Land and

African Gardens and Orchards

Growing Vegetables and Fruits

Hugues Dupriez
Philippe De Leener

translated by
Bridaine O'Meara

with advice from
H.D.Tindall

MACMILLAN

in association with

TERRES et VIE and CTA

Terres et Vie is indebted to the CTA that financed the translation of the book into English and actively promotes its distribution. The **CTA, Technical Centre for Agricultural and Rural Co-operation**, has its headquarters at Ede-Wageningen, Netherlands. It was founded in 1983 by decision of the Second ACP-EEC Convention of Lomé.

The Convention was renewed in 1984 and associates sixty-six ACP and twelve European countries.

The aim of CTA is to collect, disseminate and facilitate the exchange of information on research, training and innovations in the spheres of agriculture and rural development and extension for the benefit of the ACP States.

Headquarters: "De Rietkampen", Galvanistraat 9, Ede, Netherlands
Postal address: Postbus 380, 6700 AJ Wageningen, Netherlands
Tel.: (31)(0)(8380) – 60400
Telex: (44) 30169 CTA NL
Telefax: (31)(0)(8380) – 31052

Published in association with **TERRES et VIE**, rue Laurent Delvaux 13, 1400 Nivelles, Belgium, from the French title **Jardins et vergers d'Afrique**, edited by TERRES et VIE in association with L'HARMATTAN, APICA, ENDA and CTA.

© Copyright H. Dupriez 1989

All rights reserved. No reproduction, copy or transmission of this publication may be made without written permission.

No paragraph of this publication may be reproduced, copied or transmitted save with written permission or in accordance with the provisions of the Copyright, Designs and Patents Act 1988, or under the terms of any licence permitting limited copying issued by the Copyright Licensing Agency, 90 Tottenham Court Road, London W1P 9HE.

Any person who does any unauthorised act in relation to this publication may be liable to criminal prosecution and civil claims for damages.

English edition first published 1989 by
MACMILLAN EDUCATION LTD
London and Basingstoke
Companies and representatives throughout the world

ISBN 0–333–49076–2
ISBN 2–87105–008–2

13 12 11 10 9 8 7 6 5 4
06 05 04 03 02 01 00 99 98 97

This book is printed on paper suitable for recycling and made from fully managed and sustained forest sources.

Printed in Hong Kong

Introduction

Gardens and orchards complement and diversify the plant and animal produce of the fields where the staple crops are grown. Moreover, by the great variety of their produce, gardens and orchards are the source of a varied and nutritious diet. The housewife finds there everything needed to turn stodgy staples into appetizing meals. She has a choice of vegetables, potherbs and condiments, fruits, beverages and medicinal plants all of which are essential for good health.

Kitchen gardens, orchards and market gardens also provide a training ground where people can learn to associate plants and exploit the land in a spirit of mutual solidarity for the future benefit of the community. Here too, vegetable and fruit growing becomes an indispensable economic activity that ensures a livelihood for the family as well as adequate food supplies for towns and rural areas.

Agriculture in African Rural Communities, published in 1988, drew attention to the basic practice and theory of farming on small holdings, explaining the farmers' achievements and shortcomings, while outlining possible experimentation, and reconciling the prevailing agricultural theories with the day-to-day realities of small-scale farming, all this without advocating a too rigid programme for the future.

African Gardens and Orchards pursues similar objectives. Practical information is expanded, for example, on subjects such as planting, fertilizing, pest control and pruning. The book is a practical manual but the theory is explained, because the right course of action has to be understood before it can be applied.

The research for this book was begun by visiting rural and urban food markets and listing the most common vegetables, fruits and condiments for sale. The supply-lines which send foodstuffs daily to large markets so that urban dwellers have a wide choice of provisions were traced back to their source. These supply-lines are mostly run by women

Notable aspects of vegetable and fruit production are, first, the amazing variety of plants cultivated, second, the similar approach to gardening methods in all the countries visited, and third, the fact that information is not exchanged between men and women cultivators, even though they may come from comparable social groups, or from neighbouring regions, a discovery which led to the collection of as much concrete information as possible and to the writing of *African Gardens and Orchards* .

Much more technical information must be made available to growers and more research carried out into the properties of African food plants, in order to improve their intrinsic qualities by seed selection and the domestication of species hitherto used only in their wild state. Such an approach would help to popularise native and traditional African vegetables and stop them from taking second place to produce of European and Chinese origin. Why is a distinction made between the traditional and the exotic ? Why not, by experimentation and research, improve the quality of native produce so that a decade or so will see it rivalling foreign produce in taste and popularity ?

It is hoped that the book may be a first step towards this end, thus contributing to worldwide agrarian development in the fight against hunger.

The book is divided into two parts. Part I forms the core of the book and deals mainly with **gardening methods and practices**. It should help cultivators to think about what they are doing and to experiment with plants in order to improve their yield and their nutritious qualities. It suggests ways of ensuring a more balanced diet, controlling pests, fertilizing the soil, choosing good seed, and many other aspects of gardening. The book is not a list of recipes, but rather a manual that should encourage vegetable and fruit growers to direct their efforts towards positive effects on their usual methods of cultivation. The text and the illustrations go hand in hand for this purpose.

Part II is more descriptive, and **presents eighty-five plants**, many of which can often be found in the market-place, but tend to be overlooked by agricultural advisers in books on the subject.

Certain conventions have been used in this book : all the technical words are printed **in bold face** and explained in the text, heavy print is also used for key words and ideas.The general index gives the first and subsequent pages on which these words appear.

Italics are used for scientific and vernacular names other than those in English. Italics are also used in some tables.

The explanations for the illustrations always appear in the text itself, and the references are in boldface like this : **figure 8**, **table 9.**

Space above and below the ground is often differentiated to make certain illustrations easier to understand. It is important to understand the exact meaning of the line representing the surface of the grounds which occurs in many drawings.

There is a glossary and two indexes at the end of the book. The glossary gives definitions of the botanical terms used in Part II, in so far as they are not already defined in Part I. The index of scientific (Latin) names is useful because it removes any confusion about the names of plants in English and other languages - French, Spanish, Portuguese, Arabic. Some common names in languages or dialects other than English are also found in Part II. Lastly, the general index gives the reference pages for the subjects treated.

We are most grateful to the many cultivators we met on farms in Senegal, Mali, Burkina Faso, Ivory Coast, Rwanda, Burundi, Zaire, Togo, Benin and Cameroun. They gave us much practical information and were helpful in every way. In particular, we want to thank Bernard Njonga, Amos Nlonga, Tiéba Traoré and the Yako Development Committee (Burkina Faso) for their advice during the most important stages of our field work.

We also thank the permanent or occasional collaborators of TERRES ET VIE who contributed in many ways to this publications, especially Gilberte Van Caneghem, Michelle Favart, Rosa Micus and the Onclincx family.

We were able to write and publish this books thanks to the technical or financial help of APICA-Cameroun (Appui aux Initiatives Communautaires Africaines, the Ford Foundation, CHEMINS-PAYS, ONEM-Belgium (National Office for Employment), Broederlijk Delen and Entraide et Fraternité (Belgium), and the CTA. We thank these bodies for their effective support.

CONTENTS

Introduction

Part I
Gardens and orchards

Chapter 1
Gardens and orchards as a source of variety in food 7

Fields, gardens and orchards

Occupying land surface and volume 9

Parcelling or dividing up the land
Occupying the volume of cultivated plots : multistorey cropping 11
Plant establishment in relation to their habit of growth 12
Plant establishment related to their root system 14
Multistorey growing calls for good knowledge of plants and their environment 16
Crops in pure stands (monoculture)

Calculating yields and productivity 17

Measuring return from multistorey cropping 18
Measuring return from crops in pure stand 19
Gross productivity, net productivity 20
Measuring return and productivity - summing up 21

The species mentioned in this book

Families, species and varieties 23

Gardening as a special branch of farming 24

Gardens are places where a little of everything is found
Trees in gardens 25
Species with many uses
Small animals and bees in gardens 26
The many functions of gardens 27

Chapter 2
Vegetables, fruits and condiments - health foods 28

The food man needs

What is the human body made of ?
What should people eat to remain healthy ?

Foodstuffs 30

The chemical properties of food crops
Mineral condiments 31
Additional types of food 32
A varied diet means a balanced diet

Nutritional aspects of food processing 34

Peeling
Soaking
Scalding or blanching 35
Grinding
Refining foodstuffs 36
Drying foodstuffs
Fermentation 37
Cooking
Cooking in water 38
Frying
Grilling
Simple meals, complicated meals

Chapter 3
Laying out and preparing the land for cultivation 39

Bed preparation for seasonal crops

Earthing up 43

Planting holes 45

Some gardening tools

Additional hoeing 47

Chapter 4
Managing soil fertility 48

Fertility

Soil fertility generated on the farm 49

How is fertility generated on the farm ?
Plant mulches 51
Mulches not derived from plants
Compost 53
Green manure plants 54
Plants designed for producing mulch and compost 56
Animal manure
Other organic fertilizers 58
Burying organic manure

Ashes and cinders 59

Sources of mineral substances near gardens 60

Commercial fertilizers

Types of commercial fertilizers
Base dressing, top dressings 61
How to make the most of commercial fertilizers 62

Chapter 5

Plant spacing above and below the ground 63

Planting patterns 64

Broadcasting
Row planting 65
Growing plants in mixtures 66

Arrangement of plants above the ground 68

Air and light for shade-loving and light-loving plants 69
Staking plants
Tying plants 71
Adjusting shade
Shading young plants 72

Chapter 6

Pruning 73

Why are plants pruned ?

Promoting growth, shape and form of plants 76

Producing leaves, shoots and poles
Lopping for pole production 78
Pruning shoots and disbudding 79
Removing the flowers 80
Shaping the framework of trees
Renewal pruning 86
Techniques that help shape the plant 87
Pruning to avoid competition 88
Root-pruning
Pruning to control diseases and pests 89

Pruning practices that increase yield 90

Observations prior to production pruning 94

'Harvest pruning' 95

Ways of gathering leaves and how plant development is affected 96
Ways of picking fruits and how plants are affected
Collecting bark and how it affects trees

Pruning tools and cuts 98

When should plants be pruned ? 100

Chapter 7

Diseases and pests 101

Major plant diseases and pests

Secondary infections 103

The symptoms of disease

Some common symptoms and their causes 105

Different types of wilt
The causes of wilt
Wilts due to root infections
Wilts caused by damage at ground level 107
Wilts and blights due to attack on stems and trunks
Dieback 108
Damping off
Fruit drop
Distortions and necrotic lesions 109
Arrested growth, dwarfism and stunting
Necroses
Mosaics and streaks 111
Distortions
Abnormal growths 112
Gummosis

Plant pests

Insect damage 113
Browsing 114
Warm-blooded animals 115
Chewing pests
Piercing and sucking pests 117
Parasitic plants 118
Worms
Indiscriminate pests, selective pests 119

Friends and enemies 121

Dispersal mechanisms of pests

Chapters 8, 9, 10 and 11

Pest control 122

Chapter 8

Natural methods for the prevention of pests in cultivated plants 123

Nutrition affects the health of cultivated species

Pest control and plant environment 124

Growing crops in mixtures

Plant density and pest control 128

Sources of infection 129

Cultural practices which limit the risks of infection 131

Avoid contact between cultivated plants and sources of infection
Avoid practices and operations that transmit infection
Fire as a disinfectant 132
The rotation of cultivated plants 133

Variations in sowing dates 133
Weeding and earthing up

The use of healthy seeds of good quality 134

Importance of choosing the right seeds
Susceptibility and resistance to pests 135
Diseased or pest-infected seeds
Grading seeds 136
Seed treatment 137

Cultivating resistant varieties

Mechanical resistance to pests 138
Chemical resistance to pests
Choice of cultivated varieties in relation to pests of economic importance

Chapter 9

Natural methods of pest control 140

Natural products used for pest control

Natural products of mineral origin
Natural products of vegetable origin 141
How to prepare plant extracts for spraying 143
Animal substances 144

Mechanical methods of pest control 145

Fencing, live and dead hedging
Scarecrows 147
Control of bird pests
Baits, snares and traps 148

Food chains 149

Chapter 10

Biological control of crop pests 152

Direct biological control

Indirect biological control

Chapter 11

Pesticides 155

Insecticides

Fungicides 157

Rodenticides 158

Other pesticides

Some common pesticides

Safety in the use of pesticides 159

Summary of chapters 8, 9, 10 and 11

The choice of control measures 164

Chapters 12, 13, 14, 15 and 16

Seeds, sowing and planting

Chapter 12

Propagation by seeds and by vegetative material 165

Natural methods of vegetative propagation 166

Choice of quality planting material 168

Selecting seeds for specific conditions 169

Harvesting and storing seeds and cuttings 172

Harvesting and storing seeds
Harvesting and storing other propagating material 173

Preparing for planting

Seed preparation

Vegetative propagation 176

Stem cutting preparation
Cuttings from rhizomes and tubers 180
Shoots, root-suckers and underground stems 181

Chapter 13

Sowing and planting 182

Direct sowing in the field 183

Establishment of cuttings and tubers 184

Planting depths for seeds 185

Good sowing practices 186

Planting depths for vegetative material

Sowing varietal mixtures 187

Chapter 14

Nurseries 190

Objectives in nursery construction

Methods of nursery establishment 191

Protecting nurseries 193

Chapter 15

Transplanting 196

Transplanting techniques

Planting trees 198

Chapter 16

Timing of sowing and transplanting 200

Planting patterns

Sowing calendars 204

Sowing patterns and timing for seasonal crops
Timing for trees and perennial crop planting 210

Chapter 17
Grafting 211

Reasons for grafting
Plant structures related to grafting 212
Selecting stock plants and scions 213
Compatibility between plants and scions
Grafting tools
Positioning the graft 214
Methods of grafting and budding 215
Cleft grafting
Whip grafting 217
Budding
Approach grafting 220
Topworking
Precautions required in grafting 222

Chapter 18
The domestication of wild species of annual and perennial plants 223

How can spontaneous and subspontaneous plants be domesticated 225

Chapter 19
Gardens and water availability 227

Water requirements and the irrigation of cultivated plant
Rainfed market gardening 228
Irrigated gardens 229
Hand methods
Gravity Irrigation 232
Sprinkler irrigation 234
Valley bottom cultivation and drainage 235
Water management in perspective 236

Part II
Vegetables, fruits and condiments

Chapter 20
Leaf vegetables and pot herbs 239

SP1 Amaranths and Celosia
SP2 Baobab 240
SP3 Indian spinach 241
SP4 Basil 242
SP5 Foetid cassia and negro coffee 243
SP6 Cabbages 244
SP7 Jutes 245
SP8 Costus 246
SP9 Waterleaf and purslane
SP10 Bastard mustard 247
SP11 Lettuce 248
Nightshades
SP12 Solanum gilo Raddi 249
SP13 Black nightshade 250
SP14 Mock tomato 251
SP15 Drumstick tree 252
SP16 Roselle and kenaf 253
SP17 Leek 254
SP18 New Zealand spinach 255
SP19 Bitter Leaf

Chapter 21
Vegetable and condiment fruits 257

SP20 Eggplant
SP21 Desert date 259
SP22 Fagara 260
SP23 Fig sycamore 261
SP24 Okra 262
SP25 Indian jujube 264
SP26 Wild or Cameroun cardamom 265
SP27 Chillies 267
SP28 Ethiopian pepper
SP29 Pepper and Guinea pepper 269
SP30 Bush butter tree 270
SP31 Tamarind 271
SP32 Aidon tree 273
SP33 Tomato

Chapter 22

Cucurbitaceae 275

SP34 Chayote
SP35 Citrullus and watermelon 276
SP36 Cucumbers and gherkins 277
SP37 Bitter cucumber 278
SP38 Vegetable marrows and courgettes 279
SP39 Bottle gourd 280
SP40 Fluted gourd 281
SP41 Snake gourd
SP42 Smooth loofah 282
SP43 Bitter gourd
SP44 Melon 283
SP45 Pumpkin

Cucurbitaceae : cultivation and husbandry 284

Chapter 23

Miscellaneous fruits 286

SP46 Annonaceae
SP47 Carombola 288
SP48 Cayor cherry 289
SP49 Detar
SP50 Monkey guava 290
SP51 Strawberry 291
SP52 Cape gooseberry
SP53 Mombin 292
SP54 Cayor apple 293
SP55 Passion fruit 294
SP56 Tree tomato 295
SP57 Lannea 296
SP58 Black plum 297

Chapter 24

Seeds, nuts and kernels 298

SP59 Cashew
SP60 Kola 299
SP61 Dika nut 300
SP62 Calabash nutmeg
SP63 Akee apple 301
SP64 Shea Butter 302
SP65 Orere 303
SP66 African locust bean 304
SP67 Cowpea 305
SP68 Njansan 306
SP69 Almond nut 307
SP70 Pigeon pea 308
SP71 Annato 309
SP72 Sesame and bungu 310

Chapter 25

Palms 311

SP73 Date palm
SP74 Dum palm 312
SP75 Oil palm
SP76 Coconut 313
SP77 Raffia palms
SP78 African fan palm 314

Chapter 26

Bulb and root vegetables 315

SP79 Garlic, onion and shallot
SP80 Carrot 316
SP81 Coleus
SP82 Ginger and turmeric 317
SP83 Tiger nut 318

Chapter 27

Edible bark and flower producing trees 319

SP84 Garlic tree
SP85 Red flower silk and silk cotton 320
SP86 Triumphetta 321

Appendices

Glossary 324

English and Latin names of plants 326

Bibliography 328

General Index 330

Chapter 1

Gardens and orchards, as a source of variety in food

Fields, gardens and orchards

When we speak of growing food crops, a distinction is usually made between **fields**, and **gardens** and **orchards**. Fields produce **staple foods** whereas gardens and orchards supply the **vegetables, fruits and condiment plants** that supplement the staples at mealtimes. These **supplemental foods** from gardens are the subject of this chapter.

Figure 1 shows a typical Senegalese meal. The bulk of this meal is rice, the staple which may be grown in the valley of the River Senegal, or imported from abroad. Added to the rice are fish and vegetables that make the dish attractive and more nutritious than the rice on its own. As well as the fish which is an animal product, we find carrot, eggplant, cabbage, onion, pumpkin, sweet potato and chillies. These vegetables are mostly grown in gardens, whether they be **kitchen or market gardens.** Growing vegetables is called **market gardening**, **vegetable farming**, or **vegetable gardening**. The term **horticulture** covers gardening in general.

There is also a sauce in which many nutritive elements are mixed together. It contains groundnut oil, salt, tomato paste, garlic, parsley, and finely ground tamarind leaves. The sauce makes the dish tasty, stimulates the appetite and helps the digestion. Oil, tamarind, garlic, tomato paste and salt are **condiments** (also called **seasonings** and **relishes**) added to the sauce in small quantities.

Figure 2 shows a woman weeding a large field of intercropped groundnut, maize, cassava and cocoyam. These are all staple foods. In the woman's garden round the house shown in **figure 3**, a wide variety of additional fruits and vegetables are grown. The plants that produce these may be **seasonal, perennial and semi-perennial plants**.

1

2

Seasonal plants are sown every season. Their life span, also called the **life cycle**, lasts for a few months. The stem and leaves wilt and die after having produced seeds that fall to the ground.

Perennial plants have a life cycle lasting many years. They flower and bear fruit every season. Trees are perennials. Some herbaceous plants and lianas are perennials too; they include pepper, wild cardamom, triumphetta and elephant grass.

Apart from the two categories of plants that are seasonal or perennial, there are many plants with in-between life cycles. They are called **semi-perennial**, or **pluriseasonal**. (**Pluriseasonal** refers to plants planted in one season and harvested in another, sometimes a year later. For example, cocoyam planted in March, the first farming season, can be harvested in December, the end of a second farming season). Cassava, for instance, can live from 24 to 36 months; banana stems die after fruiting but the plants survive by producing suckers. Some varieties of okra last for many seasons. The plants bear flowers and fruit for two or three seasons before dying off. The same is true, for example, of some chillies and Indian spinach

3

Some plants which are perennials or pluriseasonal are cultivated like seasonal crops. Yam and taro are perennials but when the tubers are grown for food, they must be replanted and are treated like seasonal plants.

A typical house garden such as the one seen in **figure 3** grows all kinds of woody and herbaceous plants - seasonal, pluriseasonal and perennial. There is sweet potato with a cycle of 6 months, pineapple - cycle 18 months, roselle - cycle 4 months, pigeon pea - perennial, bush greens - 3 months, nightshade - 3 to 6 months, pawpaw and a native pear tree - perennials, castor - perennial. All these plants were either sown by the gardener herself, or seed themselves. Cultivated plants can therefore be divided into **spontaneous** (wild) plants, and **subspontaneous** plants, not seeded but encouraged to grow by man's behaviour.

Many gardens in this book are a **mixture of plants with different uses, different life cycles, growth patterns and cultural requirements.** Their main aim is to diversify production.

Sometimes, it is easy to see the difference between fields and gardens. The large field of millet in **figure 4** stretches out of sight, lightly shaded by shea butter and African locust bean trees. Millet is the staple food of this dry region and is cultivated over vast areas in order to ensure abundant supplies.

Some crops are wholly dependent on rainfall. This is **dry** or **rainfed cropping** as opposed to **wetland cropping** as it is practised in valley bottoms, on **flooded, irrigated** or **watered land.**

The **garden in figure 5** consists of a few ares from which the owner obtains large quantities of fruit and vegetables. He has a well that allows him to **water** the beds daily. Almost every day, he picks **fresh produce** which he must eat or sell quickly because fruit and vegetables are **perishable foods** that, for the most part, cannot be kept for more than a few days or they will spoil.

4

The distinction between growing staple crops in fields and growing fruit and vegetables in gardens is not always clear. Fruit and vegetables are often found growing in fields and, conversely, cereals, seeds and tubers are often cultivated in gardens.

This practice is explained by the fact that many plants have **several uses**. They can be used as a staple and a supplementary food. For example, both the tubers and leaves of cassava are edible; the leaves, fruits and seeds of beans and marrows can all be eaten.

Useful trees like shea butter (**figure 4)** may be left in the fields. These trees can reduce moisture loss by shading the crop and the soil, and shelter it from drying winds They also produce fruits that can be eaten and their seeds are processed to make butter. Or take the baobab, a familiar sight in West African landscapes; its leaves, flowers and fruit can all be eaten.

Vegetables are sometimes grown in the shade of staples. Roselle is growing under maize in **figure 6**. This is a cultural practice very common in rural Africa.

In short, fruit and vegetables growing is not restricted to gardens; it is also practised in fields and may contribute significantly to the total amount of produce harvested.

5

Occupying land surface and volume

Some production systems are described in the following pages. An **agricultural production system** is all those activities which together enable the production of crops. For instance, cropping patterns, cultural practices, the use of tools and machines, the use of fertilizers and irrigation and the role played by livestock.

Choosing a production system means weighing up the following points :

- how to avoid **wasting land resources,** especially where the area supports a large population,
- how to preserve and improve **soil structure,**
- how to preserve **soil fertility** during a cropping season and for future seasons,
- how to avoid **erosion,**
- how to let plants make the best use of **fertilizers,**
- how to reduce problems caused by **climate** and **pests,**
- how to **make the best use of available labour** for planting, maintenance and harvesting.
- how to reduce **economic risks** from price fluctuations, poor transport and the unreliable supply of production factors.
- how to divide the available land between staples and fruit and vegetable production.

The choice of production systems, for gardens and for fields, is affected by all these factors. They should be borne in mind right through the book because the choice of cultural methods often depends on the answers to the points listed.

It is particularly useful to look at the ways in which aerial and underground space and the available ground surface on a farm are occupied. This occupation tells us about the balance between agricultural, environmental and economic factors on the farm and about the improved techniques that could be applied.

We shall begin by looking at

- how land on farms is split into units or plots, and
- how cultivated plants occupy the volume of these plots when crops are grown in mixtures and in pure stands.

6

Parcelling or dividing up the land

Parcelling land refers to the way in which land on a farm or in a settlement is divided into plots and patches for a specific farming purpose : family dwelling, crops, cattle, timber, fallow, etc.

7 **Dividing up the land : the occupation of surface space**

8

On the family farm in **figure 7**, the dwelling with the corrugated-iron roof is seen in the centre. In the foreground are fields where staples , mostly maize, sweet potato, cassava, and beans, are grown on very large, rectangular beds **(figure 8)**. These crops provide the staple foods.

In association with these crops, we find vegetable marrows, bush greens, Jew's mallow, bitter tomatoes, cherry tomatoes, black nightshade, bananas. Some of the beds are bounded by a hedge of cassava grown for its leaves.

There is also a large orchard with all kinds of useful trees and lianas - palm, avocado, native pear, citrus, kola, soursop, pepper.

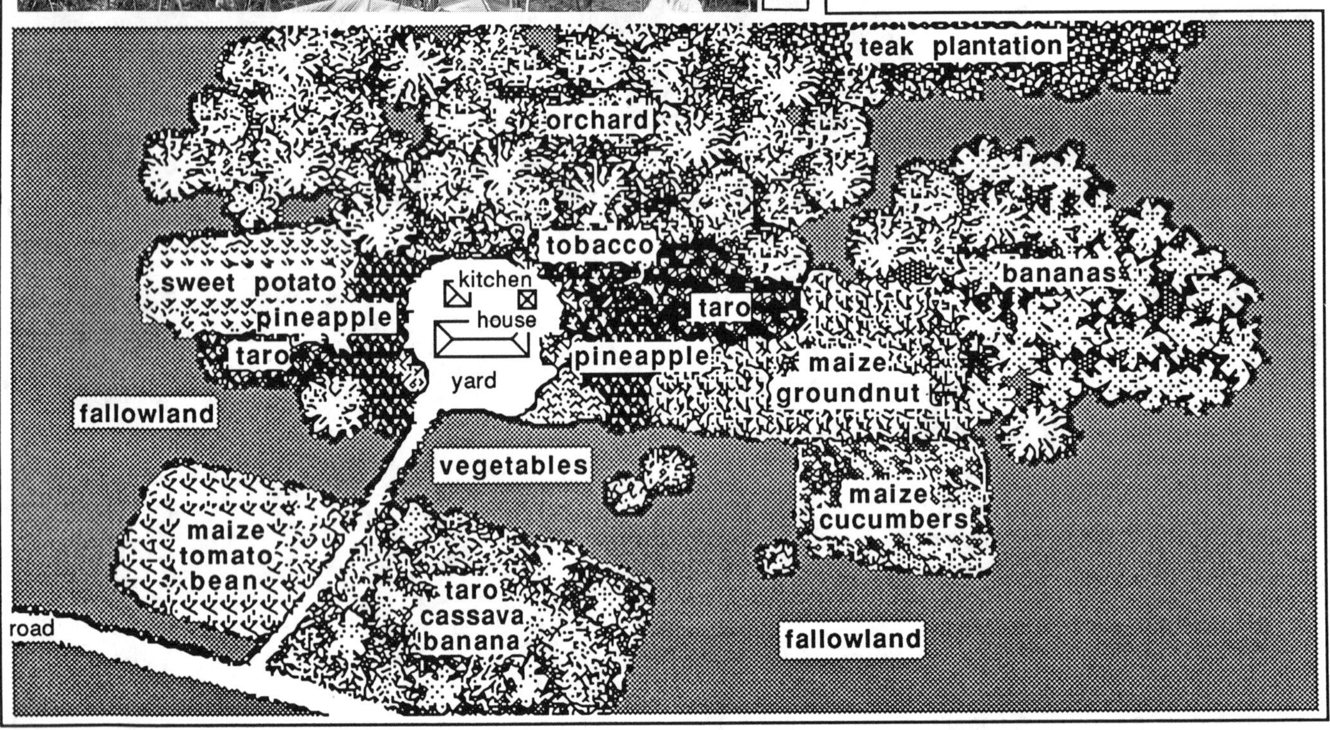

Some tree species are exploited for their timber and one plot has been planted with teak *(Tectona grandis)*. Alongside the compound, we find pineapple, tobacco, marrows and medicinal plants that benefit from the household waste cleared from the backyard every day. Some of the arable land lies fallow, fallow plants help to restore soil fertility.

This is a typical example of a family holding based on diversified production and practising what is called **mixed farming**.

Livestock is only a sideline on this farm. Some poultry, a few pigs and goats can be seen wandering about. Their excreta fertilizes the soil close to the family dwelling, but they cause damage to the rest of the farm because they are allowed to roam free.

Figure 9 shows another type of farm based on the **monoculture** of rice, this means that the farm produces only the staple, rice. This crop is grown on all the land cultivated and its production keeps the whole family occupied throughout the year. The farmer has built his farm economy on the hope of being able to produce enough rice to sell the surplus to buy other food. This is **commercial farming** whose main object is not diversified food production for the family, even though some of the rice is for domestic use. There is no room for livestock on this holding, but thanks to irrigation, there are two rice crops, or **two cycles**, per year.

The vegetable garden in **figure 10** is situated on the banks of a river and is watered regularly in the dry season. Bed cultivation is practised and there are many vegetables sown or transplanted in rows - cabbage, leek, onion, okra, eggplant, tomato, etc. One species only is cultivated per bed; there are no associated plants. Variety in vegetable production is ensured by variety in the seeds sown in each bed.

9

10

11

These gardeners concentrate on a production system inspired by **sole cropping methods,** contrary to the pattern adopted in the garden shown in **figure 5**.

Cattle have an important role to play in the garden by the river. The soil is sandy and poor, and needs fertilizing. Every evening, the vegetable growers put their cattle into a kraal for the night. Excreta are collected the next day, brought to the garden and spread on the beds.

If cattle were not used in this way, vegetable production would be very poor even though water is available. Here, the cattle are being used only for their manure. The gardeners have not yet managed to use livestock as efficiently as those shown in **figure 11** who also use oxen for lifting water from their well. These cattle have a three-fold role : **lifting water, providing manure**, and **supplying meat**.

Occupying the volume of cultivated plots : multistorey cropping

Space in a cultivated plot can be considered in three ways : surface area, aerial volume, underground volume.

Figures12 and 13 and figures 15 and 16 show how plants exploit space at different levels above and below the ground. The plants form **layers** or **storeys**. The natural arrangement of the leaf canopy is such that plants get the air and light they need for growth. Their roots vary in structure and vigour to penetrate different soil layers. **They take up different nutrient elements at different times and from different soil layers.** This arrangement of useful plants promotes complementarity between species : complementarity in yields, diversification of food crops and sources of income, complementarity in the fight against cultural hazards caused by weather conditions and specialized pests and diseases. It also creates competition because some plants do not tolerate others at certain times in their life cycle.

The art of the cultivator is to emphasize complementarity between plants, and reduce competition.

There are many ways of building multistorey canopies.

12 How the volume of a cropping field in Mali is occupied

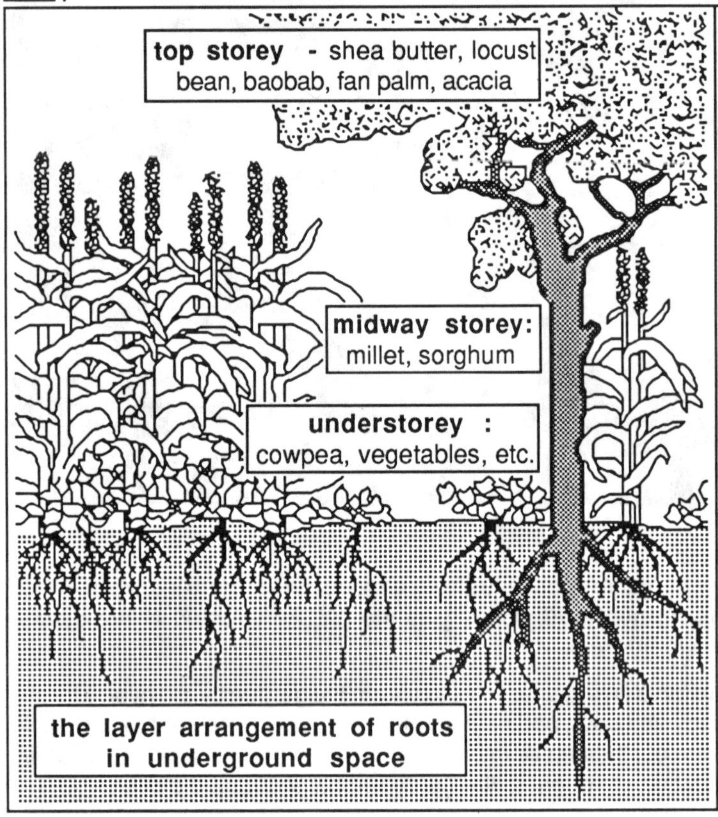

Plant establishment in relation to their habit of growth

Plants can be arranged according to their habit : giant forest trees, trees of medium height, shrubs, erect plants, low and creeping plants can be planted so that they do not compete with one another.

In this kind of arrangement, **all associated plants must find water, light and air**; otherwise, they may produce leaves but and not flower or bear fruit.

A multistoreyed garden is shown in **figure 14**. The top storey is composed of banana and pawpaw well spaced between the beds, in order to avoid too much shading.

This top storey fulfils many functions :

- it produces bananas and pawpaws;
- it produces organic matter that will rot on the ground and manure it. Banana is particularly useful in this respect;
- it gives light shade to the vegetables growing underneath. During the day, the shade revolves with the sun round the plants giving the understorey plants successive periods of cool and heat. Because low plants are never in full shade, they are not short of light;
- it gives partial ground cover during heavy rains;
- it reduces windforce, thereby reducing evaporation from the ground surface and lessening the risk of drought.

The top storey in this garden therefore **protects understorey plants and also produces fruit crops**.

15

The understorey is composed of many vegetables and herbs planted in beds or strips. Seasonal species include eggplant and native eggplant, bush greens, roselle, Jew's mallow, lettuce, cabbage, tomato, vegetable marrow, okra. Among the pluriseasonal or perennial plants, we find *Triumphetta*, bitter leaf, pigeon pea, cassava leaves, and yam.

Some plants occupy a bed to themselves as in **figure 17** where bush greens are on their own. Other beds were sown more or less densely with associated plants as shown in **figure 18**. Here, two rows of maize form **an intermediate storey** down the centre of the bed which they overhang and shade lightly. The ears of maize are between 1 metre and 1.50 metres above the ground. At the foot of the stems and on the sides of the bed, cocoyam and black nightshade grow. These tolerate shade and thus enjoy good growth conditions. Cocoyam produces tubers underground, while nightshade is cultivated for its leaves that are 10 to 30 cm above ground level.

Thus, **under the top canopy** of banana and pawpaw, some seasonal plants are grown in pure stands while others are grown in close association.

The volume of a garden in a wet region 16

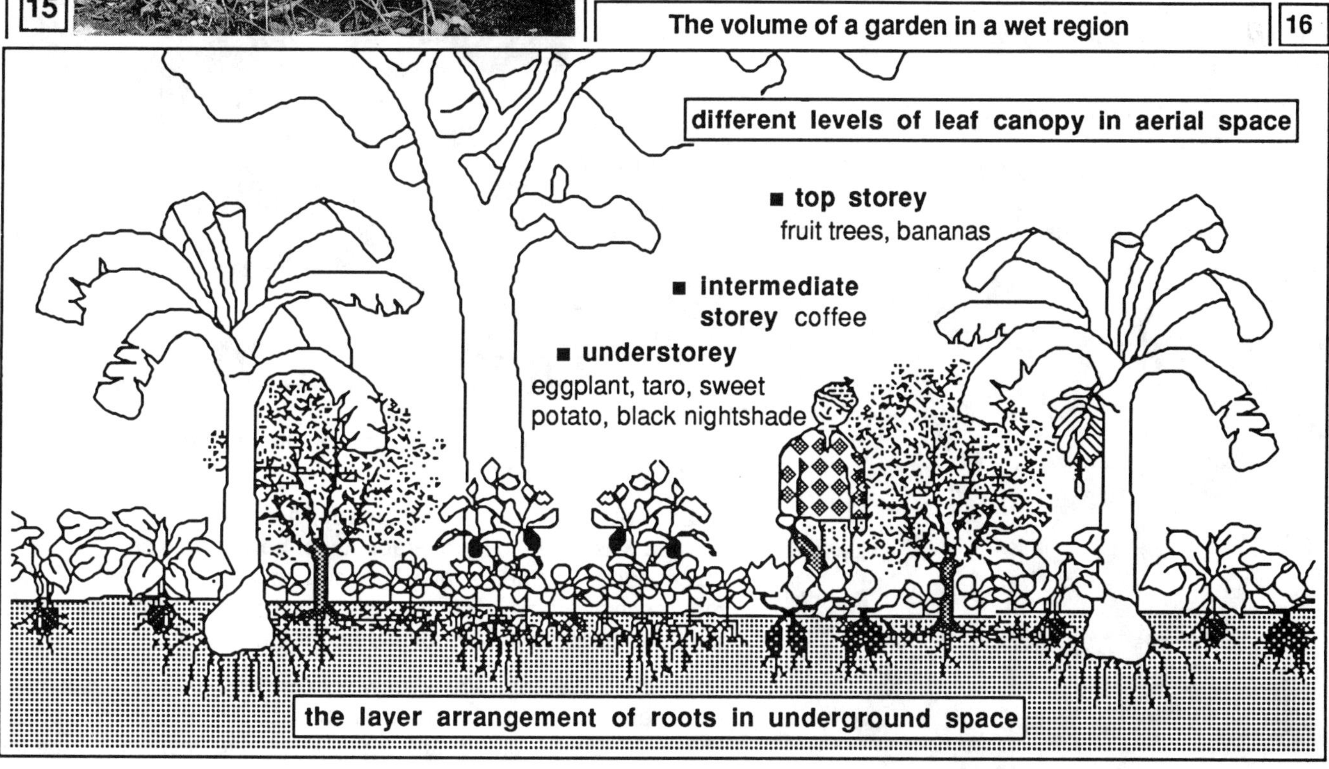

Notes

Plant establishment related to their root systems

A second method of arranging plants on different levels is to **shape the soil** so that it will contribute to the development of the roots and to their arrangement in layers in the soil **(see figures 19, 20 and 21)**.

In the first example **(figure 19)**, soil has been heaped into low mounds to suit the yam whose roots need light, well-drained soil, while the yam stems are trained on poles. Groundnuts are planted on the mounds round the yams. Groundnut roots occupy the soil in the mounds before the yam tubers are formed, and the leaves protect the mounds from erosion due to rain.

Figures 20 and 21 illustrate a much more elaborate arrangement than in **figure 19**. The soil is exploited at several levels : high mounds (sometimes called hills); beds at a lower level; and lowest of all, the soil that was not moved when forming the mounds or beds.

In this garden, the hard work that went into forming the different soil levels is justified for many reasons :

- the variety of yam cultivated can grow tubers 1 metre to 1.2 metres long. To be able to enlarge fully, the yam needs **loose, well-drained soil**. By forming **hills** as opposed to the low mounds seen in **figure 19**, the cultivator has created the right growth conditions for tuber enlargement. This was done by raking the ground and heaping up the soil;

19

17

18

- when the high mounds were ready, another part of the ground surface was raked to form larger, lower **beds** with a soil layer 25 to 40 cm deep. This soil is fairly light and penetration is easy for plant roots such as maize, bush greens and nightshade. Like the mounds, the beds consist of soil thrown up from the furrows;
- lastly, the lowest surface layer was hoed too. The soil was worked to a depth of 15 to 20 cm so that cocoyam could be planted. Rainwater drains to here and cocoyams thrive because here there is **more moisture** than in the mounds and beds.

Many points in connection with this cultural pattern are worth remembering.

A wide variety of plant species are grown and answer the need for diversified foods to be discussed in the next chapter.

The garden must be cultivated **by hand** so that the different cultural levels can be formed. It is impossible to form hills and beds with the agricultural machinery available in rural areas.

20 Surface relief and the layering of roots in a garden

Cultural methods are adapted to the characteristics of each plant :

- this yam variety needs a large volume of light, well drained soil and its leaves like full light. The yam is therefore planted on hills and its stems climb up supports;
- groundnut thrives in light weed-free well-drained soils into which it can easily thrust its pods. It also requires exposure to sun and grows well on the sides of the yam hills. To some extent, it protects the

hills from erosion by rain and does not hinder the enlargement of the yam tubers;

- maize and bush greens are good companions once the maize plants have outstripped the bush green foliage;
- cocoyam likes moist ground. Its tubers do not penetrate deeply and the soil does not have to be loosened to any great extent. In the subsoil furrow, between the mounds and beds cocoyam finds the soil moister and more clayey;
- there are also some scattered trees, planted at the lowest level of tilled soil. The shallow roots were clipped by hoeing to avoid root competition with other species.

Soil levels can be changed with every cultural season in keeping with the grower's requirements.

As a rule, **drainage and runoff** predominate in gardens of this kind, but there is no reason why they should not be watered.

Basically, cultivation on different soil levels means that, after land forming, **field space is occupied to suit the root systems of each plant**.

22 Two ways of deciding plant spacing

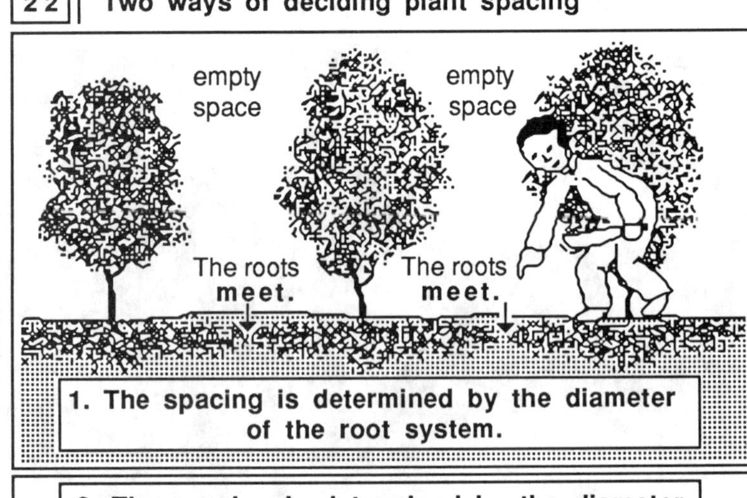

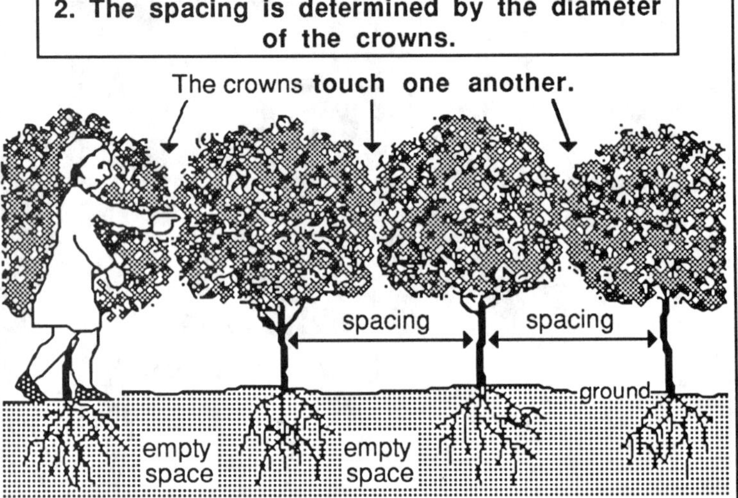

Multistorey growing calls for good knowledge of plants and their environment

The grower will obtain better results if he has a good **knowledge of plants and their growth environment.**

- He must **observe the habit of plants and know** their root systems and the shade they provide. He must know their life cycle, their water and light requirements, the best time to sow and to transplant, and the type of soil they prefer (sandy, clayey, rich in organic matter or stony).

  Again, he must observe how plants react to one another : Is there interplant competition ? Or does one benefit from the other ? Are they complementary with regard to soil enrichment ? etc.

- He must **observe the environment,** know how and when rain beats the ground and runs off, know when rain stagnates and stops root development. He must know about soil characteristics and the changes they undergo, and note the action of trees and plants on the environment.

Crops in pure stand (monoculture)

Production systems for crops in pure stand are based on the following principles :

- **Only one plant species** is grown on a given plot, and it occupies only one level of that cultivated plot;
- Each year, the farm (or garden) is divided into **plots** or beds reserved for one cultivated species;
- On each plot of land, species are grown in turn, keeping to the rules of **crop rotation**. The rotation pattern ensures that the same species is not grown for too long a period on the same soil;
- Roots and leaves each occupy **only one soil layer** and **one aerial layer**, see **figures 23 and 24** and **figures 25 and 26;**
- Plants are sown over the whole plot **as densely as possible** but with **the right spacing**. This means that the plants are close to each other to avoid wasting space, but not so close that foliage and roots overlap too much **(figure 22);**

- Maintenance is **easy** because only the needs of one plant have to be taken into account. Fertilizers and dressings are applied **uniformly**.

A pawpaw orchard is seen in **figure 24**. (The term **plantation** is also used). The trees are planted in rows; leaf canopies overlap and little light filters through. The roots, however, are not tangled because of the taproot system of this species.

This arrangement has its **advantages** :

- **high yields**,
- **easy maintenance** : few weeds tolerate full shade under trees,
- **good access** - workers can go up and down the rows during weeding, spraying and harvesting operations.

There are also **disadvantages** :

- aerial space is occupied along a belt one metre wide, at a height of between 2 and 3 metres above the ground. Air and light are not exploited throughout the available volume,
- similarly, the roots only occupy one layer of the underground space ,
- **production** is concentrated in a limited period of the year. If the pawpaw market collapses, income will be at risk.

A similar production system is used for seasonal farm crops. In the big field in **figure 25**, cabbage (foreground) and lettuce (background) are grown on a commercial scale. Selected seeds, fertilizers and pesticides are used. **Figure 26** shows how space is occupied at a particular time in the season. Actually, if the illustration was complete, it would show variations in the way in which the roots exploit the soil. At certain times, roots are very active while, at other times, they go through a resting period.

Calculating yields and productivity

The gardens examined so far show how, in practice, two production systems (crop associations and monoculture) are often **combined**. Crops can be grown in succession, either to a definite rotation plan, or to a less rigid pattern.

Whatever system is adopted, the grower should be guided by **the following principles** :

- **Good yields must be obtained and soil conservation respected;**

23 How aerial and underground space are occupied in a pawpaw plantation

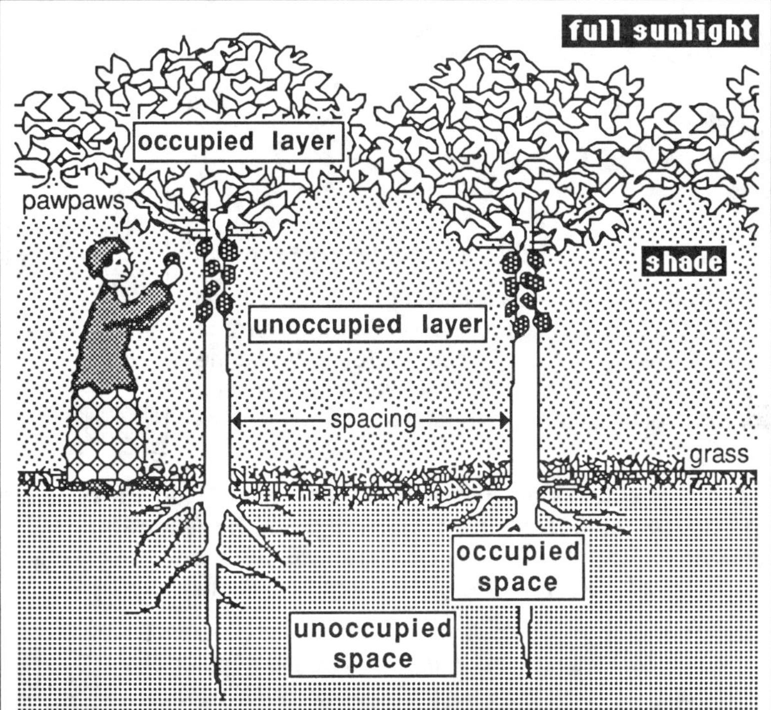

24

Let us calculate returns of different production systems.

- **Return from the land** means the amount of agricultural produce harvested during a cultural season, from an area covering 1 are or 1 hectare. The are (100 m2) and the hectare (10.000 m2) are the most usual land measures used, but other land measures, the 'acre' for instance, are also used.

- the choice of rotations or crop sequences must be such that **the same seasonal crop is not grown season after season on the same plot** (or bed), because this practice may cause soil exhaustion and contribute to the spread of diseases and pests;
- The choice of plants must consider the association of species that exploit the soil in complementary ways but have **different life cycles** (perennial, pluriseasonal, seasonal);
- The choice must be adapted to **the farmer's aims : food crops for the family** or **commercial farming.**

26 Space occupied by cabbage plants

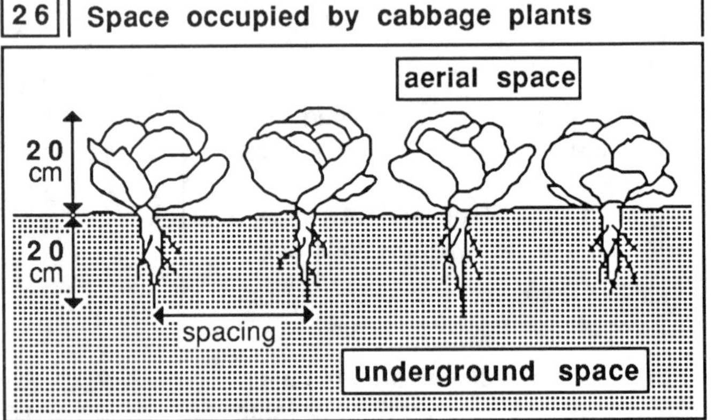

- **In order to calculate yield from a particular piece of land, the cultivated area is measured and the product obtained from that area is weighed. The second figure (production) is then divided by the first (cultivated area).** Supposing that 672 kilograms of nightshade leaves are produced on 12 ares. The return from the land is :

$$\frac{\text{672 kg of leaves}}{\text{12 cultivated ares}} = \textbf{56 kg of leaves per are}$$

- **Return from labour** is calculated in the same way, except that the number of land units is replaced by the number of working days. If 14 days were needed to obtain 672 kilograms of leaves, then return from labour is calculated as follows :

$$\frac{\textbf{672 kg of leaves}}{\text{14 days' work}} = \textbf{48 kg of nightshade per working day}$$

- The word **productivity** can be compared to the word **return,** except that the figure giving the **amount of produce** is replaced by the **value** of the same produce. For example, if nightshade leaves are worth 50 francs per kilogram, 672 kilograms are worth 33 600 francs.

Land productivity is therefore	$\frac{\text{33,600 francs}}{\text{12 ares}} = \textbf{2,800 francs per are}$	in local currency
and work productivity is :	$\frac{\text{33,600 francs}}{\text{14 days}} = \textbf{2,400 francs per working day}$	in local currency

It is not easy to compare crop returns when the quantities are expressed in vague terms – in heaps, bunches, bundles, bags, cans, baskets and so on. In this case, it is better to calculate productivity in terms of money. This is done by simply multiplying the number of bunches, heaps, bags, etc. by the sale price.

Returns from intercropped plots and plots in pure stand are not calculated in the same way. There are two ways of working out this return.

Measuring return from multistorey cropping

Yields are noted for every day of the season : so many kilos of leaf vegetables one day, of tubers the next, of fruit and so on. At the end of the season, the daily quantities are added up. **Table 27** gives the total yield, for a gardening season, from a 2-are patch.

27

Produce harvested	number of kg	Price/kg		Value of production	
		in francs	in local currency	in francs	in local currency
leaf vegetables	85 kg	110 francs		9,350 francs	
eggplants	63 kg	140 francs		8,820 francs	
bananas	112 kg	45 francs		5,050 francs	
marrow seeds	6 kg	220 francs		4,875 francs	
taros	75 kg	65 francs		4,875 francs	
cabbage	43 kg	100 francs		4,300 francs	
Total	**384 kg**			**33,705 francs**	

Return from the consumable or saleable produce of this plot can be calculated as follows :

$$\frac{\text{384 kg of various foodstuffs}}{\text{2 ares}} = \textbf{192 kg of various foodstuffs per are}$$

But this figure is more or less meaningless because we have added up quantities that do not bear comparison. A kilogram of bananas does not have the same food or market value as a kilogram of cucurbit seeds or a kilogram of eggplant.

Productivity in terms of income from the land is more significant because it is a way of of making comparisons with other production systems. Since the return from 2 ares totalled 33705 francs, we can say that

$$\frac{\text{33,705 francs}}{\text{2 ares}} = \textbf{16,852 francs per are}$$

in local currency

If 28 days were spent tilling, sowing, weeding and harvesting 2 cultivated ares, the productivity of daily labour comes to

$$\frac{\text{33,705 francs}}{\text{28 days}} = \textbf{1,204 francs per work day}$$

in local currency

Productivity can be calculated even when the produce is not sold. Its value is calculated by determining the money that would have been earned, had the produce been sold.

People who want to experiment with several cultural systems can calculate productivity in other ways, for example, by studying the **food value of the crop**. Here, productivity is expressed as the amounts of energy or protein produced by the land. Those interested in the subject can consult the appropriate chapters in 'Tropical Agricutural in African Rural Communities' by the same authors.

The estimates made so far only concern the consumable part of the production. But **there is a non-consumable part,** the part that goes back into the soil and restores its structure. This part is not usually taken into account, but it is worth allowing for when calculating the total return. **Figure 28** illustrates one aspect of the non-consumable return from cultivated plants.

It is not easy to quantify the non-consumable part of production (leaves, roots, fruit waste, etc.), but it is of real importance. Imagine the amount of manure or artificial fertilizer that would have to be purchased to enrich the soil if all this trash did not rot on the ground.

In multistorey cropping, expressing return is complicated because it means adding up vegetables, fruit, seeds, organic matter, fertility, moisture, etc. However, the fact that this return is hard to estimate is no excuse for ignoring it, particularly as the less tangible effects can be very important for soil fertility.

Measuring return from crops in pure stand

Return from crops in pure stand is measured in the same way as in multistorey farming, but the process is simplified because there is only one agricultural product. Suppose 44 days were spent growing 576 kilograms of eggplant in a 3-are garden and that the crop was sold at 80 francs per kilogram.

- ❑ **Return from the land** equals :

$$\frac{\text{576 kg of eggplant}}{\text{3 ares}} = \textbf{192 kg of eggplant per are}$$

in local currency

- ❑ **Return from labour** equals

$$\frac{\text{576 kg of eggplant}}{\text{44 days}} = \textbf{13 kg of eggplant per work day}$$

in local currency

- ❑ **Land productivity** equals

$$\frac{\text{576 kg x 80 francs/kg}}{\text{3 ares}} = \frac{\text{46,080 francs}}{\text{3 ares}} = \textbf{15,360 francs/are}$$

in local currency

❑ **Work productivity** equals

$\frac{46{,}080 \text{ francs}}{44 \text{ work days}}$ = **1,047 francs per work day**	in local currency

To complete the calculation of return, the organic matter produced by the plants and restored to the soil must be added, as in the case of multistorey farming.

28 Five ways of looking at return from a crop

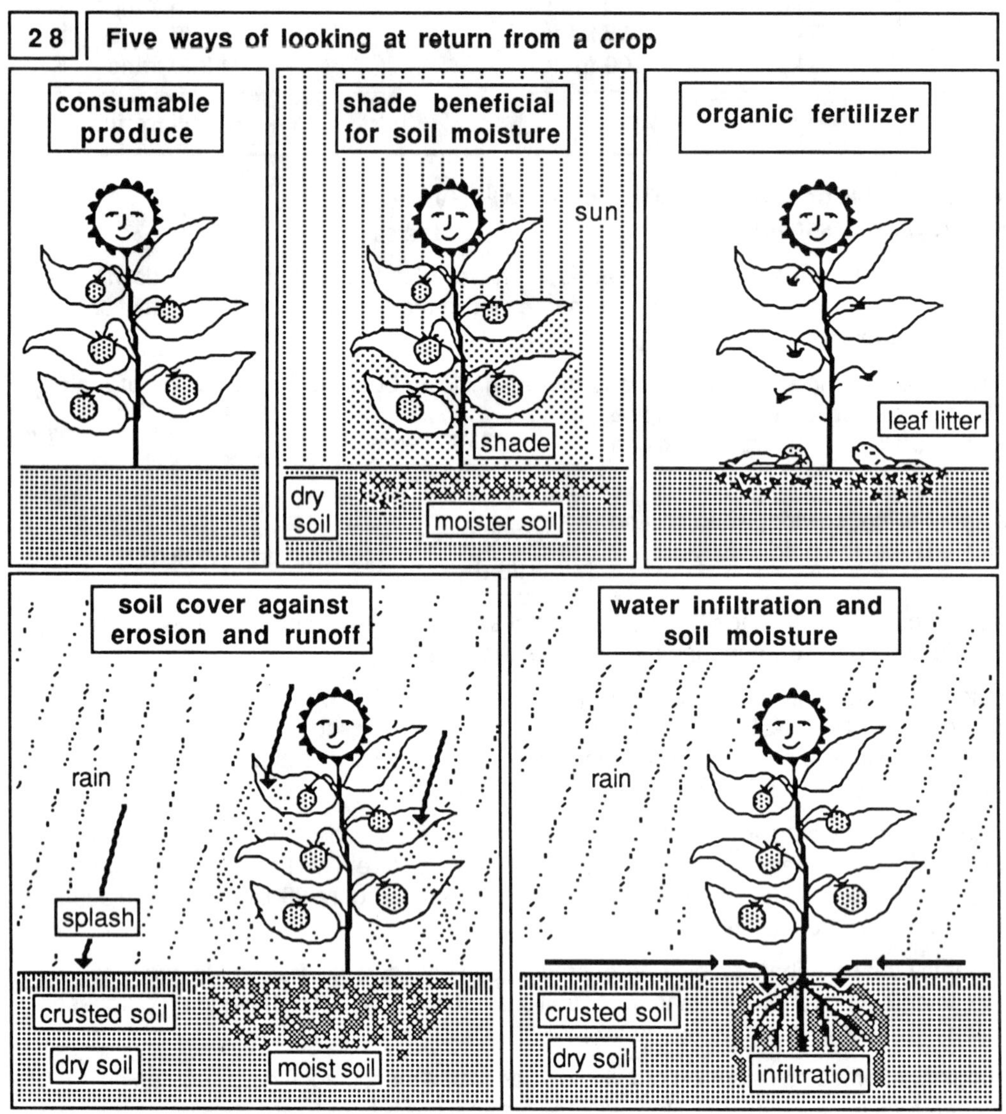

Gross productivity, net productivity

So far, we have calculated **gross productivity** from the land and from labour, only taking into account the market price of the product and **not the money spent producing it.** Gross productivity does not give the real income from the produce because production costs were incurred and not deducted.

Net productivity must be worked out to discover the sum of money earned and really in hand. **Net productivity** is obtained by **deducting production costs from gross productivity**.

If we go back to the multistorey garden in **table 27** where production costs came to 6,780 francs (seeds, tools, fertilizer, etc.) and start the calculations over again, we get the following figures :

❍ **gross productivity of the land** equals	$\frac{33{,}705 \text{ francs}}{2 \text{ ares}}$ = **16,852 francs per are**	in local currency
❍ **net productivity of the land** equals	**33,705** francs earned - **6,785** francs spent = **26,920** francs	in local currency

The sum of 26920 francs = **net product** or **net receipt**	$\frac{26{,}920 \text{ francs}}{2 \text{ ares}}$ = **13,460 francs per are**	in local currency
❍ **gross productivity of labour** equals	$\frac{33{,}705 \text{ francs}}{28 \text{ days}}$ = **1,204 francs per work day**	in local currency
❍ **net productivity of labour** equals	$\frac{26{,}920 \text{ francs}}{28 \text{ days}}$ = **961 francs per work day**	in local currency

Net productivity of labour is the actual sum the grower earns for his work. It is, at is were, the daily wage earned after the production costs have been deducted.

Measuring return and productivity – summing up

If the agricultural production of a garden or an orchard has to be calculated, all the plants exploited or present in the garden must be taken into account. Then the contribution of every species is estimated for quantity and quality.

❑ **Quantitative elements** are those that can be measured, weighed, counted, calculated, i.e. the overall 'production' from each species whether it be in the form of agricultural goods or vegetal residues restored to the land. In an oil palm plantation, for instance, production is expressed in the number of litres of palm and palm kernel oil, the weight of the palm-kernel cakes after oil extraction, the litres of palm wine tapped, the amount of leaves for home crafts or the actual number of baskets, mats and fences made from them. For crops like cassava, taro and sweet potato, the tubers and leaves harvested during their respective cultural seasons are measured. Yields from African elemi (incense tree) are found by weighing the fruit and counting the number of resin bricks. Depending on the species, quantitative elements will be more or less diversified.

❑ **Qualitative elements** are harder to estimate, but it is worth doing so in order to determine the value of a species and its role in the environment: nutritive value, soil cover, increased infiltration, loosening earth due to the root system, cooling effect on the ground surface and reduced evaporation.

The species mentioned in this book

A very wide variety of vegetables, fruits, condiments and spices are eaten in Africa and it would be impossible to cover them all in this book. Some species are known in particular regions, and unknown in neighbouring territories.

Table 29 lists the species frequently mentioned in Parts I and II of the book. These have been divided under six major headings for easier reference. The abbreviation **SP** refers to the systematic description of the plant found in Part II of this book. This gives details of structure, uses and cultural requirements, together with photographs and some vernacular names.

In this book, the user's point of view has been adopted as opposed to that of the botanist. The reason for this practical approach is simple . Produce from the same plant is often used and eaten in many ways. The cashew tree, for example, yields apples and nuts. The acid apple is eaten raw and fresh, but the nuts are dried before use. Another example – the leaves, flesh and seeds of some cucurbits are all eaten.

In addition, the same vegetable or fruit can be eaten and commercialized both fresh and dried, with different characteristics in both cases. Two examples are green beans and their dried seeds (pulses), and okra fruit fresh or sun-dried. A product is said to be a vegetable, a fruit or a condiment depending on its culinary preparation.

The **plant index** gives all the vegetable and fruit species referred to, with their scientific names.

People name plants in the common or vernacular language of their particular country or region. The name of a plant in the common or vernacular language will vary from country to country and even within the regions of a country. For example *bush greens* are called 'folong' in Ewondo (Cameroun) 'tété' in Yoruba (Nigeria), 'bura-bura-ba' in Bambara (Mali), 'imbwija' in Rwandan, 'mchicha' in Swahili, 'amarante' in French. To avoid the confusion caused by such a diversity of names, all plants have a scientific Latin name. *Adansonia* is the scientific or Latin name for the baobab tree, *Amaranthus* for bush greens, *Dacryodes* for the native pear, *Lycopersicum* for the tomato, and so on. The scientific names in Latin are recognized all over the world.

29. Main vegetable, fruit and condiment species

The reference **SP** in brackets is the number of the systematic description found in Part II of the book (Chapters 20 to 27). Some species are mentioned in two or three different categories because they have many uses.

30

Leaf vegetables and potherbs

These vegetables are usually eaten fresh, but they can also be dried and stored.

Baobab (SP2)
Basil (SP4)
Bauhinia ***(figure 32)***
Beans
Bitter Leaf (SP19)
Black Plum (SP56)
Bungu (SP72)
Bush Greens (Amaranths) (SP1)
Cabbage (SP6)
Cassava
Cat's whiskers, Bastard Mustard (SP10)
Costus (SP8)
Cowpea (SP67)
Cucurbits (Chapter 22)
Eggplants (SP20)
Fennel
Foetid Cassia (SP5)
Drumstick (SP15)
Indian Spinach (SP3)
Jute, Jew's Mallow, (SP7)
Leek (SP17)
Lettuce (SP11)
Mint
New Zealand Spinach (SP18)
Nightshade (SP 12 to 14)
Okra (SP24)
Onion (SP79)
Parsley
Purslane (SP9)
Red Flower Silk and Silk Cotton (SP85)
Roselle, Jamaican Sorrel (SP16)
Sugar Cane
Sweet potato
Taro, Dasheen
Waterleaf (SP9)

Savoury vegetable fruits, eaten raw or cooked

Most of these fruits, popularly called 'vegetables' must be cooked before eating. Avocados are eaten raw, tomatoes are eaten raw or cooked.

African Elemi ***(figure 37)***
Avocado
Bush Butter (SP30)
Chillies, Sweet Peppers (SP27)
Cucurbits (Chapter 22)
Eggplant (SP20)
Green or Garden Peas
Monkey Bread (SP2)
Okra (SP24)
Plantain
Runner or French Beans
Tomato (SP33)

Spicy fruits, flowers and barks

These are used in small quantities for seasoning relishes. They can be used fresh, or dried for later use.

Spicy fruits

Chillies (SP27)
Desert Date (SP21)
Dum Palm (SP74)
Fagara (SP22)
Pepper (SP28 and 29)
Tamarind (SP31)
Tetrapleura (SP32)
Wild Cardamom, Grains of Paradise (SP26)

Barks

Garlic Tree (SP84)
Triumphetta (SP86)

Flowers

Baobab (SP2)
Gardenia
Red Flower Silk and Silk Cotton (SP85)

Seeds and nuts

Some are eaten raw, like the cashew nut. Others are crushed and added to relishes.

African Fan Palm (SP78)
African Locust Bean (SP66)
Akee Apple (SP63)
Beans
Bixa orellana (SP71)
Calabash nutmeg (SP62)
Cashew (SP59)
Cayor Apple (SP54)
Coconut (SP76)
Cowpea (SP67)
Cucurbits (Chapter 22)
Dika Nut (SP61)
Dum Nut (SP74)
Bambara Groundnut
Gabon or African Nut (SP69)
Groundnut
Indian Jujube (SP25)
Kola (SP 60)
Njansan (Ricinodendron) (SP68)
Orere (SP65)
Palm Nut (SP75)
Peas
Pigeon Pea (SP70)
Poupartia (SP53)
Roselle, Jamaican sorrel (SP16)
Sesame (SP72)
Shea Butter (SP64)
Sunflower ***(figure 31)***

32

31

Sweet and acid fruits

They are eaten raw with meals, or on their own. They are also stewed.

African Fan Palm (SP78)
Annonaceae (SP46)
Aphania senegalensis (SP48)
Black Plum (SP58)
Cape Gooseberry(SP52)
Carambola (SP47)
Cashew (SP59)
Cayor Apple (SP59)
Citrus (Orange, Lemon, Grapefruit, Mandarin)
Date (SP73)
Guava
Indian Jujube (SP25)
Lannea acida (SP57)
Mango
Mombins (SP53)
Monkey Guava (SP50)
Papaya
Passion Fruit (SP55)
Pineapple
Poupartia (SP53)
Sapodilla
Shea Butter (SP64)
Strawberry (SP51)
Sweet Banana
Sweet Dattock (SP49)
Sycamore Fig (SP23)
Tamarind (SP31)
Tree Tomato (SP56)
Watermelons (SP34)

Bulbs, roots and tubers

African Fan palm (SP78)
Carrot (SP80)
Coleus (SP81)
Garlic (SP79)
Ginger (SP82)
Lotus ***(figure 30)***
Onion (SP79)
Shallot (SP79)
Tiger Nut (SP83)
Turmeric (SP82)
Yam

Families, species and varieties

All the plants discovered worldwide have been examined for their similarities and differences, and have been divided into **families**, **genera** and **species.**

Plants of the same species are able to fertilize one another, this capacity being the main criterion for defining species. Just as a rabbit cannot fertilize a hen, so taro pollen cannot fertilize the flower of the black nightshade growing beneath it, or vice versa **(figure 33).** Other criteria also help to differenciate species - the characteristics of the flowers, fruits, leaves, stems, etc.

Plants of the same species can differ widely, these are called **varieties** or **cultivars**. A typical example are the two varieties of sweet potato **(figure 34)** that can easily be recognized by the habit of their leaves and the colour of the tubers. Contrasts in varieties based on visible botanical differences such as structure of leaves, habit of plant, colour of flowers, kind of stems and roots, are important. But, from the practical point of view, cultural characteristics are what matter most : long or short life cycle, resistance to disease, fertility or sterility, productivity and the like.

33

34

35

These are the differences characterizing **cultural varieties**.

Some species abound in varieties, for instance, bean, banana, rice, chillies, okra.

Knowing plant varieties allows the cultivator to choose the best method of propagation, to decide crop associations, to space out seeding in time, to stagger production. Any decline in varietal stock should be interpreted by the farmer as a degradation of his economic situation until such time as he can count on the efficiency of the replacement varieties offered him.

Species of plants are all grouped into genera, which in turn are grouped into families according to similarities. The size of these families varies. In horticulture, *Solanaceae* and *Cucurbitaceae* are two important families. Solanaceae include chillies, peppers, tomatoes, eggplants, nightshades, potatoes, these are all easily recognized by their small star-shaped flowers. Cucurbitaceae are also recognized by their flowers, and their climbing or creeping habit. This family includes marrows, cucumbers, melons, watermelons, pumpkins, courgettes and gherkins.

Leguminosae, **Gramineae** and **Palmae** (respectively legumes, grasses and palms) are three well-known plant families, which include a large number of similar looking species.

Details on classifications in Botany are outside the scope of this book. We need only remember that, depending on similarities, plants belong to varieties, species and families.

Gardening as a special branch of farming

The economy of gardens is quite different from the economy of field cropping because of the great diversity of garden produce and its many uses. Gardens produce a little of everything. Some of the plants cultivated can be used in many different ways and the variety of plants can help to extend the active farming season. Gardens are places where horticulture can be associated with livestock.

Gardens are places where a little of everything is found

The family garden in **figure 5** is **a place where one should be able to find a little of everything : fruits, vegetables, condiments, medicinal herbs, dyes, wood for fires or building, poles, fibres, flowers, incense, calabashes, loofahs.**

As was already stressed, diversity in plants leads to diversity in family diet. It also ensures a **better continuity of income**. In the garden in **figure 35,** there is always some produce waiting to be picked, pulled or cut, no matter what the time of the year, whether it be njansan seeds, palm nuts, bananas, bitter leaf, citrus fruits, soursop, cassava, yam, cocoyam, medicinal herbs, calabashes or wood. When the woman of the house feels the need, she can harvest some produce and sell it. Diversity in the garden is a factor that helps spread farm income, and is therefore of considerable importance in regions where farm work in cropping fields is limited by the short duration of the rains.

36

Notes

A garden is an extension to the home for the women. There is always something to be done there, especially when work in the fields has eased off. During slack periods, the garden will supply the materials or produce the housewife needs for some household or artisan job, for example, fibres for baskets, dyes for cloth, calabashes to make bottles and containers, loofahs, medicinal herbs to be dried.

Gardens are often part of the kitchen, an extension of the housewife's realm where she finds ingredients for cooking and for sale. Unfortunately, the garden is often far too small and badly looked after. There is not enough room; water and seeds are in short supply.

Yet gardening is **an effective means of overcoming shortages due to drought,** especially if this activity is aimed at exploiting all the natural resources.

Trees in gardens

In dry regions, multi-storey cropping is an intelligent way of using the small quantities of water available during the dry season **(figure 36)**. Thanks to a shallow pool and a well, the grower can water the garden for many months of the dry season. In fact, he manages to cultivate seasonal plants from July to February, although the rains are over in October. He has to stop cultivation in March for lack of water. **The cultural calendar** can also be extended by planting trees that will stay green during the dry season, for instance, different species of acacia, cassias and neems. These trees are planted at the onset of the rains to give them time to root deeply. Rain and irrigation water help them to become well established. In the end, they will give shade during the dry season and cool the cultivated garden soil.

By planting and managing trees, the climatic conditions in the garden are modified. The cultivated trees are **ecologically useful,** because they change or conserve the environment of other plants. A few months are added to the horticultural season, and this is quite an achievement in a region where rainfed crops can only be grown for 4 to 5 months each year. Planting a range of different tree species gives the gardener a wider range of produce and keeps the **family busy** at times when farmwork is usually at a standstill.

37

38

39

Species with many uses

Many species of plants and trees are exploited in several ways. Here are some examples.

The African elemi tree *(Canarium schweinfurthii)* grows in wet regions **(figure 37)**. Elemi fruit is eaten raw, boiled, fried or grilled **(figure 38)**. The hard stones are used for handicrafts (games, clappers), or for flooring. Red-hot elemi stones dropped into a glass of water are said to make a good gargle for sore throats. Elemi also produces fragrant resin used as incense and as fire-lighters. **Figure 39** from the Cameroun shows processed resin sold in brick-form. The resin is also used to seal bottles and to waterproof containers. The caterpillars that

40

41

Managing and exploiting gardens means keeping in mind the ecological utility of the plants growing there and the countless ways in which the produce can be used.

Small animals and bees in gardens

Poultry, rabbits, and bees are all associated with gardens.

Rearing poultry (hens and guinea fowl) is combined with gardening (**figure 42**). Half the food comes from cereal grown in the cropping fields. The other half consists of garden trash - stalks and stems, fruits unfit for consumption, weeds from vegetable beds.

At the start of every cultural season, the henhouse floor is raked, crushed and spread on the beds, thus providing a rich organic fertilizer. When the

live on the leaves can also be eaten fried **(figure 40)** and when the tree is cut down, the trunk can be exploited for its hard wood.

Leaves from **bitter leaf shrubs** *(Vernonia)* are a widely used potherb. The raw leaves are used as a cure for jaundice. Unpruned shrubs supply long, thin poles used for firewood or as props for climbing plants. Vernonia plants, in association with other species, form good quickset hedges.

Oil palm, in fact all palms (African fan and date palms, for example), can also be exploited in many ways. Oil palm yields palm oil, kernel oil, palm cabbage i.e. the terminal bud, dried leaves, fibres for sponges. Note that edible white larvae make their habitat on palms. Palm roots are used in a cure for rheumatism. Decaying palm trunks provide a good habitat for edible mushrooms **(figure 41)**.

Many potherbs are used in a variety of ways. Fresh leaves from the sweet potato are used for treating burns. Moist leaves are sometimes used to poultice boils.

Seeds from **Njansan** *(Ricinodendron heudelotii)* are used in sauces, the bark can be decocted and is sometimes used for healing open wounds.

42

43

henhouse has an earth floor, the soil a few centimetres below the surface is full of earthworms that are an asset in gardens.

A rabbit hutch is seen in **figure 43**. The rabbits are reared in small wire cages. The floor of these cages is made of wiremesh to let the droppings fall onto the ground where they can easily be swept up and spread on the vegetable beds.

Rabbits are fed on waste from vegetable crops, thus turning it into valuable protein.

Beekeeping combined with gardening is a worthwhile activity **(figure 44)**. Bees produce honey and play a significant role in pollinating flowers.

Yields from certain fruit trees can be increased by between 30 and 40% when bees fertilize the flowers.

44

The many functions of gardens

The economy of gardens is different from that of cropping fields because production factors can be combined in all sorts of different ways on a very small piece of land.

The examples given below show the need to examine garden plants for the different functions they fulfil.

- They have **an economic role to play** because they yield food products and by-products, products used in medicine, in the home, in clothing, in arts and crafts. Produce can be consumed, or sold to ensure an income.
- They have **an ecological role to play.** Plants, especially perennials, influence the living and physical environments. They produce vegetal manure in the form of humus, they help to control erosion, they create shade, they intercept wind, they promote rainwater infiltration.
- Some plants have **a direct agricultural role** to play. Like legumes, they fertilize the soil, they prop up other plants, they protect others from disease (Chapter 9).
- Plants also play **a social role.** Hedges and trees delimit farm boundaries. Trees shelter family and community activities. They give shade.
- Because of their diversity, garden plants growing in association really help to ensure safe, regular food supplies. In a well-kept garden, food for a side dish or food to round off a meal (Chapter 2) will always be found to make the main dish more nourishing or to improve the children's diet. Basically, developing the family garden is a way of improving the family's health.

Chapter 2

Vegetables, fruits and condiments - health foods

If we want to produce and eat a healthy, balanced diet, we must know the substances that make up the human body and what people must eat to remain healthy. We must also know something about the value of the food we eat and the best way of preparing it.

The food man needs

What is the human body made of?

The human body is composed of :

- muscle, flesh, intestines, brain and skin are the **soft parts** of the human body;
- bones, cartilage, nails and hairs are the **harder**, sometimes rigid **parts**. The bones of the human skeleton support the softer parts;
- blood and tissue-fluids are the **liquid parts** of the human body.

45

Living beings - man, animals and plants - are all composed in a similar way. Animals are also composed of the different parts listed above. As for plants, they have rigid and soft parts in which the sap and water flow.

All the parts of the human or animal body and of plants are made from chemical substances that are classified under the following major headings:

- **lipids** (fats, oils, butters),
- **carbohydrates** (sugars, starches),
- **proteins,**
- **vitamins,**
- **mineral salts,**
- **water**.

All these substances, each in its own way, help build living organisms, keep them alive and active.

In the context of this book, there is no need to explain in detail how the human body uses these substances. But it is vitally important to know that, **to be well-fed and in good health, man must eat a balanced diet containing all these substances. This can be achieved by eating all the varied plant and animal foods to be found in the environment.**

What should people eat to remain healthy?

A balanced meal is on the lines of ' tchébou djène', the Cameroun dish (**figure 1)** or of the Burkina dish 'soumbala' in **figure 45**. It is composed of a **staple food, complementary foods** and a **sauce** with condiments.

Table 46 summarizes what we need to know about healthy eating.

46 What makes a diet healthy

Staple foods give the **energy** we need to move, lift heavy objects, walk and run. The human body uses these foods whenever it needs **movement.** Staples containing a large proportion of carbohydrates are the foods needed after a hard day's work and should be eaten too, before people set out for work.

Staples **fill the stomach.** Quantity is more important than quality.

Among the energy-giving foods we find flours, couscous, cereals like rice, millet, sorghum and maize, banana, bread, pulses and tubers.

a staple food

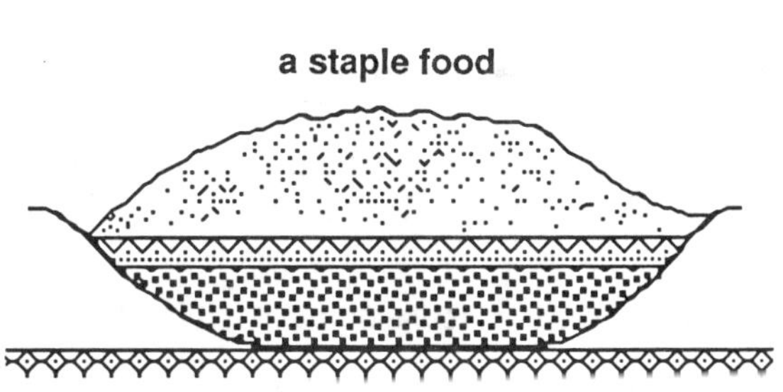

complementary foods

Complementary foods are those that lend variety to diet. **They add a little of everything :** glycosides, lipids, proteins, vitamins, mineral salts. All these substances make for a **nourishing**, balanced diet. Thanks to them, the body finds everything it needs **to make it healthy.**

As for quantity, in a balanced meal complementary foods are less abundant than staples and in a well-composed diet, they come to between 10 and 30% of the weight of the total food ration.

All vegetables, fruits, meat, fish, eggs, seafoods, cheeses, milk and mushrooms are suitable complements for staple foods. Their real value lies in the fact that they supply the body with lots of **proteins**, **mineral salts** and **vitamins**.

Condiments and extras are added in small quantities to the foods mentioned. As a rule, condiments are thoroughly mixed into the accompanying sauce that makes the dish tasty. Condiments are not to be despised because

- they improve the **aroma** and **flavour** of foods,
- they change the **texture** and **consistency** of sauces, for example, by making them thick or sticky,
- they increase the number of nutritive elements on which the body is fed,
- they can change the **colour** of sauces or **make other foods tender**,
- some of them are **good for health**, or **may have curative properties**.

condiments and extras

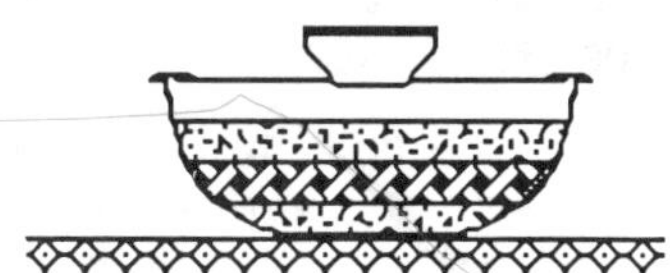

Condiments are of vegetal and mineral, rarely of animal, origin. Condiments are described in detail later in the book.

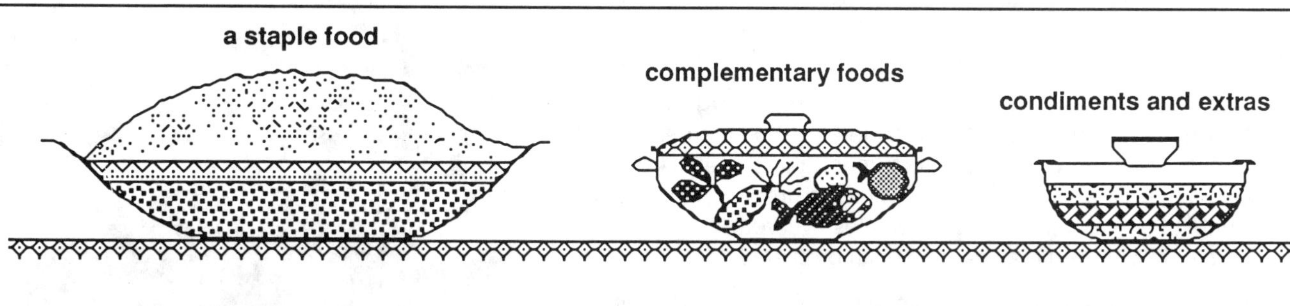

A balance between these three kinds of foods makes for **a balanced diet.**

Lack of any of these categories or **eating too much** of any of them will cause **ill health.**

Foodstuffs

The chemical properties of food crops

It is not easy to group foodstuffs into well-defined categories because their chemical composition is very variable. Generally only the proportions of fat, protein, carbohydrate and mineral salts need be taken into account.

However, to make discussion easier, it is usual to separate foods into **a few major categories** :

- Groundnut, sunflower, shea butter, njansan *(Ricinodendron heudolotii)*, oil palm, moabi *(Baillonella toxisperma)*, soya and sesame all yield **oilseeds with** a high oil content ranging from 10 to 25% of total weight. There are also valuable **oily (oleaginous) fruits,** such as avocado and akee apple.

  These foods contain other chemical substances. The **oil cakes** left over after oil extraction from seeds and fruits contain proteins, sugars, mineral salts, and cellulose fibres. These fibres are also found, for example, in straw, banana and baobab bark, palm leaves, pea and bean pods. Human and animal organisms need cellulose to help the digestion. This is called **roughage**.

- Vegetable marrows, peas, cowpea, locust bean, pigeon pea, groundnut, Bambara groundnut, soya, cashew, coconut, and roselle are examples of plants yielding **seeds rich in protein**. They are excellent complementary foods, of particular value to children and to people suffering from malnutrition.

  All **legume seeds** are rich in protein and this is a major reason for associating legumes with cereal crops. In fact, most edible nuts and seeds coming from species other than legumes are also rich in protein and make first-class complementary foods. Proteins and oils are often found together in seeds and nuts. Groundnut, soya, cashew nut and some cucurbita are in this category.

- The word **cereals** describes the seeds borne by grasses, i.e. plants from the **Gramineae** family that includes millet, sorghum, fonio, maize, rice, wheat, elephant grass, tef. Cereals contain mostly carbohydrates, and from 7 to 12% proteins. Some cereal germs, maize for instance, contain a fair amount of oil. Cereals are excellent staple foods because the ratio of protein to starch is greater than in tubers.

  Tubers - cassava, sweet potato, taro, cocoyam, potato, coleus, yam - are **starchy foods**. Banana, breadfruit **(figure 47)** and baobab fruits (monkey bread) are also rich in carbohydrate. All these make good staple food. Their protein content is insignificant (at most 3%) and they contain no fats. The advantage of starchy plants is their high crop yields per unit/area.

  Starches on their own are not healthy foods. They provide bulk. People who only eat starchy foods, without animal products, vegetables and fruit, suffer from malnutrition and poor health with diseases like kwashiorkor and are liable to succumb to infections.

  The advantages of starchy plants is their high crop yield per unit area.

- **Vegetables, fruits and condiments** are nourishing foods because they contain **a little of all the substances** man needs : proteins, some mineral salts, sugars, vitamins, aromatics, colouring agencies, iron and essential oils, that increase man's resistance to disease.

- Indeed, in this class of food, man finds the wide **range of nutritive elements he needs**. Vegetables are therefore complementary foods of the first order, and are much more important for man's health than products of animal origin. Nobody will suffer from eating quite large amounts of different fruits and vegetables, whereas eating too much meat is pointless and may cause health problems.

  Most fruits, especially acid fruits like pineapple, lemon, mango, fresh grains of paradise and cashew apple contribute to good health because they contain **vitamins.** Vitamins are complex chemical compounds which are essential in very small quantities for the normal activities of the body. Vitamins increase the body's resistance to disease and without them, the body will show symptoms of ill health. About a dozen vitamins and their characteristics are known to scien-

47

tists. Vitamins are necessary for healthy skin and bones and all parts of the body.

Since **vitamins are often destroyed in cooking, fruits and raw vegetables**, carefully washed, **must be eaten regularly**.

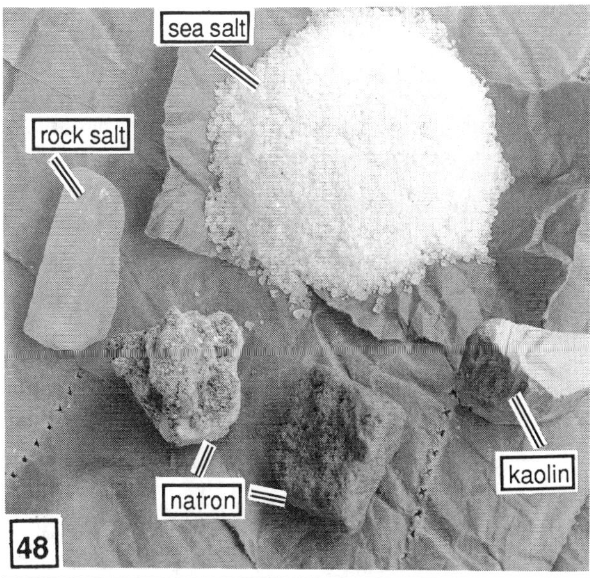

48

Mineral condiments

Most condiments are of mineral or vegetal origin; a few are of animal origin.

Many vegetal condiments are mentioned in this book (see **table 29** and Part II) and there is no need to discuss them here at length. However, a word should be said about those condiments of mineral origin that are used all the time in cooking - sea salt, rock salt and natron **(figure 48)**, ashes, edible clays, kaolin, etc.

- **Sea salt** is obtained by evaporating sea water in salt works. All countries with coastlines are able to produce salt. Sea salt is good because it contains many mineral elements and is therefore preferable to refined salt.

49

- **Refined salt** comes from sea salt. The latter is worked until the cristals only contain sodium chloride, a chemically pure substance. Where nutrition is concerned, there is nothing to be gained from refining salt. Salt is refined for commercial reasons only. Refined salt is less water-retentive than sea salt that gets damp quickly and is harder to store.

- **Rock salt** is extracted from mines situated in deserts. Entire seas evaporated in ancient times, leaving large, grey, translucid cristals on the spot. These cristals have qualities comparable to those of sea salt and can be used by man and animals.

- **Natron,** seen in two forms in **figure 48**, is a **mixture** of salts, clays and some impurities. It contains sodium chloride and **bicarbonate of soda.** This substance is used by doctors to help **digestion,** and by housewives to soften vegetables during cooking and to give them a good colour.

The impurities in natron have their nutritional use because they give the body mineral elements which are not found in over-refined, purified foods.

- **Home-made salts** are produced by artisans who filter salty earth or boil filtered water. In **figure 49**, earth collected in a mangrove is filtered in order to extract the salt. The salty solution is then heated and evaporated until dry cristals are obtained **(figure 50)**.

The same method of filtering and evaporation is used to extract **vegetable salts** of which there are many kinds - from banana, palms, reeds, etc. The plants are heated on a metal sheet until they turn to ashes. The ashes are then put into a filter similar to the one in **figure 49** and washed with water, after which the salty solution is evaporated as in **figure 50**.

50

- **Kaolin** is used in small quantities to thicken sauces. Its food value should not be undervalued. It contains a considerable number of rather rare minerals which the body needs in tiny doses.
- There are also composite commercial condiments produced on an industrial scale, items like maggi cubes and meat extracts. These artificial commodities are being used more and more widely, especially in urban areas.

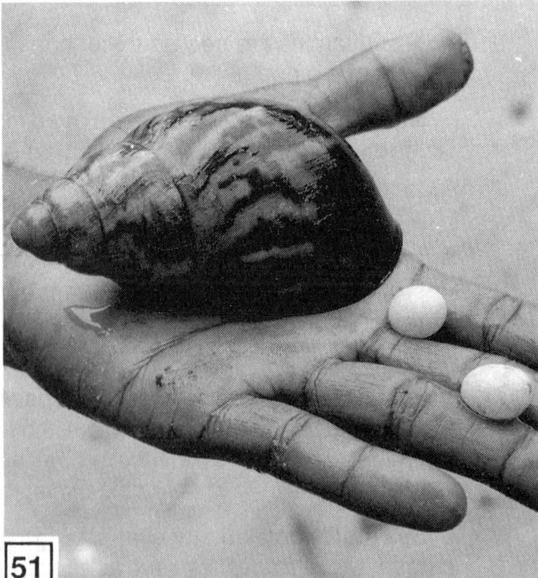

51

Provided they are used in small quantities, mineral condiments are essential for health. Here too, diversity in mineral intake is important.

52

Additional types of food

We all know foods that seem exceptional, because they are unusual, or taste different or have to be specially prepared. We realize that these foods are not really necessary, but they are very much appreciated. They can be paste made from cucumber seeds seasoned with brown piquant ants, or a dish of palm worms or grilled crickets, or yoghurt.

Congealed blood, shellfish and oysters, some termites, caterpillars or insects, eggs or snails **(figure 51)**, edible mushrooms such as *Termitomyces* that grow on termite hills **(figure 52)** or raw fruits, belong to the 'extras' containing all kinds of vitamins and substances essential for human health.

Beverages also round off meals. They contribute the water which is essential. (The body consists of about 80% water.) Some drinks are nutritious and/or good for the health in general - milk, palm wine, beers made from sorghum, millet and banana, fruit juices, herbal infusions.

Other drinks are not so beneficial, especially when certain substances are present to excess. High alcohol-content in palm wine and beers has detrimental effects on the nutritional value of these drinks. Drinks that have been sweetened and coloured artifically, lemonades, for instance, serve to quench one's thirst but are useless nutritionally. In fact, the colouring agencies used are often harmful.

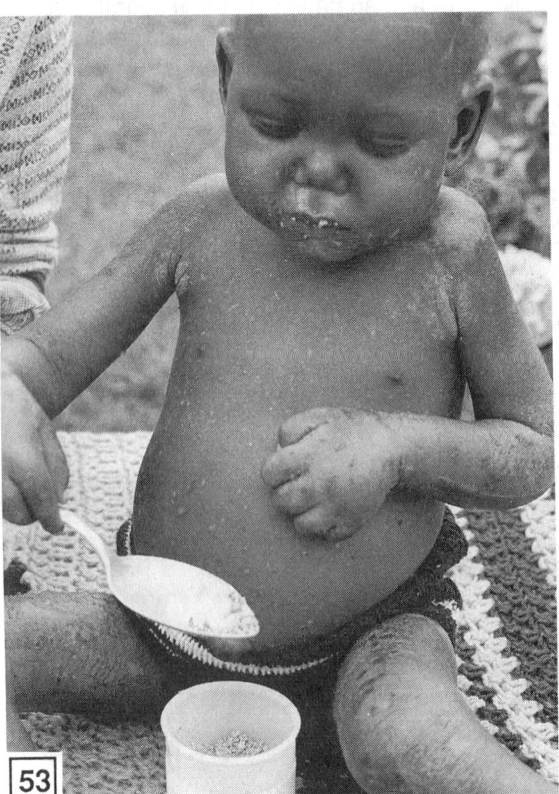

53

A varied diet means a balanced diet

The child in **figure 53** is obviously suffering from malnutrition. He has kwashiorkor, a disease caused by imbalance in diet. The child **gets enough starchy staples but too few complementary foods.**The belly is swollen, the skin whitish, tissues are soft.The victim is weak and often sick. He will only recover if he gets a properly balanced diet with the right amount of fruit, vegetables, meat, fish, milk, etc. Marasmus is another children's disease brought about by malnutrition. Children get marasmus when they are deprived of good food in sufficient quantities.

Although diseases caused by **malnutrition** are unfortunately all too frequent, there are also diseases caused by **overeating** or eating the wrong kinds of foods which are very common. Some forms of obesity are due to an unbalanced diet, that is to say, eating too many foods and drinks loaded with sugars and fats. People who eat too much meat may get liver and heart complaints or diseased arteries. People who use excessive amounts of salt may damage the arteries, and those who live on banana beer or palm wine may end up by developing cirrhosis of the liver.

In Bamileke country in Cameroun, there is an expression that sums up the best way of preparing family meals and especially 'nkwi' sauce. It is 'dom pa, dom na' which, translated literally, means 'so much couscous, so much sauce'. This means that couscous on its own will not nourish the family, but neither will sauce.

In conclusion, we can say that **being healthy involves eating a little of everything in sufficient quantities but not to excess**.

Nutritional aspects of food processing

The way in which foodstuffs are processed, stored and cooked alters their value both nutritionally and economically. Crushing, drying, cooking, soaking, salting, fermenting, all these operations change the chemical composition of farm produce. These methods also allow food commodities to be stored without rotting, and their sale value is often increased.

In some cases, food must be treated before consumption. Bitter leaf and bush greens must be cooked before eating ; bitter cassava must be fermented to rid it of toxins; locust bean seeds must be cooked and left to ferment for quite some time.

Here are some ways of treating food.

Peeling

The skin of some produce cannot be eaten either because it is **too tough** (banana, avocado, mango), or because it is **toxic** like the skin of raw potato. Certain skins can be eaten (tomato, eggplant, sweet peppers) and have a **nutritive value**.

The need to peel vegetables sometimes depends on the degree of ripeness. Beans picked when still green can be cooked and eaten in the pod. Pods are a useful food because of the proteins and roughage they contain. However, the skin of ripe beans is hard and only the seeds (pulses) can be eaten.

Fresh produce that is going to be stored or sold should not be peeled. Every effort should be made to **avoid damaging skins and barks,** because cuts and bruises allow bacteria that cause rotting to enter.

Mortars and pestles, huskers, or mills are used for husking cereals. The grains and chaff (the husks or hard outer skin of the grains) are then separated by using a winnowing fan **(figure 55)** or a winnowing machine. Cereals should not be completely husked as this removes some of the nutritional value. The chaff need only be removed without peeling the grain.

Figure 54 shows the different parts of a grain of rice - chaff, germ, and outer layer called the aleurone. Chaff cannot be eaten and must be removed. The outer layer is full of vitamins and minerals, so that husking should avoid removing this very rich part of the grain. The reason behind pearling and polishing rice is purely commercial and is senseless with regard to food value because the best part of the grain is either thrown away or used for animal feed.

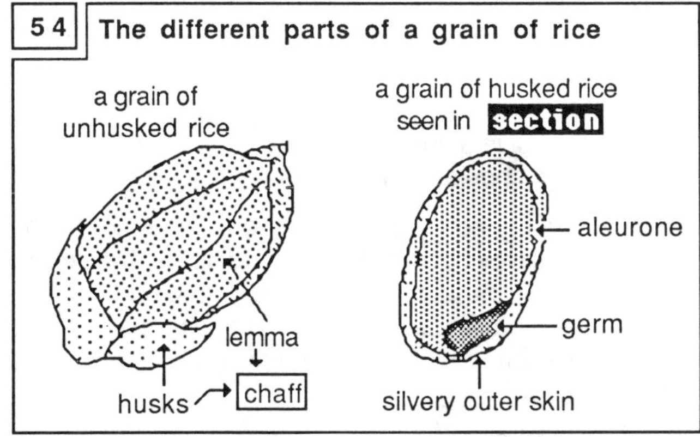

As a general rule, **white, refined flours from which the bran and germs have been removed are not as nourishing as whole flours obtained by merely grinding whole grain.**

Figure 56 shows how groundnuts are skinned in order to prepare a seed sauce. The nuts are scalded (see below), so that the seed coats peel off easily.

Soaking

Some dry produce must be **soaked** for a number of hours before cooking. Items like dried beans and peas are

56

soaked to absorb water and soften. Soaking shortens cooking time. Once they have been soaked, pulses cannot be sold because they ferment quickly.

Soaking is also a way of cleaning food and getting rid of impurities : empty seeds, little bits of straw and wood float, while pebbles sink to the bottom of the bowl.

Scalding or blanching

Scalding means plunging food rapidly into boiling water. There are two main reasons for this method:

- **it makes skinning and shelling easier.** The skin of a fruit or vegetable seed is loosened by the action of hot water, and is easily removed by hand ;

57

- scalding is frequently used to **eliminate bitter flavours**. Some bitter leaf is being scalded in **figure 57**. The leaves are plunged into boiling water for a minute, then drained and pressed to remove all the bitter green liquid. They are then cooked in a second lot of water.

Soaking and scalding are often necessary as we have just explained, but these preliminaries have their disadvantages too. The water in which food is soaked or scalded absorbs the bitter flavour but, at the same time, removes other elements, more specifically mineral salts and vitamins. **Scalding must therefore be done as quickly as possible and in a minimum of water if vegetables are to retain all their nutritive qualities.**

Grinding

Grinding foodstuffs means **turning them into flours** or powders when they are dry (cereals, dried leaves, etc.), or **into pastes** when they are wet (banana, groundnut, pistachio nut, leaves).

When dry food is ground into flour or powder, the process helps cooking water to penetrate the food mass and make it stick together in lumps or balls. On the other hand, if food is moist when ground, it tends to lose its juices that are transformed by contact with air. If the ground product is let stand, it will ferment quickly.

58

Apart from flours and very dry powders which can be kept in damp-proof containers and bags, foodstuffs should be pounded only just before use.

Stone grinding and pounding are the most traditional ways of grinding foods at home **(figure 58).** But as these tasks are often slow and tedious, women are only too pleased to use mechanized mills when it comes to grinding cereals or dried tubers.

Refining foodstuffs

Refining is the process of removing all the impurities from a product to make it more useful or palatable or to improve the keeping qualities. For example, pressing oil seeds separates the oil from the cake or fibre. Unrefined oils are coloured - palm oil is reddish, shea oil brownish. The colour is caused by the impurities in the unrefined oil which will make it go rancid or sour quickly. The oil can be filtered in factories to remove the impurities leaving an almost colourless oil.

Flours can be refined by repeated sieving to remove all impurities leaving only the white starch. However, this removes the bran and the crushed germs (embryos) which are the most nutritive parts, containing proteins, vitamins and minerals. These parts of the seed removed by overrefining can be used for the manufacture of animal feed.

When people eat white rice, bread and pasta, they are getting excellent energy foods but are forfeiting the benefit of the proteins, vitamins and mineral salts originally contained in the grains that served to make these white foods.

Just as unrefined oil goes rancid, so whole flour can go sour because of the impurities it contains. Refined flour keeps longer and is therefore more commercial.

As with salt mentioned earlier in the chapter, sugar can also be refined and becomes snow white as opposed to the yellowy or brownish colour of unrefined sugar.

59

60

61

Refining foodstuffs, a practice uncommon in homes, entails more disadvantages than advantages when examined from a nutritional angle. Foodstuffs are refined for reasons connected with marketing and storage.

Drying foodstuffs

Harvested produce always contains water. Water in fresh vegetables and fruits can account for 80 to 95% of their weight, whereas it accounts for only 12 to 15% of the weight of dry nuts and.seeds.

Water in harvested produce encourages the growth of fungi that cause fermentation and rot. **Drying consists in lowering the amount of water in the product so that the development of fungi is inhibited.** It is generally considered that a product with less than 10 to 12% water cannot be spoilt by microorganisms. Drying foods therefore involves lowering their moisture content to below these percentages. Remember, however, that drying does not prevent insect infestation.

Drying is carried out by evaporating the water contained in the product. When the air is very dry as in Sudan and the Sahel, the product need only be spread on the ground, preferably on matting as in **figure 59**.

Figure 60 shows sixteen vegetables dried in this way in Northern Burkina Faso. After drying, the produce is stored in jars like those seen in **figure 61**.

It is better to dry food slowly in the shade, rather than expose it to direct sunshine. In the shade, drying depends on the difference in moisture between the food and the air.

In wet regions where the air is humid, drying in the shade never suffices to lower the moisture content to below 10 or 12%; drying in the sun or in drying sheds will be needed. Once dried, the produce must be immediately stored in airtight containers (bottles, glazed jars, plastic bags). If the dried foods are exposed to air, they will absorb moisture once more.

62

Heating foods may degrade their nutritive qualities and should therefore be avoided, especially for fruit and vegetables. Heat is not so important where tubers, seeds and nuts are concerned.

Foods can be dried artificially by means of hot air that is made to circulate through each layer of the produce. This hot air removes the water contained in the food.

Fermentation

There are many kinds of fermentation some of which are valuable in processing food, others are not so important while still others are dangerous. A change in the appearance or taste of foods is one sign of fermentation. Gas bubbles form in liquids and break on the surface ; products become vinegary or alcoholic; there is a characteristic smell.

Uncontrolled fermentations lead to putrefaction, whereas **controlled fermentations give valuable results** :

63

- Fermentation changes food and makes it more **digestible.** Fermented seeds from the locust bean are used, for example, in soumbala because they can only be digested after fermentation.

  Curdled milk, yoghurt and cheeses are products obtained by fermentation from fresh milk.

- Fermentation **enriches** foods. The microorganisms that cause controlled fermentation give people a supplementary food and add variety to diet. Moreover, microorganisms are needed to make the digestive system function properly ;
- Fermentation can be used to **keep** some foods. A large dose of vinegar or alcohol produced by controlled fermentation prevents spoilage. Beers brewed from sorghum, banana and barley, wines and vinegars are simply fermented drinks that can also be distilled. The alcohol produced by microorganisms stops the proliferation of other microorganisms likely to cause putrefaction.

Cooking

Foods are cooked to make them tender and digestible, and to destroy the germs of most disease.

Many foods can be eaten either raw or cooked : cabbage, onion, bittereggplant, carrot, turnip, figs, jujubes, to mention a few. Cooking merely softens and heats these foods to make them into different, perhaps more attractive dishes, but does not increase their nutritional value.

Other produce must be cooked to make it digestible, for instance, runner beans, pulses, the leaves of nightshade and bitter leaf, okra, potato. Here, cooking **transforms** the chemical substances contained in the food and makes it palatable.

64

Softening, heating and transforming foods are important aspects of cooking. But cooking also makes food wholesome by getting rid of harmful microorganisms and germs adhering to it : amoeba, worms, germs of typhus, cholera and dysentery. The high temperatures of cooking kill most bacteria and their spores, if carried out long enough. This includes the bacteria causing fermentation and putrefaction.

Cooking is often necessary but overcooking has its drawbacks : it decomposes the food and causes loss of vitamins. Besides, cooking calls for wood, coal or gas. Why waste these fuels if the human body derives no benefit from overcooked food ?

There are many methods of cooking, each of which transforms food in different ways.

Cooking in water

Cooking in water is the most usual method **(figure 62)**. While the food is being cooked, it absorbs a certain amount of water and swells. Couscous, rice and millet are examples of food cooked in water.

Cooking water dissolves the mineral salts contained in the food. The longer the cooking, the more salts are lost with the discarded water. From this point of view, cooking chopped vegetables increases the loss of nutrients because the juices of the vegetable are dissolved into the water. It is, therefore, a good idea to save the cooking water, either to prepare other foods or just to drink the vegetable broth.

Braising means cooking in a little water in a tightly-lidded saucepan. It is a good method because the juices are saved to a large extent. In urban areas, some housewives **steam food** by using special saucepans called pressure cookers. The food is steamed in very little water.These cookers require a constant source of heat and are dangerous when used on open wood or coal fires. However, they preserve the food's nutritive qualities.

65

Regional cooking in West Africa : Tô

The basic ingredients for this dish are couscous, millet or sorghum. The sauce may contain soumbala, a fermented preparation with locust bean seeds, tamarind fruits and leaves, and roselle or bauhinia leaves ***(figure 32).*** *This is the general recipe for tô, but, depending on the region and the produce available, other ingredients might include :*

- *fresh or dried leaves of Jew's mallow, horseradish, baobab and foetid cassia,*
- *groundnut, Bambara groundnut, cowpea, cucurbit, roselle or other seeds,*
- *eggplants, tomatoes, okra, etc.,*
- *spices obtained from desert dates, jujubes, chillies, or silk cotton flowers,*
- *fats in the form of shea butter, groundnut oil.*

Tô becomes more nutritious when more ingredients are added.

Frying

Frying means cooking in oil. This method is appropriate for foods that cook fast and do not require much preparation. There is a difference between **shallow frying** when a little oil or fat is used (fried eggs are shallow-fried) and **deep frying** when food is plunged into a deep pan of oil as with fritters **(figure 63)**.

Frying is always faster than cooking in water. Fried foods deteriorate less because mineral salts are not so soluble in oil as in water and because a hard, protective coating quickly seals the fried food. Fried foods absorb a lot of overheated oil. Eating food fried in oil overheated again and again is not good for one's health. This is why frying oil must be changed at regular intervals to avoid ill-effects.

Grilling

This is a quick way of cooking without any liquid **(figure 64)**. Nutritive loses are minimal except in the burnt parts that are changed into charcoal.

Simple meals, complicated meals

Frying and grilling are simple ways of preparing food but there are more complicated ways, e.g. cooking in sauces. Regional cooking usually combines the simple and the complicated. 'Ndolé', a well-known regional dish from Southern Cameroun illustrates this point. It is prepared as follows :

- bitter leaf is washed and scalded,
- dried meat is soaked in hot water,
- onions are fried in the pan,
- groundnuts are scalded, peeled and crushed,
- the mashed leaves, onions and meat are then deep-fried in oil,
- plantain bananas and cassava flour are cooked in water.

Various condiments are used during preparation : bicarbonate of soda is added to the cooking water in order to make the bitter leaf tender and preserve its nice green colour. Salt, chillies and garlic complete the seasoning.

In urban communities, housewives tend to simplify food preparations because they cannot find all the vegetable and mineral ingredients of traditional regional dishes. This is an unfortunate trend nutritionally speaking. It is always advisable to diversify regional cuisines, to keep up and improve recipes. Such efforts encourage people to eat a varied diet as is shown in **table 65** where all the produce found in 'tô' a West African dish, is listed.

We have mentioned the different ways in which garden vegetables, fruits and condiments are processed and prepared in the home. The same methods are, for the most part, applied in industry. Food in factories is ground, milled, fermented, refined and cooked in order to sell or stock it. Industrial processing covers a great number of methods whose description, even in general terms, lies beyond the scope of this book. Readers interested in the subject should refer to our reading list.

Chapter 3

Laying out and preparing the land for cultivation

Since plant roots supply the water and mineral salts to the stems, good root growth is essential for strong, productive stems. If the roots are sickly, the plants cannot thrive and yields are low.

Tilling and seedbed preparation are very important because they establish the right soil conditions for good root growth. In order to obtain these conditions,

- the soil must be **loosened** to the right depth, i.e. one that allows roots to penetre with a minimum of effort,
- the soil must be **moist**, but **not wet**,
- it must be **aerated**,
- it must be **fertile and living** (Chapter 4).

This chapter deals with the many, varied practices that promote these soil conditions. The methods used are chosen to suit the land, the climate and the crops planned. A series of factors must first be considered :

- **the kinds of plants** one wants to cultivate and their root requirements : do the roots tolerate very wet, or waterlogged soils, or do they prefer dryer soils ?
- **the type of soil** : clayey soil, difficult to drain or hard to irrigate, is not tilled in the same way as sandy soil where water infiltrates easily;
- **water management and availability :** must the soil be drained or soil moisture retained, or must it be irrigated ? Is the soil moisture-retentive or does it dry out quickly ?
- **the kind of manure** that must be mixed into the cultivated soil : dung or well-decomposed vegetable manure, lightly decomposed trash, compost, green manure, etc.;
- **the methods** needed to care for the plants and harvest them;
- **the tools used** - hand or mechanical;
- **the topography** - flat or sloping;
- **land exposure** to sun and wind.

66

67

Bed preparation for seasonal crops

Gardening involves a variety of routine tasks. Tilling, seeding, pricking out, pruning and trimming, crop protection, and harvesting come one after the other in the cultural season. **Easy access** to the cultivated plants is essential; the gardener must be able to get at them without trampling on them.

68

This explains the need for **beds and strips** separated by paths **(figures 66 to 72)**. The width of the beds is determined by the length of the gardener's arms. He should be able to reach the centre of the bed without stepping on it.

The young man **(figure 67)** is hoeing the right-hand plot **(figure 66)** but he cannot reach the centre without treading on the plants.

The beds are often casually marked out as in the garden pictured in **figure 14**. Haphazard marking does not matter when there is plenty of land. However, when the garden area is limited, it is better to delineate beds with the help of a string This avoids wasting cultivable soil and cuts down on the area used for paths **(figures 68 and 72)**.

The beds can be raised higher than the paths like those in the foreground of **figure 68** or, as in the background, they can be surrounded by little ridges on which the paths are laid out. The reasons for these arrangements are explained later on.

The tracing-string seen in **figure 68** is useful for two reasons. It helps

- **establish straight edges** and save space;
- **level the surface of the patch** in order to stop rain or irrigation runoff.

The string must be well stretched between the marking pegs and not catch on any little twig or unevenness in the ground.

When the position of the beds is more or less permanent, they can be edged with stones or wood. **Figure 69** shows beds neatly outlined by

69

70

Notes

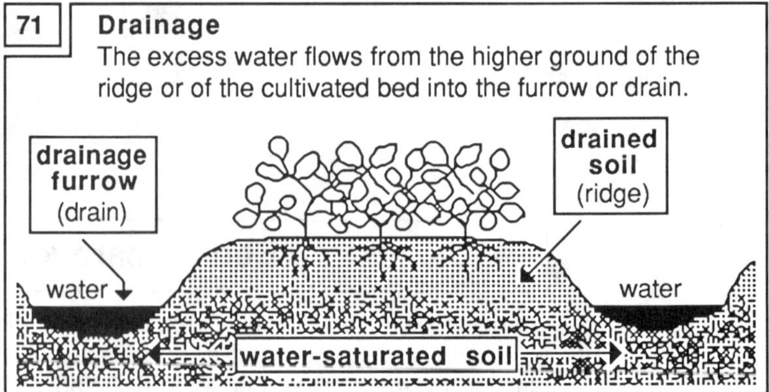

71 **Drainage**
The excess water flows from the higher ground of the ridge or of the cultivated bed into the furrow or drain.

hardwood poles pushed into the sloping ground to form an edge and prevent earth being washed away by runoff.

The poles, fixed horizontally, are held in place by small bamboo or wooden stakes. If there is a likelihood of termites attacking the wood, it is better to use stones.

The choice between raised and sunken beds is decided by soil characteristics, water availability and the type of plants to be cultivated Raised beds are above the level of the ground whereas sunken beds are below that level.

Figure 70 shows a garden in a valley bottom subject to flooding. The problem here is one of **drainage and how to let water flow away to avoid asphyxiating the roots**.

When soil is waterlogged, the roots of most plants are no longer able to breathe, and they rot. This is why the beds are built to a height that will give roots an adequate layer of drained soil **(figure 71)**.

Sunken beds is the term used to describe cultivated patches surrounded by small dykes **(figure 72)**. The dykes, also used as paths, are built to prevent rain and irrigation water from leaving the beds. The beds are **levelled so that water spreads evenly over the whole surface**.

Coleus (SP81, Part II) was sown in the patch in **figure 73**. This vegetable is a small tuber picked from the soil without destroying the plant as shown in **figure 74**. In order to be sure of the crop, the gardener had to earth up very narrow beds that look like ridges. A single row of *Coleus* was seeded in each bed.

The roots of certain plants must have a large volume of well-drained, loose soil at their disposal. This is particularly true of tubers that do not tolerate waterlogged soils. Tuber growth is restricted when the soil mass presses too heavily on the young tubers. Raised beds with soil tilled to a depth of 30 to 60 centimetres, sometimes more, suit these species better than sunken beds not worked to such a depth and designed to trap water instead of allowing drainage.

Figure 76 shows a bed growing a variety of sweet potato with elongated tubers The bed is 60 centimetres high, and its edges are somewhat higher so that irrigation water poured onto the surface is forced to infiltrate the loosened soil rather than flow away down the sides.

When raised and sunken beds are being prepared, it is important to incorporate manure and organic matter in order to ensure good yields. When manure is well broken down and decomposed, it is easy to turn it into the soil by using a hoe, a fork or a spade. This can be done on the beds or in the bottom of the

72

73

74

75

76

sunken beds **(figure 75)**. However, when the material to be buried is barely decomposed (straw, millet stalks, banana bark, etc.), it is impossible to turn it in. Consequently, soil is thrown on top of the trash to let it rot slowly in the bottom of the bed **(figure 77)**. This method is inappropriate for sunken beds because too much soil would have to be moved.

Figure 78 shows a plot in the Sahel where trees have just been planted. Rains are sparse and infrequent. Land forming was needed because the plot lies on a gentle slope. Circular hollows were dug out and protected by semicircular ridges shaped like half-moons. This arrangement forces runoff water to accumulate at the foot of the trees and to infiltrate.

There is another method suitable for trees that dislike excessive moisture. The orange is a species liable to gummosis of the trunk; this disease often occurs when the foot of the tree stands in water. In **figure 79**, two hollows were dug round the orange tree. For health reasons, one hollow was dug right round the trunk so that the root collar would never come into direct contact with water. The second hollow forms a wide circle round the trunk and serves as an irrigation ditch. It is under

78

77

this ditch, sometimes filled with straw and other mulches, that the roots grow best. As the mulch decomposes, it gradually feeds the roots of the tree **(figure 80)**.

Other ways of preparing beds are directly linked to water management. For example, eggplant was seeded in shallow holes that are watered daily **(figure 82)** whereas two rills were formed lengthwise on the levelled surface of the bed of basil so that the irrigation water poured into the rills flows from one end of the patch to the other without draining away onto the paths **(figure 81)**.

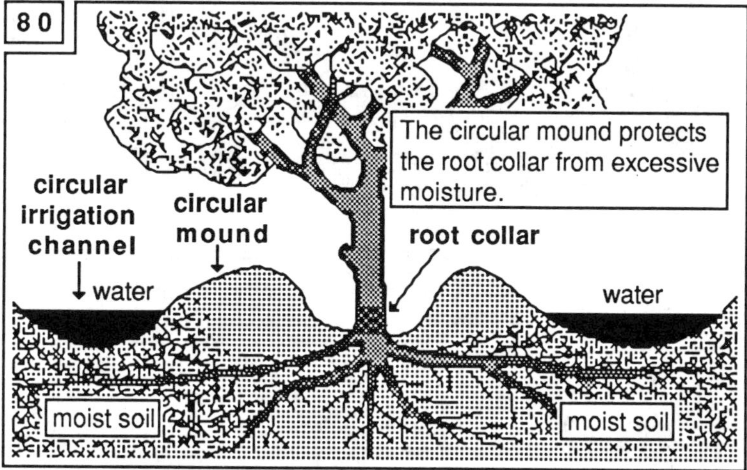

Notes

Earthing up

The term **earthing up** has two meanings. Firstly, it can denote a form of tillage whereby soil thrown up into mounds or ridges provides good growth conditions for the roots of plants about to be sown.

Secondly, earthing up can take place round established plants **(figure 83)**, in which case the aims are

- **propping up young plants** with a tendency to droop because soil is compacted or eroded;
- **developing adventitious roots** that will feed the plant better;
- **burying weeds** which compete with the cultivated species;
- covering developing tubers.

The plants that benefit most from earthing up are those that grow adventitious roots, i.e. roots that grow above the root collar **(figure 84)**.

To be effective, earthing up must be carried out some weeks after sowing and emergence, that is to say, before plants develop young adventitious roots (for example, tomato, maize, *Triumphetta*), or just when the roots on which the first tubers will grow start to appear (potato, sweet potato, yam). Tuberous plants must be earthed up in such a way that the actual tubers are never exposed to light. Exposure makes them turn green or dry up.

Here are examples of when to earth up :

83 **Reasons for earthing up**

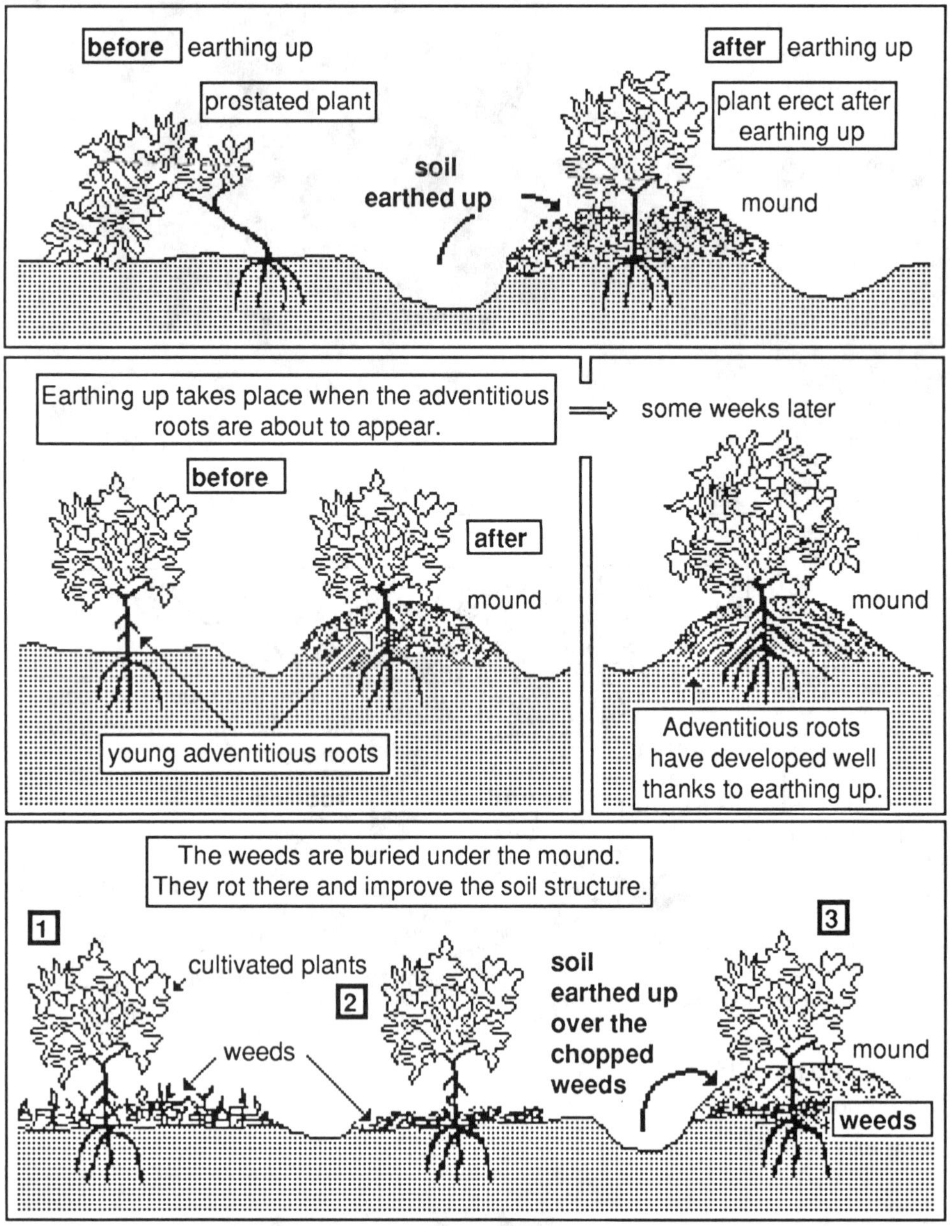

before earthing up
prostated plant
soil earthed up
after earthing up
plant erect after earthing up
mound

Earthing up takes place when the adventitious roots are about to appear.
some weeks later
before
after
mound
young adventitious roots
mound
Adventitious roots have developed well thanks to earthing up.

The weeds are buried under the mound. They rot there and improve the soil structure.
1
cultivated plants
2
weeds
soil earthed up over the chopped weeds
3
mound
weeds

84

- **tomato :** 4 to 6 weeks after transplanting when the first flowers appear;
- **sweet potato :** about 5 to 6 weeks after planting when the main creeping stem divides into many vines;
- **maize :** about 4 weeks after emergence when the stems start to grow rapidly;
- **potato :** 4 weeks after emergence, when the stems are about 20 cm high.

Figures 85 and 86 illustrate a special way of earthing up tomatoes. The seedlings are transplanted from the nursery into a trench the bottom of which is filled with plant manure **(1)**. When the plants develop, a little soil is put back into the trench to promote the growth of the first adventitious roots **(2)**. Later, soil is earthed up over the base of the plants to encourage the growth of more roots **(3)**. The advantages of this method are as follows :

- the first roots are established deep in a layer of soil that is less prone to drying out than shallower layers. Burying organic manures and irrigating are relatively easy;
- next, adventitious roots develop from the covered stem. The plant develops more vigorously than if rooting were restricted to the primary roots situated under the root collar.

To start with, the trenches are watered. Then, when mounding is finished, irrigation water is brought to the furrows that separate the rows of plants.

Whatever the method used, earthing up never fails to **loosen and aerate** a certain volume of soil. This is what makes it a worthwhile practice, especially on farms where machinery for deep tillage is not available.

Ridging is as useful as earthing up. Ridges are long, narrow mounds separated by furrows.

Planting holes

85 Transplanting into a trench followed by earthing up

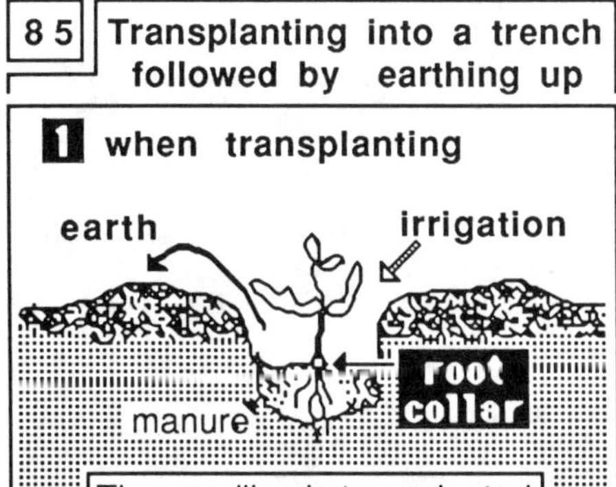

The seedling is transplanted into a small trench.

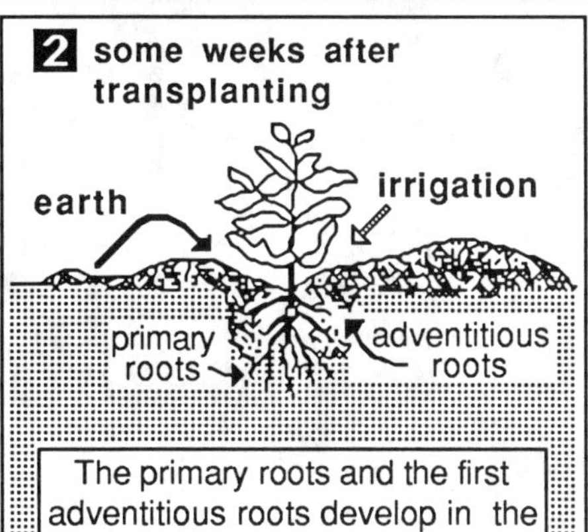

The primary roots and the first adventitious roots develop in the soil thrown back into the trench.

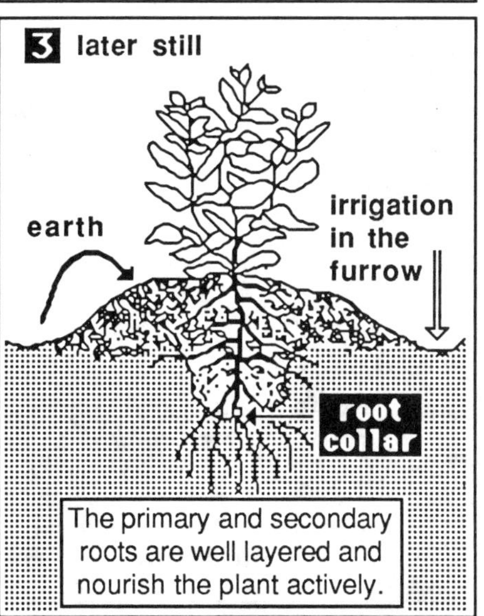

The primary and secondary roots are well layered and nourish the plant actively.

When a tree is to be planted, the ground must be prepared to allow the first roots to develop as effortlessly as possible in soil with the right structure.

The planting hole is dug out where it is intended to plant the tree. The greater the volume of the hole, the more easily the young tree roots will develop when the hole is filled in with loosened earth. As a rule, holes should be 50 to 70 centimetres wide with a depth at least equivalent to their diameter. If there is a taproot system, the hole must be deeper; if the root system is extensive, the hole must be wider.

86

Holes are dug some weeks before planting and should

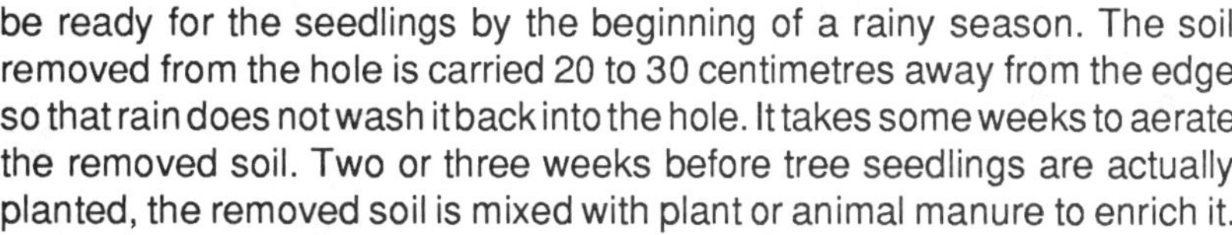

be ready for the seedlings by the beginning of a rainy season. The soil removed from the hole is carried 20 to 30 centimetres away from the edge so that rain does not wash it back into the hole. It takes some weeks to aerate the removed soil. Two or three weeks before tree seedlings are actually planted, the removed soil is mixed with plant or animal manure to enrich it.

At planting time, the soil, now aerated and fertilized, is put back round the base of the tree and the gardener treads it firmly with his feet.

This operation therefore covers three successive phases :

- **digging the hole** some weeks or months before planting time;
- **improving the structure of the soil** taken from the hole by mixing it with plant or animal manure shortly before planting;
- at planting time, **filling the hole** with enriched, well-structured soil.

87

Some gardening tools

Hand tools are used most of the time in gardens and orchards. The mechanical equipment on sale is expensive and rarely adapted to soil conditions in African farms and gardens, conditions such as dry, hard soil, land riddled with stumps, land that needs forming into ridges and mounds. Considerable research is still wanting in the matter of mechanical tools suitable for African gardens.

Here we shall limit ourselves to hand tools and the jobs they have to do.

Hoes are the basic tool for preparing vegetable beds. There are many types of hoes. Flat, heavy hoes are used for trenching and moving soil. Others are wider and bent, and are designed for turning over soil and making the required ridge or mound **(figure 87)**.

Picks and mattocks are use for breaking up the ground to a depth of 40 or 50 centimetres. These tools are very handy for seedbed preparation because they make deep cracks that let water and air circulate under the cultivated patches.

The tined hoe is a strong, forked tool that penetrates the soil easily **(figure 89)**. The cast-iron tines are perpendicular to the handle so that the user can strike the ground, making the hoe penetrate to a depth of 20 to 30 centimetres and loosening the soil thoroughly.

Tined hoes help the gardener to break the soil into clods and remove the roots and rhizomes of weeds. These hoes are useful tools for primary cleaning and for breaking up the soil.

Spades are blades of hard metal, flat or slightly dished in cross-section. They are used for turning soil **(figure 88)**. Spades are easy to handle when the ground is clean, but are not practical for dealing with tree stumps, branches and stones. When confronted with this type of soil, gardeners can use **a spade-fork**, also called **a digging fork**, consisting of three or four strong, heavy-duty tines like those of the hoe in **figure 89** but instead of being perpendicular to the handle as in **figure 89**, they are a straight extension to it.

All these tools are equipped with handles of varying lengths. The length and shape of the handle depends on how the tool is used. Short-handled tools are used when the gardener is crouched or bent over his work; long-handled tools are suitable for work done standing up.

Ploughs and other mechanical implements are rarely used in gardens because the surface of the cultivated beds is usually too small to allow the passage of oxen or machines such as tractors.

After the soil has been tilled by one of the hand implements, it must be levelled and worked to a fine tilth before it can be seeded. For this secondary tillage, pronged tools like **rakes (figure 88)** and **harrows** are used and are most effective when clods are friable. A pass with these tools is easier when, during primary operations, the clods are broken down and crumbled by breaking up with the back of a hoe or spade.

88

89

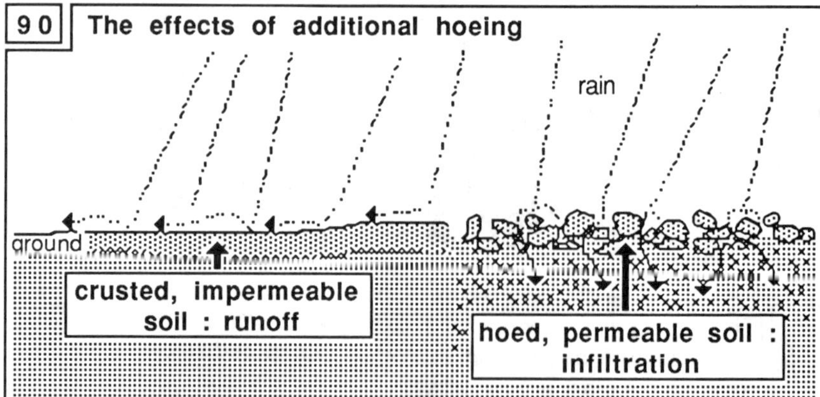

90 The effects of additional hoeing

When it comes to watering the beds, the surface must be perfectly level. Otherwise, irrigation water will spread unevenly with the consequent risk of erosion : higher ground in the beds is eroded by water runoff and the clay particles are washed down to the lower sections. The surface of the bed is levelled by stretching strings horizontally from end to end and then running a rake or a plank under the strings to make the surface even.

Levels like those in **figure 91** can be used to make sure that the surface is horizontal. The first level is an ordinary isosceles triangle with a lead weight or plumb bob fixed to the top of the triangle. The median of the triangle is clearly marked. When the bob and the median tally, the crossbar forming the base of the triangle is perfectly horizontal.

The second instrument is a water level consisting of transparent plastic tubing laid on the ground. The string is stretched so that both ends are exactly level with the water in the ends of the tubing. A bricklayer's or carpenter's level can also be used if available.

When the strings are truly horizontal, it is quite easy to level the ground with a plank or a rake. Small stakes with ends exactly the same height as the strings are notched to serve as guide marks for levelling.

91 **Two ways of levelling cultivated beds**

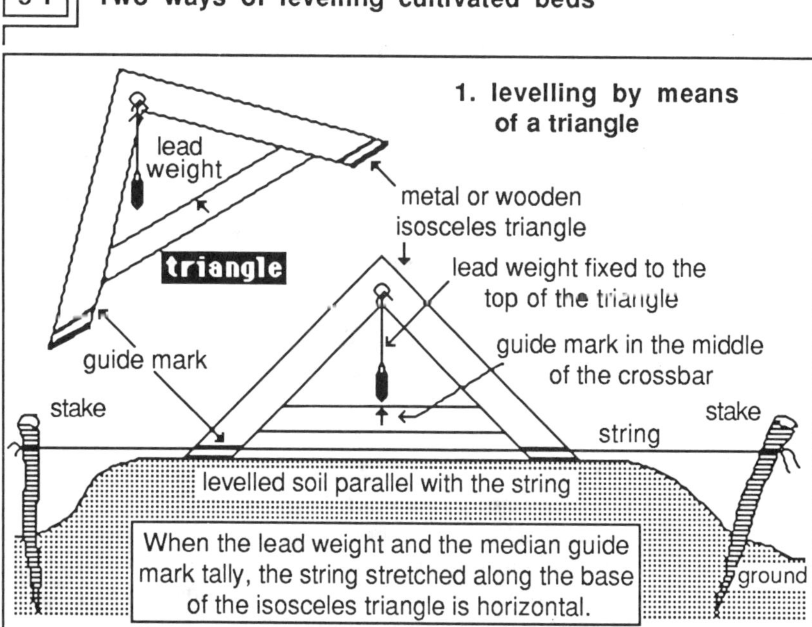

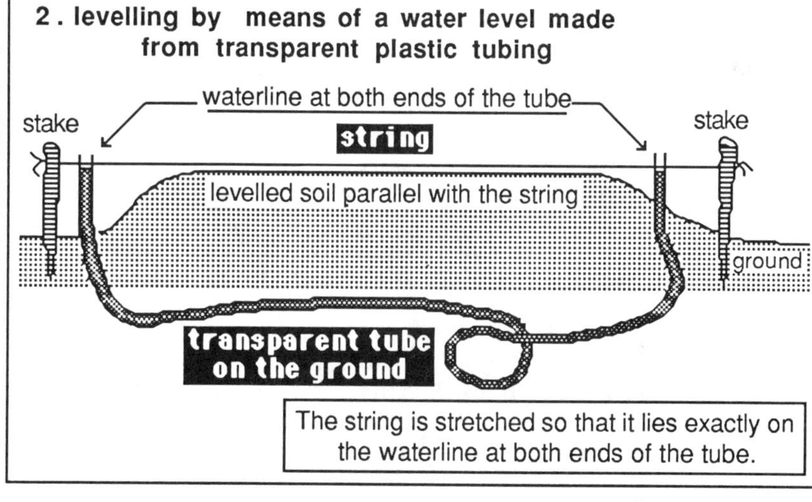

Additional hoeing

Secondary hoeing, as opposed to hoeing for land clearance and seedbed preparation, is aimed at maintaining cultivated soil. It involves breaking up the superficial soil layer hardened by erosion and evaporation **(figures 90 and 92)**. Raindrops compact the soil forming a hard crust some millimetres deep. When it rains again, the water runs off the impermeable layer instead of infiltrating in depth.

Because it breaks up the impermeable layer, hoeing makes infiltration easier. After hoeing, small clods of broken-down, crusted soil cover the soil layer just below the surface and, like a kind of mulch, protect it from overheating (Chapter 4) and reduce evaporation on the surface of the soil.

92

The effects of hoeing are not as lasting as those obtained by mulching. Beating rain quickly disperses the small soil clods, and a hard crust forms again.

Garden hoes with the blade set forward across the end of the handle and one-pronged hoes as in **figure 67** are used for secondary hoeing operations which should be carried out when the soil is fairly dry and breaks up easily.

There is some overlap between **weeding** and **secondary hoeing.** Weeding sets out to eliminate weeds competing with cultivated plants to no purpose. Weeding, properly carried out, chops unwanted plants just under the root collar to prevent them from growing again. Weeding-hoes penetrate crusted soil and usually break it into clods, which is what happens during secondary hoeing operations.

Chapter 4
Managing soil fertility

Fertility

Vegetable growing is a type of **intensive farming** that produces a great deal on a small area of land. Cultivated plants feed heavily on the mineral salts in the soil. When agricultural produce leaves the field or the garden, the mineral salts it contains are carried away. The process is expressed by saying that mineral salts are **exported (removed)** from the land **(figure 93)**.

If agricultural produce is removed from fields season after season without any attempt to replace the mineral salts taken up by the roots, the layer of arable soil becomes exhausted and return from the land decreases.

If the gradual decline in production is to be avoided, **the stores of mineral salts taken up by plants must be constantly replaced.** These salts are found more particularly in clay, humus, manures, ashes and chemical fertilizers. They are present, but to a lesser extent, in sand and gravel. The most fertile soils are usually those in which all the soil components are found in the right proportion. The proportion of the various components determines the **soil structure,** and a good structure is needed to make soil fertile (*).

Maintaining good soil structure is a prerequisite for preserving fertility and is as important as the replacement of the mineral salts that plants can assimilate.

Soil fertility is also linked to water availability. Water is essential for root absorption of mineral salts. **Establishing and maintaining sufficient moisture is therefore a third aspect of soil fertility.**

Water can however also harm fertility. When water infiltrates through the cultivated layer in large quantities, it dissolves the mineral salts present there and removes them to deeper soil layers. In other words, the cultivated layer is **leached**. Since roots absorb water before it percolates to greater depth and becomes inaccessible, only intense activity by the roots can prevent **leaching in a small way.** Erosion and runoff also seriously affect fertility. Erosion degrades soil structure, and runoff carries away the most fertile substances such as clay and loam, and significant amounts of mineral salts.

93 The removal of nutrient mineral salts

The store of mineral salts that was depleted by cultivation and was removed from the garden along with the harvested produce must be put back into the soil layers exploited by plant roots.

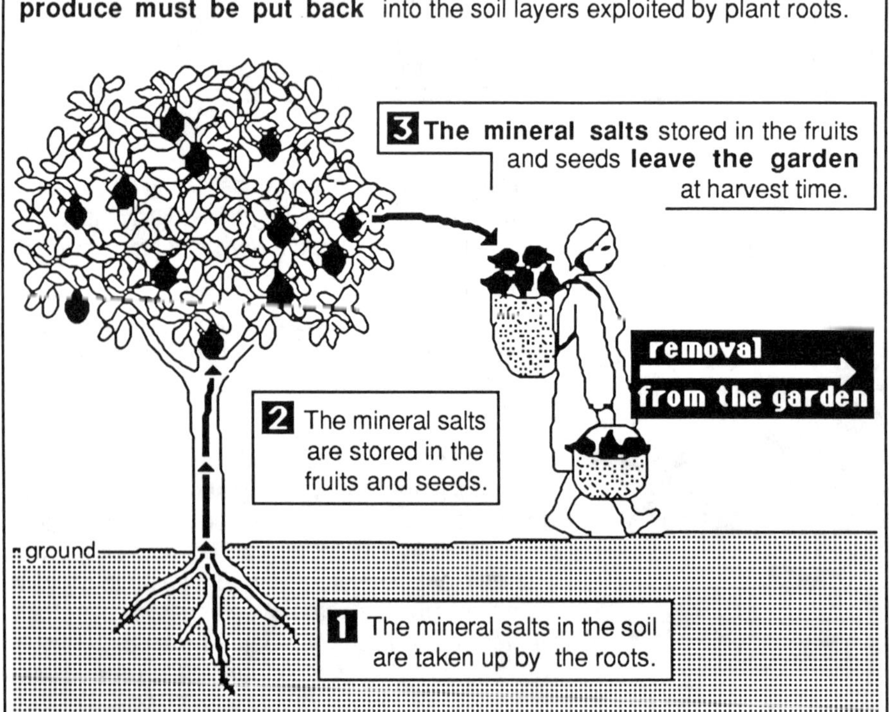

There are three fundamental conditions for fertilizing soil, particularly the layers exploited by the roots of cultivated plants. They are :

- **restoring to the arable layer mineral salts that can be assimilated in quantities equal to those removed from that layer** at harvest time;
- **preserving and improving soil structure in the arable layer**;
- **maintaining good moisture levels.**

This chapter deals mainly with the first two points. The third point will be discussed in Chapter 19. However, these three aspects of gardening are inseparably linked.

There are two main ways of fertilizing the arable soil layer. **The first way is**

* See *Tropical Agriculture in African Rural Communities*, Chapters 18 and 19.

based on the use of substances produced or extracted on and near the farm. The second way uses substances found in mines or manufactured by chemical industries unconnected with the environment of gardens.

We shall start with the first way of building up fertility and with the fertilizers that can be produced on the rural settlement itself. Chemical fertilizers sold by national or international firms will be discussed afterwards.

Fertility generated on the farm

How is fertility generated on the farm?

Plants and animals play an essential role in supplying gardens with natural fertilizers. Plants form their organic matter by taking up mineral salts from the soil. This organic matter is called **vegetable biomass**. It includes roots, stems, leaves, sap, fruits, moulds, fungi, microorganisms, etc. The remains of mammals, reptiles and insects form the **animal biomass**.

When some of the vegetable or animal biomass dies and lies on the ground, it is decomposed quickly or slowly, as the case may be, by innumerable insects, worms, ants, fungi and microorganisms. All these living beings help to convert **organic matter into minerals**. This means that the mineral salts contained in the dead biomass are returned to the soil and can be absorbed once more by plant roots. There is, therefore, a **cycle** of organic matter and mineral salts. The words **organic matter** and **humus** denote the substances in various stages of decomposition that result from the dead biomass.

Table 94 illustrates the cycle undergone by organic matter, and the arrows show how mineral salts travel. A distinction is made between those mineral salts removed from the soil and those restored to it. We see that when animals eat fodder, they only create a temporary deviation in the cycle of mineral elements because their excrements end up in the soil. Note, however, that if the farmer sells cattle or milk, he is also removing mineral salts from the farm.

94 **The cycle of organic matter and mineral salts on and round the farm**

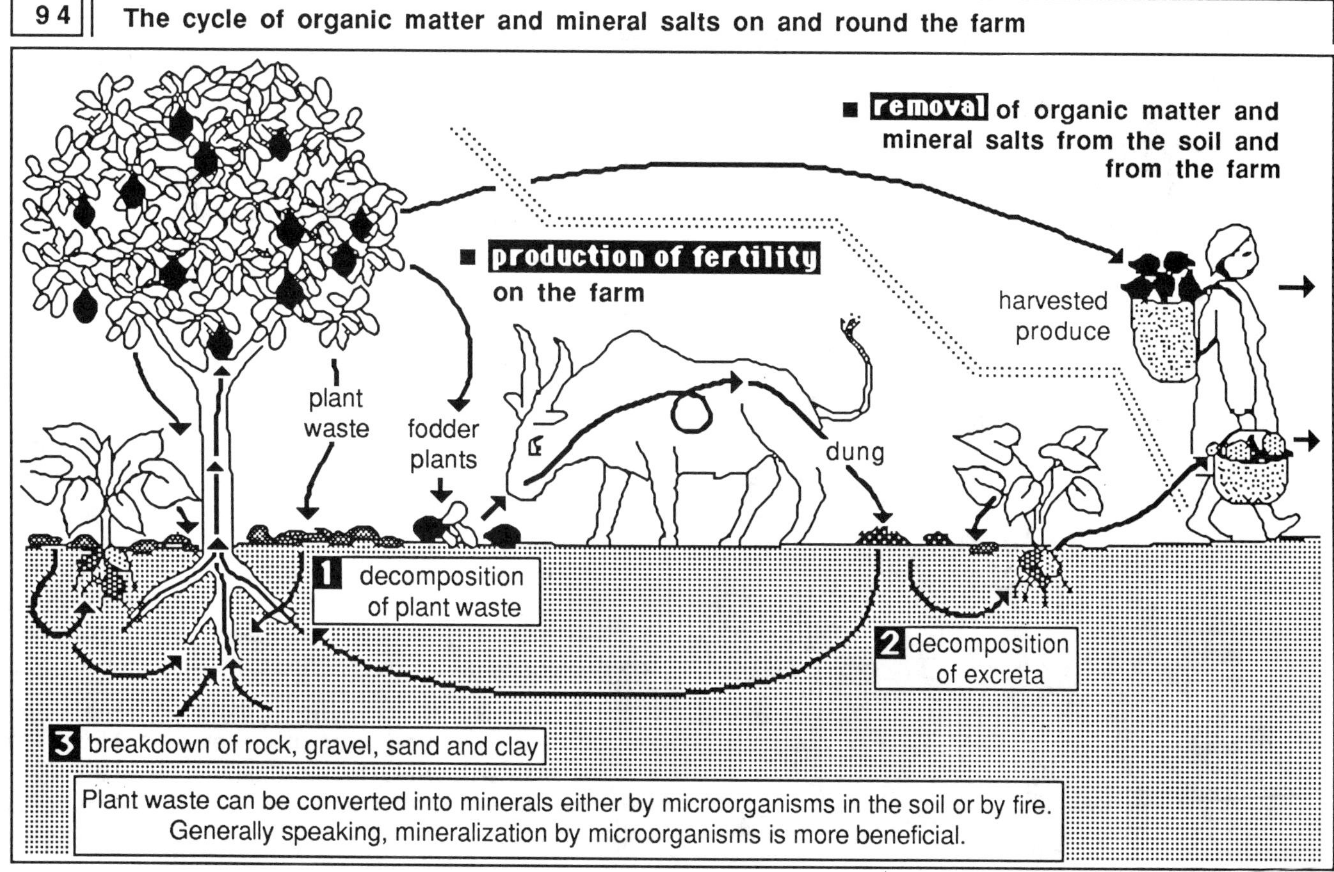

Plant waste can be converted into minerals either by microorganisms in the soil or by fire. Generally speaking, mineralization by microorganisms is more beneficial.

We can now grasp the need to take two inseparable aspects of farming into account :

- **producing maximum quantities of consumable produce** - fruits, vegetables, seeds, fibres, wood, remedies, etc.;
- **producing maximum quantities of organic matter and returning it to the soil in order to preserve fertility.**

A balance between these two aims must be kept all the time. Growers only interested in the first aim are bound to observe dwindling returns from their land as the seasons pass; restoring the fertility of the soil will cost a lot of money.

However, both aims can be pursued at the same time by many cultural practices such as using mulches, making compost, growing green manure plants, using animal manure and other organic fertilizers, spreading ashes, cinders and other mineral substances to be found near the farm. The effectiveness of these methods can be reinforced by mixing in commercial chemicals.

What exactly are these cultural practices ?

96

97

95

Plant mulches

Mulching means covering the soil surface by spreading layers of straw, leaves and other vegetable trash in order to :

- protect the soil from rain erosion and especially from rainsplash,
- improve water infiltration,
- conserve soil moisture by preventing desiccation through surface evaporation,
- enrich the soil with nutrients when mulches are decomposed,
- encourage microorganisms living in the soil,
- improve soil structure,
- reduce weed growth near cultivated plants.

The sloping ground of the banana plantation **(figure 95)** is covered with a mulch. Dead leaves and felled banana trunks are being used for this purpose. The trunks have been arranged at right angles to the slope to let them control runoff. This mulch is produced in the plantation itself. Some of the mineral salts which were taken up by the bananas will be returned to the soil when they rot.

In this instance, **natural mulches benefit soil moisture and structure. They do not increase the amount of mineral salts** in the shallow soil layers, but they activate organisms living in the soil.

98

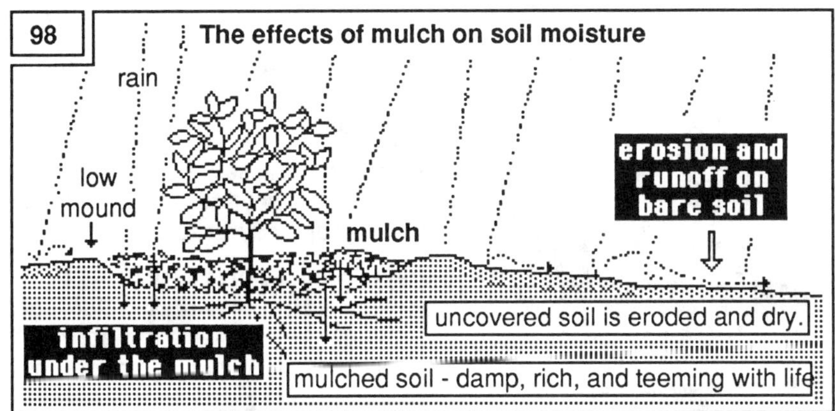

The straw mulch in **figure 96** protects the soil from evaporation and rain erosion. The vegetable bed has just been sown and the straw arranged in neat rows. When the seeds germinate, the mulch will be removed to prevent damage to the small plants. Once the roots have grown a few centimetres, there is less likelihood of wilting, even if the superficial soil layer suffers from drought. The straw cover therefore provides valuable protection to the young seedling because it preserves moisture in the top few millimetres of soil.

The photograph in **figure 97** and the corresponding illustration in **figure 98**, show a chilli seedling in sandy garden soil. Mulch was spread round the plant to cover an area the size of the root diameter of the mature plant. The surface was hollowed a little to stop irrigation water from flowing away.

The mulch in this garden comes from an outside source. It is composed of shredded straw mixed with animal dung and is beneficial for many reasons : it protects the soil from the harmful effects of climate (erosion, evaporation, drought), it contributes to soil life as it decomposes, it feeds the soil and promotes the infiltration of irrigation water.

Mulch can be made more effective by using urine and slurry. However, these could be a serious health hazard and strict hygiene precautions such as washing hands are essential.

Mulches not derived from plants

Some of the effects of mulching can be obtained by using soil cover other than vegetable waste.

A layer of pebbles will protect the soil from erosion due to heavy rainfall and will aid infiltration by preventing compaction of the soil surface. Pebbles will protect the soil from the effects of intense sunshine and will radiate this heat during the night. Dark coloured pebbles will cool quickly at night allowing dew to form in humid climates.

99

100

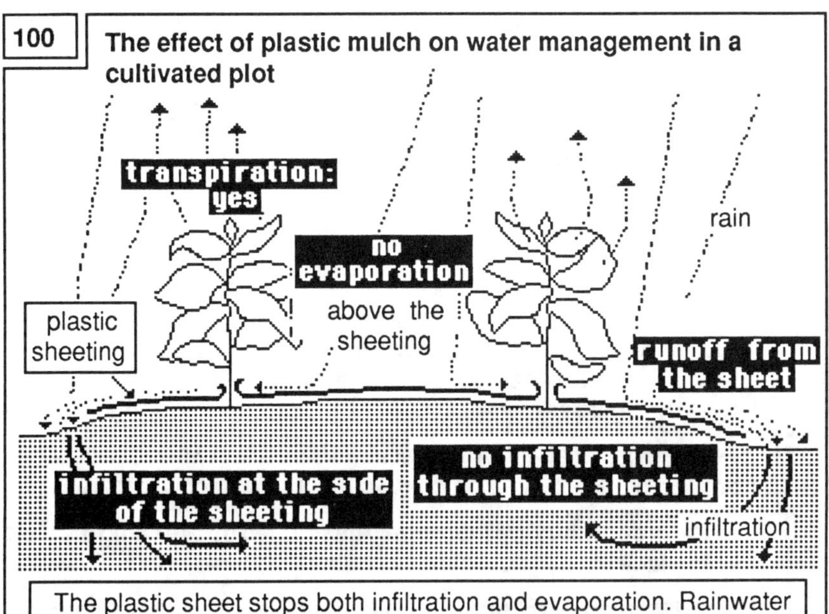

The plastic sheet stops both infiltration and evaporation. Rainwater runs to the edge of the sheet, then percolates vertically and laterally.

Another practice, inspired by mulching techniques, consists in spreading a sheet of waterproof plastic over a cultivated patch. The three rows of pineapple in **figure 99** were planted through this type of sheeting that prevents soil water evaporation and the growth of weeds - all welcome benefits. However, rainwater only infiltrates along the sides of the plastic cover. Hence the need to use plant mulch between the plastic strips to let the ground absorb water.

This practice helps to preserve soil moisture but does hardly anything for soil structure or mineral enrichment **(figure 100)**.

101 The use of plastic mulch when planting young trees

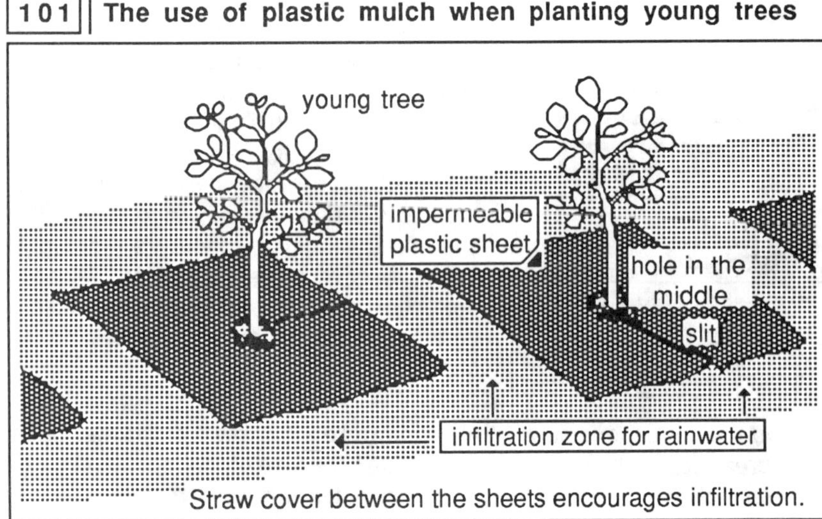

Plastic sheets are useful in many ways :

- unlike plant mulches, **they do not rot** and, with due care, **can be used again and again**,
- **they are labour-saving** because unlike plant trash, they do not have to be chopped up and transported,
- **they let plants derive even benefit from soil water for the whole cultural season,** in contrast to the effects of plant mulch which vary as the season progresses,
- finally, **plastic sheets smother weeds** more effectively because they cut out the light.

As plastic sheeting tends to be expensive and is not easily obtainable, it is worthwhile saving cover material such as old fertilizer sacks, cement bags and flour bags; all are particularly handy for tree seedlings (**figure 101**). Even heavy-duty paper can be used.

There are many kinds of plastic sheeting, of varying thicknesses, different colours and different textures (smooth or porous). Thickness affects the resistance of the plastic. Colour affects soil temperature : dark coloured materials get hotter in the sun and cool off quickly at night; light colours keep the covered soil at a more even temperature. Smooth, unperforated sheets do not let rainwater or evaporation through. Perforated and porous sheets let a certain amount of water through, but limit evaporation. This is true of sacks made of braided plastic fibres that are often used commercially for selling cereal grains, flours and other produce.

102 Some tips about mulching

- *The plant waste used for mulching must not contain any seeds or propagation material. The gardener must avoid spreading unwanted plants that will have to be controlled later on.*
- *There are two reasons why the layer of mulch must not be too thick : first, it must not be allowed to absorb all the water during light rains, nor prevent air from reaching the soil. A layer between five and ten centimetres thick is usually just right.*
- *The layer must not be too thin because it would not give effective cover and might rot quickly.*
- *Mulches are only spread on soil loosened by tilling or weeding. When soil is compacted under cover, mulch does not stop runoff completely and has only a limited effect on water infiltration.*
- *Mulch must let rainwater filter through. Large, spreading leaves should be avoided because rainwater falling on them flows away from the cultivated plants.*
- *Chopping up mulches is really worthwhile because it makes the layers of waste more permeable and speeds up rotting. A straw chopper or compost crusher will do the job.*
- *Direct contact between plant leaves and mulches must be avoided because fungal diseases can be transmitted in this way.*

103

Two **special precautions** must always be taken when plastic sheets are laid on a cultivated patch or round the base of young trees :

- **the ground must be thoroughly moistened before fixing the sheet in place** and, if necessary, abundantly watered;
- **water infiltration around the plastic cover must be encouraged** by the right technique - tilling, straw cover, stone mulch, etc.

Compost

Compost is fermented plant waste, heaped up and partially decomposed by microorganisms which convert it into minerals. This plant manure is remarkably good for preserving and improving soil structure. **Composting** means making compost from vegetable refuse.

There are two ways of making compost : by cold fermentation and by hotbed fermentation.

Cold composting is taking place in the pit in **figure 103**. All sorts of household garbage is thrown in every day and spread in thin layers. After a few months, it turns into a dark, sticky mass swarming with living organisms - earthworms, larvae, insects, slugs and microorganisms. Decomposition is slow and often incomplete. After many months, branches, straw, half-rotten bark and seeds ready to germinate can still be found in the heap. Half-decomposed trash of this kind cannot be used, just as it is, on the vegetable beds and must be removed from the mass of cold compost before being spread on cultivated soil.

Cold composting is improved by mixing the waste and turning it over from time to time. Two pits can be dug side by side for this purpose. One pit is filled with trash and then emptied into the second pit so that, in the transfer, half-rotted waste lies in the bottom and rotted waste on top. One must, at all costs, avoid putting unwanted seeds or propagating material in with the compost as these would then grow in the vegetable beds.

Cold composting is a convenient method when waste accumulates gradually, as is the case with kitchen garbage.

When large quantities of organic matter are available at the same time, **hotbed composting** can be carried out. Hotbed composting gets its name because, three or four days after heaping up, the compost temperature rises sharply **(figures104 and 105)**.

Certain conditions have to be observed in order to make hotbed compost successfully.

104 Hotbed composting

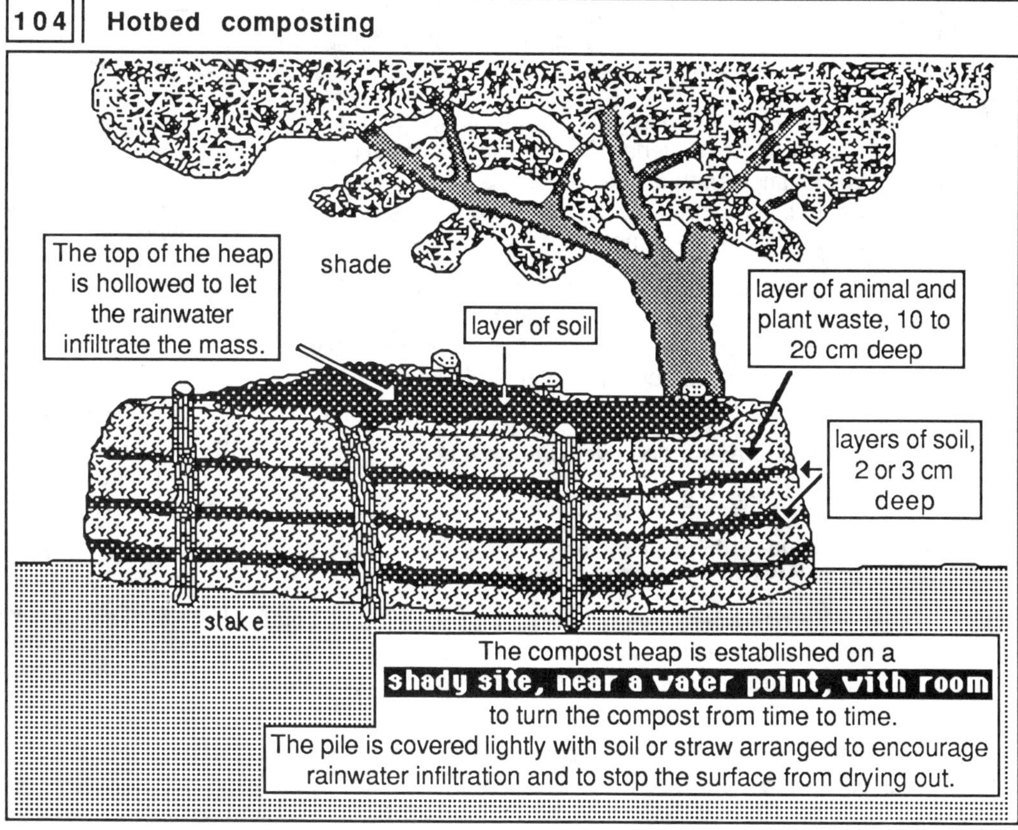

- **Quantities of organic matter are needed, enough** to make a volume of compost that will allow internal heating. The pile in **figure 104** has a base 2 metres x 2 metres and is 1.20 metres high. These dimensions ensure satisfactory mass and compact volume so that the pile heats up and is not cooled off too quickly by surrounding air.
- **The trash** in the compost heap can come from **various sources** (leaves, grasses, dung, straw, etc.) but it must all be **chopped up** because long stalks, branches , barks and similar residues slow down decomposition. As well as this, a **balance must be struck between fresh materials** (leaves, pulp, suckers, shoots, etc.) that generate heat as they rot, and **dry materials** that ferment. Dry trash can be crushed if the right equipment is available.
- The layers of vegetable refuse can be alternated with layers of dung and thin layers of soil, ashes and lime. Small amounts of commercial fertilizers are also a possibility (see page 65).
- When decomposition starts, **moisture in the heap is very important** because the microorganisms that act as rotting agents are only active in moist conditions. If the heap dries up, it must be watered. Again, watering is sometimes necessary to avoid overheating and fire. Slurry and urine can be added to the water.

105

The compost is ready after three or four months. Apart from bits of branches and roots, waste materials (leaves, stalks, fruits, pulp and so on) are now indistinguishable. The compost is a damp, blackish or brownish mass and, when properly decomposed, teems with earthworms, centipedes, larvae and other living beings.

When the waste to be composted consists of branches and straw, these must be chopped up; it is also advisable to mix in moister material and/or dung. Hand and motorized crushers specially designed for making compost are on the market. This equipment could be a first step towards mechanization in gardens.

Hotbeds have three advantages over cold heaps :

- organic matter rots faster and more thoroughly;
- the seeds of unwanted plants are destroyed by the heat and can no longer invade plots when compost is applied;
- in the same way, parasites, larvae and eggs that cause human and animal diseases and are present in the composted waste, are destroyed and replaced by living organisms harmless to man, animals and plants.

- The heating period may last anything from ten days to three weeks and calls for great vigilance. If the pile overheats, it must be completely turned over so that the drier materials on the top and sides are inside the heap and vice versa. Two or three turns may even be necessary during heating, followed by two or three extra turns at intervals depending on the degree of decomposition.
- The compost heap must not be exposed to direct sunshine because it would dry out, nor to heavy rains that might cool off the compost too much during the heating phase and leach out minerals. Consequently, the heap should be **in the shade of a tree** or protected by matting.

106 Practical advice about sowing after burying green manure

- *Do not sow straight away after burying green manure. Wait until decomposition has well and truly set in.*
- *When fresh trash such as leaves and green stems have been turned in and the soil is wet, wait about two weeks before sowing.*
- *When dry trash is turned in and the soil is dry, you may have to wait from 6 to 12 weeks before planting.*
- *In dry regions, good results are sometimes obtained by burying green manure at the end of the rainy season, i.e. at the end of the growing season, for the benefit of crops in the next cultural season.*
- *In gardens, irrigate plots that have been fertilized with green manures. Do this for a few days before sowing in order to speed up the decomposition of the organic waste that has just been turned in.*

Compost is spread on cultivated plots as soon as it is ready, and mixed at once into the arable layer. It is not left to dry on the ground surface. Success with hotbed composting comes with experience and practice. The method is rewarding particularly in gardens where enough organic waste can be collected. Composting is a labour-saving boon for the gardener and, as we shall see below, it may be worthwhile encouraging or cultivating certain plants in order to compost them.

Green manure plants

Green manures are plants grown specially with a view to fertilizing the soil. At a certain stage in their development, they are buried in the ground where they rot and, in so doing, improve fertility.

All plants that put organic matter into the soil can be called green manures. Some, however, are much more effective than others. The best-known are those belonging to the legume family. Often, they are able to fix atmospheric nitrogen thanks to the presence of *rhizobia*, microorganisms that live on the roots in little knots called **root nodules.** Among seasonal legume plants used solely as green manures or as animal feed, we find *Pueraria* (tropical kudzu), *Centrosema* , *Stylosanthes* , *Mucuna* , *Vigna*, some varieties of bean. Trees such as *Acacia albida*, African locust bean, *Leucena*, *Flemingia* (shrub) and tamarind are remarkable fertilizers.

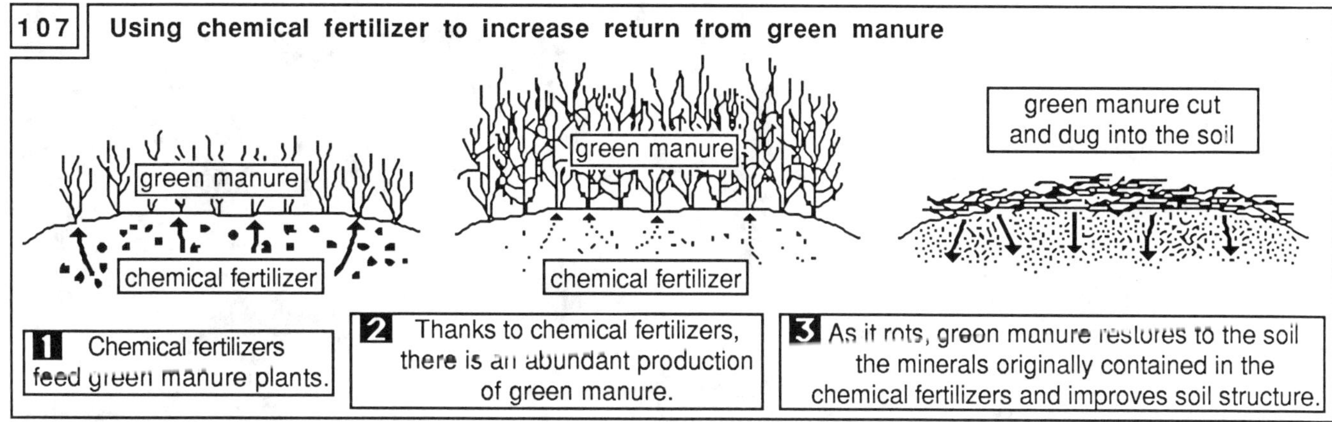

Some seasonal grasses also make good green manure provided they are cut and ploughed into the soil when they are young. A farmer with a supply of cheap seeds - millet, sorghum or maize, for example - can sow them densely on land to be fertilized. When the plants are 30 to 50 centimetres high, they are cut and buried in the field.

Green manures have a three-fold effect on soil fertility :

- **they produce large quantities of vegetable matter** that improves soil structure as it rots. This matter is produced in the soil (in roots) and in aerial parts (stems and leaves);
- their extensive roots break up the clods of soil and promote infiltration;
- Leguminous manures take up atmospheric nitrogen through the bacteria in their roots. The nitrogen finds its way back into the soil when the plant rots.

108

Green manures can be interplanted with other crops, perhaps half-way through the rainy season. By that time, crops seeded earlier on are well-established and their development will not be retarded by competition from the green manure plant. The green manure is either left standing during the dry season, or buried at the end of the rainy season, in which case the practice is called **relay intercropping** of green manure.

Only seasonal grasses propagated by seed and with easily harvested seeds can be used in this way. When these grasses are used as green manures, they must not be allowed to produce seeds on the land that needs fertilizing. Perennial grasses and those propagated by cuttings must be avoided because they are too hard to eradicate when the land is cultivated at a later stage.

Whichever green manures are used, they must be buried and given time to rot by the action of soil microorganisms before crops are grown again.

Small quantities of chemical fertilizers can give good results when spread on green manure rather than applied straight onto crops. This is the sensible thing to do, especially when the fertilizers in question encourage the growth of stems and leaves **(figure 107)**. Unlike cultivated plants, those intended for use as fertilizers are sown very densely and are consequently able to take up mineral fertilizer quickly and transform it into living matter (biomass). When this biomass is cut and spread on cultivated patches it decays slowly and releases the mineral salts it contains, including those salts derived from chemical fertilizers.

This method of **using mineral fertilizers indirectly** is beneficial in many ways not only from the point of view of soil fertility and structure but also where the health of cultivated plants is concerned. When the soil feeding them is rich in organic waste, cultivated plants are often hardier and healthier than when nutrients come to them straight from factory-made minerals.

Plants designed for producing mulches and compost

When the land is underpopulated and vegetation is abundant, it is easy to find mulching material or plant waste in the vicinity of gardens. On the other hand, when the settlement is densely populated and vegetation is sparse, **the value of organic manure in gardens proves how right it is to set aside some plots for the purpose of producing the mulches and the compost needed to enrich the soil.**

The plot of *Flemingia* (**figure 108)** is situated near a garden with the aim of producing mulch. The stalks are cut before they harden. Cutting back the plant makes new shoots grow. *Flemingia* is useful because it is a prolific plant belonging to the legume family that fixes atmospheric nitrogen in the soil.

109

Tithonia seen in **figure 109** is often grown in hedges. It is productive and its exploitation is worthwhile for improving soil fertility, especially in composts.

Mulch can be produced underneath cultivated plants. Associated plants, both cultivated and weed plants, can contribute to mulch production.

The fertilizing qualities of certain aquatic plants, of which azolla **(figure 110)** is an example, should not be forgotten. Azolla is a small plant easy to propagate. It grows fast in ponds and quickly covers the entire surface of the water. Azolla feeds fish. The plant can also be pulled and used for mulch or for composting. In China, azolla is sown in flooded paddy fields where fish feed on it. Then, when the paddies have dried out, the plant rots on the ground and enriches the soil.

Other fertilizing plants such as algae and water hyacinths can be exploited too.

110

111 Some straw-producing plants useful for cultivation in gardens and orchards

■ **Herbaceous plants**

Elephant grass, ***Setaria***, *Brachiaria* (palisade grass, Surinam grass), ***Cenchrus*** (African foxtail), ***Panicum***, *Pueraria* (tropical kudzu), *Mucuna, Desmodium* (tick clover), *Derris, Stylosanthes, Canavalia* (jack bean, sword bean), ***Vigna***.

■ **Woody plants**

Tephrosia, Calliandra, Tithonia, Flemingia, Sesbania, **pigeon pea**, ***Prosopis***, some **cassias and acacias,** *Leucena.*

(Plants in bold grow well in dry regions).

Animal manure

All animal excrements, liquids and solids, can be used for fertilizing gardens. **Animal manures** include cow dung, droppings (horses, goats, sheep, rabbits, poultry) and slurry. Human excrements can also serve as manure.

The fertilizing substances contained in animal dung all come from the fodder which the animals have eaten. As a rule, animal manure contains more concentrated substances than plant manures.

Collecting dung means that animals have to be kept in enclosures, in stalls or kraals. Collection is not easy when animals are allowed to wander, or herds are migratory.

The pigs in the back-yard enclosure **(figure 112)** are fed every day on household garbage and fodder (grass, spoilt fruit, tubers and the like). Dung in the enclosure is raked up regularly and spread on the garden plots.

Stabling is a more developed technique than fencing in. The dirt floor of the stable is packed and hardened, or it can be cemented over. Liquid and solid excrements are heaped up or put into pits and are left for some time before being used on cultivated land.

All domestic animals can be stabled : oxen, horses, sheep and goats in stables, pigs in pigsties **(figure 113)**, hens in henhouses. Whenever animals are stabled, the farmer must plan for adequate supplies of fodder and water.

Kraaling is often observed in regions where pastoralism is a way of life. This practice consists in penning the cattle at night for their security and in order to let dung accumulate. The manure is used later for fertilizing gardens. The advantage of kraaling is that the excreta produced from grazing a large area of pasture during the day is ejected in the restricted area of the kraal **(figure 114)**.

Like plant manure, dung restores mineral elements to the soil and changes its structure. However, as dung is more concentrated, it is best **mixed in about equal parts** with straw or other plant trash. To ensure a good mix, the plant waste can be spread in the kraal or stable so that it can be trampled on, or it can be chopped up and mixed into the dung if a straw chopper is available. The combined dung-and-plant fertilizer can be used in gardens or added to compost heaps to produce top-quality compost.

Droppings are poultry excrements. They can be applied in thin layers or in the form of dry powder. They can also be mixed into water or slurry and then used for watering plants.

Urine is the liquid excreta of animals. When urine flows into a channel sweeping some solid dung along with it, it turns into a green, foul-smelling liquid called **slurry.**

Urine and slurry contain nitrogen and mineral salts valuable for soil fertility. They activate soil bacteria and contribute to the decomposition of organic matter. Pure or diluted urine is used for watering or spraying. But applications must be diluted correctly and care taken to prevent too much liquid from landing on plant leaves because of the risk of scorching. Hygiene precautions are very important.

112

113

114 **Kraaling**

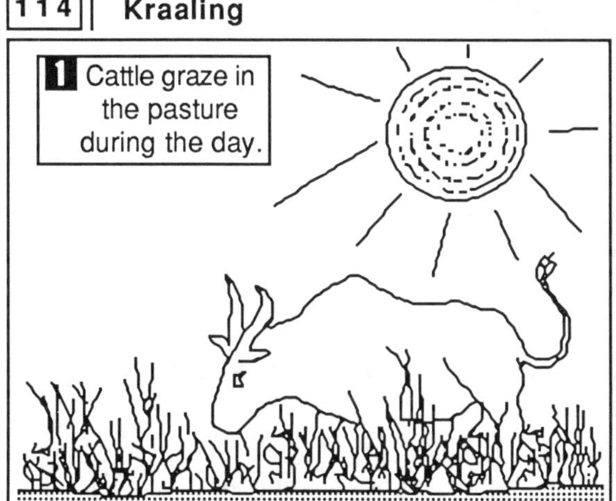

Fodder plants take up mineral salts from pasture soil. These salts are concentrated in cattle excrements and ejected in the kraal or stable, wherever the animals are confined.

When crops are mulched, it may be worthwhile spraying them with urine that has fermented for two or three weeks. Spraying encourages the growth of microorganisms acting as decomposing agents and improves soil structure. Urine can also be used when compost heaps have to be sprinkled to keep them moist.

Although animal and human manures are always valuable fertilizers, they are not without danger to man since they are germ-carriers. Consequently, these manures, and particularly pig and human excrements, must be handled with caution because they transmit diseases such as typhus, hepatitis and dysentery, and may cause worm infestation. **The manures must never be applied on produce ready to be harvested and consumed. When handling these manures, farm workers must never put their hands to their mouth, and must wash carefully when the job is over.**

When contamination of foodstuffs by human or pig manure is suspected, the food must be boiled before consumption.

115 | Practical advice on making animal manure

- *Keep the enclosure small.*
- *Feed and water the animals at regular intervals.*
- *Throw all household and farm waste into the enclosed area, except metal objects, glass and waste materials that do not rot.*
- *Do not throw in thick branches or bulky waste which would obstruct the collection of manure at a later stage.*
- *At regular intervals, spread a little straw or plant trash evenly over the floor to let the cattle tread on it.*
- *See that the enclosure is cool. It should be established, in a shaded area, under a tree or under a roof.*

Every season, litter 10 to 30 centimetres deep can be used. Bulky waste is removed before the manure is applied on the cultivated plots.

116

Other organic fertilizers

Many kinds of waste and various by-products can be used to fertilize gardens - household garbage, contents of septic tanks and latrines, industrial waste from agricultural and food-processing plants, brewer's draff (spent hops), coffee pulp, fruit pulp, fish waste, blood, etc. and all and any organic waste.

However, these wastes have their drawbacks. City garbage as seen in **figure 116** may contain unwanted materials - scrap iron, plastics, silver paper, broken glass, beer cans and so forth. The waste may not be fully decomposed, it may be too rich in vegetable trash (in this case, maize husks), or infested with parasitic worms and toxins dangerous to man. Untreated sludge from septic tanks is also a possible source of disease.

Precautions have to be taken before fertilizers of this kind are applied. After the waste has been sorted out and sieved, it is best to let it rot completely before use - for example by heaping it up for one or two months away from cultivated plants or, better still, by composting it. The waste can also be transformed into biogas in tanks used for the purpose. This worthwhile process is little practised in Africa, but is widespread in Asian countries. The products of this transformation are biogas for heating and lighting, as well as innocuous manure removed from the biogas tanks when gasification is over.

Burying organic manure

As was already stressed, animal and plant manures left to dry on the ground lose many of their fertilizing qualities. Hence the need to bury them. The way in which organic fertilizer is buried has a considerable effect on the development of soil structure and on plant uptake.

Three main factors are involved : the kind of manure, the kind of soil and its preparation, the reasons for applying the manure.

- **Long stems and bulky waste** are not easily buried. This is why waste of this kind is used for mulching on the surface or, as in **figure 77**, spread round the base of ridges when tilling starts, Or, again, it can be spread on the ground a long time before the next cropping season (at the end of the rainy season), so that decay by termites and other soil insects will have set in by the onset of the rains.

  Fine waste is incorporated fairly easily.

Some vegetable residues rot more easily than others. Leaves, fruits, and young green shoots rot quickly in or on the ground. Branches, trunks, stems and barks contain substances called lignin and cellulose that are hard to break down and rot very slowly.

Wood and cellulose waste must not be mixed into arable soil in too great a proportion. When this happens, the microorganisms that activate decay take up many minerals and nitrogen from the soil to the detriment of roots, and keen competition for food is sparked off between plants and the microorganisms that cause wood and straw to decay.

117 Three ways of spreading organic manure

Example of brewer's draff as used in Cameroon

1 The draff is spread on the surface of the ridge.

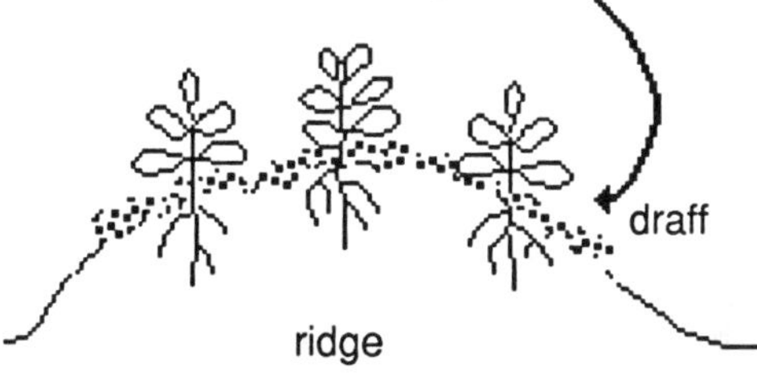

The manure acts **fast if moist conditions speed up decay. It acts slowly if it dries out in the sun.** If the manure is merely left on the soil surface, it is in danger of being carried away by runoff water.

This method is not recommended.

2 The draff is mixed into the soil on the ridge during seedbed preparation.

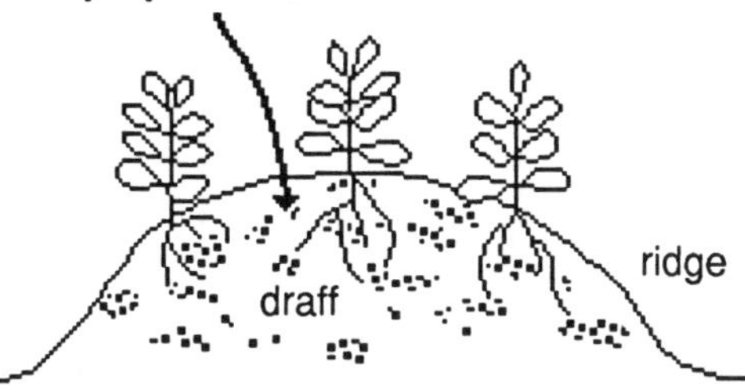

The manure acts **fast** because air and soil moisture contribute to its decay. The minerals contained in the draff are quickly restored to the soil and can be taken up by plant roots.

3 The draff is spread at the base of the ridge before ridging starts.

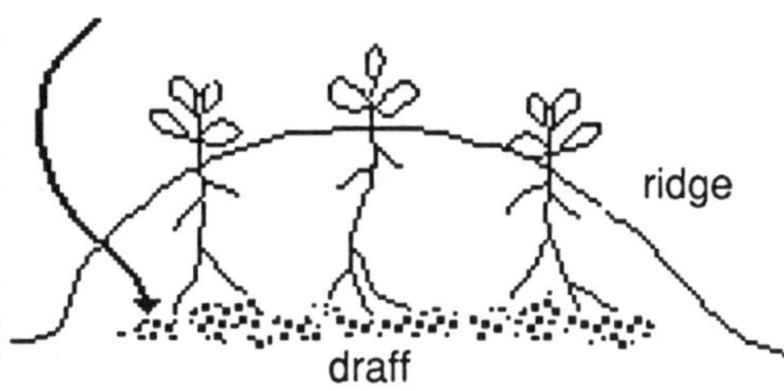

The draff lying at the base of the ridge is compacted by the weight of the earth thrown on top of it when the ridges are formed. Deprived of air, the draff decays slowly. The roots penetrate deeply before reaching the manure. The effects of the manure are **slow** and **lasting**.

- **Animal manure** must be buried evenly. Compact, solid lumps of manure that would scorch or smother any penetrating roots must be avoided. Many small clods are better than one big mass.

  The same rules apply to **hot compost** with or without animal excrements. Hot compost is easily dug in because it is thoroughly decomposed.

- Manures blend differently into soil depending on the sand or clay content of the soil itself. **Sandy soils lend themselves better to mixing than clayey soils** that stay cloddy. On the other hand, **organic matter and humus fix better in clayey soil** with a greater exchange of mineral salts.

  Gardeners can have different aims in view when spreading manure.They may be looking for **slow or quick results.** How long these results last depends on how the manure is applied. **Figure 117** shows the effects of brewer's draff (spent hops) applied to ridges in three ways.

Ashes and cinders

Ashes are obtained from burning organic matter and therefore their mineral composition is very similar to that of the source matter. The mineral salts they contain are almost as **diversified** as those in vegetable waste decomposed by microorganisms. Mineral salts in ashes dissolve faster in water and are therefore **ready for plant uptake quicker** than salts present in organic matter. However, these ash minerals are rapidly leached by infiltrating or runoff water, something which is to their disadvantage.

All plants react to ash fertilizers but in varying degrees. Some plants , react strongly; they include onion, taro, black nightshade, cucumber, banana, millet, eleusine. This is why women like to sow these plants in areas where field trash was burnt. Kitchen ashes can be saved and if kept dry can be spread round the base of plants later.

After charring, some animal by-products provide powders rich in minerals, for instance, oyster shells, fish scrap, bones and dried blood. These products are charred by prolonged heating on an iron sheet. They are usually rich in lime and phosphorus, and make excellent compost additives.

Lebu women on the Senegal coast were photographed smoking fish (**figure 118**). Groundnut shells are burnt to keep the fires going. When the task is over, there remains a whitish powder full of different mineral salts from the shells and fish waste. Some of the mineral salts that were contained in the manures used for the groundnut crop are found again in the ashes. The variety of materials burnt and charred makes the resulting powders into quality fertilizer.

118

A common practice called **burning-over** involves burning vegetable waste collected from all over the farm and charring clay at the same time **(figure 119)**. The dry trash is heaped up, covered with soil, and set on fire. The waste burns slowly under the layer of soil and is reduced to ashes. The soil is overheated and some of the clay charred. In the process. The clay is transformed and releases certain mineral salts which would otherwise remain in the soil.

Burnt-over sites are sown or planted with species tolerating ashes. Burning-over is sometimes done on sites intended for fruit-tree seedlings.

Sources of mineral substances near gardens

Other useful minerals can be found near gardens. One example is basalt rock that outcrops in some volcanic regions. This dark, porous rock is finely ground and when spread on cultivated beds is a most effective base dressing (see below).

Alluvial clay and silt collected from gullies, water channels and sewage drains can be spread on sandy plots. These alluvions are rich in mineral salts and improve the structure of sandy soils.

Marling is a similar practice. Alluvions deposited on banks and shores by the ebb and flow of water in rivers, lakes and ponds, are removed and spread on fields.

119

Commercial fertilizers

Types of commercial fertilizers

Many natural and artificial fertilizers are available commercially. (Natural fertilizers are those existing in nature and collected in their natural state; artificial fertilizers are factory-made). T**able 120** gives a list of the fertilizers most frequently on sale. Commercial fertilizers are always composed of **mineral salts soluble in water.** Some of these fertilizers dissolve very quickly and have an immediate effect on plant nutrition, while others dissolve very slowly with effects lasting many weeks or months.

Fertilizers must be applied in the right quantities and at the right time. In insufficient quantities they are useless. In excessive quantities, they are not completely taken up by plants so that some fertilizer is leached away by infiltrating water and runoff - this is a complete waste of money. The overdose simply poisons the plants.

The choice of fertilizer and application method depends on many factors :

- **soil** characteristics : composition, water content, capacity for retaining fertilizer. Compared to sandy or gravelly soils, clayey soils rich in humus retain fertilizers and release them to plant roots in a more satisfactory way;
- the characteristics of the **plants** to be enriched : root system, nutrient needs, vegetative cycle;
- **the results sought** : is the grower looking for immediate fertility for a single growing season, or long-lasting fertility through several cycles;
- **the effects of the fertilizer on the soil** : fertilizers can make soil acidic or alkaline. They may increase soil salinity. They can supply trace elements, or have the opposite effect by removing them. **Trace elements** are mineral substances present in the soil in minute quantities; they are absolutely essential for plant health;
- **the characteristics of the fertilizer** itself : is it a straight or a compound fertilizer, does it dissolve fast or slowly ?
- **the cost** of the fertilizers and the return obtained from them.

As so many factors have to be taken into account, practical experimentation in fertilizer applications is very important and must be carried out in gardens in accordance with advice from researchers and suppliers. The book 'Agriculture in African Rural Communities' discusses the subject of fertilizer applications in detail.

120. Main commercial fertilizers

- **Natural organic fertilizers**
  - *droppings of birds and bats (guano, viano),*
  - *oil cakes, dry or wet waste from food-processing plants,*
  - *dried algae,*
  - *blood meal, bone meal*
  - *peat.*
- **Natural mineral fertilizers**
  - *ground-rock dust,*
  - *basalt dust,*
  - *phosphates*
  - *limestone, lime,*
  - *dolomite,*
  - *alluvial clay*
- **Artificial fertilizers**

  Depending on which fertilizers are used, they supply the following mineral elements - nitrogen, phosphorus, potash, calcium, magnesium, trace elements, etc.
  - *nitrate,*
  - *phosphate,*
  - *sulphate,*
  - *carbonate,*
  - *chloride*
  - *urea,*
  - *slag*

They are divided into simple or compound fertilizers depending on the number of minerals they contain.

Base dressings, top dressings

A distinction is usually made between top dressings and base dressings also called pre-seeding or pre-planting dressings.

Top dressings are characterized by **immediate results.** They directly benefit the plants near which they are spread. No trace of them is found in the soil at the end of the growing season because during that time they are taken up by the plants or leached by infiltrating water. Return from top dressings must be tangible during the growing season, i.e. fertilizer expenditure must be immediately compensated by increased yields and income.

As a rule, chemical fertilizers which are highly soluble in water are considered to be top dressings. They can even be applied on land not permanently cultivated provided dosage is correct.

The effects of **base dressings last for many cultural seasons**, because the organic or mineral elements they contain decompose or dissolve slowly. Most natural fertilizers, especially those produced from ground rocks or hard materials, fall into this category.

121

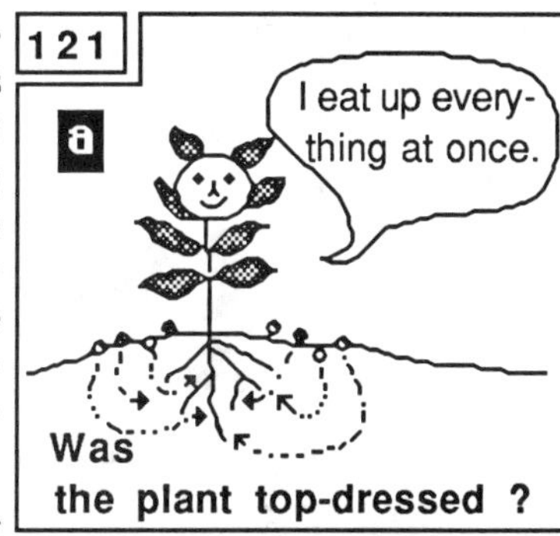

Was the plant top-dressed ?

Was a base dressing applied ?

122

- **Fertilizers that dissolve or decompose quickly and can be used for top-dressing the soil :**

  poultry manure, blood meal, bone meal, lime, green manures, ashes, nitrate, chloride, superphosphate, sulfate, urea.
- **Fertilizers that decompose slowly or are barely soluble, suitable for base dressings :**

  oil cakes, algae, peat, ground-rock dust (lime, phosphate, dolomite, basalt), slag, animal or vegetable manures, compost.

Base dressing is **a land investment** because it improves the soil on a lasting basis. The expense involved becomes profit-earning with the passing of many cultural seasons. Therefore, to make the investment profitable, the farmer must be sure of exploiting the land for several seasons.

123

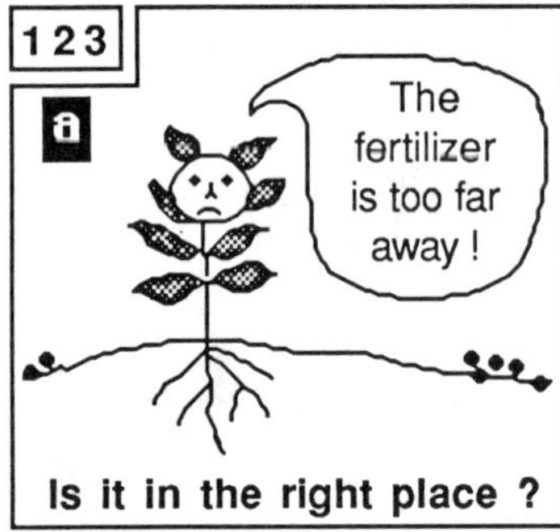

Is it in the right place ?

Is it in the right place ?

at the right time ?

at the right time ?

In the case of valley bottoms flooded every year, there is no point in applying base dressings because the cultivated beds and plots have to be established again after the annual floods.

Good base dressings, also called **soil conditioners,** should, by themselves, be able to improve soil structure, whereas top dressings in general use existing structures without modifying them.

How to make the most of commercial fertilizers

The following points should be borne in mind **in order to obtain maximum benefits from fertilizers**:

- ❏ apply fertilizer **at the time when plants need it and can use it** - time of growth, time of fruit set and fruiting;
- ❏ apply fertilizer **near the roots**, not too near the stem, but within the root zone;
- ❏ **choose fertilizer after deciding how long its effects should last**;
- ❏ apply fertilizer **in small successive splits** rather than in heavy spreads. This stops surplus fertilizer not used by plants from being leached down by rainwater;
- ❏ only apply fertilizer **on well-structured soils** containing enough organic matter and humus because these materials are able to retain mineral salts for a certain length of time;
- ❏ **vary the fertilizers** used, do not apply the same one all the time;
- ❏ do not mix chemical fertilizers on your own initiative because such mixes are not always effective. Indeed, they may have harmful effects on the soil.

If in doubt as to application methods and quantities, it may be wiser to use artificial (factory-made) fertilizers indirectly on a green manure crop as was explained earlier on **(figure 107)**.

The proper use of artificial fertilizers on horticultural produce is not easy to determine, and the amounts required to obtain the best results for particular plants growing in a tropical environment are not always well known. The reasons for this are :

- ■ fertilizer tested for specific crops such as cotton, coffee, pineapple, palm or banana can have unexpected, unwanted effects on other plants. Nitrogenous fertilizer, for example, can make eggplant leafage overvigorous with a reduction of fruit production;

the right amount ?

Is it the right food ?

Is the diet varied ?

- too much fertilizer can **poison**, or at least scorch the cultivated plant. Scorching occurs when too many fertilizer granules dissolve in contact with plant tissues;
- the wrong use of fertilizer may be **wasteful**. For example, when nitrogenous fertilizer, e.g. nitrate or urea, is applied to legumes, they absorb less atmospheric nitrogen and take up bought fertilizer, which is a waste of money;
- artificial fertilizer is also food for soil microorganisms These are activated to such an extent that organic matter in the soil is converted into minerals so fast as to destroy soil structure. When no organic matter is left, these microorganisms die and soil life comes to an end to the detriment of crops. **Wrong dosage can kill off soil life;**
- fertilizer can also have adverse effects on plant health and on the quality of harvested produce just as an unbalanced human diet causes disease through malnutrition (kwashiorkor and obesity, for example). Fruits and leaves produced after heavy fertilizer applications are often less nourishing and more delicate. They rot faster. They may even taste peculiar.

All these risks that are associated with the wrong use of fertilizers indicate that natural manures are often preferable to artificial fertilizers.

Natural products are always better balanced and their supplies of mineral salts more varied. We can compare natural manures to the balanced meals people should eat (Chapter 2).

124

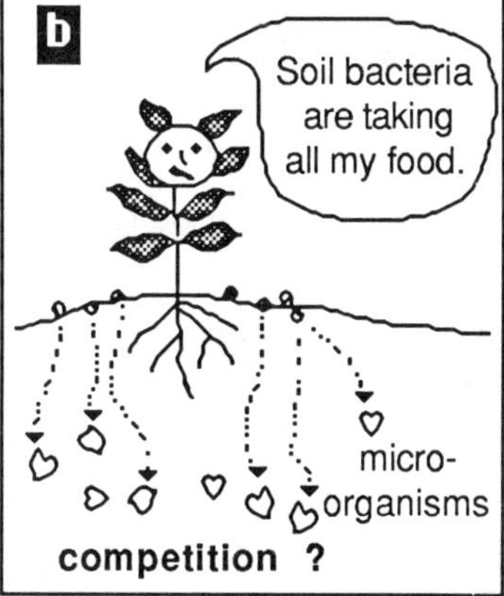

Chapter 5

Plant spacing above and below ground

The way plants are arranged, particularly when grown in a mixed stand, has far-reaching effects. Some of these will be discussed in this chapter.

The right arrangement reduces **competition** between plants with the same cultural requirements. It can also increase the **benefits between different plants**. These benefits can take many forms, such as enriching the nitrogen content of the soil, repelling pests or giving shade. Plants can be complementary, exploiting different soil levels and aerial space, and thus increases the total production from an area.

Planting patterns can affect the use of **labour** and the access for workers and for machines for cultivation and harvesting.

The distances between plants will also affect the **microclimate** particularly with reference to wind and moisture.

Crop protection and spacing are dealt with in Chapter 8.

We shall first deal with sowing and planting patterns and then with the spatial arrangement of plants

125 **Broadcasting of seed**

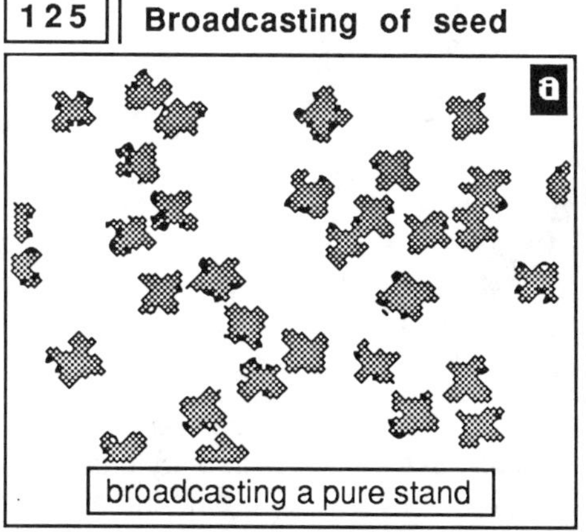

broadcasting a pure stand

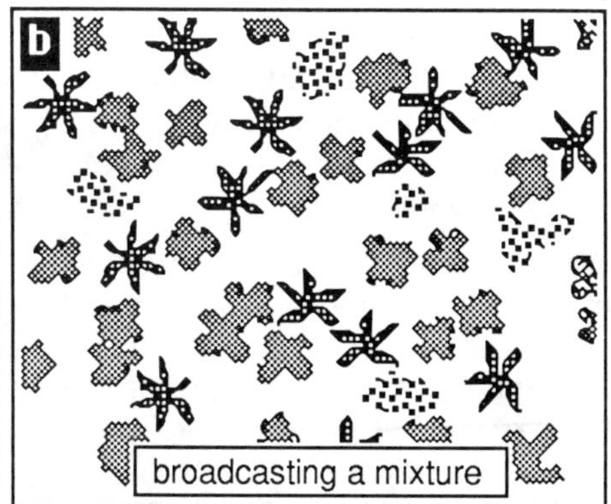

broadcasting a mixture

Planting patterns

There are countless ways of spacing plants. Observations of the morphological characteristics of the plants together with experience will help the gardener to choose the arrangement best suited to local conditions.Some sowing patterns are random while others are organized.

Broadcasting

As a rule, **broadcasting seed** is not a good way of controlling plant density **(figure 125)** When this method is used, seeds are not scattered uniformly. This gives rise either to gaps between plants or to overcrowding. Where gaps occur, the soil is not as fully occupied, as it could be; where plants are too dense, they compete with one another for soil, water, light and air.

However, broadcast seed does not require much labour or equipment. It is done by hand and can take into account the presence of trees and plants which are already established. This is an advantage when cultivated plants have different life cycles (perennial or seasonal), different habits (creeping, erect, bushy, etc.), different ways of propagation (by seeds or by cuttings).

Broadcasting is a method typical of manual farming using only simple tools. It is not adapted to animal-pulled or motorized cultivation.

The vegetable plot in **figure 126** was broadcast. Taro, nightshade, bush greens, okra and cassava are growing in confusion and the bed looks like uncleared bushland. There is a little of everything in this bed but, unfortunately, none of the plants enjoy good conditions for growth and production. Some of them are stunted and straggly, many of the leaves are yellow for lack of light, fruits are hidden and their development cannot be checked easily. Under the mass of foliage, there will be high humidity and shade; a good breeding ground for countless insects, slugs and snails that damage leaves and fruit, and spoil them for market or for domestic consumption.

Broadcasting must always be carefully planned in order to avoid an unproductive tangle. The sower has to know :

- **the number of seeds to be sown on a given surface** so that plant density or population is satisfactory;
- **the proportion of seeds of each associated plant** to be added when the seed mixture is being prepared;
- **the right spacing, that is, the approximate distance needed** between seedlings of the same species.

Where tiny seeds are involved, for example, bush greens, sesame and nightshade, it is usual to mix the seeds in a certain proportion in the bottom of a basket before broadcasting. The proportion of each kind of seed in the mixture determines seedling density.

127 Plant density is determined by spacing in the rows and between the rows.

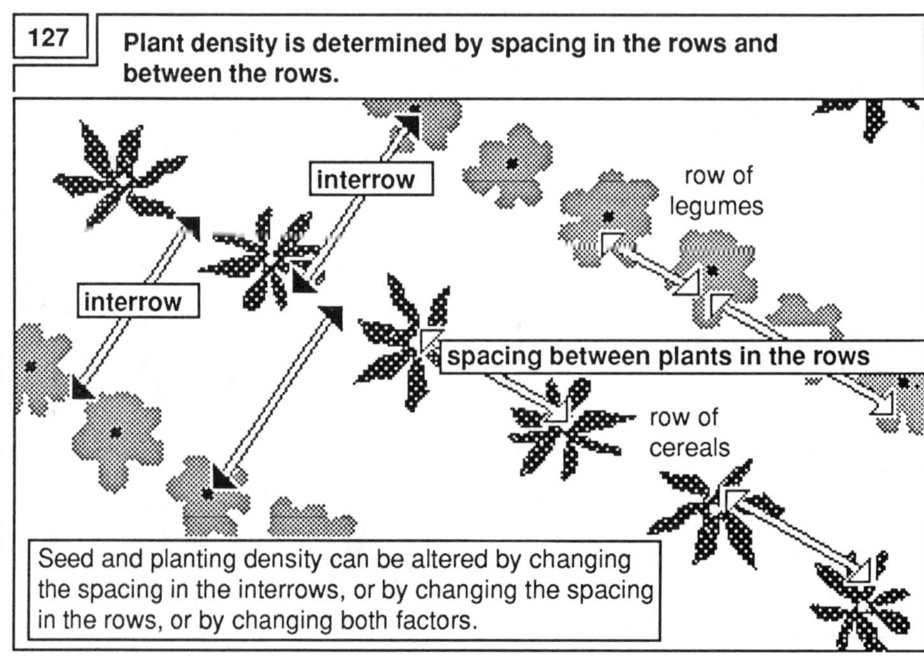

Only by practice does the sower acquire the knack of broadcasting more or less uniformly over the ground surface.

What looks like a broadcast pattern is sometimes the result of natural reproduction. When seeds grow spontaneously in gardens and fields, the gardener may decide to keep some young plants and eliminate others by thinning rather than remove the whole lot. For tree seedlings, roughly the right density can be kept.

Row planting

Row planting must be adopted when it is intended to seed, weed and harvest with animal-drawn or motorized implements. Row planting allows the passage of cultivators and machinery. It also makes it easier for hand operations such as hoeing.

When planting in rows, a distinction is made between :

- **the space** or **distance between two rows (interline spacing) and**
- **spacing in the row itself**, i.e. the distance between two plants sown in the same row **(figure 127)**.

128 Some sowing patterns for row planting

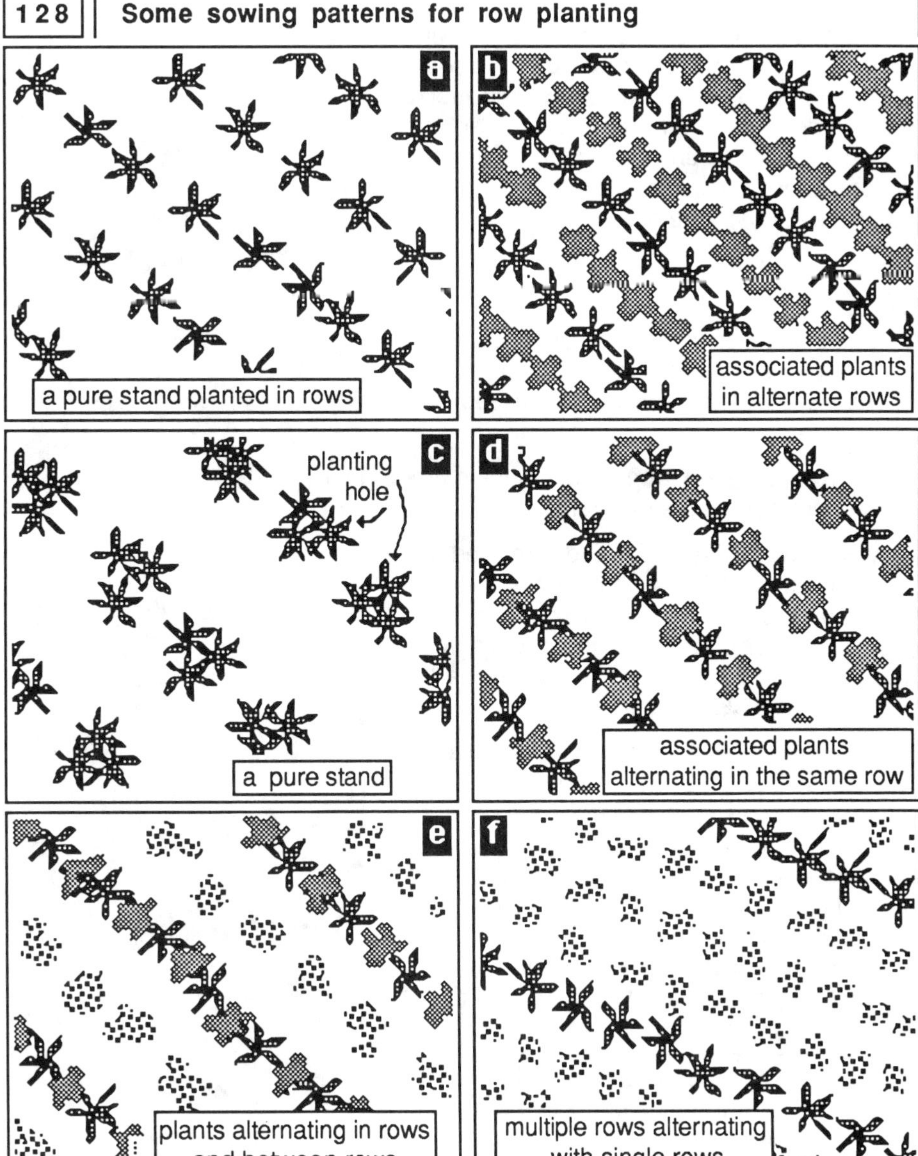

129

The distances between rows and in the rows themselves determines the amount of space that is available for each plant. To choose the right spacing the following should be considered :

- **the shape of the root system**,
- **the growth habit** of every species,
- **the development of the root system and of the foliage** during the cultural season.
- the **benefits** the plants obtain from each other.

Chapter 44 in *Agriculture in African Rural Communities* deals with this subject in detail.

Some of the numerous seeding patterns for row planting are illustrated in **figure 128.** Experimentation will show the most suitable pattern.

Growing plants in mixtures

Here is a small field in which maize and cherry tomato are interplanted **(figure 129).** The seeding pattern is particularly **suited to the maize crop which is dominant here**. The maize was dibbled in rows whereas the tomato seeds were broadcast and their stems will gradually cover the whole surface of the field.

There are two reasons behind the choice of cherry tomato :

- its stems cover the ground completely and stop weeds from growing under the maize. Thanks to the tomato, there is less weeding to be done;
- **the tomato yield supplements** the maize crop, providing more food and money.

It is worth noting that hardy seeds are used because selected varieties would not tolerate the shady conditions under the maize. In order to grow these types of tomatoes, more space would have to be left between the maize to give the tomatoes sufficient sunlight.

Figure 130 shows a planting arrangement associating trees (mango) and seasonal plants (sweet potato). The trees were planted in rows but the potato mounds were heaped up at random. Sweet potato is a light-loving plant but, because the dwarf mangos were spaced well apart, it is not affected by shade from the trees. This planting arrangement means that two distinct soil layers can be exploited, one for the benefit of the sweet potato - the layer turned over and heaped up to form the mound - and the other for the benefit of the mangos, i.e. the layer situated under the ground floor. Thanks to the mounds, the roots of the seasonal crop are raised thus lessening competition between the crop and the trees whose roots develop in deeper layers **(figure 20)**.

The planting arrangement of the trees is fixed once and for all because of their long life, but the layout of the lower storey can be changed from one season to the next : mounds placed at random, ridging in straight lines, crops in rows on the flat, etc.

Another planting arrangement is illustrated in **figure 131**. Here trees were

130

131

132 Arrangement and orientation of rows of trees growing in a plot of mixed crops

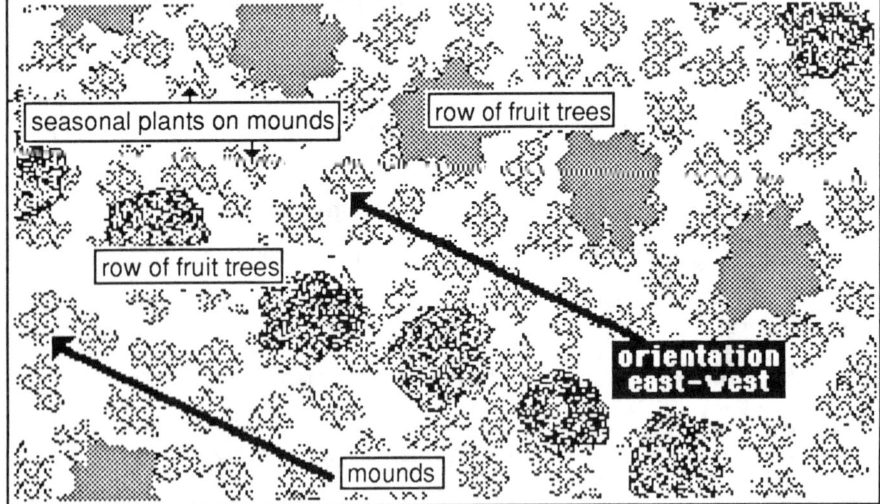

The rows of fruit trees are oriented east-west to let the seasonal plants get as much sunshine as possible during the day.

133 **The way lines of trees are oriented determines variations in shade during the day.**

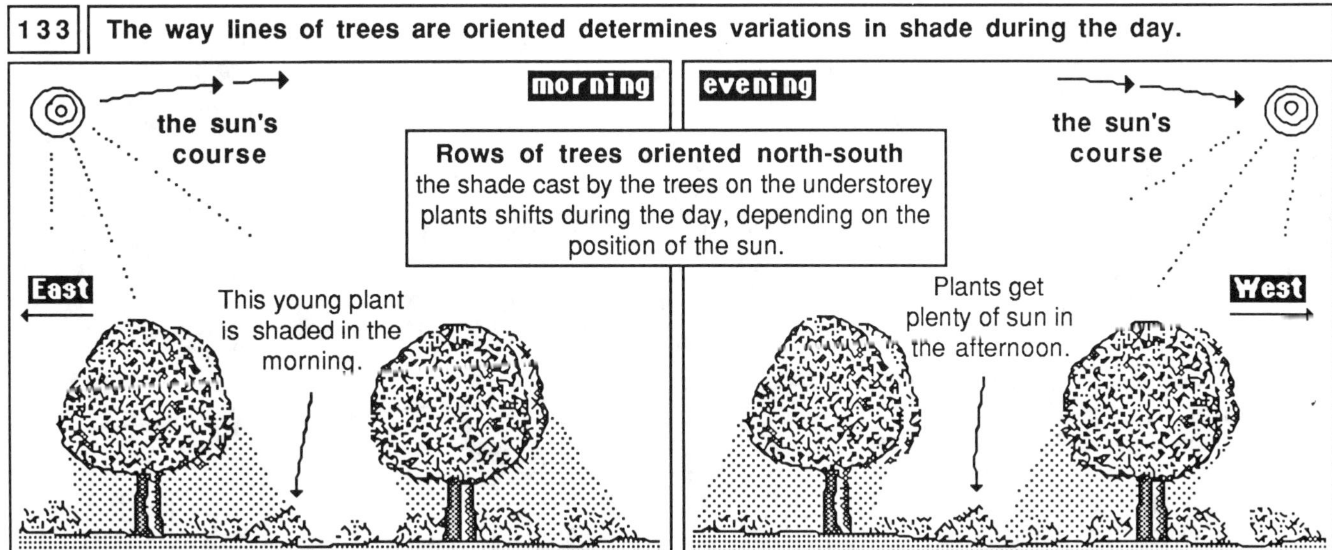

planted in parallel rows as close as for a hedge. In the foreground, we see a row of sweet limes (citrus fruit) planted close together. In the background, a row of mangos also closely spaced. Other rows of trees follow with spaces of between 10 and 20 metres between the rows. The garden is therefore a series of parallel rows of trees separated by strips of seasonal crops **(figure 132).** In this instance, the lines of trees and shrubs are each composed of one species but the gardener could just as easily have mixed different species within the rows.

The orientation of rows of trees is also an important factor in gardening. When the rows are oriented from east to west, seasonal plants growing between the rows are in full sun all day **(figures 132 and 134)**. On the contrary, when the rows of trees are oriented north-south, the sun's path lies across the rows. Consequently, plants growing between the rows enjoy alternate periods of shade and sun **(figure 133)**.

134 **Rows of trees oriented east-west**

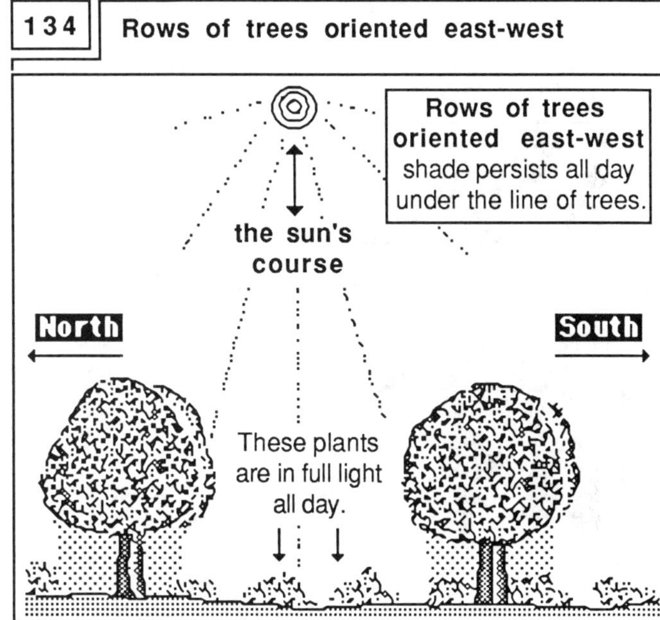

135 **A garden planned round two clusters of fruit trees**

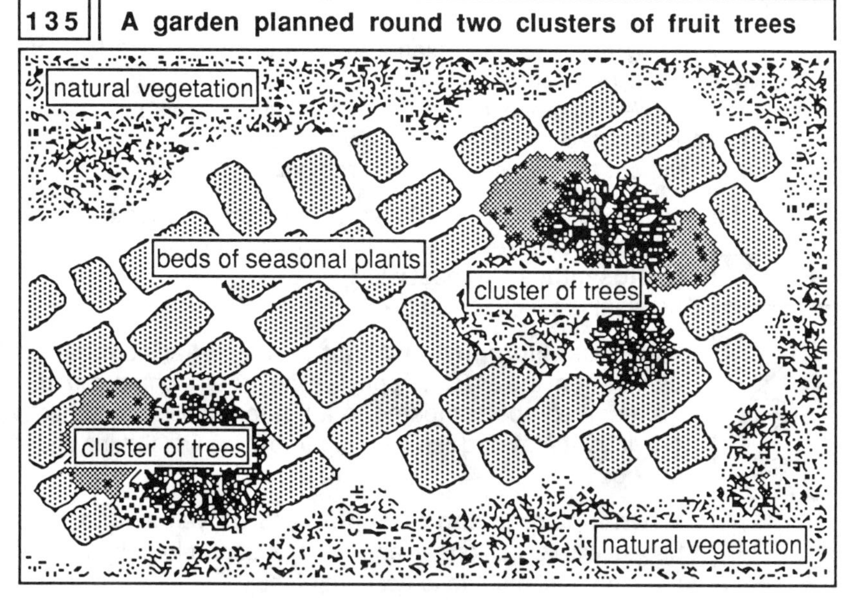

Row orientation will modify the drying effects of the prevailing winds. A sheltered environment with low wind speeds will reduce the amount of evaporation from plants and soil. Rows orientated at right angles to the prevailing wind will shelter each other. Winds coming from different directions will be best modified by rows planted in a crossing pattern. Large trees and bushes provide a little shelter on the windward side, but much more on the downwind side. Gaps between large trees in a row and rows of tall plants oriented in the wind direction cause a funnelling effect with much higher wind speeds.

In some regions, gardens are laid out in a concentric pattern with, say, a cluster of trees surrounded by patches of seasonal plants. In **figures 136 and 137**, some palms give shade to annato trees. Palm and annato are the core-plants in the garden. The foreground is occupied by various seasonal beds : tiger nut on the right, sweet potato on the left, staked eggplant and tomato in the centre. On the edge of the trees, plants that tolerate shade and cool conditions can be seen.

One of the advantages of this concentric plan, represented in **figure 135**, is to create a whole range of microclimatic conditions. There is cool, moist air inside the cluster of trees, while all around the trees, there is a zone protected from winds, and a few metres away, a drier area.

136

137 Plant layers in a garden planned round clusters of trees

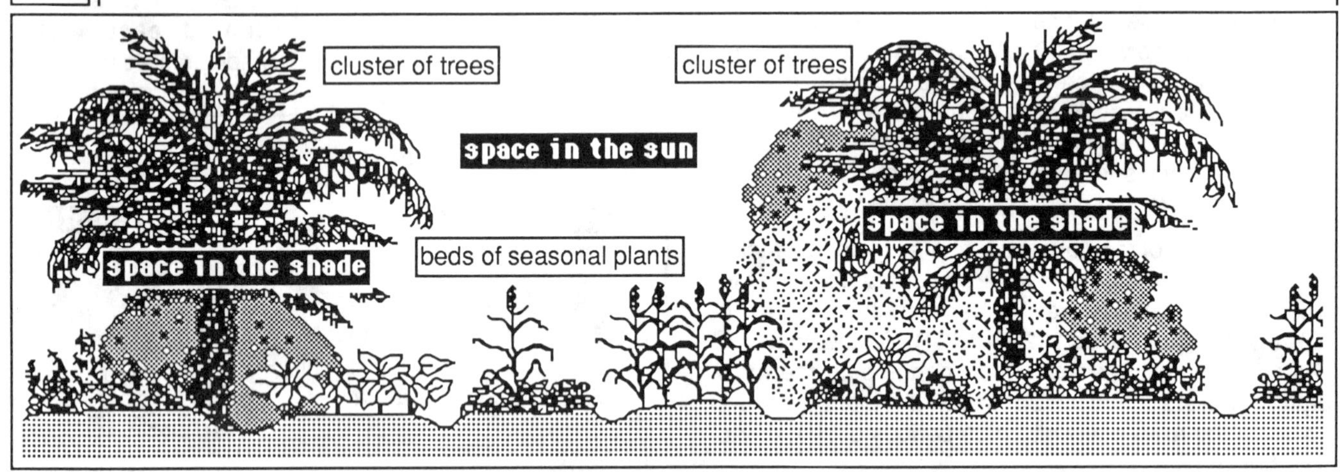

Arrangement of plants above the ground

Plants need air and light to produce living matter. From air, plants extract **carbon which is the most abundant chemical substance in living matter**. Carbon is the main component of sugars (carbohydrates), fats (lipids) and proteins. We can grasp the importance of carbon in plants by taking charcoal as an example. Charcoal is obtained by burning wood (living matter) under a layer of soil deprived of air. After combustion without air, only black carbon remains.

Plants absorb air and the carbon it contains through small holes called **stomata** situated on the surface of leaves. Plants then transform the air through **photosynthesis** without which no plant growth and therefore no plant production can take place.

138 The effects of the lack of space

healthy plant
ground
This plant is smothered.

Plants use **chlorophyll and light**, in order to transform carbon dioxide from the air. Chlorophyll is the green pigment found in leaves; it can be compared to a pot for cooking food. Light provides energy and can be compared to the fire burning under the pot.

When a plant is short of light, it turns yellow and wilts because it is no longer able to produce chlorophyll. Plant management must take account of this.

Air and light for shade-loving and light-loving plants

It is important to ensure that plants are not smothered as in **figure 138**, but even more important is to see how they are exposed to light.

Some plants like to be in full light., others prefer to be in the shade. Still others are happy to be in partial shade. Some produce abundant vegetation when shaded but do not bear fruit. Light requirements can also vary during the life cycle of the plant.

Okra, groundnut, chillies, tomato, eggplant, shea butter, pineapple, cabbage, citrus, oil palm, sweet potato, are all **light-loving plants**. It is useless sowing them in the shade if they are to produce satisfactory yields. **When these plants are grown in shade**, it can be seen that

- they stretch towards the light and **the stems are noticeably elongated** between the leaf nodes. The leaves are abnormal and unhealthy **(figure 139)** ;
- **they turn yellow** quite quickly. Only the heads that reach full light are really green;
- **they yield little or no fruits**. The fruits that set are small and fall off easily before ripening.

On the other hand, when these plants are in full light, their growth habit is normal, leaves are green and strong, flowering and fruiting are abundant.

139 Lack of light and how it affects one of the intercropped species

1 Overcrowded planting

Some plants are short of light. They are elongated and underproductive.

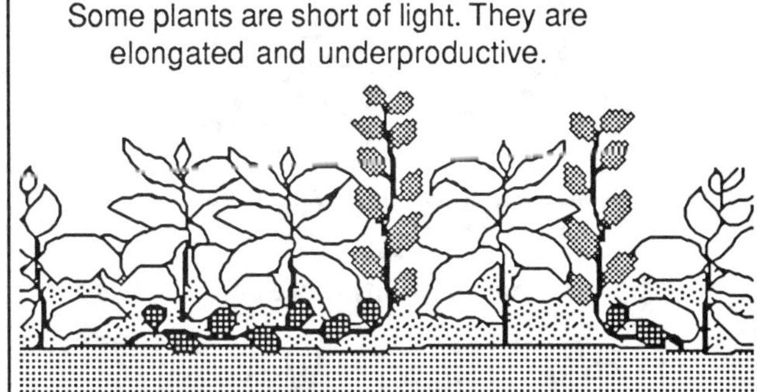

2 Correct plant population

Plants of both species have enough light.

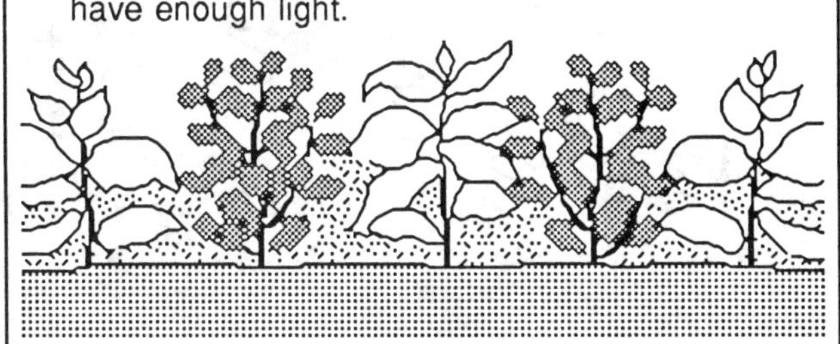

The reaction of **shade plants** is very different. They grow naturally in cool, shady places, for example, such plants as grains of paradise, cocoyam, hilleria, some cucurbits, and pepper. They develop well in shade, their leaves are deep green, they flower and bear fruit normally. When these plants are left in full sun, they droop and wilt after germination, the leaves are small and tough, the stems short between the leaf nodes, flowering and fruiting are disappointing. Seedlings look stunted.

Many species can be called **indifferent** - they thrive equally well in shade and in full light. It may be, however, that flowering and fruiting are affected by light conditions. Some plants develop abundant leaves in the shade but bear no fruit. If they are grown for their leaves, they can be left in the shade without any problem, but if fruit is wanted, they have to be established in full light. **Figure 140** shows how plants of the same species develop very different growth habits and appearance depending on whether they are in the shade or in the sun.

The way plants are grown must therefore take into account the reactions of plants to light and shade. Here are some ways of dealing with shading.

140 Two plants of the same species have different growth habits, depending on whether they grow in the shade or in the sun.

in the shade

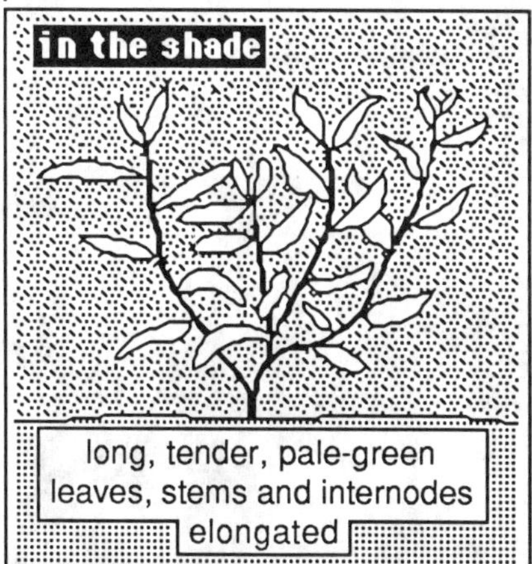

long, tender, pale-green leaves, stems and internodes elongated

in full sun

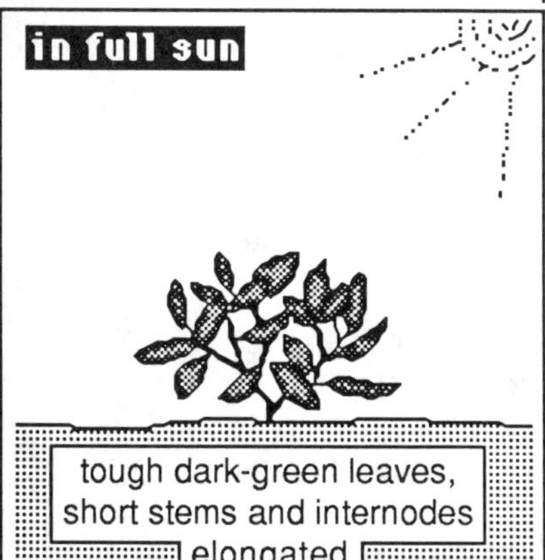

tough dark-green leaves, short stems and internodes elongated

Staking plants

Staking plants meaning providing plants with **stakes** or **props** to which the stems can cling naturally or be tied. Stakes are usually wooden poles, bamboo canes, or branches. Trees, bananas, millet and maize stems, etc. can also be used for supporting plants.

141 Staking

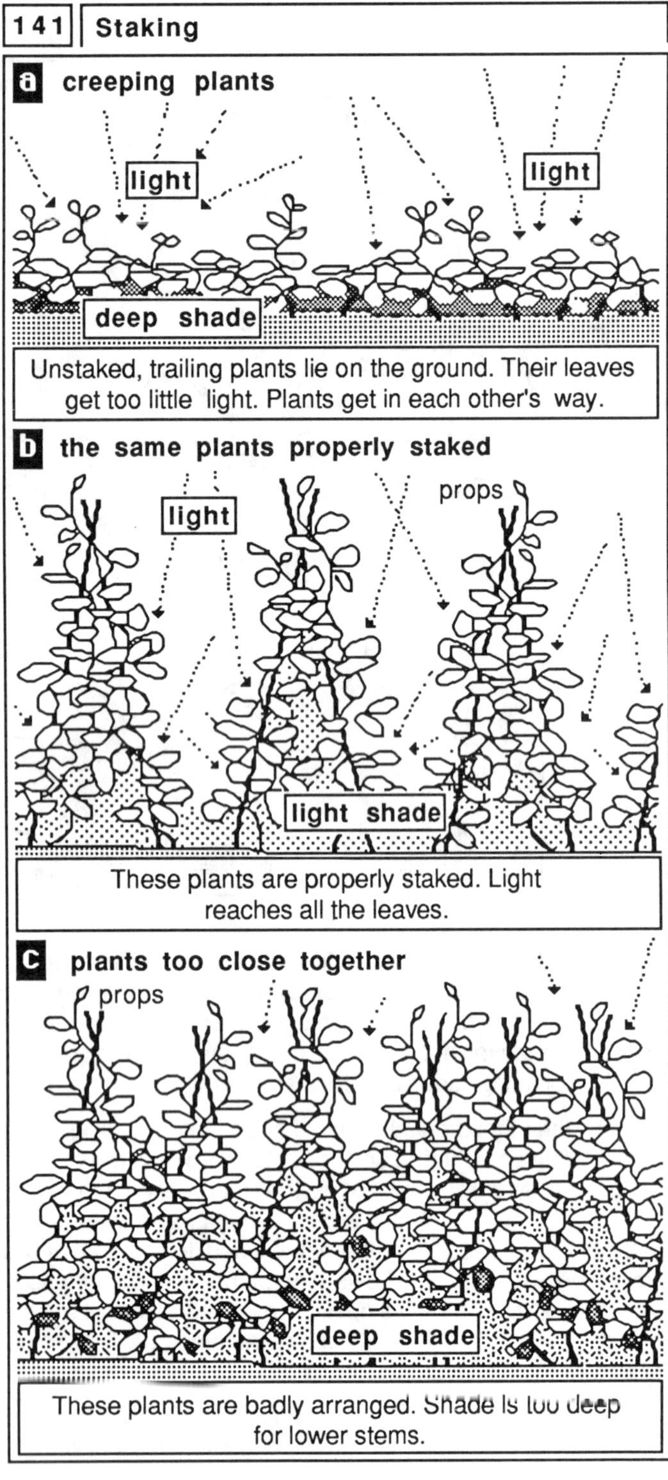

142

143

Stakes must be pushed firmly into the ground to prevent them being knocked over by wind or by the weight of the staked plants.

Figure 142 shows a field of staked tomatoes. The stakes are made of five or six dried elephant grass stems stripped of their leaves They are arranged round the plant like a pyramid and tied together at the top. The pyramidal structure makes for stability.

Staking suits **trailing plants** that tend to creep and spread on the ground.

144

When crops grow in association or relay intercropping is practised, some species can be supports for other plants as illustrated in **figures 143 and 144**. Here yam is growing up a maize plant for support, while passion fruit is twining round a *Leucena* trunk. It should be noted that passion fruit is a long, vigorous climber that thrives in shade but whose flowers and fruits only develop well in full light.

Tying plants

Tying plants serves the same purpose as staking. Plants are tied to a vertical support on a surface along which stems and creepers can develop. Tying can be done against a wall with the help of branches **(figure 145)**, or by fixing nails into a wall, or by attaching string, or wire to a living or dead hedge **(figure 146)**. This practice is particularly suitable for creepers like passion fruit because the stems can be tied as they grow.

Adjusting shade

When garden-trees throw heavy shade, they can always be cut or pruned to admit more light to the plants below. Pruning can be done with the help of a machete, a bow saw, or shears.

Before adjusting shade, the orientation of the garden must be studied so that the pruning

The benefits of staking are illustrated in **figures 141 and 197** :

- **stems** do not trail on the ground nor get entangled as they would if they were not staked. **Every staked plant occupies less ground surface and more volume in height.** Seed density is therefore increased because the plants are staked;
- the foliage of staked plants is arranged so that **leaves get plenty of light,** even those nearest the ground. The seeding pattern must fit this goal;
- **air circulates freely between the young plants;**
- **leaves and fruit do not come in contact with the ground,** thus minimizing disease infection and rotting.
- **it is easier to look after and harvest the crop** because the grower can pass up and down between the plants without damaging the stems;
- for plants erect by nature, staking is also used **to prevent lodging** (beating down by wind or tornados).

145

146

decided upon lies on an east-west axis, that is to say, the course of the sun. Shade can also be altered so that it becomes diffuse. This is done by lopping off branches and creating light paths through the thinned branches **(figure 147)**.

It is not advisable to let intense shade develop in gardens. The choice of large trees for gardens and their planting pattern should, as far as possible, allow for the needs of the plants below.

Shading young plants

Quite often, young plants do not grow well in full light particularly in dry weather and when the roots are not fully established. This means that temporary shade may be needed.

Young seedlings cannot survive long exposure to sunlight because the rootlets are unable to absorb water quickly enough to compensate for the loss of water from the leaves.

147 Adjusting shade in a many-layered garden

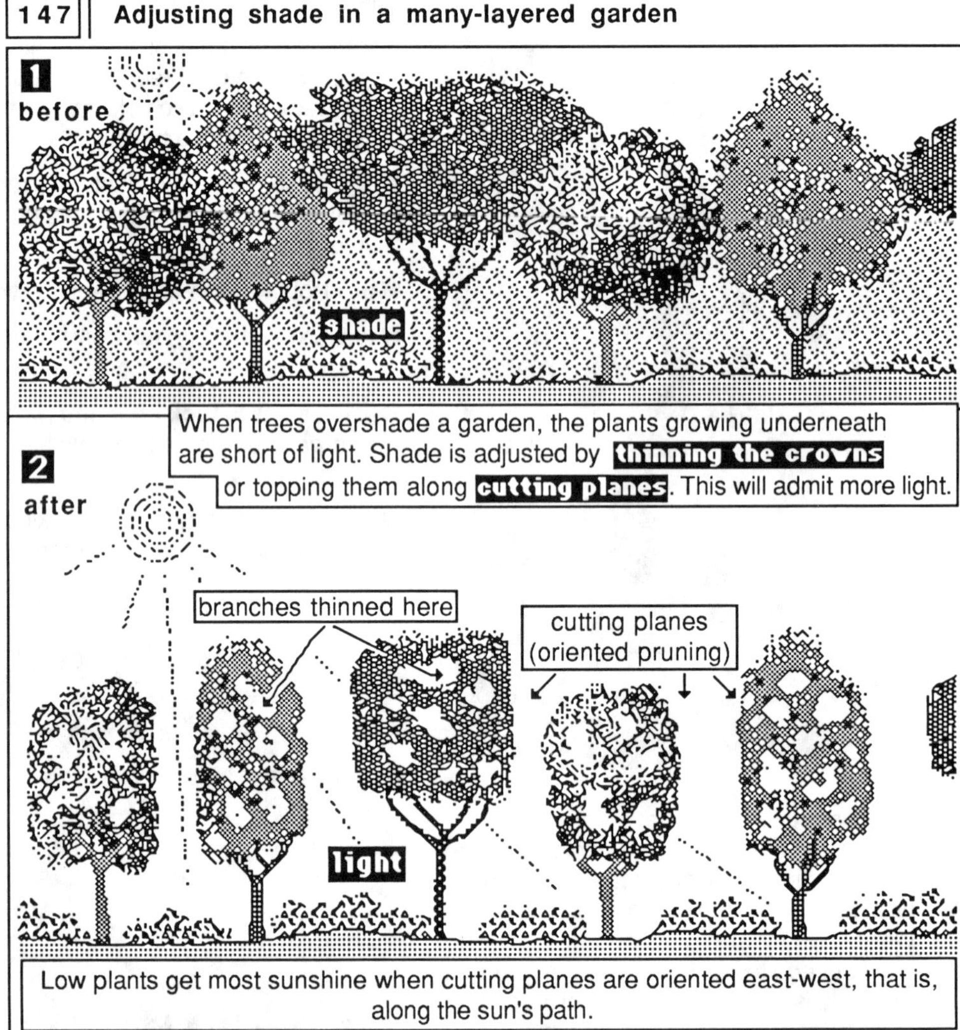

Low plants get most sunshine when cutting planes are oriented east-west, that is, along the sun's path.

148

There are many ways of creating temporary shade for seedlings. For instance :

- the sowing of associated plants can be staggered so that light-loving plants are able to shade plants that do not tolerate sunlight quite so well;
- palm or other leafy branches can be used to establish shaded nurseries **(figure 384);**
- young plants can be covered individually as demonstrated in the pineapple plantation in **figure 148**. The shoots are protected from light and heat by other shoots not used for propagation. In this instance, the young plants are protected not so much from light as from high temperatures. This technique is also used when the first fruits appear and sun scorch must be prevented.

Chapter 6
Pruning

Why are plants pruned ?

The growth of leaves, stems and roots depends very much on the sap circulating in them. Sap moves in two directions : from the roots towards the leaves, and then from the leaves to all the other plant parts **(figure 149)**. **Water and mineral salts** travel from roots to leaves where they are converted into **soluble organic compounds,** which help to build all plant organs - stems, roots, leaves, fruits and tubers.*

149 The role of leaves in plant life

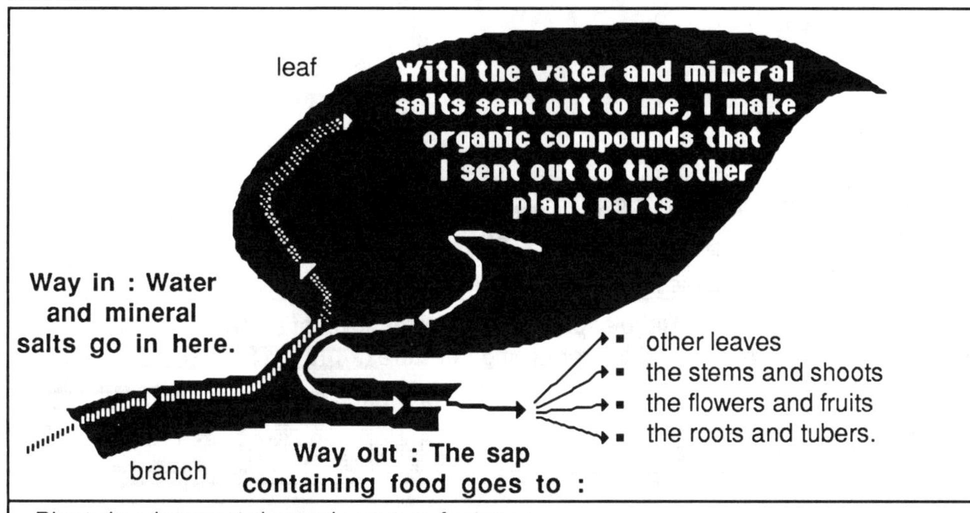

Plant development depends on two factors :

- the **amount of water and mineral salts** that the roots take up from the soil in order to make the food. Well-established roots are needed for this task ;
- the **ability of the leaves** to transform carbon dioxide from the air, and water and mineral salts into organic compounds with the help of sunlight. Healthy, abundant leafage is needed for this task.

Cultivated plants are pruned in order to **direct the sap towards the organs one would like to develop.** Gardeners who spend time pruning cultivated plants or who go to the trouble of cutting them back at harvest-time want to encourage production. The aim is to channel the work of the plant so that it will provide more of the desired agricultural produce. If fruits are wanted, then steps are taken to encourage these. If leaves are wanted, the plant is stopped from wasting energy on producing unwanted flowers or fruits.

- Therefore, before pruning begins, the first question to be asked and answered is : **Which plant part is to be harvested :** leaves, shoots, flowers, fruits, tubers, barks, roots ?
- In nature, there is always a balance between the power of the roots to make the water and mineral salts ascend to the leaves, and the power of the leaves to convert them into organic compounds which are sent back to other plant parts. Man can alter this natural balance in favour of the parts he wants to harvest, but he must do so carefully and know exactly what he is aiming at.

150

* The subject is discussed in greater detail in "*Tropical Agriculture in African Rural Communities*", lesson 23.

151 **Growth competition betweeen runners and fruits**

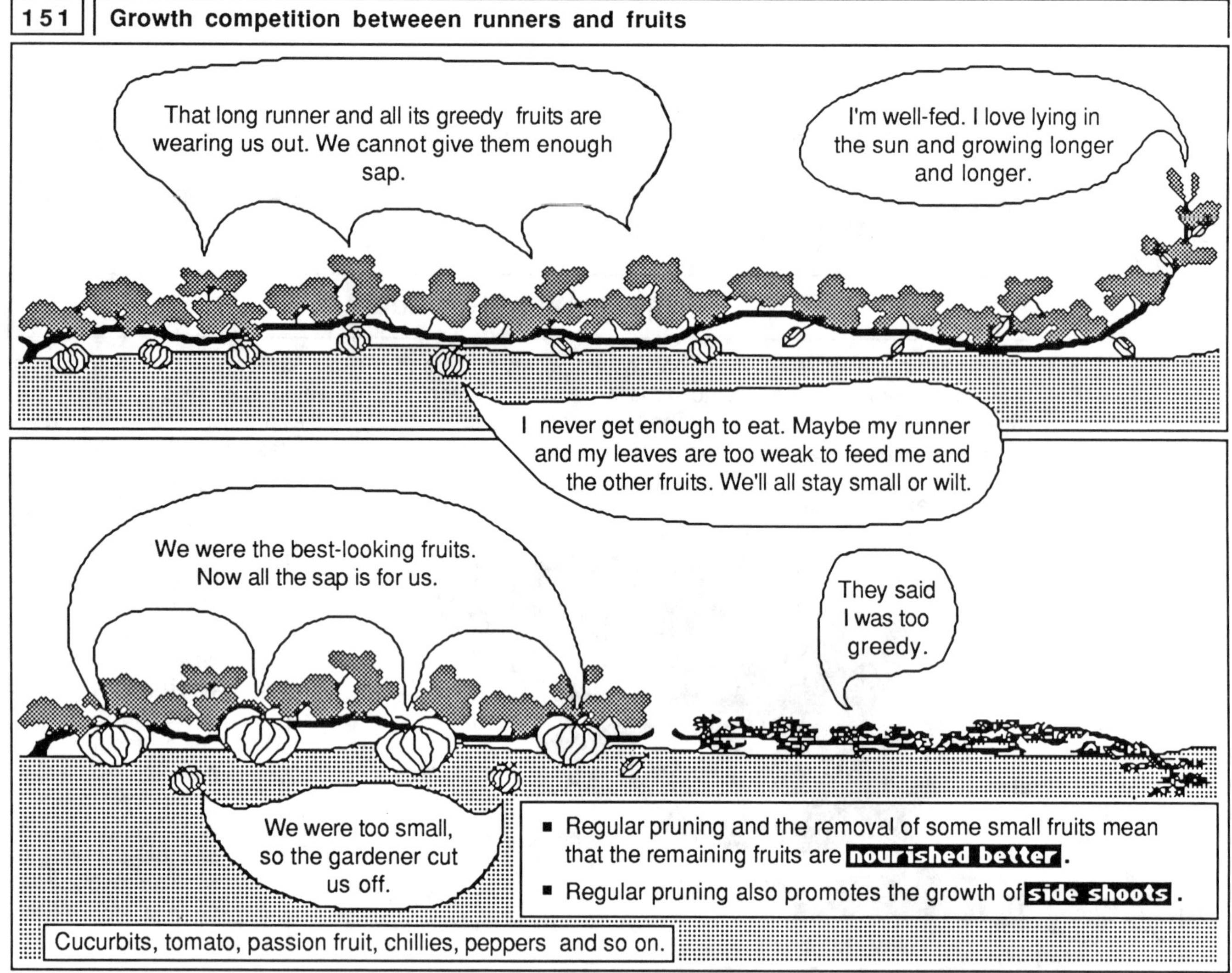

Figure 150 illustrates the danger of cutting off too many leaves. In contrast, **figure 151** shows how it is possible to achieve a balance between vegetative growth (development of stems and leaves) and fruit growth. A cucurbit was chosen as an example but the same remarks apply to erect, shrubby and bushy species.

Plant development depends on two factors :

- the amount of water and mineral salts that roots take up from the soil. Well-established roots are needed for this task ;
- the ability of the leaves to transform carbon dioxide from the water and mineral salts into organic compounds with the energy from sunlight. Healthy, abundant leafage is needed for this task.
- When the gardener knows exactly the produce or result he is looking for, he goes on to **observe the plant from the point of view of its morphology and its growth pattern. Morphology** is the scientific term used to describe the shape (form) of a plant : shape of its leaves, arrangement of shoots and branches, shape and position of leaves and fruits, root system, etc. The illustrations in this chapter show us which morphological aspects of cultivated plants should be observed and the practical conclusions to be drawn from our study.
- It is quite easy to observe the arrangement of leaves, shoots, flowers and fruits on a plant, but it is not so simple to follow the change in these plant parts as a result of pruning. Changes depend mainly on **how the food supply is distributed** to the different plant parts, and particulary to the parts one wishes to harvest.
- Pruning is only worthwhile and efficient if it is **properly timed** and has a **definite effect** on the unpruned parts of the plant.

152 **Getting to know plant parts before pruning**

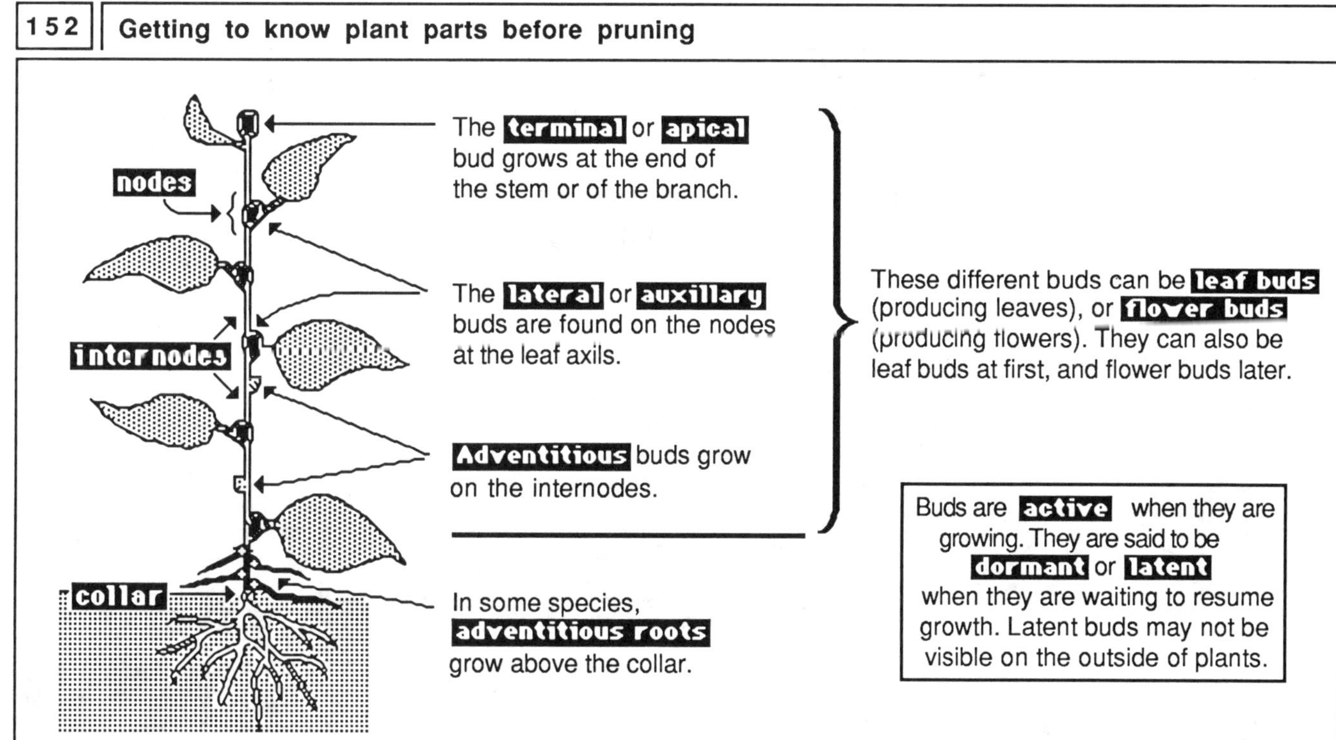

■ Some plants respond well to pruning, some do not. Frequent pruning is of benefit to fruits such as guava and mango because, after cutting, they produce many buds. In similar fashion, pinching out the main stem of cucumber, tomato and bush greens does not kill the plant but stimulates the growth of replacement stems. This means that pinching out promotes the production of auxillary (or lateral) shoots.

The opposite is true of other plants such as palm, millet and maize. The removal of the terminal bud kills the plant.

153 **Different types of stems and branches**

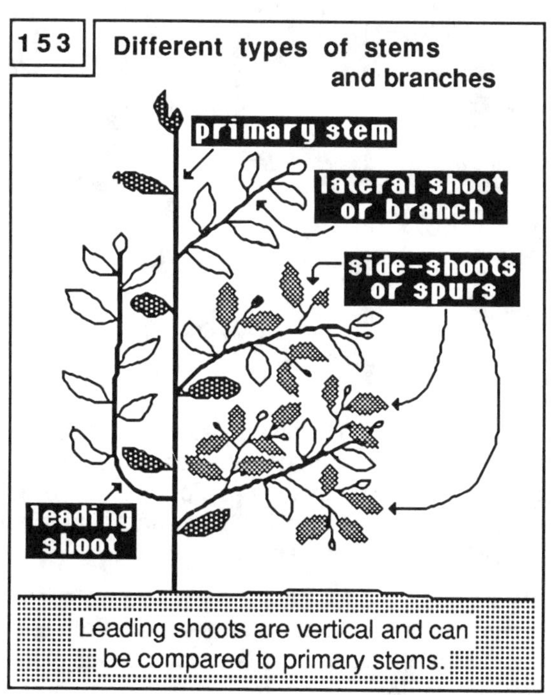

Leading shoots are vertical and can be compared to primary stems.

Figure 152 shows the different types of leaf buds to be found on a plant. When they develop, buds can grow into two kinds of stems easily recognized by their growth habits. **Primary stems** grow upwards, they are vertical. **Secondary stems or laterals** spread sideways from the primary stems, growing horizontally or obliquely. Primary stems are those that lend height to plants (or length, in the case of creepers). Laterals lend breadth to plants. When referring to trees, one can also speak of "primary wood" and "secondary wood" **(figure 153)**.

As was said earlier, trees are pruned for definite results and these should be clearly understood before any cutting is done, or irreparable mistakes could be made.

Observation and experience are the best guides for pruning. Growers must observe the various patterns of plant growth and try out different pruning techniques checking the results on plant shape and on production.

The following section describes how best to observe and experiment. The diagrams explain some certain pruning techniques. Some species are mentioned by name but readers can add their own examples.

154 **The dominance of the apical bud and the effects of pinching out**

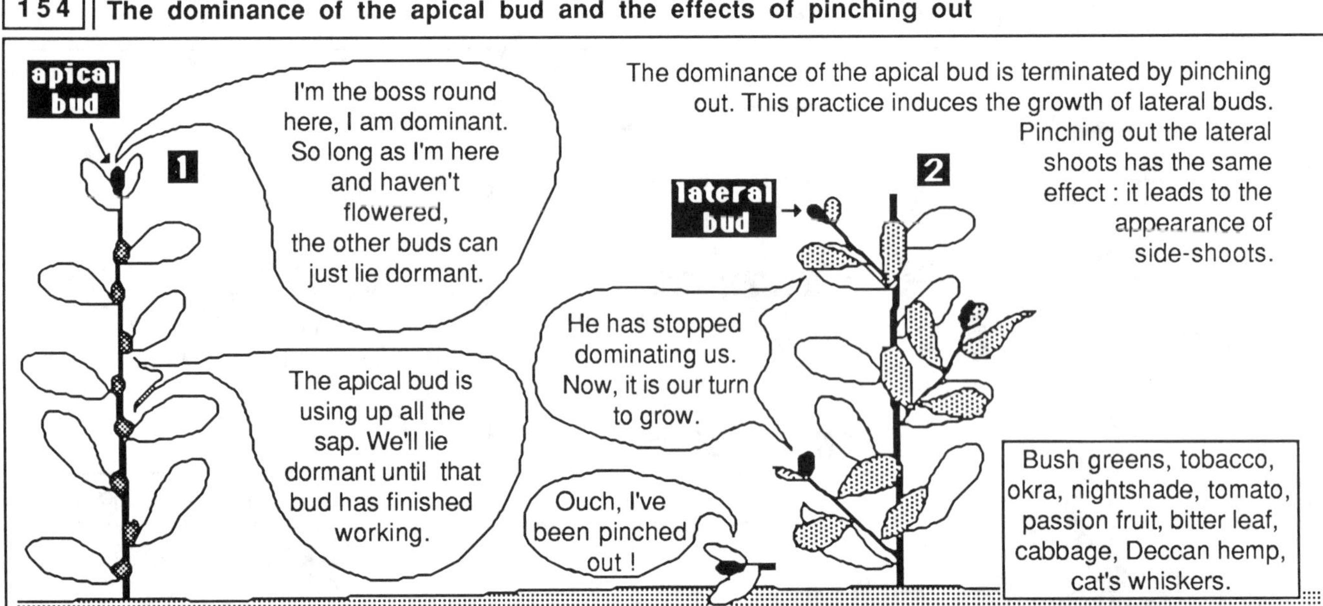

Promoting growth, shape and form of plants

Producing leaves, shoots and poles

Plants grown for their leaves like bitter leaf, bush greens, cassava and Indian spinach are easily pruned. Pinching out the terminal bud of a stem or a shoot stimulates the growth of side shoots ; these new shoots will themselves be cut back at a later stage **(figure 154)**.

155

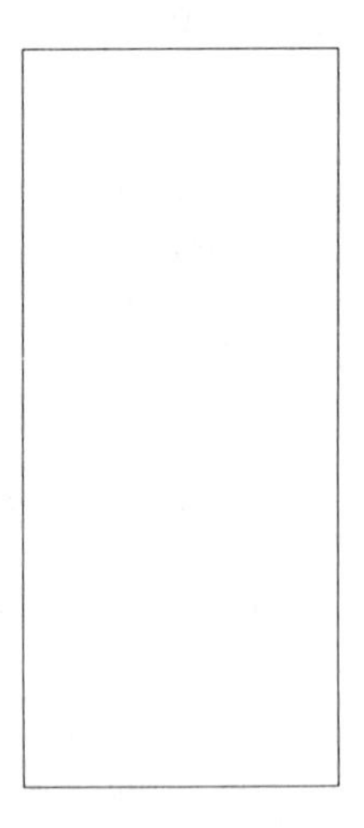

156

Figure 155 shows a bush green plant. The primary stem was cut before the apical (terminal) bud had flowered. Three lateral shoots have grown to replace the primary stem. They will never be as vigorous as the first stem but together they will yield a quantity of leaves at least equivalent to that which would be picked off the primary stem.

If the three new shoots are again pruned back, they will be replaced in turn providing one or two nodes with buds have been left. With bush greens, the first regrowth is satisfactory, but the second is less plentiful. Frequently, the first cutting (leaves from the primary stem) is sold and the second crop is used for home consumption only.

Figure 156 shows the top of a cassava stem being used for its leaves. When the terminal tip of the regrowth shoot was pinched out, other shoots sprouted. They were cut, and have already been replaced by fresh growth.

By repeatedly gathering the young shoots, the gardener has checked the growth of the plant including tuber enlargement **(figure 150)**. Cassava grown for leaves and tubers are often grown on different sites. Tuber-cassava requires fairly loose, well aerated soil while better yields of leaf-cassava are produced on moist, clayey soils where tubers do not thrive. This is why leaf-cassava is frequently found growing by ditches or in hedges whereas root cassava is a field crop.

Although all varieties of cassava can be grown for their leaves, some are more productive and more highly rated that others. Sometimes, varieties liable to mosaic virus, and therefore with low tuber yields, and mottled leaves are considered a delicacy.

The young drumstick tree growing in a bed of seasonal plants **(figure 157)** was cut right back (pollarded) to within 70 cm of the ground and produced a close growth of bunchy, leafy shoots on the top of the trunk. These shoots are cut repeatedly and replaced by others. Gradually, a swelling appears on the top of the stem and produces a close rounded head of young branches. Pruning the shoots again and again encourages budding on the head. However, the head may need replacing from time to time either by cutting back to the stem lower down, or letting one of the shoots grow and then topping this in order to produce another head.

160 Producing a head

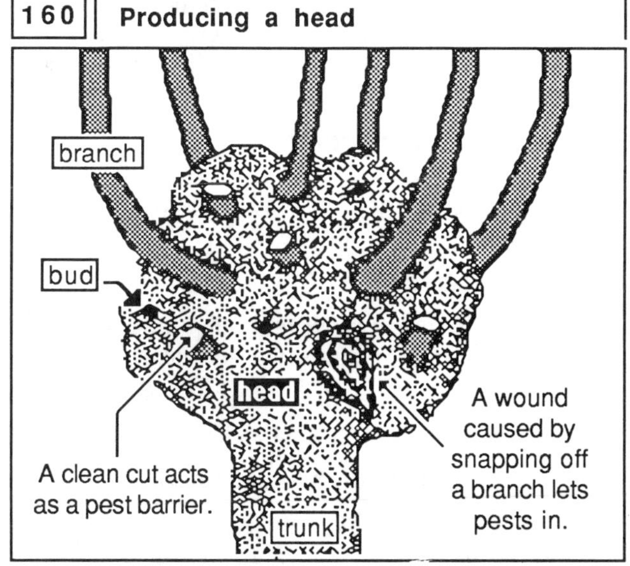

Pollarding is often practised in order to produce poles. The tree in **figure 158** was cut back to a height of 2.5 metres. A great number of shoots appeared, growing rapidly to reach the light. The shoots require light and therefore grow very few secondary shoots. Given two or three years, this sort of tree is capable of producing many poles suitable for fencing, roofing, plant supports, etc.

The height at which the main stem is cut off is important because of the shading of nearby plants. If forage plants are cut in this way, they must be high enough to prevent cattle eating the young shoots.

These shoots can be exploited simultaneously for their leaves and for poles as illustrated by the drumstick tree in **figure 159**. Some shoots are left to grow into poles while others are removed while still young, and used as vegetables.

To prevent attack by disease or pests, only very sharp pruning tools should be used. Wounds caused by breaking off branches allow the entry of pathogens **(figure 160)**.

161

162

Another technique similar to pollarding is shoot pruning often carried out on baobabs. The small shoots are pruned off and this gives rise to little swellings on which new buds keep appearing **(figure 161)**. Again it is important to use a sharp tool when removing shoots so as to avoid unnecessary tears. Three baobabs pruned in this way are shown in **figure 162.** Bark from the base is used for rope-making.

Lopping for pole production

Lopping trees means cutting back laterals growing up the trunk as other laterals develop higher up.

Lopping is practised

- **to force the tree to grow vertically rather than let it spread.** This produces straight trunks of the kind valued by lumberjacks and carpenters,
- **to thin out the lower branches** for the benefit of associated plants,
- **to get rid of unhealthy branches** that might contaminate the trunk.

The trees on the edge of the maize field were lopped. The first row of maize In the foreground is shaded by branches left behind **(figure 163)**.

163

Lopping for pole production means cutting back branches in order to produce poles or scaffold-poles **(figures 164 and 165)**. This type of pruning can be practised on species whose stems grow high because the terminal bud remains alive for a very long time.

This kind of pruning means that all the **lateral branches and buds are eliminated.** The buds are removed while still very small by running one's

165

164

hand up and down the trunk ; the laterals are pruned with a sharp cutting tool or shears. Only the crown is left, and as it receives all the sap, it grows very vigorously.

Lopping can be practised on the primary stem or on multiple shoots. The young drumstick trees planted in the garden **(figure 164)** are being grown for their poles. After a few years, the stems will be cut hard back to the ground and replaced by two or three selected shoots **(figure 165)**.

Pruning shoots and disbudding

Pruning suckers consists in removing all the shoots that sprout on the primary stem and use up the sap which should nourish productive branches **(figures 166 and 167)**.

Disbudding consists in removing some buds. Removing the terminal bud is called **pinching out or heading.** Disbudding stops the branches and stems from growing, so that sap is directed to other plant parts.

166 **Why cut back the suckers ?**

167

169

Pruning and disbudding are practised to stop the crown of a tree or the top of a plant from becoming too dense and to prevent too much energy going into leaf production. Overcrowding can cause shading which reduces cropping.

Removing the flowers

Figure 151 shows how competition can exist between the production of fruits and flowers and why it may be advisable to remove the flowers from plants grown for their leaves.

168

Cat's whiskers *(Gynandropsis gynandra)* is growing in the patch in **figure 168** but its flower clusters have been removed. This practice allows the plant to use all the sap to grow leaves. In many plants, leaf shoots stop growing when flowers appear. In order to grow, the fruits take up food from the leaves that lose their nutritive qualities and become tasteless. The leaves harden, turn yellow and wilt.

Shaping the framework of trees

Shape or form pruning refers to those pruning practices that aim at shaping and maintaining the framework of the branches and shoots that bear the products of the tree. This type of pruning is practised on **woody plants,** that is to say, on plants producing wood (trees and shrubs).

The tree in **figure 169** is badly shaped and had to be propped up to prevent it from collapsing with all its fruits. The same tree is illustrated again in **figure 170** and is contrasted with a well-shaped tree whose four strong, branches are arranged evenly from the trunk and support the crown and the fruiting branches.

These are the advantages of a good framework :

- **there is no risk of the tree collapsing** or of branches breaking,

170 The framework of fruit trees

- **the tree does not have to devote energy to bearing the lopsided weight**,
- **maintenance, harvesting and routine pruning** to increase the amount of fruit **are easier**.

The citrus trees in **figures 171 and 173** are laden with fruit. The trees in **figure 171** are cylindrical in shape. The fruits are growing on the outside and can be picked easily, except for those at the top of the tree.

171

172

The second lot of trees **(173)** are out of reach. No pruning was done to build up a framework. Numerous branches shot upwards to reach the light and are now propped up to prevent breaking.

In fact, it is now imperative to rejuvenate the trees (see below for this pruning practice), or to replace them by planting new seedlings.

When trees are too high and badly shaped, fruit can only be picked by **beating (figure 172)**, that is, beating the branches with a stick to make the ripe fruit fall off.

Beating fruit trees has three drawbacks :

- **it breaks shoots** and wounds the tree,
- some unripe fruit is likely to fall ;
- **ripe fruit hitting the ground may split or get bruised.** It may also **get dirty** by falling into mud and become harder to sell.

Fruit-picking is made much easier, and damage to trees can be avoided when trees are pruned regularly to give them a good framework.

This type of pruning begins by carefully observing the tree's habit and seasonal development. **Figures 174 to 177** point out the features that must be noted. **Figure 174** starts with the basic question of the choice of framework - the shape, height and breadth one would like to achieve.

Having decided on the framework, the gardener must now prune the shoots and branches properly in order to build the desired shape.

173

174 | **Deciding on the right framework**

Before he starts pruning, the gardener must know exactly what shape he wants to achieve — wide-branching frame, cylindrical frame, U-frame.

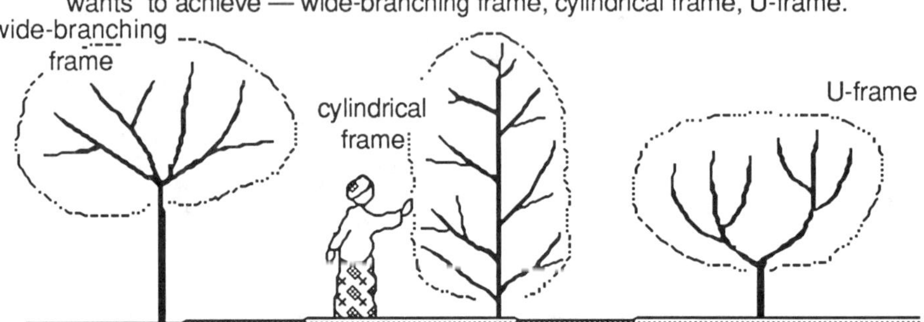

The right framework is decided by taking a series of factors into account :

- the growth habit of the trees to be shaped and their **natural shapes**;
- the **strength of the wood**. Soft wood snaps easily under the weight of fruit, and branches must not be allowed to grow too long ;
- the **location of the tree** in the garden or field, and the plants to be grown nearby. Spreading trees do not give the same **shade at ground level** as cylindrical U-shaped trees ;
- **ease** of maintenance and of picking.

It takes years to build the right framewwork. However, once built and correctly maintained, the framework will last as long as the tree.

Figure 175 describes step-by-step pruning for wide branching and cylindrical frames.

When dealing with tree species that normally throw choots, form pruning can be carried out directly on them, rather than on laterals or side-shoots. When the terminal bud on the main stem has been pinched out, some shoots will appear. The ones growing most vigorously are kept, the others removed. When the selected shoots have elongated, they are treated in similar fashion, as illustrated in **figure 177**.

175 Practical advice on how to shape fruit trees

1 Wait until the seedling has reached a good height.

- Prune the tree for the first time when it is two or three years old and is established in its permanent site.

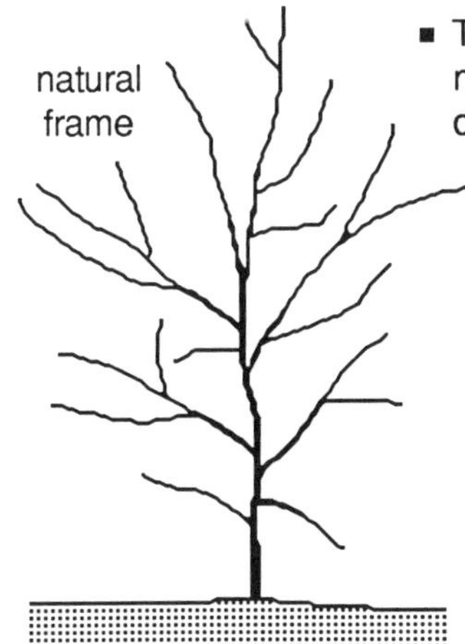

- The tree must be sturdy and its natural frame already developed.

- If the plant is not growing vigorously enough or its natural frame is not clearly visible, wait one or two more seasons before starting to prune.

176

2 Get rid of some branches, keep those that will become the main framework .

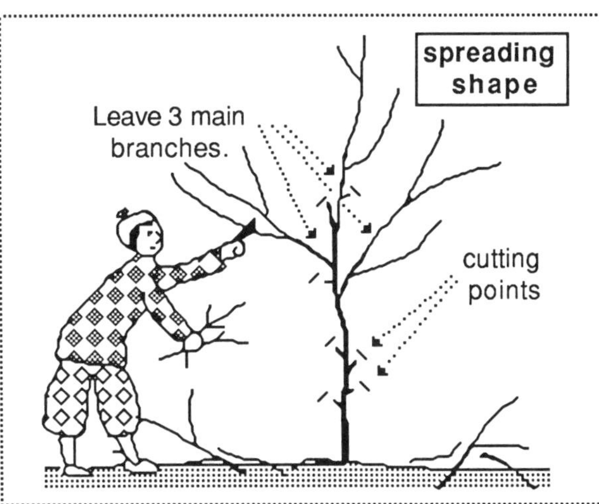

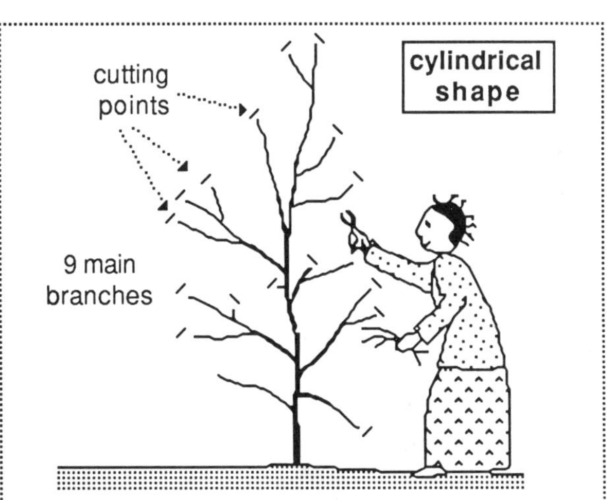

Pick out, on the natural frame, the most vigorous shoots destined to become the main branches.
They must be at a **wide angle** to the trunk.
Make sure that the chosen main branches are arranged **all round the trunk** so that the weight of the crown is evenly distributed.
Inside the crown, cut out all the shoots growing vertically or turning inwards.
The underneath part of the crown must be thinned and opened up so that **air circulates freely**.

To build a spreading shape, let the buds on the main branches develop. To obtain a cylindrical shape, the main branches must be distributed right up the trunk ; these branches are disbudded to within a certain distance of the trunk, the distance being the same on all branches. Disbudding encourages the growth of branches that make the crown broaden out.

(table 175 contd.)

3 The framework is strengthened and improved during subsequent seasons.

spreading frame before
shape pruning is practised for the second time

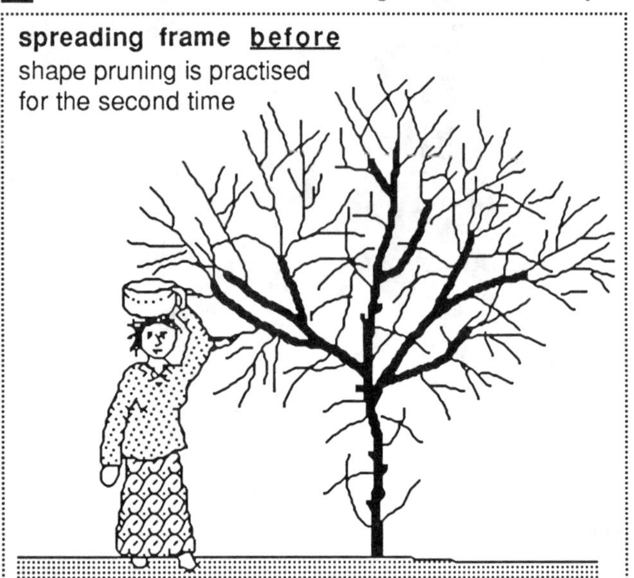

spreading frame after
shape pruning for the second time

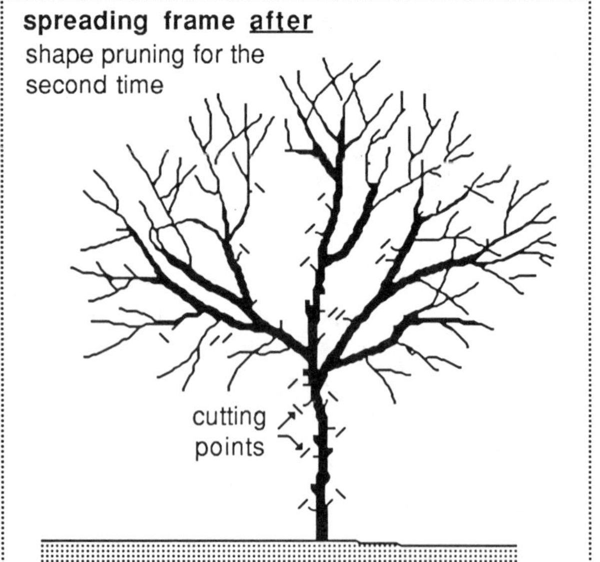

One or two seasons after the first shape pruning, weak laterals and side-shoots are cut back ; likewise those growing in the wrong places, i.e. those developing **inwards** under the crown.

When several branches are **too close to one another**, the most vigorous and growing in the best direction are kept, the others are pruned.

Diseased shoots and those **growing above** the crown are also cut back.

cylindrical frame before
the second pruning

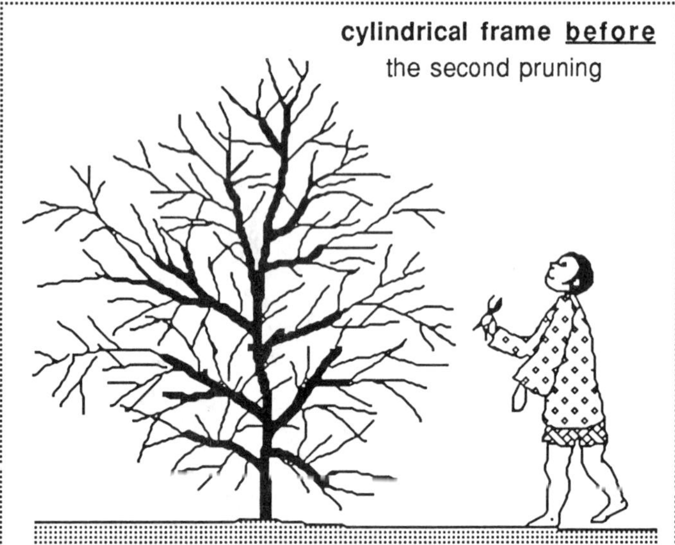

cylindrical frame after
the second pruning

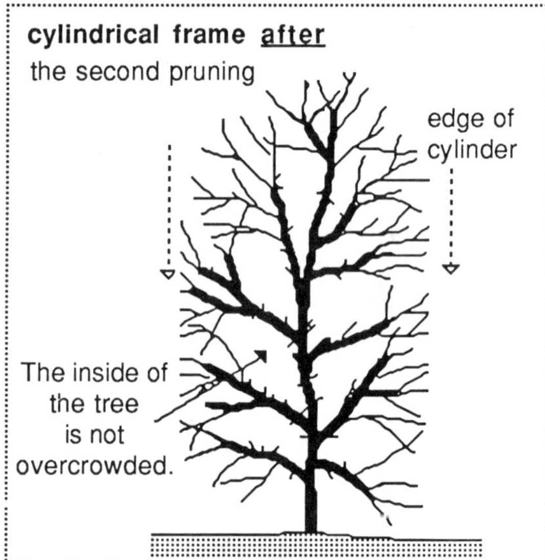

When the cylindrical framework is well established, maintenance and improvement pruning is done every year where necessary. Fruiting is on the laterals and spurs that develop on the outside of the cylinder.

Figure 178 shows how unusual form pruning was practised to shape a nettle tree *(Celtis integrifolia)*. This tree is grown for its leaves which can be eaten raw or cooked. The grower built a frame shaped like a ladder in order to make picking easier. As it grew, the tree trunk was bent and trained into the desired shape by tying it with string. Laterals were cut back almost to the trunk; small heads formed

178

179 Incision of the bark

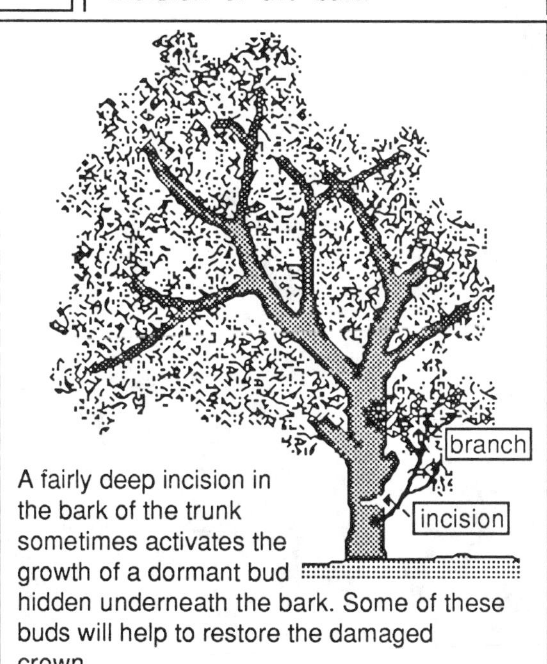

A fairly deep incision in the bark of the trunk sometimes activates the growth of a dormant bud hidden underneath the bark. Some of these buds will help to restore the damaged crown.

177 Using suckers to form side shoots

1 When the tree is about 70 centimetre high, pinch out the terminal bud. This results in the growth of several shoots.

2 Now remove all the new shoots except three or four that are growing vigorously and are well-distributed round the stem. At about 1.30 metres, pinch out the growing tips.

3 New shoots will grow on the pruned branches. Leave two on every branch of this second storey, and pinch them out at about 1.90 metres. After that, prune regularly, cutting back new shoots. Only laterals are retained.

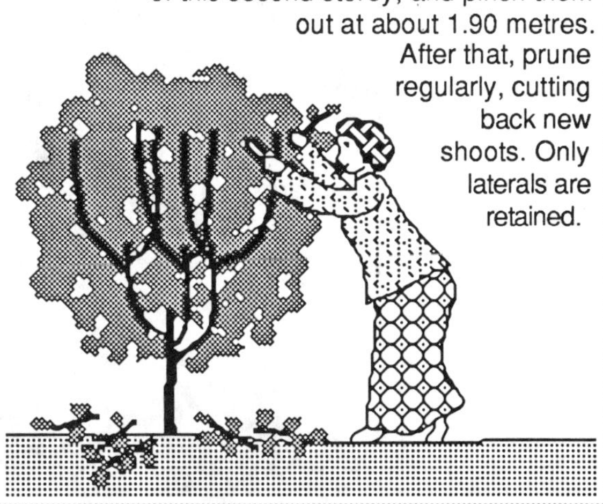

on the tips of the cut-back branches, and produced the leafy shoots that are gathered for eating. Ladder pruning like this makes it easy to climb the tree and harvest the produce.

180

Renewal pruning

Renewal pruning will build a new frame from an old stem. It is practised when the branches of a tree are too leggy, diseased or dead.

Renewal or rejuvenation usually involves cutting the tree back hard to ground level and letting one or several replacement shoots grow **(figure 181)**. When the shoots are sufficiently developed, pruning on the lines of **figures 174 to 176** is carried out.

It is sometimes possible to stimulate the growth of shoots by making a deep incision in the bark at the base of a tree **(figure 179)**. The incision can cause a flow of sap to that spot, thus activating the growth of a dormant bud. However, the older the trunk, the harder it is to force buds to resume growth under the bark.

With bushy species like bitter leaf, for example, the plant is sometimes rejuvenated by leaving all the frame branches **(figure 180)**. Shoots then appear at the end of every branch.

This practice suits plants whose shoots and leaves are used as a vegetable as they grow.

The coffee tree in **figure 181** was cut back to ground level a short while ago. The main stem was left lying on the ground and three replacements grew on the stump. This method allows the original stem to go on producing some berries, while the growth of new shoots is fostered. The stump here is split lengthwise, and this is bad for the health of the plant.

Cutting back to ground level is necessary when witches'-broom forms at the end of branches as in **figure 182**. This abnormal growth occurs when a stem is maltreated; for instance, shoots are broken off instead of being cut off cleanly, the head on which shoots form is allowed to age instead of being rejuvenated, pest attack increases because of the many wounds caused by repeated cropping.

181

182

Rejuvenation is not restricted to trees and perennials. Renewal pruning was practised on black nightshade plants in **figure 183**. Just before flowering, the main stems were all cut off. They will be replaced quickly by fresh shoots that are already sprouting from the old stumps.

183

Techniques that help shape the plant

There are practical ways of altering the natural position of frame-forming branches, especially by using devices such as spreaders, stakes and stretchers **(figure 184)**. After a few months, the separated branches thicken and adopt their new shape permanently.

184 Three ways of separating future main branches when shaping the framework

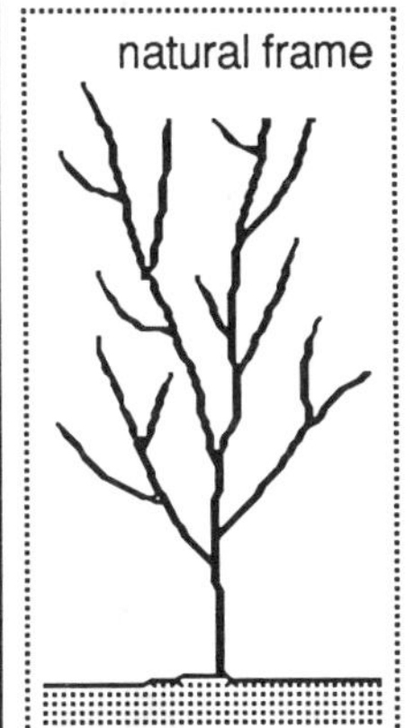

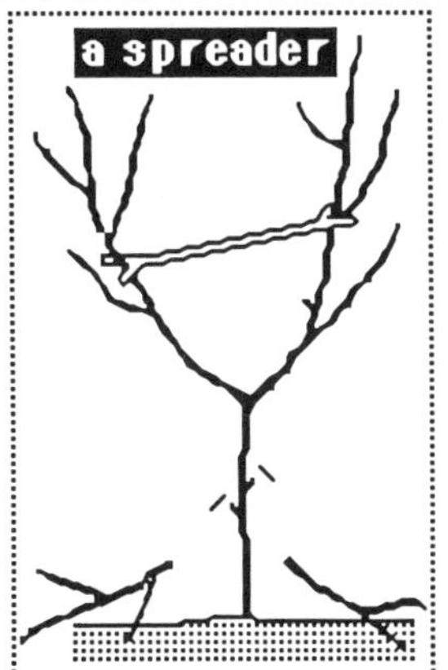

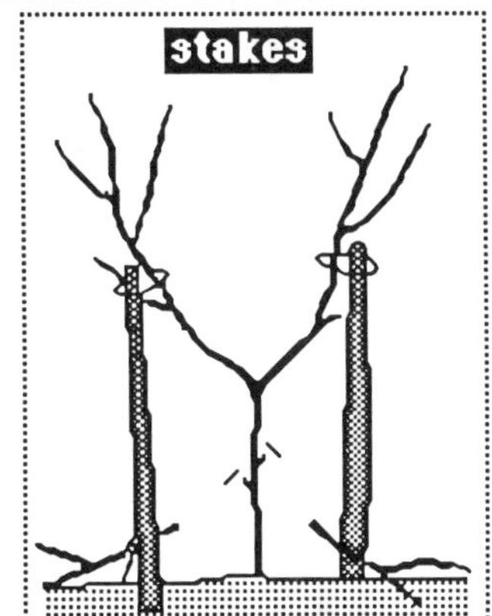

Routine and maintenance pruning

185

Thinning out

Thinning out aims at making tree crowns lighter and, at the same time, obtaining the following results :

- **get rid of shoots and branches causing dense shade underneath the crown** and taking up sap which could be used for cropping;
- **admit more light** to foliage and shoots developing inside the crown;
- let light penetrate **for the benefit of plants growing underneath (figure 147)**;
- **reduce the weight on framework branches** that might break under their own weight;
- **get rid of diseased or unproductive branches.**

Thinning cuts can be carried out at any time.

Pruning to avoid competition

Some cuts are carried out with the sole aim of avoiding excessive interplant competition and, in particular, competition for light. Take, for example, the sweet potato plantlet growing on the edge of a patch of Indian spinach with drumstick trees **(figure 185)**. The sweet potato runners are shortened when they start to overrun the associated plants. As soon as the productive cycle of the Indian spinach is over, the sweet potato will be allowed to cover the patch. Pruning the runners for a few weeks does not encourage tuber production but, on the other hand, keeps the potato in a state of vigorous activity capable of providing stem cuttings.

Thinning can be carried out on seasonal plants or on trees in order to control the density of light, leaves, roots, etc. The techniques described above are used for this purpose - pruning to form cylindrical or U-shaped frameworks, lopping, thinning, plant sanitation, etc.

186

Root-pruning

Generally speaking, pruning is carried out on the aerial parts of plants, but there are also ways of pruning roots. This involves cutting certain parts of the root system to stimulate growth, stop them spreading, or harvest root crops..

Figure 186 shows how to prune in order to limit surface root spread in a tree or a row of trees. There is a pawpaw plantation on the left and a row of eucalyptus on the right. A trench 40 cm deep was dug out between the two sets of trees, as shown in **figure 187**, to stop the eucalyptus roots from spreading towards the pawpaw. This practice forces the eucalyptus roots to penetrate deeper into the ground, and competition between the roots of the two species is avoided.

187

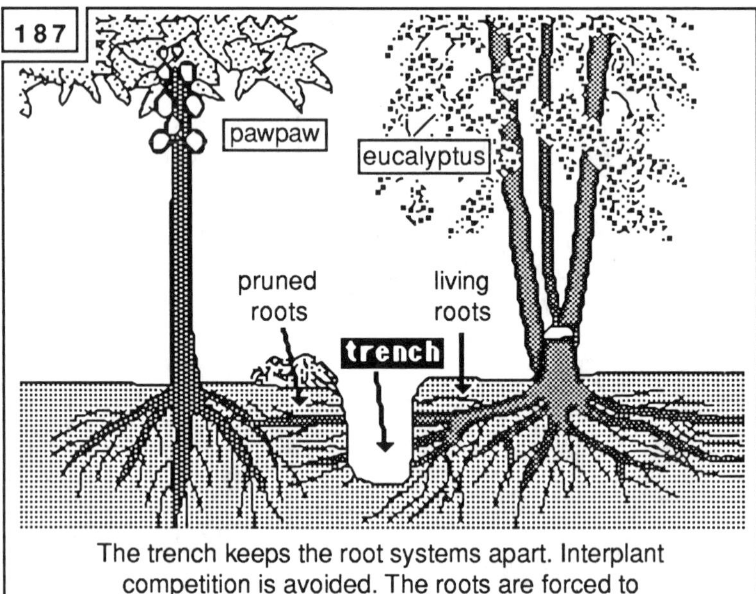

The trench keeps the root systems apart. Interplant competition is avoided. The roots are forced to grow downwards instead of spreading.

188 **Stimulating the roots by hoeing**

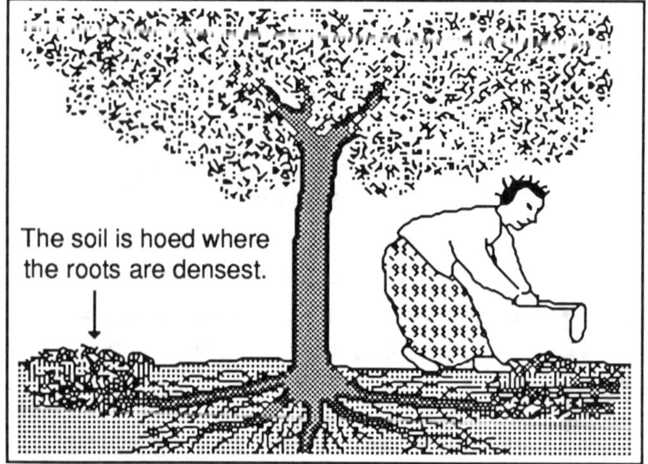

This same pruning practice can be applied round a tree or a group of trees by digging a circular trench.

The trench must be at least one metre from the tree trunk and is usually in line with the outer edge of the crown. Excessive root-pruning can obviously damage plant production and, as with all pruning, a balance must be struck between the advantages and disadvantages of this cultural practice.

After a few years, it may be advisable to stimulate tree roots by ploughing or hoeing. This operation cuts some roots and forces the tree to renew them **(figure 188)**. Roots more active than the old ones then grow in the loosened soil. However, care must be taken to avoid destroying too many roots.

This kind of root-pruning can be accompanied by interplanting herbaceous plants. Growing cereals, legumes or green manure plants in the tilled soil can benefit soil fertility and the renewal of tree roots.

Actually, every operation carried out round the tree for the associated plants - be it weeding, hoeing, mounding or tilling - leads to a certain amount of root-pruning which invigorate their growth. During these operations, it is important not to sever thick roots growing close to the trunk.

The coffee orchard in **figures 189 and 190** is situated in the Ivory Coast. All the coffee shrubs were cut back to ground level not long before the photographs were taken. The shrubs were then interplanted with yam and okra **(figure189)**, and their roots were pruned for the first time when yam mounds were earthed up and okra sown at the base of the mounds. During the following season, the mounds were flattened **(figure190)**, and groundnuts were sown.

The roots of the regenerated coffee trees were therefore stimulated several times :

- when the yam mounds were established,
- during the hoeing operation that prepared the groundnut seedbed,
- when the groundnuts were pulled up.

Each time, the soil was loosened and root activity encouraged.

Root-pruning is best carried out at the start of the rainy season. It is not recommended during the dry season when trees need as many roots as possible to obtain sufficient water.

When tree seedlings are about to be transplanted, the roots are pruned **(figure 191).** All the lateral roots are cut back close to the taproot. In the same way, all the leaves and shoots are removed to control loss of water. The pruned plant is therefore in two parts : the stem with a single terminal bud, and the taproot all of whose buds are dormant. When the plants are transferred to the planting holes, young roots grow fast on the taproot and feed the terminal bud.

191 **Pruning to control insect borers**

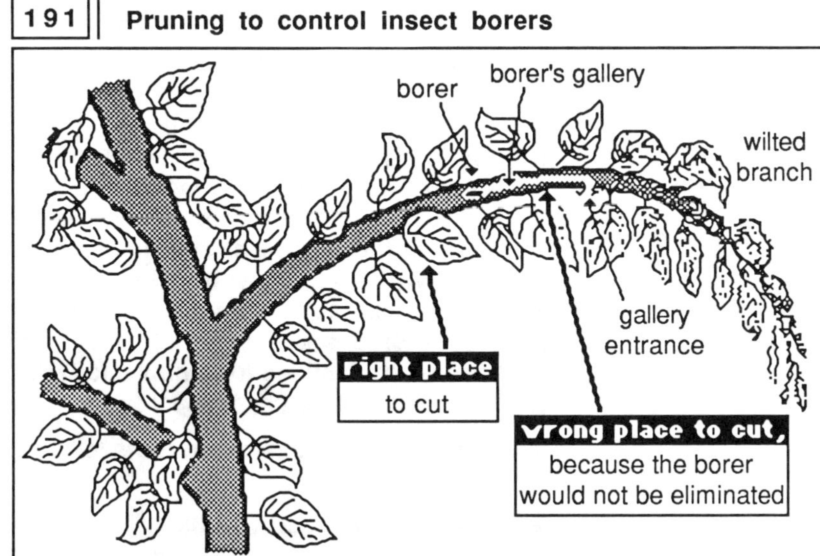

Root-pruning also takes place when certain crops are harvested. **Figure 74** illustrates this point. When the farmer wants to pick a few tubers he sometimes cuts through a yam or a cassava plant as he digs into the mound. Just as with aerial pruning, unnecessary damage to roots should be avoided ; clean, sharp cutting is desirable.

Pruning to control disease and pests

Pruning can be an effective means of pest control. **It consists in cutting off and burning all the branches, stems and fruits that are**

infested, blemished, dried up, or diseased. By acting in this way, pests which would otherwise spread are destroyed.

During pruning, the following precautions must be taken to halt disease and infestation :

- **clean, very sharp tools are used** ;
- **unhealthy shoots are severed cleanly above the diseased sections as in figure 192.** Again, when borers infest a branch, it must be cut below the part chewed out by the larvae so that only healthy wood remains ;
- **the parts cut off must be burnt at once** in order to kill pests. Insects and other pests can survive in the removed part and spread from there to healthy plants;
- when pruning, **do not touch healthy plant parts** after handling diseased parts, so as to avoid transmitting infection by manual contact ;
- when a plant is extensively infested, it is better to **dig it up or cut it** right back before it becomes a source of contamination for other plants.

192 Preparing seedlings

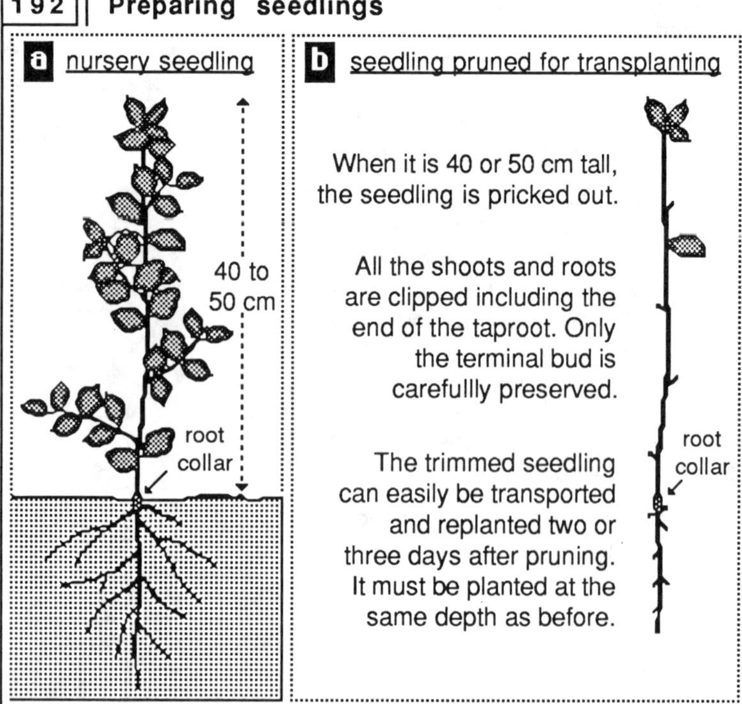

194

195

The timing of this kind of pruning depends on the development of the pest itself. If branches wilt because of **bacterial or fungicidal infection**; they are cut back **immediately** at a safe distance from the diseased part.

When plants are attacked by **borers**, be sure to prune before the borer **moves away** from the damaged branch and starts invading other branches or other plants. The right time for pruning is determined by observing the life of the pest and spotting the pest invasion the moment it starts. Pruning and burning of the affected parts must take place between the larval stage and hatching (chapter 8).

Pruning practices that increase yield

Pruning practices that set out to increase fruit and seed production are quite different from those designed to increase leaf yields. As a general rule, these practices are much more complicated because they try to establish **a balance between the production of the vegetative organs**, i.e., stems, leaves and roots, and **the production of the reproductive organs** in the form of the flowers, fruits and seeds **destined to be harvested**. This balance can be characterized as follows :

- **produce enough leaves and roots** to let the plant feed its fruits,
- **not produce too many fruits** so that leaves and roots are able to feed them adequately,

- **not produce too few fruits,** otherwise pruning is not worthwhile,
- **produce as many flowers as possible** on the pruned branches**, even if some immature fruits have to be removed later on**.

Two photographs **(figures 194 and 195)** were taken of a branch of chillies whose zigzag morphology or shape is explained in **figure 193**.

The first photograph **(194)** shows the unpruned branch with some flowers and the first chillies. The second photograph **(195)** shows the same branch, pruned this time in order to increase fruit-bearing during the present season and the following season.

Pruning in this case consisted of topping all the shoots ; all the existing adult leaves were left intact but growth of new foliage was arrested. Topping is practised just above the fruit to be encouraged, while care is taken to leave the leaf nearest the fruit. The effect of this pruning is to let the leaves devote all their energy to producing fruits that will be bigger and better than if the plant had been left unpruned.

193 The natural zigzag habit of some species

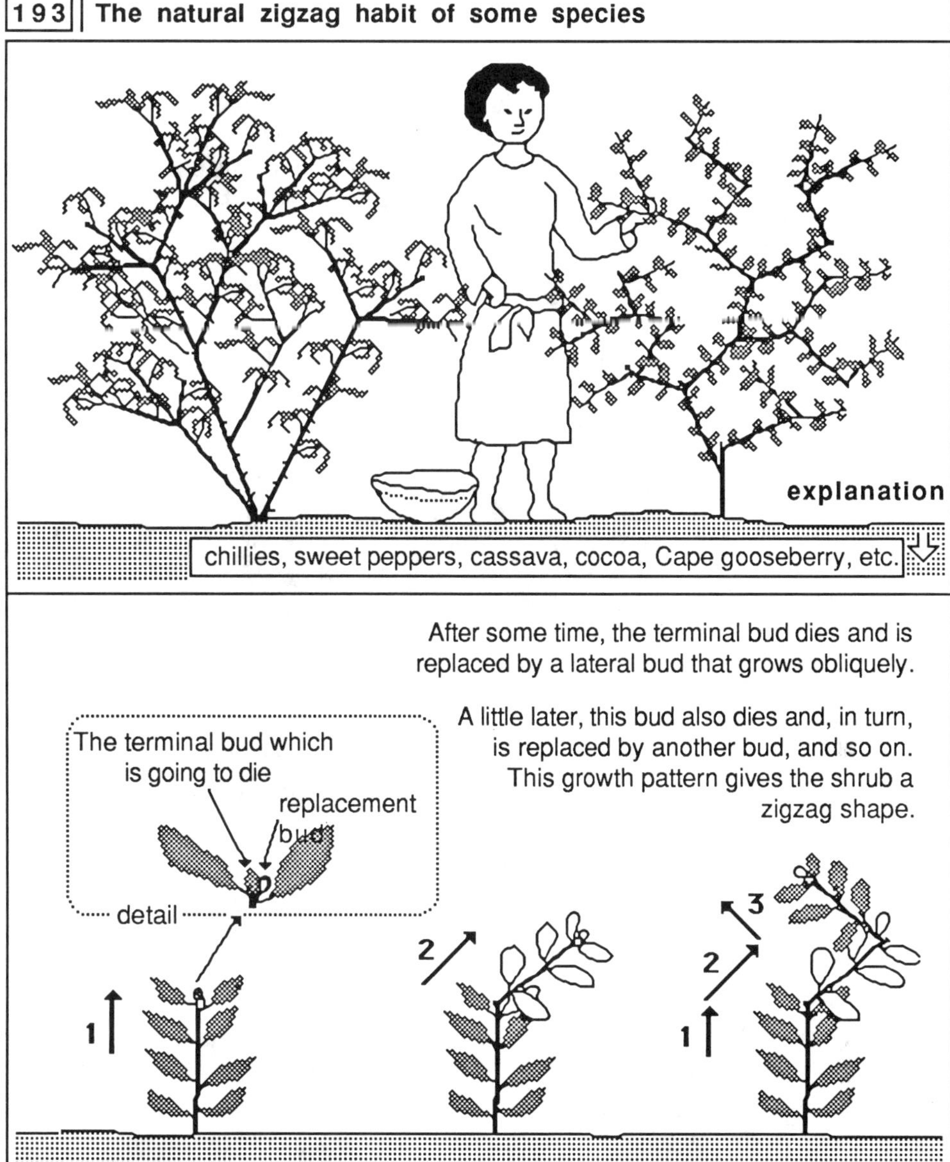

196

Pruning also helps to take weight off the branch and admit more light to all plant parts, increasing the crop.

This routine pruning leads to the following results :

- **the growth of shoots is halted temporarily**, and the sap they were taking up is sent to the fruits;
- **the fruits are fed properly** because they are relatively few in number;
- some time after topping, **new shoots grow** on fruit-bearing stems. This new growth will itself bear fruit the following season if the chilli plant has a life cycle of two or more seasons.

What would have happened if the shrub had gone unpruned ?

- Elongation and subdivision of the shoots would have continued, making the shrub bushier and bushier. The lower layers of foliage would have been shaded. The leaves would have become less productive and started turning yellow;
- The elongated branches would have born many flowers but many of them would have failed to set. Then, of those that set, some fruitlets would have dropped. **Fruit drop** is the term used to describe badly nourished fruitlets that dry up and fall to the ground. It is as though the plant itself deliberately sacrifices some fruitlets because it is unable to feed all those that set;
- More fruits might have matured but they would have been smaller because of poor feeding.

197 Pruning and staking tomato plants

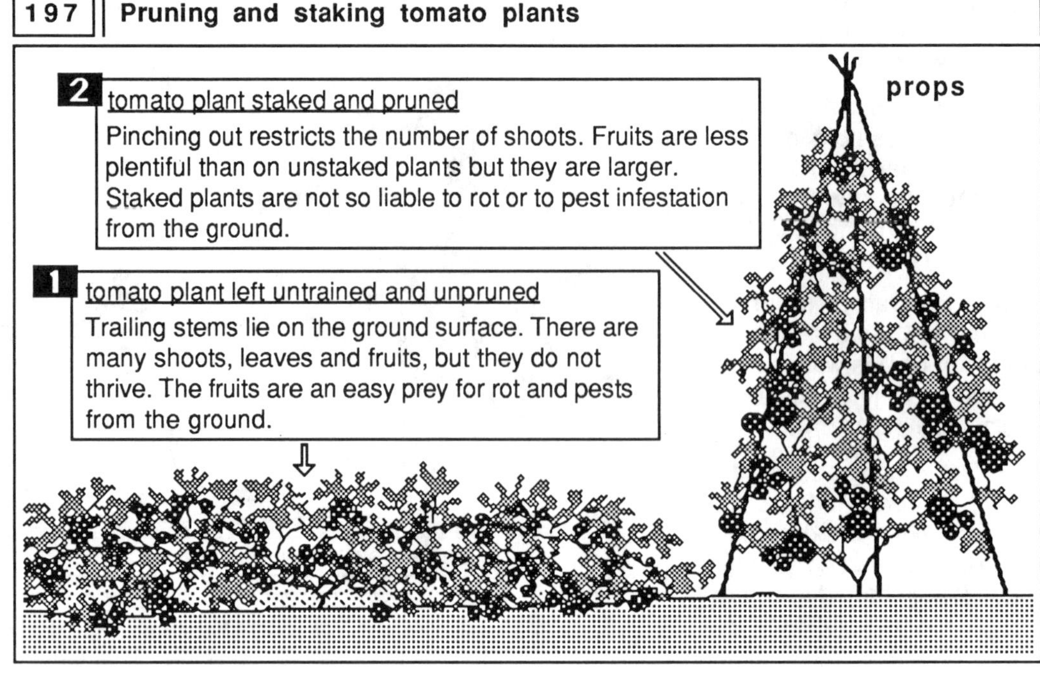

The type of production pruning practised on the chilli plant is also suitable for other annual herbaceous plants, shrubs and trees, and can be combined with removing some of the fruits so that the remaining ones grow better. Mottled, diseased, badly developed fruits, and even those in excess of requirements are removed. The gardener is simply getting rid of all the fruits on which the plant would have devoted its food to no purpose.

What pruning techniques can be practised on the marrow in **figure 196** ? We see that the stem has four nodes each composed of a petiole (leaf stalk), a tendril that serves to attach the plant to some kind of support, a tiny shoot, a flower and here and there an adventitious root.

Routine pruning along the principles explained in **figure 151** would suit this marrow. On observing that there are already four young fruits on the trailing stem, the gardener can choose between :

198

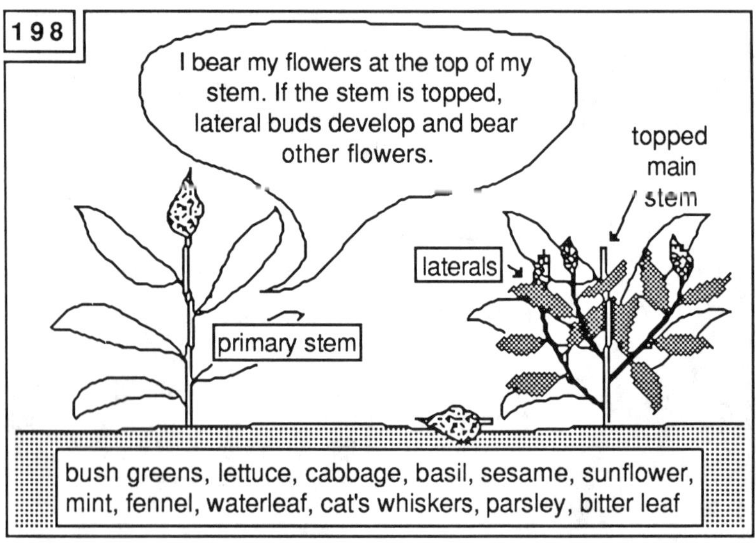

199

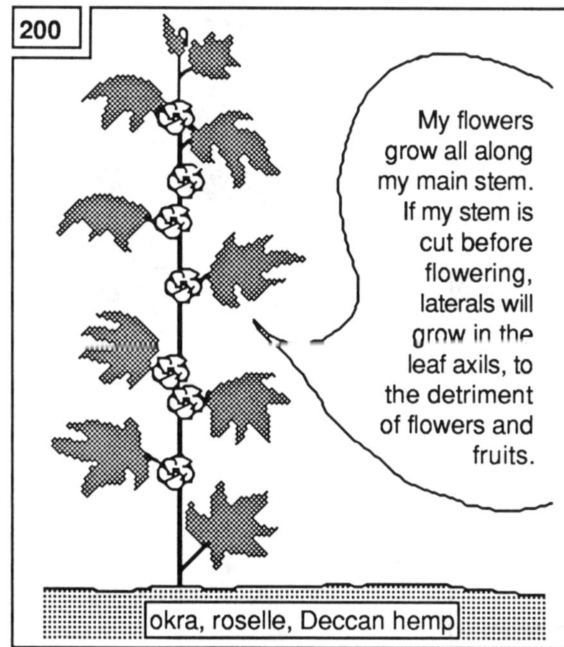

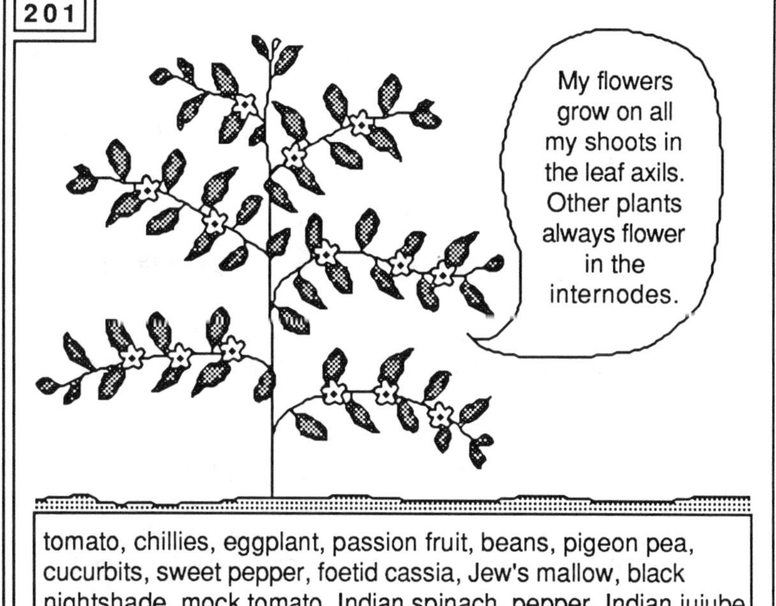

202 Flowering branches

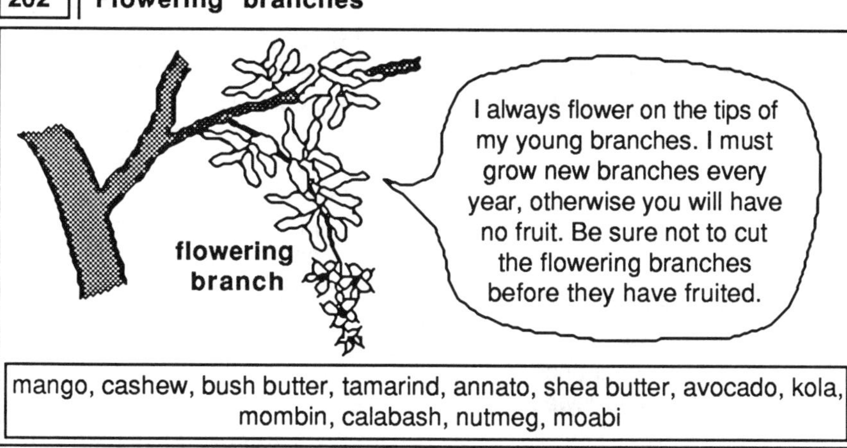

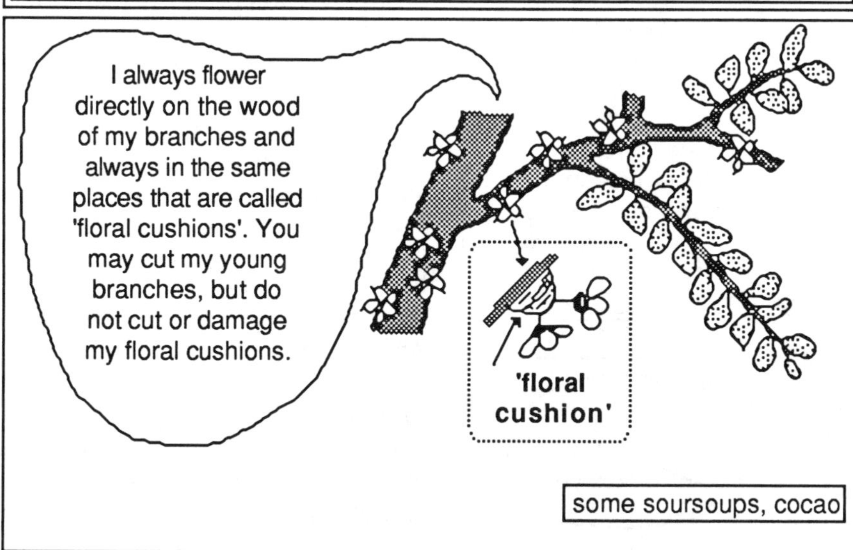

- **removing the tip** of the runner to stop it from growing longer. It is cut a little above a node, care being taken to preserve a leaf on the node, because the leaf will feed the fruit beside it;
- **topping the stem** to avoid elongation as above and removing some of the fruitlets so that each fruit is nourished by several leaves.
- Gardener know that topping the creeper automatically encourages the growth of shoots in the leaf axils and that new shoots compete for food with the young fruits especially if shoots and fruits are growing on the same nodes. Consequently, growers **only allow some shoots to develop** so as to ensure new fruit formation in the following weeks. The other shoots are all cut back.

It is assumed that the gardener who wants to carry out these cuts checks the garden regularly every day and keeps an eye on the growth of vegetative parts and fruits.

Tomato plants are very similar to those of cucurbits. A shoot tends to grow in every leaf axil and a flower truss at every internode. Given a free rein, the laterals and fruit trusses become so numerous that the plant cannot feed them all. Some fruits dry up and fall; the remainder do not develop properly **(figure 197)**.

Tomato plants are pruned in the same way as cucurbits. Plants must be checked constantly in order to

- eliminate unwanted shoots and top those that grow too long,
- pick ripe fruits,
- note the number of fruits ripening,
- note the number of flowers that, in the following weeks, will replace those that have fruited and been picked.

Good management of tomato plants is characterized by a balance between the production of new leaves and fruits throughout the season.

Pruning practises that increase productivity can be used on herbaceous plants as well as shrubs and trees as long as the vegetation to be pruned is accessible The return from pruning must be worthwhile because the time spent pinching out plants or removing sickly or overabundant fruits must be paid for by increased yields in quantity and in quality. Practical experience alone can determine the economic value of these cultural methods.

204 Flowering follows after a year's leaf growth

203 Sessile and pedunculate flowers

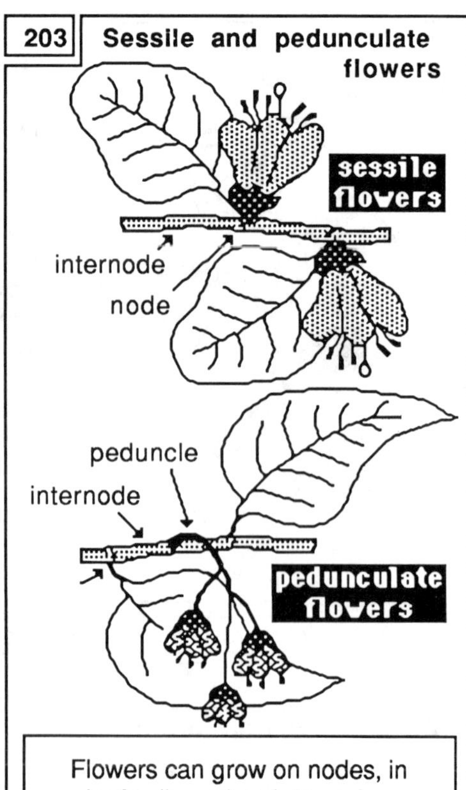

Flowers can grow on nodes, in leaf axils and on internodes. They can be sessile, that is to say, attached directly to the branch, or they can be pedunculate, meaning fixed on special little stalks bearing one or more flowers.

Observations prior to production pruning

Gardeners who intend pruning are guided by observation of plant shapes and behaviour. Experiments based on figures **198 to 219** can be attempted. Begin, for example, by pruning a shoot or a flowering stem and wait for a few weeks to see how the plant reacts. Have new shoots or new flowers appeared ? Or do we have to wait until the following season to see new flowers grow ?

When experimenting with pruning, it is a good idea to mark the cut stems and shoots with raffia fibre or a length of straw to make it easier to identify the plants later.

205

207

Notes

'Harvest pruning'

The way in which leaves, fruits, branches and barks are harvested can greatly influence production in the following weeks or years. The expression "harvest pruning" is therefore used to mean controlled or uncontrolled effects on the subsequent development of plants.

Harvest pruning must take into account

- **the exact nature of the desired produce :** leaves, shoots, fruits, barks, roots,...to be consumed at once, to be stored, to be sold fresh or dried, etc.,
- plant reactions after harvesting : new shoots, senescence, etc.
- health risks to which the plant is exposed as a result of wounding,
- ease of harvesting operations.

Ways of gathering leaves and effects on plant development

Leaves have just been pulled from the roselle (Jamaican sorrel) in **figure 205**. The housewife tore off the leaf blades (green part of leaves) leaving the petioles or leaf stalks which together with the veins form the framework of the leaves **(figure 206)**. She did this by pinching the base of the stalks between her fingers and then running her fingers to the top of the stalks tearing off the blades on the way.

206

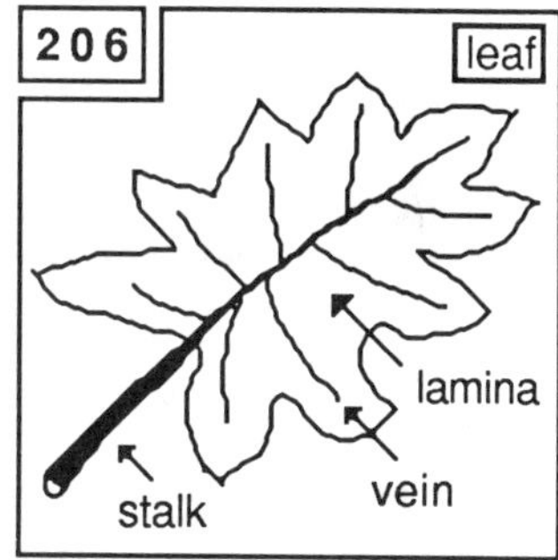

This is an easy way of gathering leaves because the housewife only gathers the amount she is going to use. (If she picks whole leaves, she still has to remove the stalks before cooking). But this easy way is only possible if the produce is consumed or dried at once. The leaf blades are damaged in the picking ; when heaped or tied into bundles in this state, they ferment quickly and cannot be sold.

Picking whole leaves (i.e. with the stalks) takes more time than tearing them off, but leaves and stalks remain intact and the vegetable can be sold more easily.

208 Do not injure the floral cushions

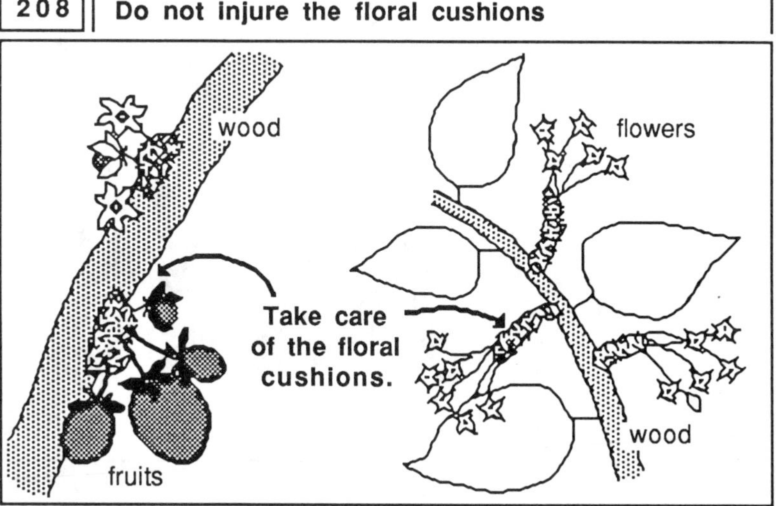

The effects on the plant are the same whichever way the leaves are gathered. Because the plant is short of foliage for photosynthesis, it will quickly produce shoots that in turn grow leaves to replace those torn off, season permitting, of course.

The woman in **figure 207** is picking Indian spinach leaves by running her fingers from the bottom to the top of the stems. The stripped stems are seen in the foreground. To promote regrowth, she then cuts the stems right back to within twenty or thirty centimetres of the base of the plant. The cut shoots are used as stem cuttings to start new beds.

The bitter leaf seen in **figure 209** is gathered either for its leaves like roselle and Indian spinach, or for its shoots.

Harvesting shoots is sensible if the produce is for sale. The leaves are whole and remain fresh longer than if they had been picked one by one, but they are not all at the same stage of development Cutting the shoots means that the woman removes some leaf nodes on which new shoots would have developed.

When shoots are harvested, **enough buds and leaves must be left behind so that new shoots have a chance to develop.**

209

Ways of picking fruits and how plants are affected

When picking fruits, it is important to **avoid damaging the fruits themselves and the plants that bear them**. First, damaged fruits lose market value because, for example, they are dirty or sticky, rot quickly or attract flies. Second, injuries to plants are gateways for disease, and also jeopardize future harvests especially if specialized branches or 'floral cushions' have been damaged **(figs 208 and 202).**

If you examine ripe fruits, you will often notice the exact **breaking points** that plants actually provide either close to the main stems or a little distance from them. In fact, even before ripe fruits fall, plants have a plan to close the door, as it were, and keep out disease. This is why fruit picking that respects nature causes no injuries.

The tomato plant is a case in point **(figure 210)**. The fruit is attached to a peduncle (fruit-bearing stalk)) divided into two parts. When the tomato is really ripe, the stalk snaps without any trouble if it is lifted where it swells slightly. When the fruit is picked properly it comes away with a piece of stalk still attached to the top. But when unripe fruit is pulled off, it can get torn at the top and will therefore rot quickly.

If for any reason the fruit does not come away by itself, cut the stalk between the fruit and the breaking point with a well-honed blade. In any case, the fruit must not be pulled off.

When handling fruits that grow on specialized cushions, as with cocoa, it is most important to

210 Harvesting tomatoes

To keep the fruits and branches healthy, pick tomatoes by lifting the stalks and snapping them at the **breaking points** provided by the plants themselves. The stalks break easily when the fruits are **really ripe**.

When necessary, cut the stalk between the breaking point and the fruit. Do not pull off the fruits because infections enter via the tears.

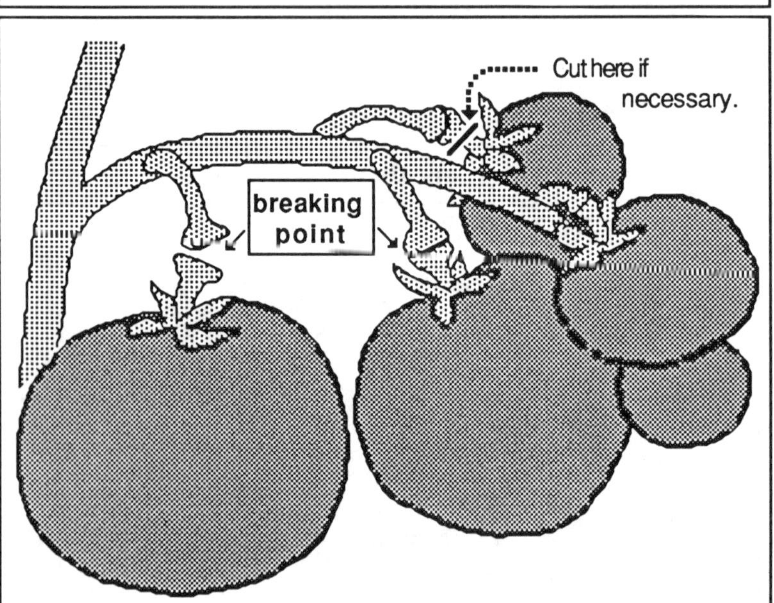

pick them the right way. Pulling the fruits and injuring the cushions can damage future crops.

Collecting bark and how it affects trees

Some trees are exploited for their bark (garlic tree, baobab, quinine).

Trees are always at risk when large pieces of bark are removed.This is because it causes a great wound. The bare wood is moist and attracts all kinds of insects and pests. Stripping bark therefore calls for many precautions even more stringent than those connected with fruit picking. Bark is being removed from a garlic tree with the help of a machete **(figure 212)**, a tool too rough and clumsy for the job. The machete tears off the bark and cuts

211 The right way of collecting

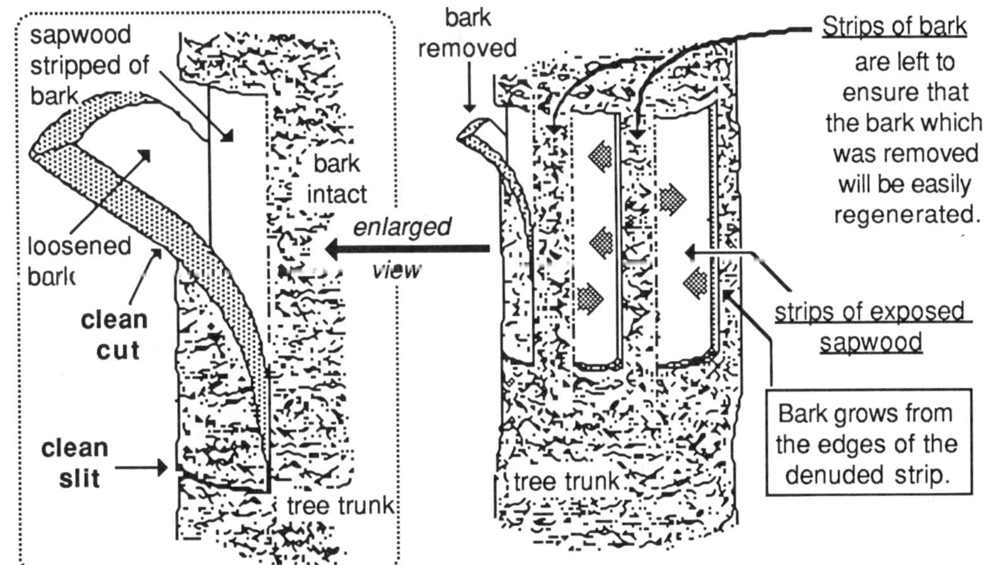

- Removing bark is a delicate operation for the health of the tree. Once bared, the fresh, sweet sapwood is a wide-open door for insects and pests.
- The strips must be removed with a **very sharp cutting edge**.
  The blade must not penetrate the fresh wood (sapwood). The strips of bark removed must be separated by **strips of intact bark** that can grow and replace what has been cut off.
- If the strips removed are too wide, the tree will not recover and may die.

212

213

into the wood underneath, causing damage to the vessels carrying the sap. Obviously, this method cannot be recommended.

It is better to use tools with sharp cutting edges and to remove the bark according to a definite cutting plan **(figure 211).** The operation should preferably be carried out in the middle of the rainy season when wood and bark are really wet and can easily be separated one from the other.

If bark is for home use only, scrape some off superficially without going near the wood.

Some removal of bark and incision practices aim at stimulating the development of branches or fruits.

In some species, removing bark from a young tree by cutting a fairly wide section some centimetres in length can stimulate the growth of new branches or shoots The bark, however, should not be too thick.

Figure 213 is another example of growth stimulation. A machete was used to make slanting gashes in the trunk of a young mango tree. The aim of this practice, is to stimulate fruit-bearing in trees four or five years old. The advantages of this system need to be checked.

Pruning tools and cuts

We have stressed many time that all wounds inflicted on plants are a source of pest infestation and disease. Whatever pruning cuts are made - shape pruning, production and harvest cuts, pollarding, etc. - wounding must be avoided at all costs.

Cuts must be neat and clean. Large cuts should be made slanting so that rain flows off them **(figure 218)**. Water stagnating in cracks in the wood causes rotting **(figure 216)**.

When cuts are fairly wide, they can be protected from pests by sealing with birdlime, wood tar, or clay paste to which some fine ashes may be added.

214 Controlled felling

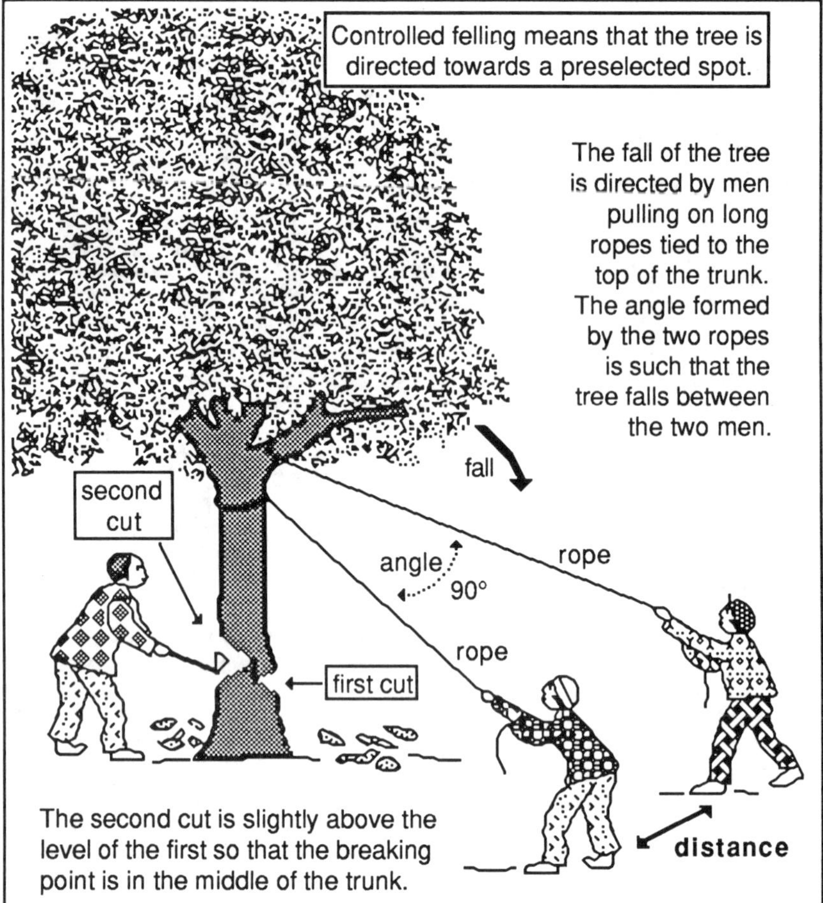

219 Cutting a large branch
(read **1** then **2** in that order)

First, cut upwards from below, then cut downwards to meet the first cut so that the branch breaks in the very middle.

2

branch to be chopped off

1

trunk

When cutting a big branch, begin by cutting the branch from below and cut one-third of the way through.

Very sharp knives, secateurs and bow saws are used for smaller stems and branches **(figure 215)**. A machete can be used if the cutter knows that his tool cuts because of its sharp cutting edge and not because of the power behind the blow.

Machetes, axes, hand and power saws are used for cutting thick stems, branches and tree trunks. Before cutting, it is a good thing to decide on a cutting plan **(figures 214 and 219)**. After the trunk has been felled, the top of the stump can be cut to an angle like a roof to help rain to run off. This will prevent the stump from rotting.

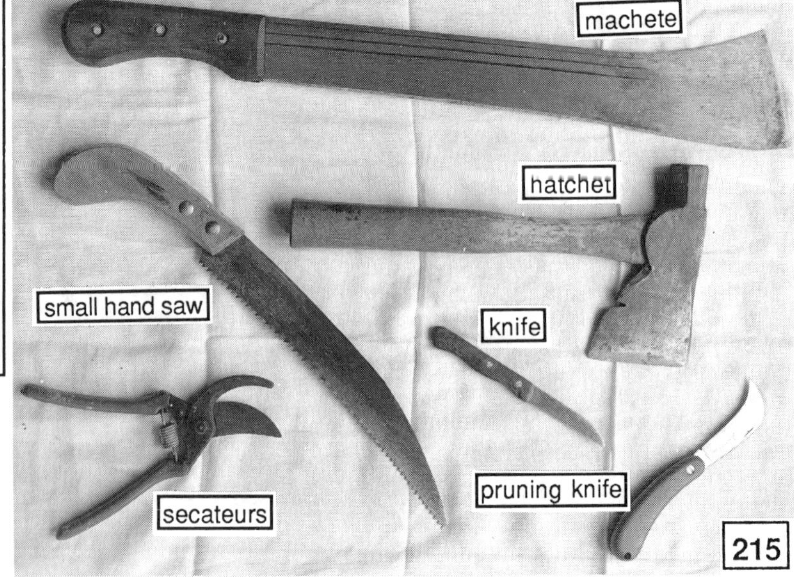

215

216 Do not wound trees when chopping and felling.

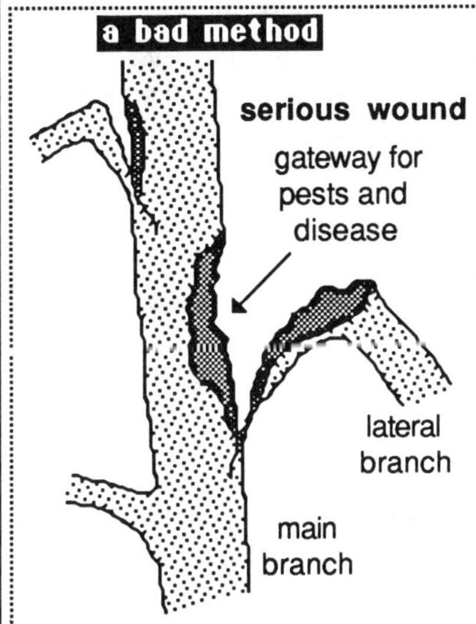

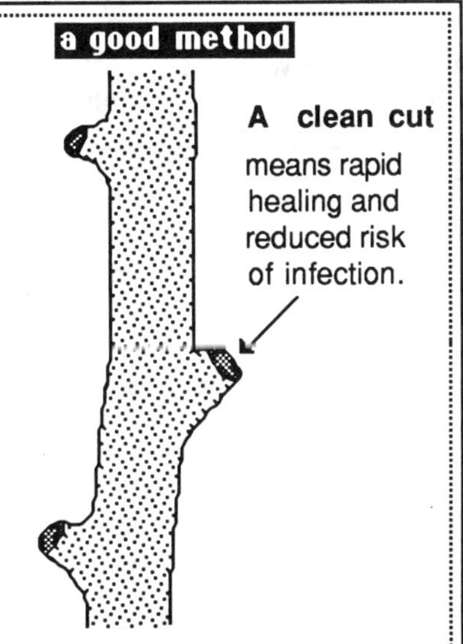

Wounded trees devote a lot of energy to self-defence and the healing of injuries. They are exposed to disease and pests.

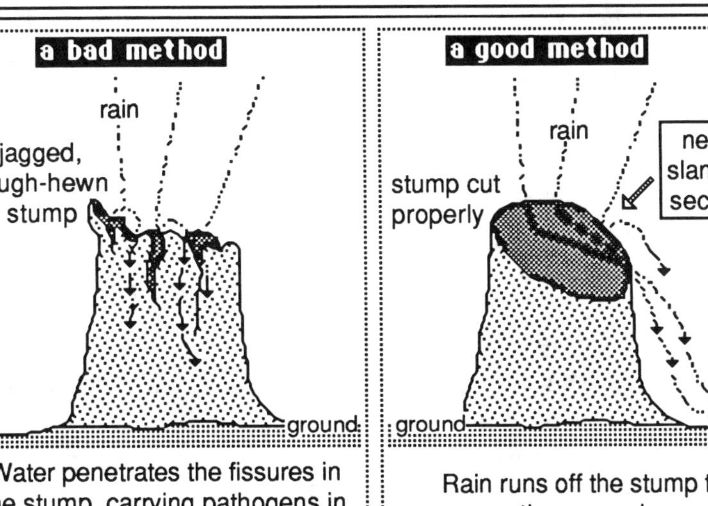

Water penetrates the fissures in the stump, carrying pathogens in with it and causing the wood to rot.

Rain runs off the stump to the ground.

217

218

Notes

When should plants be pruned?

Gardeners should be guided by personal experience when it comes to choosing the best time to prune. Everything depends on the aims and the pruning practise one has in mind. **Table 220** gives some pointers on the subject.

220 Pruning aims and seasons

Pruning aims	Pruning seasons
Restrict the spread of foliage	*Light pruning is acceptable all the year round. If severe pruning is planned, it must take place during the rainy season.*
Restrict the spread of roots	*End of the dry season and onset of the rains.*
Shape plant framework	*At the start and the first part of the wet season. Form pruning takes many years.*
Remove suckers	*At any time, whenever they start growing.*
Pollarding, topping and pinching out plants to promote growth of shoots or branches :	*When the rains are well established.*
Pinch out the side-shoots of seasonal creepers to promote fruiting	*When a sufficient quantity of fruitlets have set -about the middle of the rainy season, and as soon as useless shoots appear.*
Rejuvenate crowns	*At the end of the dry season, or at the very start of the rains.*
Stimulate tree roots by root pruning	*When the rains start, or at the end of the dry season during seedbed preparation.*
Lop trees	*In the dry season.*
Thin out crowns	*During the dry season, or in any case, before fruiting.*
Fight bacterial or fungicidal diseases	*As soon as the disease is spotted.*
Control borers	*While the pest is still inside its gallery, before it has had a chance to move elsewhere.*
Thinning associated plants	*The best time will depend on the problems connected with the particular plant association.*

Chapter 7

Diseases and pests

Major plant diseases and pests

The leaf blades of the soya plant in **figure 221** are discoloured, and only the veins are green. Although the soya has enough light and ground water, it is sick. It is suffering from malnutrition, that is, it is not getting a balanced diet. The plant is short of one or more nutrients to keep it healthy and allow it to manufacture chlorophyll on which photosynthesis depends. The plant is like a child suffering from kwashiorkor : it has nutritional deficiencies **(figure 53)**.

Deficiency diseases in plants are mostly caused by the lack of one or two specific mineral salts in the soil.

221

222

223

The opposite situation arises when plants absorb excessive quantities of mineral salts and are poisoned just like people who fall ill because they eat too much salt or too many fatty foods.

Figure 222 shows a vegetable marrow with some diseased leaves. Whitish blotches suddenly appear on the leaves which looked healthy a few days earlier. A **microbial disease** has attacked the plant, this is caused by a **fungus** growing on the leaves. Some days later, the fungus enters the leaf blade. At a later stage the fungus produces seeds called spores. These are scattered by wind and rainwater to other leaves. This disease can be compared to human **tinea** or ringworm which is a fungal disease ; this develops in the tissues of the human body and spots form on the skin.

Microbial diseases are legion but they are not always as spectacular as the one photographed in **figure 222**. **Microorganisms are divided into three main groups - fungi, bacteria and viruses**, all of which can cause diseases and considerable damage to crops. Groundnut rosette is an example of a **viral disease**, i.e. caused by a virus **(figure 223)**. Plants struck by this disease are unable to produce full, healthy pods and yields are severely affected.

Deficiency and microbial diseases are not the only cause of reduced agricultural yields. More than anything else, farmers have to reckon with **attacks**

by all kinds of pests that feed on cultivated plants at some time during the life cycle and bring about **massive plant destruction**.

In **figure 224**, we see an insect chewing a marrow leaf, rather like a sheep chews grass. This particular **chewing insect** is unobtrusive and does little harm to crops. However, other insects like the migratory locust cause damage of catastrophic proportions because they come in swarms and devour all the greenery in their path. Chewing insects in general can attack any part of a plant - leaves, flowers, stems, fruits and roots.

Some insects lay their eggs in fruits, branches and leaves. **Figure 225** shows a young tomato cut in two; the eggs of a fly developed there into larvae that have eaten away the inside of the fruit. When they become adult, the larvae change into flies in search of more fruit.

224

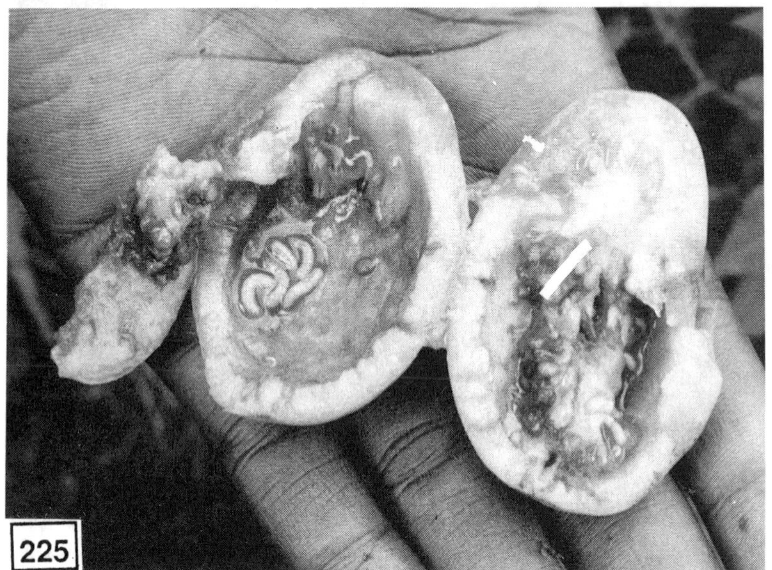

225

Larvae that burrow galleries in branches, stems and trunks are called **borers (figure 192)**. Those that burrow galleries in leaf blades are called **leaf miners**. Even though the skin covering the leaf blade is not pierced, pale-coloured lines on the leaf surface are a sign of leaf miners at work.

226

Some pests are associated with cultivated plants. A colony of **leaf-curling ants** is established at the foot of an orange tree **(figure 226)**. Damage to the plant itself is not extensive but these biting ants are a nuisance for workers during maintenance and harvesting.

Striga is a **parasitic plant (figure 227)** that clings to sorghum roots and feeds on their sap. The mistletoe which invades the crowns of some trees is also a parasitic plant whose roots become entwined in the branches.

227

Parasitic plants must not be confused with **epiphytic plants** that simply root in soil that has accumulated in the hollows and holes of branches and trees.

Finally, wild and tame animals are a frequent source of crop devastation : birds swoop on cereals and fruits; rodents, monkeys, gazelles and hippototamus, for example, go on the rampage. Domestic animals left to wander can cause considerable crop losses in some regions.

Secondary infections

"It never rains but it pours". This is an apt proverb where plants pests are concerned.

One of the two groundnut plants displayed in **figure 223** was attacked by rosette virus and is stunted and weak. The virus did not enter the plant by itself. It was injected by an aphid (*Aphis craccivora*) which pierced the plant to suck its sap. In the same way, man contracts malaria when the *Anopheles* mosquito injects him with *Plasmodium*, the parasite that causes malaria. Another example is sleeping sickness transmitted by the tsetse fly.

228

Generally speaking, all damage inflicted on plants produces openings through which other pests can enter. This fact is illustrated in **figure 228** where a watermelon pierced by a cucurbit fly, *Dacus frontalis*, can be seen. The holes in the melon rind stand out clearly. If you cut the fruit open, you would find white larvae inside.

All round the holes and inside the fruit, there are dark brown spots capped here and there by white fruiting bodies. The spots are caused indirectly by the fly and its larvae that let rot into the fruit. The insect destroying the watermelon is the *Dacus* fly and not the fungus that causes the spots. The fly is the pest to be controlled before it pierces the fruit, and not the fungus which only thrives because of the entry holes.

The two examples chosen show how important it is, when faced with diseased plants, to distinguish between the pest (aphid or fly) which introduces the pathogens and the fungus, bacteria or virus which actually cause the disease and are secondary infections. Good results can be obtained by waging war on the carrier the minute it shows signs of activity, but there is usually no way of controlling the diseases transmitted to the plant except by burning the infected parts.

The symptoms of disease

Symptoms are the specific manifestations that reveal the presence of a particular disease. Every disease is accompanied by precise symptoms in the living organism affected. Diseases are distinguishable by the symptoms associated with each disease.

Suppose we look at two children's diseases, measles and kwashiorkor. The symptoms of measles are a runny nose, temperature, cough, an eruption of little spots first on the face, then on the whole body; the spots disappear after a few days forming little scabs that peel off. The symptoms of kwashiorkor are the formation of soft swellings (oedemas) on the body, along with weak, emaciated muscles, discolouration of the skin that starts peeling off, discolouration of hair, diarrhea, arrested growth, apathy. The symptoms of measles are therefore quite different from those of kwashiorkhor.

Measles and scarlatina both cause rashes on children's bodies, but the other symptoms are different. Marasma and rickets are two other diseases caused by malnutrition but without discolouration of the skin.

In order to diagnose the disease to be cured, a doctor must weigh up **all** the symptoms he has observed. It is not enough to say that a child has measles because he has a temperature, or that he has kwashiorkor because his skin is discoloured. **A set of symptoms taken as a whole point to a disease, not just one symptom on its own.**

It is the same with plants. If you want to identify a crop pest or disease, you must observe the signs of its presence and the overt symptoms of disease.

Some crop pests are **easily identified** because the symptoms are obvious. Take, for instance, the damage caused to sweet potatoes by **defoliating caterpillars** (*Acraea acerata*) **(figure 229)**. These are larvae living on leaves, in nests wrapped in a kind of thread-like silk. As the caterpillars grow into larger greenish caterpillars with rough bristles, they spread out and chew the leaves cutting large holes as they go. The chewed plants are weakened because their leaf surface which photosynthesises is reduced. Once the holes are apparent, it means that the caterpillars have already infested the plant and it is too late to take effective measures. On the other hand, while the larvae are still grouped in their nests as in **figure 230**, it is fairly easy to capture and destroy them.

Other pests are **much harder to identify,** because they operate inside plants, with nothing visible on the outside. This is so with fungi that attack stems or roots and end up by clogging the sap-transporting vessels, so that an apparently healthy tree may wilt permanently in a few days or weeks.

Locate the presence of pests, determine the characteristics and timing of their attack : these are the basic steps in the war against crop pests.

The observations that help identify a pest attack or a disease by examining the symptoms must come from answers to such questions as :

- does the disease cause **overall plant blight** (drooping, wilting and death) or wilting of some parts only - leaves, buds or shoots, flowers, fruits, stems or branches, roots ?
- what are the signs of dieback ? Are they any of the following : wilting **(231, 237, 238, 239, 240)**, scalding **(242)**, discolouration **(221, 232, 245)**, streaks **(246)**, bites **(253)**, rot **(228)**, development of larvae **(225)**, twisting of side shoots or leaves **(247)**, necrosis (death of some tissues) **(241)**, cankers, translucent spots, white downy mildews **(222)**, or black mildews on the surface of leaves, stunted growth **(247)**, blisters **(247, 251)**, witches'-broom **(182)**, holes, abnormal fruiting, resin or gum secretions, fruitlet drop, concentric circles, galls on the roots **(236)**, leaf curling, crinkling **(245)**, stunted growth of fruits or stems, chewing of leaves **(224, 229, 254, 273)** or of fruits **(225)** ?
- at what time of the year do the symptoms appear :
  - first, in relation to the **seasonal calendar** : onset of rains, end of rains, in a given month ?
  - **in relation to unusual weather conditions** : after particularly heavy rains, during a drought period ?
  - **in relation to the life cycle of the diseased plants** : when the stems start to grow, during flowering, all the time, sporadically ?

229

230

Observing fieldcrops throughout the whole life cycle of cultivated plants is the first step in crop protection and sanitation. The range of plant destruction and symptoms to be diagnosed is so huge that we shall concentrate on recognizing the commonest symptoms so as to be able to decide the best way of combatting pests. A specialized technician or a reliable textbook can be consulted if needs be. Pratical publications in this field are listed at the end of the book.

Some common symptoms and their causes

Different types of wilt

The causes of wilt

It is not unusual for a whole plant or part of a plant to wither more or less quickly. Wilt is sometimes preceded by a warning sign as with the marrow attacked by a fungus in **figure 222**. White powdery mildew covers the surface of some leaves which have been chewed away inside and will wilt fast.

In other cases, however, there is no warning signal.Suddenly, the plant dries up and dies. The potato plant in **figure 231** has been destroyed. by bacterial ring spot, a wilt found in potato. Young bush greens are seen in **figure 239**. Inspected the previous day, this plant seemed perfectly healthy. By the following morning, the plant had toppled to the ground, leaves withered, collar limp and rotten.

231

The causes of wilting can be grouped under three headings : **physiological** causes, **pathological** causes and **mechanical** causes.

Before discussing physiological wilt, it should be noted that a seasonal plant normally withers **when its life cycle is over.** Since plant reproduction has taken place, the plant no longer needs its foliage. Wilt of this kind is normal and is no cause for concern.

Physiological wilt springs from plant malnutrition that can be so marked as to kill off the affected plants. Here are some of its causes :

232

- prolonged soil **drought** leads to permanent wilting which takes place slowly - its cause is obvious;
- wilting may be due to **root asphyxia** caused by stagnant water; the roots are deprived of air and cannot grow properly in the ground;
- **plant poisoning** by natural or artificial chemicals is another possibility, e.g. accumulation of rusty scrap-iron, discharge of chemical products including detergent soaps, overdoses of fertilizer, herbicide spill, factory waste, etc.;
- dieback may result from a **deficiency,** meaning that the plant is short of one or more specific mineral salts that are not available in the soil, rather like a child that does not get enough milk and green vegetables and is therefore short of calcium and iron to manufacture his bones and blood.

The citrus plant in **figure 232** is suffering from a deficiency. As with the soya plant in **figure 221**, the leaf blades are discoloured; only the veins and their edges are really green.

Tracking down a deficiency is not an easy task. Its exact nature can only be determined by chemical analyses of the soil that must be entrusted to specialized laboratories. But it is safe to say that signs of deficiency always result from an imbalance in soil fertility :

- **overexploited soil,** for example by a crop in permanent pure stand,
- soil that is **too acid** following water stagnation,
- **wrong doses of chemical fertilizers** that make the soil acid or saline.

Just as human nutrition can be improved by eating a varied diet (Chapter 2), so plant deficiencies can be treated by diversifying manures, using compost, vegetable and animal wastes, and household ashes, especially when these fertilizers come from a variety of places other than those where the deficiences are present.

Chemical fertilizer sometimes succeeds in getting rid of deficiencies when specialists have studied the fertilizer and determined how it should be applied. But, at other times, the fertilizer itself causes a particular deficiency. A simple comparison illustrates the point. A meal consisting of a bowl of couscous and two spoonfuls of sauce is balanced and easily digested. Two bowls of couscous and the same amount of sauce would make a heavy meal, whereas no one would get through three bowls of couscous served with the same two spoonfuls of sauce.

233 Attack at ground level

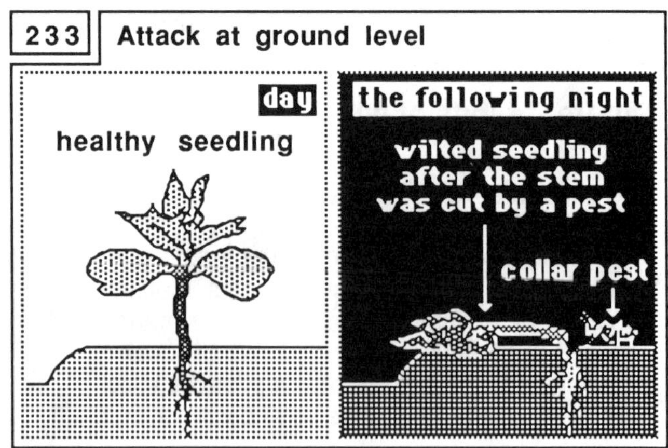

234 Root rot

section through stem and roots of a tree attacked by **root rot.** The white or coloured filaments found under the bark obstruct and destroy the vessels conducting sap through the tree.

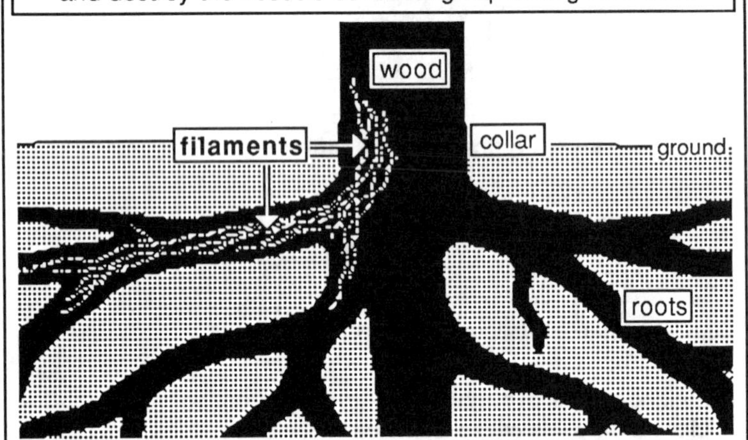

235

Chemical fertilizers can be compared to couscous sauce. A balanced meal is composed of dishes served in the right proportions. When fertilizer application is too heavy in relation to soil reserves of certain types of minerals, plants suffer from deficiencies. The minerals that are needed in minute quantities are called **trace elements**. Deficiencies are often caused by the lack of one or more of these elements. But wilts arise from other causes too, especilly **pathological** causes which are dealt with later in the chapter.

Figure 233 illustrates a **mechanical** cause of wilt. An insect moving on the ground surface chewed the collar between root and stem the way a woodman cuts down a tree at its base. When the bite went deep into the stem, the intact part was not strong enough to support the plant which collapsed. A slug could make the plant collapse in the same way. Mature plants and trees suffer similar damage, often toppling in a gust of high wind or during a tornado.

Wilts due to root infections

The roots of plants, particularly those of trees, are frequently attacked by a fungus whose filaments called hyphae block the sap-conducting vessels. When the root is infested throughout, it begins to rot and dies **(figure 234).** By degrees, the fungus invades the other roots of the tree which will die in the end. Sometimes the fungus spreads to the roots of other trees and infests the whole plantation, moving from one plant to the next.

Such fungi are called **root rots**. You will find them by clearing the soil away from the damaged roots. Scratch them with a knife, and the white or coloured hyphae appear. Depending on the species, the fungus grows on the outside or in the wood of the root. Sometimes, the fungus shows characteristic fruiting bodies on the roots themselves or on the collar.

The fungus may have completely rotted the main roots of the tree without leaving any outward sign of internal damage. Suddenly and unexpectedly, the tree is toppled by heavy winds.

Another example of root disease in the form of many **galls** or swoollen root-knots is seen in **figure 236**. The roots here were invaded by small root-feeding worms, called **nematodes** or **eelworms**. This pest stunts and deforms the root system.

The **scale insects** in **figure 235** also suck and exhaust the plants on which they settle. Here they fed on a groundnut plantlet and killed it.

237 | Wilt attacks the whole crown.

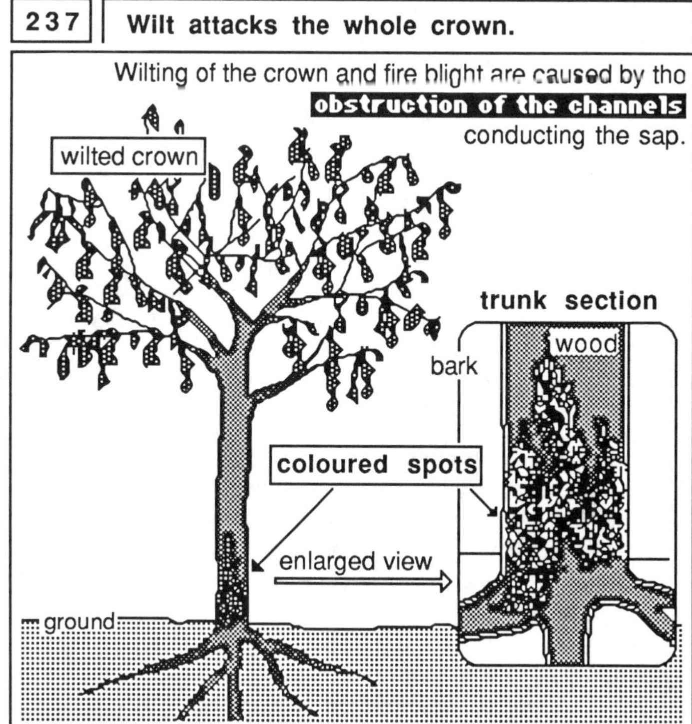

Wilting of the crown and fire blight are caused by the **obstruction of the channels** conducting the sap.

Wilts caused by damage at ground level

The collar is the region where the transition from root to stem occurs. When germination takes place in the normal way, the collar is situated on the soil surface. Collars are an easy prey for all kinds of chewing and biting insects moving on the ground, for example, beetles and caterpillars; slugs and snails also attack in this region. When well-established plants are attacked, little damage is caused but with seedlings most of the tissues needed for sap circulation may be destroyed.

This type of devastation is common in nurseries or on freshly sown beds. Most of the seedlings may wilt in a matter of hours and the whole seedbed can die off.

Fungi and bacteria also attack root collars, obstructing the sap-conducting vessels and causing wilt.

238 | Wilt attacks part of the crown.

Borers **destroy the sap-conducting channels** by burrowing through the bark and wood. Deprived of sap, the branches wilt.

withered branches
healthy branches
trunk section
borer
galleries
enlarged view
ground

Wilts and blights due to attack on stems and trunks

Figures 237 and 238 show two examples of wilt. The first figure shows how a tree suffered permanent wilt because the vessels were completely blocked by a microorganism. Sometimes disease affects the tree and kills it in a day or two. This kind of sudden death is called **wilt** or **fire blight** because the tree looks as thought it had been devastated by fire that makes the plant dry up completely. When caused by a fungus, fire blight is called **tracheomycosis.**

Wilting is also caused by **borers** that burrow galleries in the stem and/or branches and stop the circulation of sap. **Figure 238** shows how a borer damages the trunk of a tree, but similar damage can be observed on all kinds of herbaceous and woody plants. Two common examples are the maize stem-borer (*Busseola fusca*) and the banana weevil *(Cosmopolites sordidus).*

The pest tunnels away without showing any visible sign of activity. Then suddenly the infested plant breaks, revealing the pest's presence.

Borers are also responsible for blighting branches but they do not remain hidden like microorganisms. On the contrary, their presence is detected by the holes they make in the bark and wood. The best thing to do is to cut the diseased branch off in order to track down the pest and make sure, as far as possible, that the insect found is the real pest and not merely a small visitor that took advantage of the gallery burrowed by the main invader which has left.

Termites should be mentioned as a special case. They generally infest dead wood or old trees where they burrow many galleries. Sometimes certain termites are known to attack young trees and are therefore an obstacle to establishing plantations.

Dieback

Dieback is the progressive withering of plants, particularly trees, from the shoots inwards. The wilt works its way from the outside to the inside of the crown, often as a result of microorganic activity. On the whole, dieback strikes plants weakened for want of proper nutrients **(figure 240)**.

Damping off

Damping off is a hazard associated with seedlings that have just emerged, nursery seedlings being particularly at risk. Usually, the seedlings are attacked in batches. The collar goes limp, the seedlings fall over and rot **(figure 239)**. Filaments become visible on the collar or roots and indicate that damping off is caused by fungi.

Fruit drop

Fruit drop is the term used when almost all the flowers that have just set or the fruitlets themselves dry up and fall to the ground. As a rule, fruit drop can be traced to physiological causes - the plant is no longer able to feed the fruits, either for lack of moisture, or because the soil is exhausted. Watering and fertilizer applications guard against fruit drop but cannot stop it once it has started.

Blossom drop is sometimes caused by the total or partial absence of fertilisation, especially in plants that are not self-pollinating - this is true of **dioecious species.** Plants belonging to these species bear flowers of one sex only.

240 The dieback of branches

The two main causes of dieback in branches are

1 fungi or bacteria clogging the sap-conducting vessels,

2 borers feeding on the wood.

A third cause is **plant malnutrition.**

1 Dieback caused by wilt

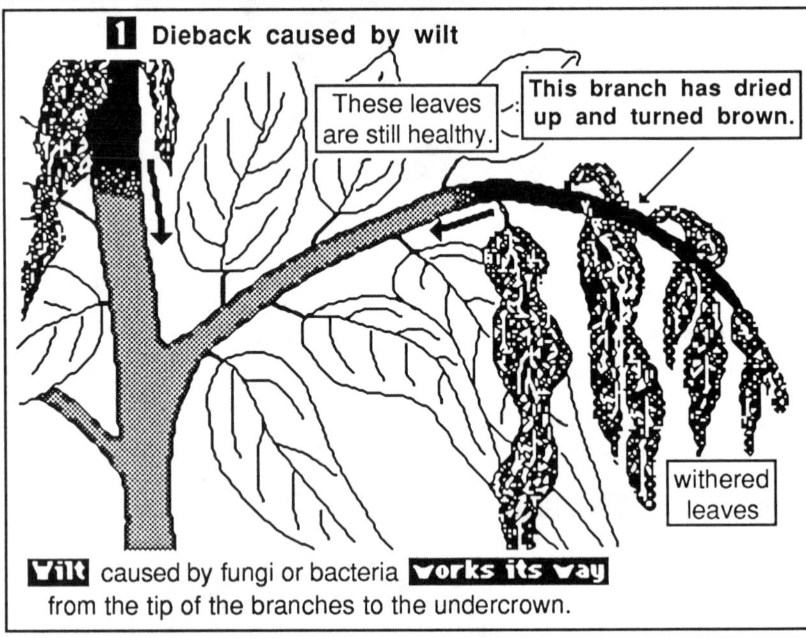

Wilt caused by fungi or bacteria **works its way** from the tip of the branches to the undercrown.

2 Dieback caused by borers

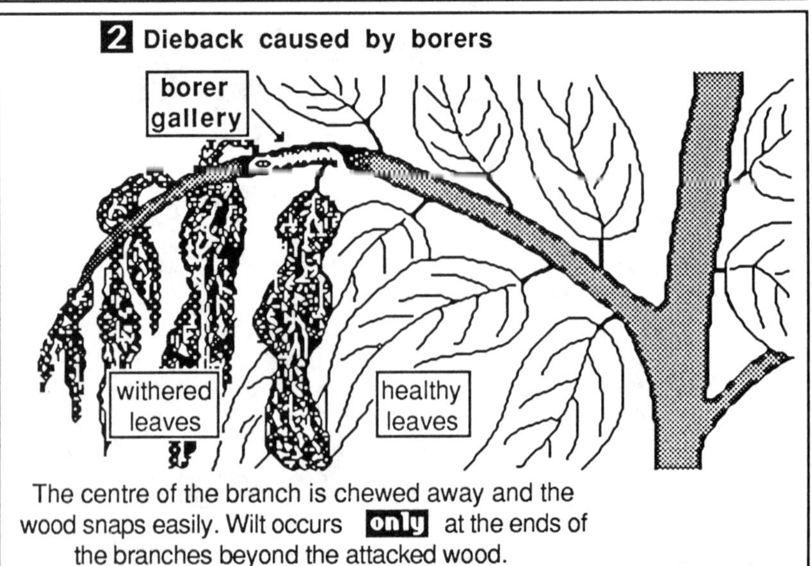

The centre of the branch is chewed away and the wood snaps easily. Wilt occurs **only** at the ends of the branches beyond the attacked wood.

239

241

Ways of avoiding blossom drop in orchards include

- ❍ **interplanting many varieties of the same species,**
- ❍ **not planting isolated trees,**
- ❍ **not using chemicals that kill pollinating insects,**
- ❍ **keeping bees.**

Distortions and necrotic lesions

Arrested growth, dwarfism and stunting

When plants are badly nourished or infected by viruses, they stop growing. Stems and leaves are stunted, leaves are abnormally coloured. Examples are cassava attacked by mosaic disease **(figure 245) or** groundnut stunted by rosette virus **(figure 223)**.

As a rule, stunting arises from many interconnected factors and especially from nutrient deficiencies that make plants an easy prey for viruses.

242

Necroses

Necroses are small spots of dead tissue that appear on the surface of leaves, branches or fruits.

Here are some examples of necroses. Bean **anthracnose** is seen in **figure 241** and is caused by the fungus *Colletotrichum*. Necrotic lesions appear on the fruits as well as on the leaves (see foreground). The spots are irregular in shape with reddish or black borders, paler in the centre.

Anthracnose affects the leaves, stems and fruits of many cultivated species such as bean, cassava, sorghum, tea, coffee, avocado, marrows, melons, banana, tomato. The plants may be severely damanged, and diseased fruits unfit for consumption.

Potato, tomato, tobacco, sweet potato and cotton are sometimes attacked by **early blight** brought on by a fungus causing lesions in concentric lines, alternately pale and dark in colour. The spots spread from the bottom of the plant to the top. The diseased leaves, fruits or tubers dry up eventually and fall off.

243

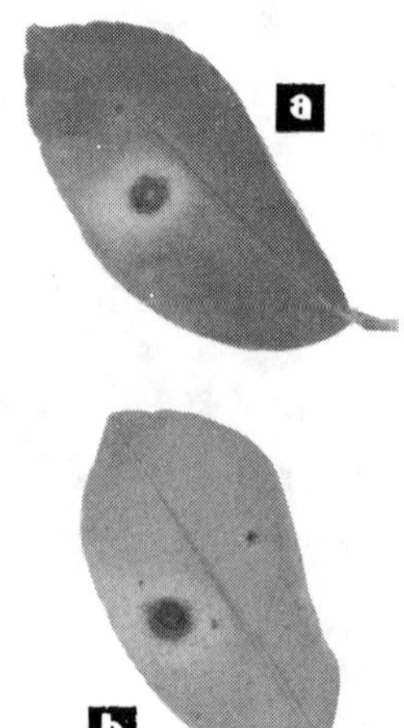
a
b

Mildews and blights are serious diseases occuring frequently in plants such as potato, tomato, tobacco, onion, lettuce, cabbage, and cucurbits. Small brown spots appear on the leaves; they enlarge and meet until the diseased parts are permanently wilted.

Figure 242 shows a potato plant struck by the first spots symptomatic of late blight that will destroy it entirely. The row of tomatoes in **figure 244** has already wilted permanently after being attacked by the fungus *Phytophthora.*

Cercospora, another fungal species, causes leaf spot or blotch. It attacks various cultivated plants such as marrows, citrus, groundnut, sorghum, tobacco, oil palm, banana, cassava and potato. The orange tree in **figure 243** is suffering from leaf spot. Here, the fungus forms round lesions which are pale in the centre with darker borders and a yellowish or greenish halo. The upper surface **(a)** and under sides **(b)** of a diseased leaf are shown in detail.

There are many other necrotic diseases caused by fungi or bacteria, for example, **rusts, spot (figure 222), bacterial galls, scalds, brown and black rots, smuts.**

The first step in effective crop sanitation is to observe damaged plants with care and accuracy.

244

You must first note :

- the **species** and sometimes the plant variety affected,
- the **form** of the necrotic lesions and their **development**,
- their exact **position** on the leaves, shoots, fruits and tubers,
- the **fruiting bodies** and their position,
- if leaves are diseased, the **side** on which the lesion is visible (one or both sides), and the side with the fruiting bodies,
- the **exact time** in the season when the disease appears.

With this information to hand, you can profitably consult specialized books on plant diseases (see list appended) or a plant pathologist (a plant doctor).

Mosaics and streaks

Mosaics and streaks of which examples are shown in **figures 245 and 246** are infections caused by viruses.

Cassava mosaic is a common disease (**figure 245).** It shows up in a set of angular, discoloured spots whose angles and edges touch one another. The leaf blades become distorted as the disease progresses. Mosaics, sometimes called **mottles,** are also found on tobacco, potato and sweet potato.

245

246

Streak viruses are more commonly associated with grasses such as maize **(figure 246)** and sorghum. They take the form of discoloured lines between the leaf veins.

Plants completely infected by viral diseases such as mosaics and streaks suffer severe exhaustion and become stunted because photosynthesis by the distorted, discoloured leaves is impaired **(figure 149)**. Sometimes, however, the virus is limited to certain plant parts.

Incidentally, where leaf cassava is concerned, housewives often prefer mottled to healthy leaves because they are more tender.

Distortions

More often than not, distortions affect the leaves but they are also found on side shoots and fruits.

248

Bugs have pierced the tip of the okra plant in **figure 248** and caused internal lesions and distortion; the damaged parts stopped growing whereas the healthy parts went on developing, with resulting plant distortion.

The distorted leaves of a tree tomato suffering from viral **blisters** are seen in **figure 247**.

Some parasites cause leaf-curling. This distortion hampers photosynthesis and the movement of sap.

247

Abnormal growths

The **witches'-broom** seen in **figure 182** grew on the end of a branch of bitter leaf because of the many wounds inflicted on the plant when the shoots were harvested. The plant became infected and reacted by multiplying buds able to grow into shoots. This process is a sort of defense mechanism against invading microorganisms.

249

250

Certain diseased trees react by producing flowers and fruits in profusion and then dying. Luxuriant growth of this kind may occur when the soil is exhausted, or when the stem is attacked by wilt or by root rot. After such excess growth, trees wilt quickly.

If the problem is due to soil infertility, it can be solved by spreading organic and mineral fertilizers, but if wilt or root rot are present, trees are condemned and must be removed and burnt at once.

Gummosis

Gummosis is the term used to describe abnormal exudations of gum on the surface of tree trunks followed by splits and foul-smelling bark rot. Gummy bark diseases are typical of citrus and particularly of lemon. They are caused by a fungus *(Phytophthora)* that attacks the tissues of the plant making it exude gum in self-defense.

Gummosis must not be confused with the natural flow of resin in certain trees, or the flow occuring after incisions in the bark, e.g. acacia, African elemi *(Canarium schweinfurthii)*.

Cankers

Typical cankers are illustrated in **figures 249 and 250**. **Cankers** are growths resulting from the multiplication of diseased tissues. When invaded by a fungus or by bacteria, the plant reacts by quickly reproducing more tissues that will themselves succumb to disease. The sick tissues are fissured and distorted, while the trunk or branch slowly withers away.

If the canker is superficial and in the early stages of growth, it can sometimes be removed and the wound treated locally. Otherwise, the diseased branch must be chopped off and burnt.

253 **Two ways in which insects affect the aerial parts of plants**

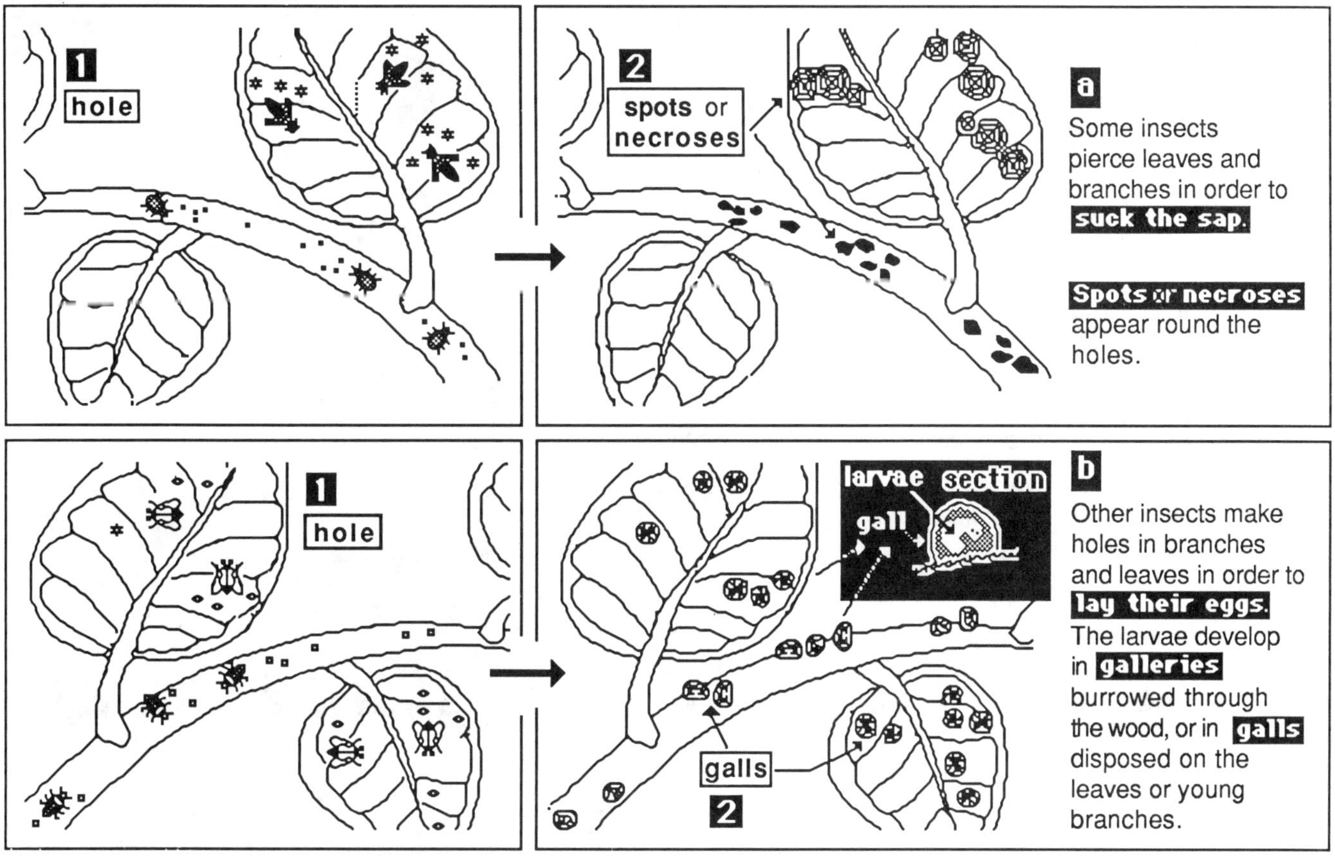

1 hole

2 spots or necroses

a Some insects pierce leaves and branches in order to **suck the sap.**

Spots or necroses appear round the holes.

1 hole

larvae section

gall

galls

2

b Other insects make holes in branches and leaves in order to **lay their eggs.** The larvae develop in **galleries** burrowed through the wood, or in **galls** disposed on the leaves or young branches.

Plant pests

Insect damage

Insects and spiders attack different plant parts - leaves, shoots, flower buds, flowers, fruits and roots. They do so for two reasons **(figure 253)** :

- **in order to feed** on the sap,

252

251

- **in order to lay eggs.**

The harm done varies from being very limited to damage of catastrophic proportions. Isolated insects are not of great concern but when they come in swarms **(figures 265 and 266)**, they are capable of wiping out entire harvests.

What happens when harvests are threatened by suctorial insects ?

- when the pest sucks the sap, **it weakens the plant;** shoots may suffer permanent wilt;
- by piercing the plant in order to suck it, the parasite may inject toxic saliva;
- sometimes they introduce microorganisms in the form of fungi, virus or bacteria that develops later, causing necrotic lesions, mosaic disease, streaks, distortions and cankers.

It is not the initial piercing of the plant which is injurious but the diseases they transmit to the plant.

When insects damage plants in order to lay eggs, the plants are affected in different ways. The eggs change into larvae which develop

- either inside the organs in which they proceed to burrow **holes (figures 225 and 228)** and **galleries (figures 238 and 240)**,
- or inside **galls** that grow on the surface of the parts attacked.

Figure 252 shows galls developing on the upper side of leaves. Turn over the leaves and notice the little sunken black spots. A larva is lodged in the middle of each gall.

The gall in **figure 251** is sometimes present on black plum leaves.

In small numbers, galls are not particularly harmful. However, when they proliferate as illustrated in **figure 252**, they cause distortion, and photosynthesis is reduced in the infected leaves. Gall-bearing parts should be burnt before the larvae hatch out.

Remember that every insect has its own particular habits that must be observed accurately. Some strike any or all plant parts. Others attack specific organs in specific places - leaf blades, their under or upper sides, leaf veins, terminal buds and the interior of fruits.

Nematodes or eelworms are responsible for a special type of root gall mentioned earlier in connection with **figure 236**. These small worms live in the soil, settling and feeding on roots.

Browsing

Some animals nibble at the aerial parts of plants the way cattle browse grass. The pests responsible are adult insects **(figure 224)**, caterpillars **(figure 255)**, snails and slugs **(figure 254)**. They destroy organs vital to plant life, for example, the foliage needed for photosynthesis.

As a rule, nibbling is from the outside in, but **leaf miners** are also known to eat leaves after penetration. Galleries can be observed between the upper and lower sides of the leaves that remain intact on the surface.

We have studied the various **symptoms** of disease and damage in cultivated plants and seen how important it is to ascertain them accurately in order to discover the cause. The expression **causal agent** of disease or damage refers to the animal, microorganism or plant originally responsible for the diseas. Here are three examples of causal agents already mentioned : the fungus *Phytophthora* for potato mildew, the aphid *Aphis craccivora* that injects rosette virus into groundnut, and the fungus *Cercospora* causing leaf spot in citrus.

The main types of pests, from the biggest to the smallest, must now be reviewed. Some of these are quite visible to the naked eye but others are microscopic, i.e. invisible to the naked eye.

254

255

Notes

Warm-blooded animals

Birds and wild or domestic mammals are among the warm-blooded animals causing crop devastation : they include monkeys, gazelles, elephants, rats, wild pigs, goats, sheep, cattle and pigs.

Some chew or smash everything in their path. Others attack particular plant parts like the rodent that came to nibble a cassava stem at its base, almost at the root collar **(figure 256)**.

Many birds, isolated or in flocks, eat fruits and seeds in gardens. The most dangerous are birds belonging to the species *Quelea quelea* that de-

scend on the crops and seem to be particularly destructive when neighbouring savanna lands are bare of wild grasses due to grazing or drought.

Quelea and other bird species called weavers also use the leaves of certain trees to build their nests. Palm and coconut, for instance, are sometimes stripped of foliage and die as a result.

Domestic animals - goats, sheep, and pigs - are known to cause extensive havoc when left to wander and can make establishing village gardens out of the question. When this situation arises, the only solution is to draw up community rules which pastoralists and farmers with stock respect to the letter, notably by tethering, or by fencing off enclosures. Pastures and crop land must be strictly demarcated.

257 Slugs and snails

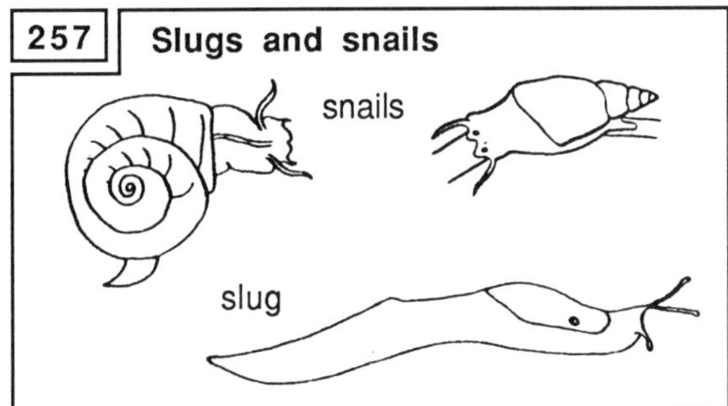

258 Centipedes and millipedes

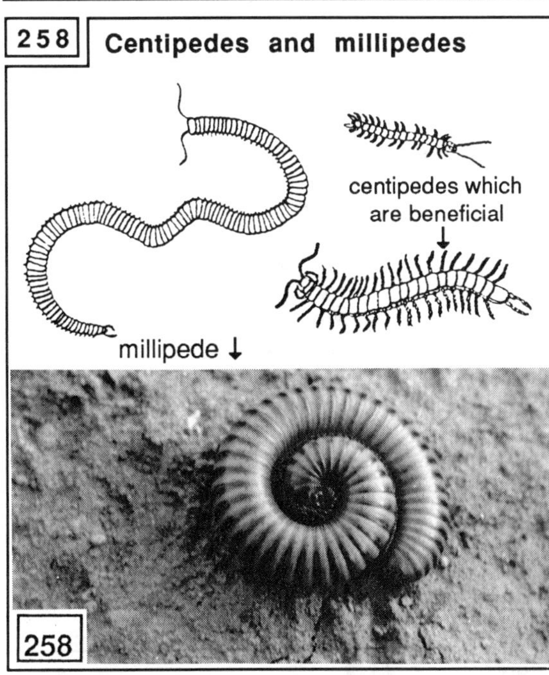

259 Locusts and African mole-crickets

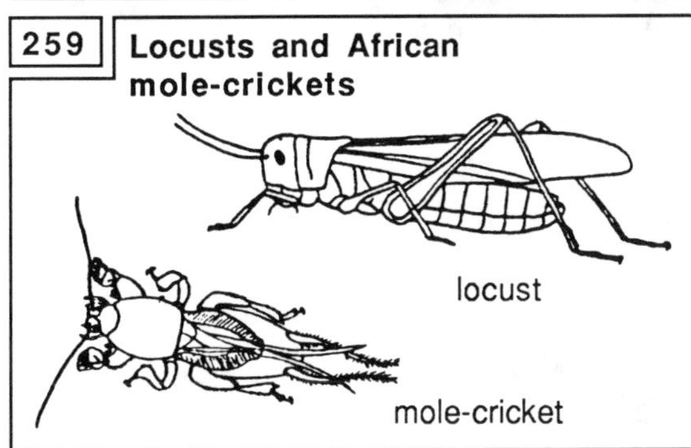

Chewing pests

Damp, shady sites and swamps are the favourite habitat of **slugs and snails (figure 257)**. When they attack mature crops, damage is insignificant **(figure 254)**. On the other hand, they are capable of razing germinating shoots as these emerge above ground. Wrecking usually takes place at night; during the day, slugs tend to hide in holes in the ground. Their presence is detected by the shiny trail they leave behind on the ground.

Millipedes are small, brown or blackish animals of cylindrical shape. Their bodies are formed of many segments each of which have two legs. If you touch them, they curl up (photograph and drawing **258**).

These animals live in the superficial soil layers. They eat seeds or seedling collars. Population is usually small and rarely a threat of any importance.

Locusts seen in **figure 259** are voracious insects that devour all the tender parts of plants. They always cause very severe damage to invaded crops especially when they overrun fields in swarms. Locusts are leaping insects with powerful, muscular hind legs that fold back when at rest.

African mole-crickets (figure 259) belong to the same family as locusts but are different because they live in the soil and feed on underground plant organs - roots and root collars.

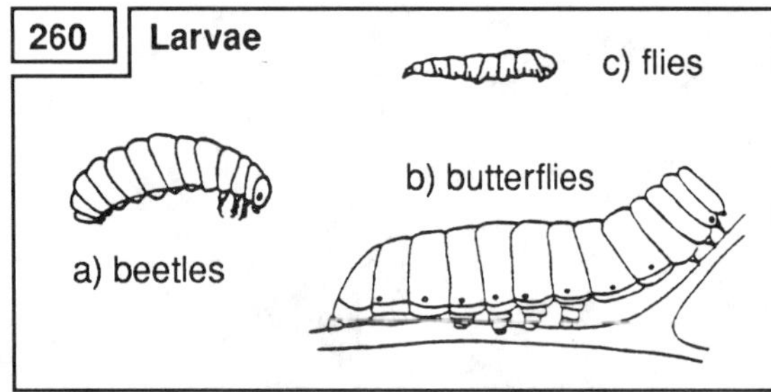

Termites are insects that almost always live in large colonies, hiding in the dark in galleries or in termite hills. The galleries are burrowed through woody structures or built of earth and clay on their surface. Termites feed mostly on dead wood but certain species also attack live wood. The presence of termites is sometimes an obstacle in establishing plantations of young trees.

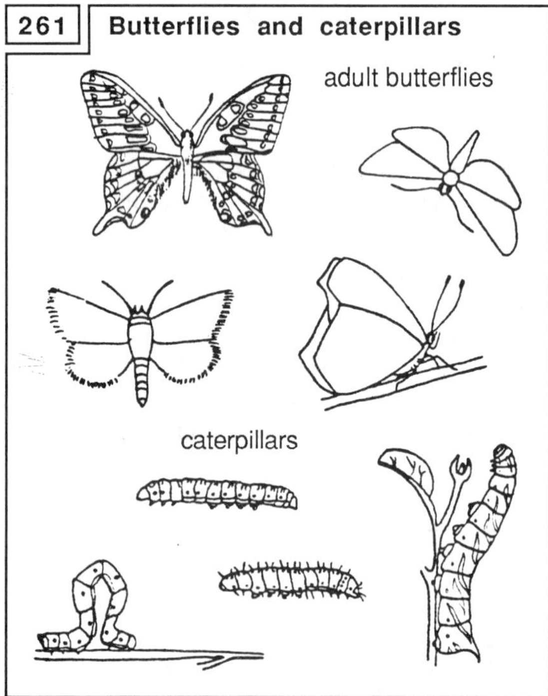

Larvae are the immature forms of insects. They are hatched from the eggs of the insect and gradually change into adults - into flies, ants, butterflies, beetles etc. Just like adult insects, larvae find food for themselves. They are able to chew wood, leaves, fruit, etc. and are at times more destructive than adults. Not infrequently, their life cycle is much longer than that of the corresponding adult.

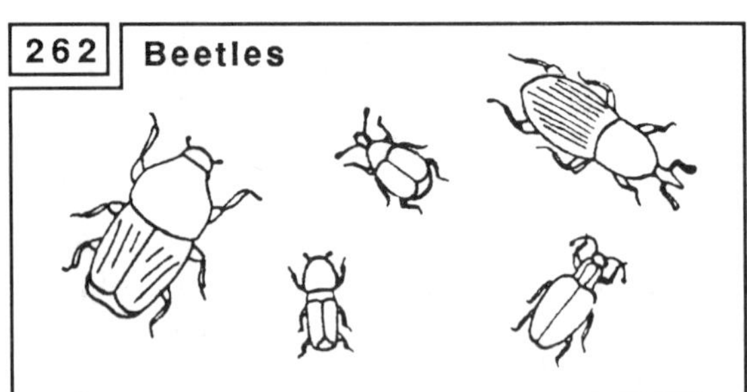

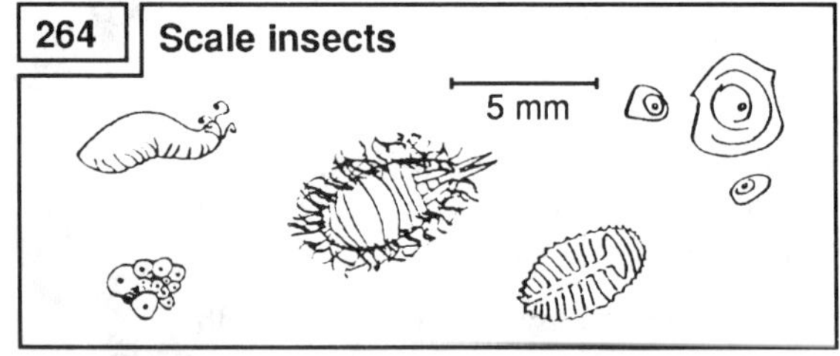

Caterpillars (figure 261) are also voracious pests, capable of destroying large areas of leaves and shoots in a few hours. Caterpillars are the larval stage of butterflies that lay their eggs on the surface of plants or in the soil.

Butterflies and moths form two groups of insects belonging to the same order (Lepidoptera). Butterflies are active during the day, moths are chiefly night-flying. The insects themselves cause little damage but their caterpillars can be exceptionally destructive, especially when they are found in large numbers.

Larvae do not reproduce. This is the role of the egg-laying adult. There is often no point in waging war on the larvae because they are hard to get at once they have colonized their host-plants. On the whole, better results are obtained by fighting the adults as they move from one plant to the next and before they start laying eggs.

It is sometimes possible to determine the order to which an insect belongs by examining a larva **(figure 260)**.

The larvae of butterflies and moths, i.e. caterpillars, have three pairs of front legs and two, three or four pairs of additional legs **(260b)**. The larvae of flies have no legs and an indistinct head **(260c)**. Beetle larvae may have three pairs of legs or no legs. They are frequently U-shaped and have a distinct head **(260a)**.

Most **weevils, borers, pulse and bark beetles** belong to the same order (Coleoptera) of insects **(figure 262)** of which there are a great number of species varying in length from 1 or 2 millimetres to 5 or 6 centimetres. Adult coleoptera have two pairs of wings, the front pair being horny and tough, the hind pair membranous. The hind wings propel the insect during flight and are covered by the front wings, called elytrons, when the insect is at rest.

Weevils attack roots, bulbs and tubers. **Bark beetles** and **borers** burrow galleries in stems, branches and fruits. **Pulse beetles (figure 309)** attack grain, seeds and ears of cereals.

267 Homoptera and thrips

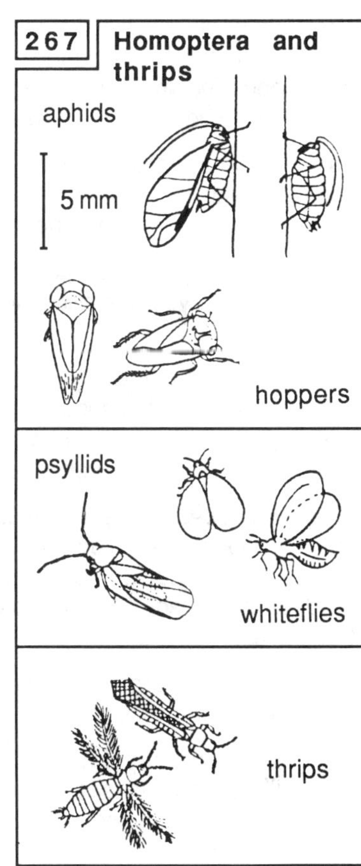

268 Mites

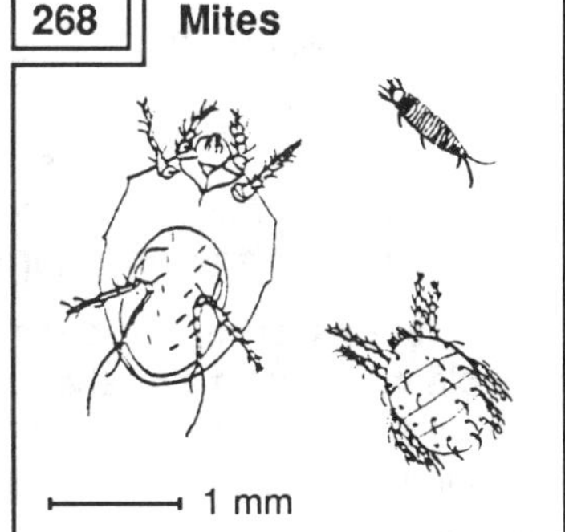

269 Bugs

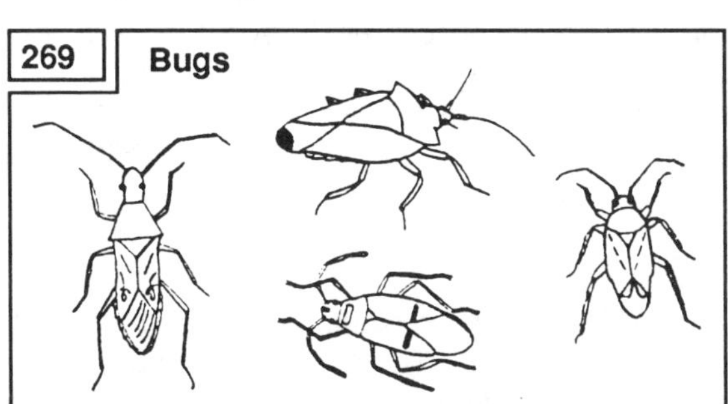

270

Larvae must not be mistaken for worms of which the best known are earthworms and, in man, threadworms, tapeworms, pinworms, and Guinea worms. Most worms do not change form, but larvae finally change into insects with legs.

Piercing and sucking pests

Scale insects live in more or less densely populated colonies, making their habitat on stems and branches. They look like small, brownish or whitish balls, they are waxy or downy and cling to the plant surface **(figures 235, 264 and 265)**. They are 3 to 5 millimetres long and often have a small scale or shell.

Scale insects transmit viruses to their hosts and inject them with toxins. Moreover, they produce whitish or blackish waste on which some ant species love to feed. The **ants**, in turn, breed colonies of scale insects and are thus an effective agent in the dispersal of these pests.

Aphids behave rather like scale insects. They often live in colonies on young branches which they pierce in order to suck the sap. They secrete a sweet substance called **honey dew (figure 266)**.

Aphids breed very rapidly. Several generations are sometimes seen on the same shoots. The young are like miniature adults without wings and are called **nymphs**.

Innumerable species of differently coloured aphids exist. Certain aphids attack a variety of plant species; others prefer specific plants and are called by the name of their hosts - the black bean aphid, the mealy cabbage aphid, the dark green melon aphid etc.

The honey dew produced by these aphids is often exploited by ants some of which breed regular colonies of aphids in their anthills. The honey dew is quickly invaded by a black fungus called **sooty** or **black mould** that does not attack the plant directly but stops light from reaching the leaves.

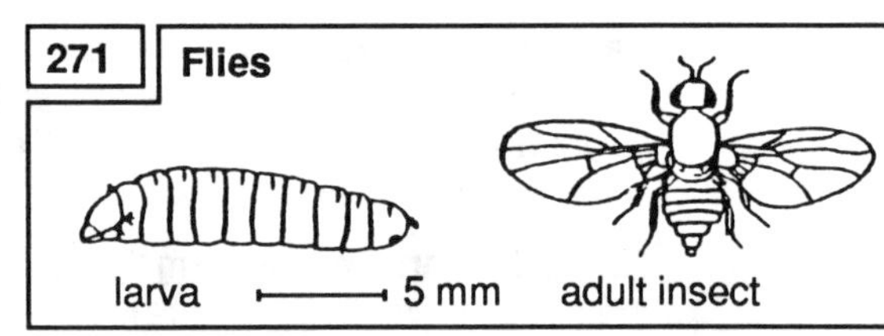

271 **Flies**

272

Other bugs also suck plant organs **(figures 269 and 270)**. They exhaust plants by sucking their sap and allow the entry of microorganisms.

Whiteflies, hoppers and psyllids are other piercing-sucking insects that inject viral diseases. They belong to the sub-order of insects called **Homoptera (figure 267)**. They are small and mobile, often whitish in colour. Unlike aphids and scale insects, they do not live in colonies although they aggregate. They are usually found on the undersurface of leaves and in the axils of leafy shoots. These insects are 2 to 5 mm long and are able to fly or hop.

Thrips (Thysanopters) are tiny sucking insects with narrow fringed wings often found in flowers.

Flies are highly mobile insects. They have a single pair of transparent wings, and their bodies, like those of all insects, are divided into three distinct parts - head, thorax, and abdomen. Certain species attack plants in order to lay their eggs. The larvae have no head or legs. They develop inside the plant and occasionally cause gall formation **(figures 271 and 272)**.

Spiders differ from insects because they have four pairs of legs as opposed to three. They are rarely a nuisance for plants because almost all of them are carnivorous. Their presence in gardens is desirable because they live on insects of which some are plant pests. However, some species of spiders attack plants by piercing and sucking them. They are called **mites,** are very tiny and hard to locate **(figure 268)**.

273

Parasitic plants

These plants live off other plants by sucking their sap. The parasitic roots become established under the bark of stems or roots. When growing on trees, they are commonly referred to as **mistletoe**, a name borrowed from a parasitic plant native to Europe but not to Africa. As a rule, these plants do little damage to crops.

Striga or witchweed is a parasitic plant growing on millet and sorghum roots in poor soil **(figure 227)**.

Worms

Nematodes, also called eelworms, are the only worms of real threat to crops. They are minute and live mostly in the soil. They sometimes penetrate the roots and stimulate the formation of galls

263

(**figure 236**). When present in large numbers, nematodes stop proper root function; the plant does not thrive, it turns yellow and suffers from partial or permanent wilt. Examining the roots of a diseased plant is the best way of finding out if nematodes are present. **Figure 263** shows an eggplant wilting after an attack by eelworms. It is difficult to get rid of this major pest in gardens. Specially-planned crop rotations and the use of resistant varieties are two ways of controlling infestation.

Indiscriminate pests, selective pests

There are indiscriminate parasites that live at the expense of many plant species. They act like cattle that eat almost all the grasses in pastures although they have certain food preferences and therefore avoid some plants. When these pests are few in number, crop damage is restricted. But should a multitude swarm over fields, the consequences are dramatic as when migratory locusts strip crops of all their green parts, or *Quelea* birds devour the grain.

Although they are very destructive, certain pests only feed on specific parts of one plant species or a handful of species. The shea butter branches in **figure 273** illustrate this point. **Leaf-eating caterpillars** have chewed all the leaf blades of which only the erect petioles or leaf-stalks remain. These caterpillars are voracious but **selective.** They eat a lot but only attack shea butter. In the background are other tree species untouched by the pest.

274

Another selective pest is the weevil *(Cosmopolites sordidus)* that bores holes in shoots and stems. It causes great havoc but keeps strictly to banana plants.

Some pests are more selective than others, that is to say, they concentrate on one plant part only - leaves, floral buds, fruitlets, mature fruits, young or old stems, etc. Moreover, invasion takes place at a definite point in the life of the pest or the plant. It is vital to determine this point in order to control the pest efficiently.

Other insects are a nuisance although they neither chew nor pierce plants. Damage here is indirect. This is true of some species of **ants** that make their nests by curling the leaves and distorting them **(figure 226)**. Certain ants interfere with work in fields and gardens because their bites are very painful. Mosquitoes are irksome for the same reason.

These insects do little damage to crops but are vectors of disease to man and animals, for example, malaria, and filariasis.

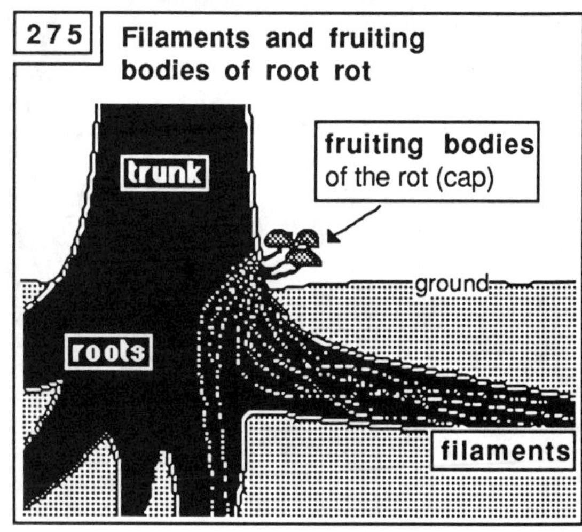

275 Filaments and fruiting bodies of root rot

Fungal infections

'Micro' means very tiny. Micro-organisms are living organisms that are often invisible to the naked eye. Yet their presence is easily demonstrated when they are the cause of disease **(figure 274)**.

Plants are attacked by many kinds of fungi that are detected when the fruiting bodies grow and the following symptoms are observed :

- powdery **stains**, white, black or coloured, on the surface of the diseased parts **(figure 222)**,
- **rough patches,** relatively damp, white, black or coloured, that rub off like fine powder on the surface of the host **(figure 274)**,

- toadstools or stems surmounted by umbrella-shaped caps in various colours. They sometimes grow on roots or on trunks, never on more tender organs such as leaves or fruits **(figure 275)**.

Fungi are microscopic organisms in the form of little balls or filaments invisible to the naked eye. The fungus in **figure 277** was photographed with the help of a microscope. This is an instrument used to see very tiny organisms.

The seeds of fungi are called **spores.** They form a white dust on the surface of the infected leaves or on the underside of the caps. Myriads of microscopic filaments unite to form the fruiting bodies **(figure 276)**.

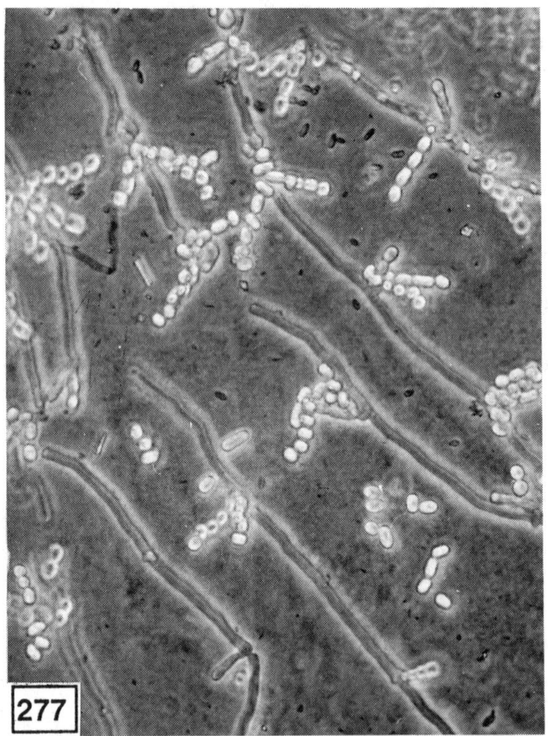

277

278

276 Filaments and fruiting bodies of a fruit fungus

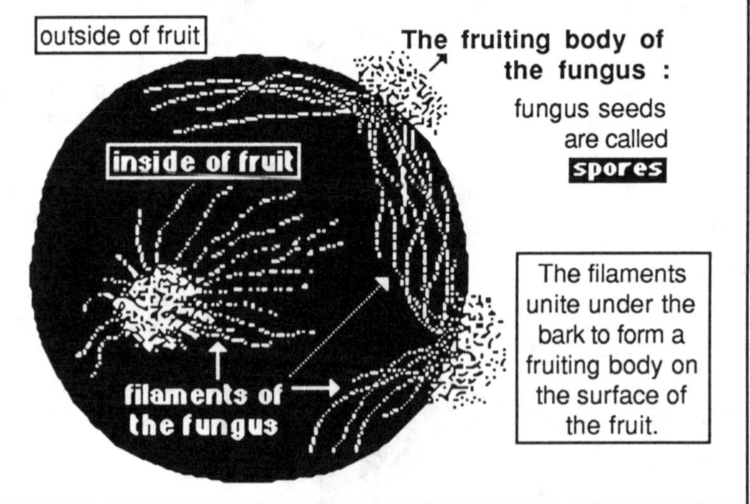

Spores are very easily dispersed by wind and rainwater, and by contact. By touching healthy plants after having touched plants covered in spores, man transmits **cryptogamic or fungal diseases**, the name given to diseases caused by fungi.

When they attack branches, trunks or roots, fungal diseases are often recognizable because of the white or coloured threads encircling the diseased organ on the outside, or running between the bark and the wood.

Fungi sometimes cause cankers and cracks in fruits **(figures 249 and 250)**.

Bacteria are responsible for what are termed **bacterial diseases**. Whereas bacteria are the source of many infections in human beings and animals, there are fewer bacterial than fungal diseases in the plant kingdom.

Unlike fungi whose spores and filaments are sometimes visible, bacteria are always invisible to the naked eye. However, their effects are manifest in leaf spots with geometric shapes, in brown or black rot, occasionally wet and foul-smelling, in dieback and wilt **(figure 240)**, in secretions of resin or whitish or transparent gum, as was mentioned earlier on.

Viruses are organisms even tinier than bacteria, and can only be seen through very powerful microscopes. The symptoms of viral diseases have also been described - discolourations, mosaic spots and streaks, distortions **(figures 245, 246, 247)**, stunting and dwarfism **(figure 223)**. Viruses are conveyed from one plant to the next in two ways :

- through **sucking insects** that travel from virus-infected to healthy plants,
- **through the seeds** of plants suffering from viral diseases.

Plants with viral diseases often remain alive but are weak and underproductive.

Friends and enemies

Horticulture plants, both vegetables and fruits, are threatened by many animals, insects and microorganisms. But enemies are heavily outnumbered by those living beings that do not present the slightest threat to these same plants, and in many cases, are useful or even necessary to them.

Take, for example, the nitrogen-fixing bacteria (*Rhizobium*) found in the nodules of legume plants Or ladybirds that eat aphids, spiders that eat insects, and the many insects and microorganisms that change organic waste into humus. Nature everywhere, be it in forests or savannas, in fields or gardens, is always full of living beings feeding and interdependent on one another.

Tho prcocnce of certain beings is sometimes essential for the proper development of others. Honey-gathering insects such as bees **(figure 278)** are extremely useful, sometimes indispensable, for fertilizing flowers. Again, there are many kinds of edible mushrooms and insects.that do not harm plants.

In nature, living beings are interdependent. This factor must be borne in mind when controlling pests, especially when damage to crops is fairly limited.

Dispersal mechanisms of pests

279 Every pest has its own dispersal patterns and it is wise to know them before attempting pest control.

Viruses

- by **insects** such as aphids, scale insects and other bugs. Here, transmission of the virus depends on the insect's capacity to travel from plant to plant and pierce the leaves or stems;
- by **propagation.** The seeds of a contaminated plant - seeds, cuttings, grafts - contain the virus that will thrive in the seedling;
- by **contact.** Tools used to cut contaminated plants are capable of carrying the virus to other plants.

Bacteria

- like viruses, bacteria can be transmitted by **insects** (this is rare, however), by **seeds,** and by **contact;**
- **rain** is an important dispersal agent **(figure 283)** because of runoff on plants and on the ground, and because droplets hit the ground and bounce onto plants;
- spreading organic matter, or infected compost prepared by the coldbed method;
- insects travelling from plant to plant carry bacteria on their bodies and legs.

Mites

- these tiny spiders are **mobile** and move round a lot;
- **they cling** to seeds or cuttings, to clothes and to animals;
- since they are tiny, some mites are also **wind-borne**.

Fungi

- like viruses and bacteria, fungi are dispersed by **water, contact and seeds;**
- **wind** disperses their spores when the fruiting bodies appear;
- **filaments** spread gradually in the soil, or from one root to another;
- **insects** and **animals** carry spores on their bodies and deposit them at random.

Nematodes

- they are **mobile** but cannot travel far;
- they are sometimes found **on seeds**.

Insects

- Adults can fly or walk and some travel great distances. Their eggs are carried by ants to chosen breeding sites.
- Larvae can crawl over limited distances.

Parasitic plants

- these are dispersed **by propagation**. The seeds are sometimes carried a few metres away by air or water;
- by **their spreading stems** or creepers;
- by **birds** that eat the seeds and excrete them some distance away;
- by certain **cultural practices**.

Chapters 8, 9, 10 and 11

Pest control

Many farming practices have been devised in order to protect crops and harvests from attack by pests. Some of these practices are based on natural means of control, for example, mineral, vegetable or animal products found in nature, or beneficial insects. Agricultural practices can also help control pests in a natural way. These methods come under the heading of **natural** and **biological control**. Other methods depend on the use of **chemical products** that are poisonous to the target pests. Some of these products are present in nature, but most of them are manufactured in chemical plants.

War on plant pests can be launched **before** the pests attack the plants. **Crop protection** or **preventitive control** is the name given to preemptive measures that, as a general rule, are the most effective and the most rewarding because they prevent the onset of crop damage.

Sometimes, control is directed at a given pest because its spread was not checked in the first place. This kind of control is **curative;** it is initiated when the disease is actually present or the pest already causing damage.

The choice of control measures is guided by three factors :

- **economic efficiency :** the value of the produce saved must be greater than the cost of the pest control,
- **technical efficiency :** the control methods must be appropriate, that is, the one most likely to achieve the hoped-for result. There is nothing to be gained by trying to kill fungi with insecticides or spraying a crop if the insect to be killed is not present or has already disappeared,
- **ecological efficiency**. Some pest control methods respect the living environment while others are very harmful. DDT is a well-known example because it kills all insects indiscriminately, the good along with the bad, and is also a serious health-hazard for man. DDT is therefore technically efficient, but biologically and ecologically dangerous.

Today, people are too inclined to believe in the superiority of chemical products and to underestimate the value of methods that respect the natural environment. At the same time, it is widely accepted that the increase of many plant diseases and pests are due to man's treatment of the ecosystem.

Pest control is discussed in four chapters as follows :

- Natural methods for the **prevention** of pests in cultivated plants (Chapter 8);
- Natural methods for direct and indirect **biological control** of pests (Chapters 9 and 10);
- **Use of pesticides** (Chapter 11).

Chapter 8

Natural methods for the prevention of pests in cultivated plants

There are many natural ways of controlling crop pests. They include :

- making sure that cultivated plants are **properly nourished,**
- **adapting the ecological environment** to the advantage of cultivated species and the disadvantage of their major pests,
- **limiting the risk of infection**,
- adopting the **right farming techniques** - removing diseased plant material, pruning, trapping, etc.,
- obtaining **resistant plant varieties and clean seeds**.

Nutrition affects the health of cultivated species

As was explained in Chapter 7, **deficiency diseases** are caused by the lack of a particular nutrient - one or more of the essential mineral salts may be lacking. How can the farmer identify and treat this deficiency without the help of a laboratory ?

Specially formulated chemical fertilizer may correct the deficiency, but this may not be available to the farmer. The best general solution is to apply **a generous amount of animal or plant manure**, which preferably should.come from an area not showing signs of deficiency. Sometimes it will be worthwhile for the farmer to get expert advice on which mineral nutrient should be added in tiny quantities.

When cultivated plants are weakened by poor feeding, and even if they show no deficiency symptoms such as discolouration, stunting, leaf or fruit fall, they tend to be more prone to **'weakness' pests**. These pests are always found in the environment but only cause significant damage when plants lack vigour.

Vigorous plants that are well-fed and regularly watered are quickly able to replace the sap sucked up by aphids and are strong enough to develop new shoots and leaves. Weak plants will wilt when attacked by aphids and will not be able to compensate by rapid healthy growth.

In the same way, certain fungi, viruses and bacteria are not so dangerous for vigorous plants whereas they destroy weaker specimens. In some cases, healthy plants are able to produce certain substances that fight the attacking microorganisms.

The lack of vigour which increases the risk of damage by 'weakness' pests may be due to various adverse conditions such as

- lack of water due to drought or **inadequate irrigation**,
- lack of oxygen caused by stagnant water,
- **impoverished soil,**
- **too much or too little light,**
- **faulty use of chemical fertilizers.**

The first four factors are easy to relate to poor growth, but the fifth needs some explanation.

Chemical fertilizers speed up plant growth and increase yields, two results that make their use worthwhile. At the same time, they often lower plant resistance and make them more attractive to pests. This is why farmers who feed their crops exclusively on chemical fertilizers, and on nitrogenous fertilizers in particular, may have to turn to pesticides in order to compensate for the low resistance of their plants. A plant reared only on chemical fertilizers is like a man who decided to live on a diet of cassava with no vegetables, cereals, milk or meat. He would have a full stomach but he would catch all kinds of diseases.

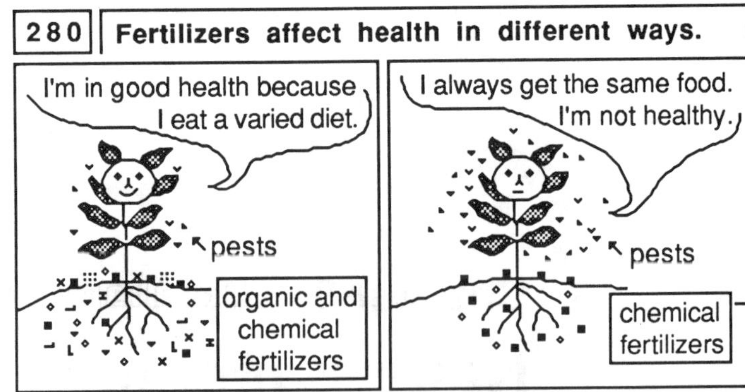

Organic manures and natural materials make a big contribution to plant health. Plants find in them a whole range of the substances they need in order to thrive and withstand the attacks of microorganisms. These natural, diversified manures feed plants just as human beings derive energy from a varied diet **(figure 280)**.

Tilling, mulching, organic manures, well-chosen fertilizers, irrigation, drainage **and all practices that enrich the soil and improve its structure, increase crop vigour and resistance to disease.**

Pest control and plant environment

Every living organism requires specific living conditions, whether it be water or dry land, sun or shade, heat or cold, a habitat in the soil or on another living being. In all these ways, pests and destructive microorganisms are no different from other living organisms - plants, animals and man.

If you observe a plant feeder right through the year, you will discover its way of life. You will find out if it walks or flies, if it lives on the upper or underside of leaves, if it is found in the soil or on plants, and where it lives during the dry season. You will know the stages of its life cycle and when it reproduces.

Equipped with this information, you will be able to take practical decisions about intercropping plant species or varieties, about crop rotation and the sowing calendar, about light and shade conditions.

Growing crops in mixtures

When a field or a patch contains only one plant species, its pests are able to develop and proliferate. On the other hand, if many species are interplanted, the spread and multiplication of the pest associated with one plant is restricted by the presence of the other species.

Here are examples of such interactions.

281

- The bacterium *Pseudomonas solanacearum* causes bacterial ring spot or wilt in potato. Rapid spread is noted when the seed tubers are densely planted in pure stand, but spread slows down considerably when potato is associated with another crop as illustrated in **figure 281 and 282**.
- Intercropping maize and erect or creeping plants is an excellent way of reducing cassava blight caused by the bacterium *Xanthomonas manihotis* **(figure 282)**. The bacterium is mainly transmitted by rainwater bouncing and splashing from plant to plant. Spread is hindered by the associated barrier plants.

The two examples chosen demonstrate the **barrier formed by mixing plants. It is important that the plants grown together are not susceptible to the same diseases and do not share the same pests.**

282 Maize or another plant intercropped with potato reduces the incidence of bacterial wilt.

1 Potato with high planting density

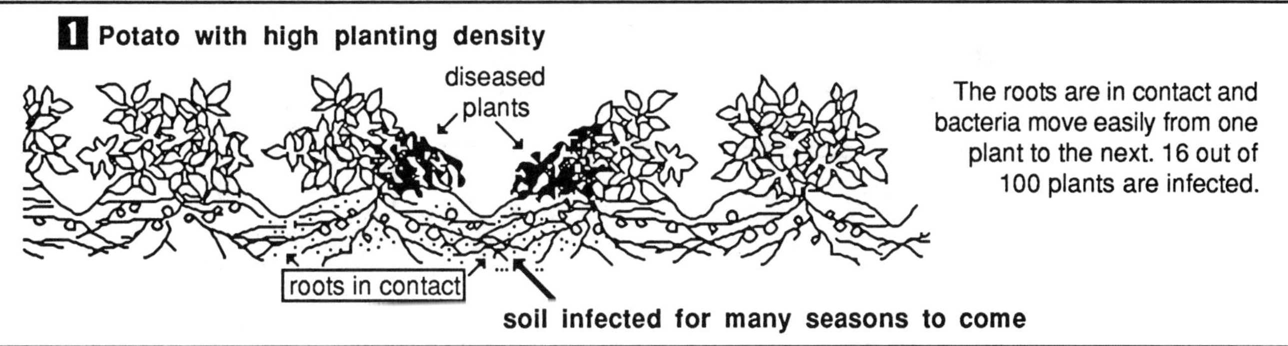

The roots are in contact and bacteria move easily from one plant to the next. 16 out of 100 plants are infected.

2 Potato with low planting density

There are fewer plants per are than in **1** . The roots are not in contact. Bacterial movement from plant to plant is restricted. Only 8 out of 100 plants are infected.

3 Low planting density combined with interrow maize crop

The maize roots also help to interrupt the spread of bacteria in the potato crop. 6 out of 100 plants are infected. Beans are an even more effective interrow barrier crop - only 4 out of 100 plants are diseased. The interrow crop compensates for lower potato yields.

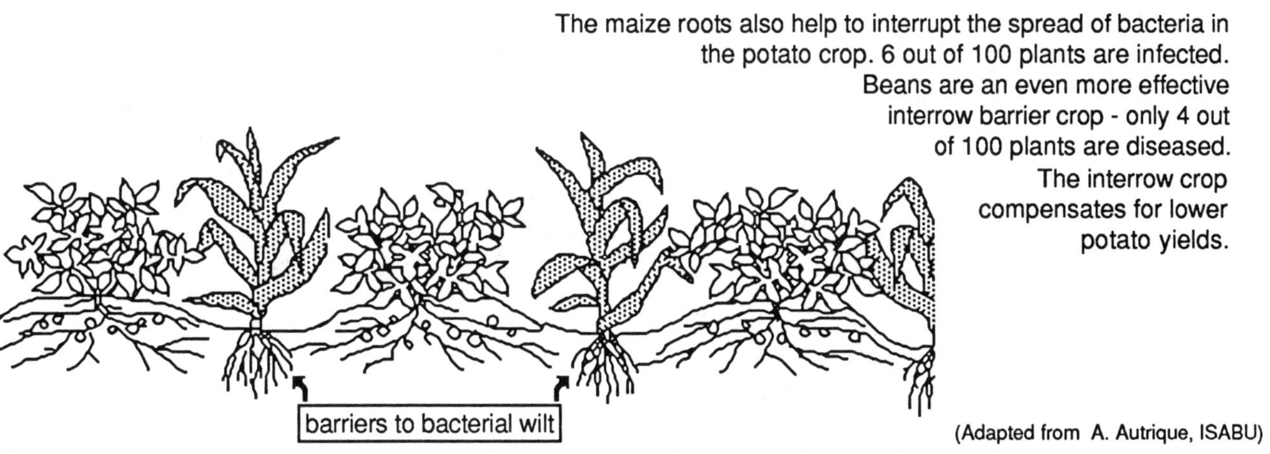

(Adapted from A. Autrique, ISABU)

Two important reasons for preventing the spread of bacterial wilt :

- crops in the current season are protected ;
- soil infection for the following seasons is avoided.

The bacterium *Pseudomonas* is capable of surviving in the soil for many seasons. If the infection is not curbed in one growing season, the field may become unfit for potato cropping for a very long time.

Notes

283 Maize intercropped with cassava reduces the spread of cassava bacterial wilt.

Cassava bacterial wilt is marked by the appearance of irregular leaf spots and stem wilt. By mixing maize or other plants with cassava, the spread of bacterial wilt in the contaminated field is reduced.

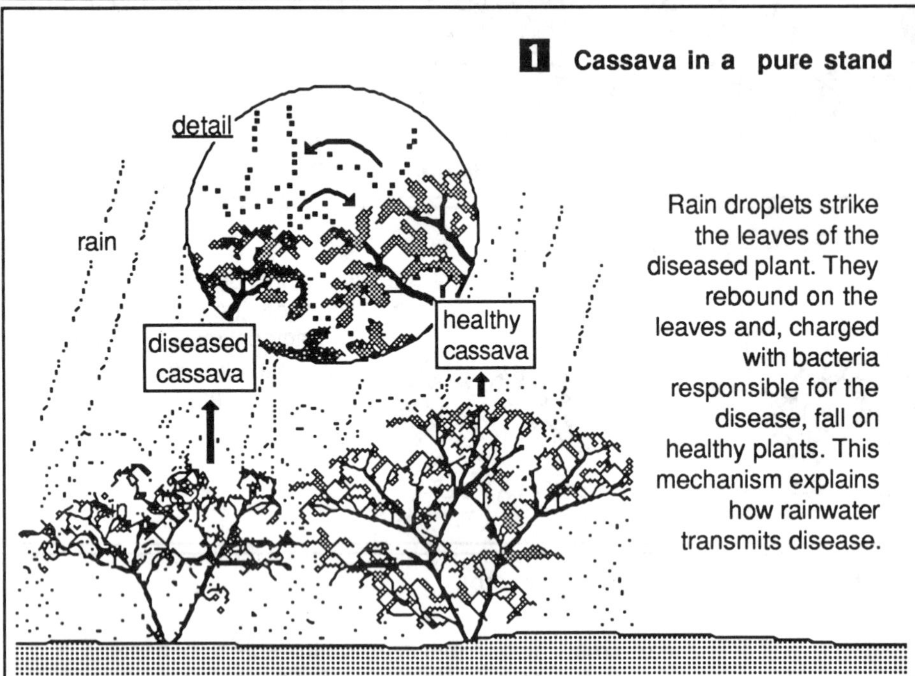

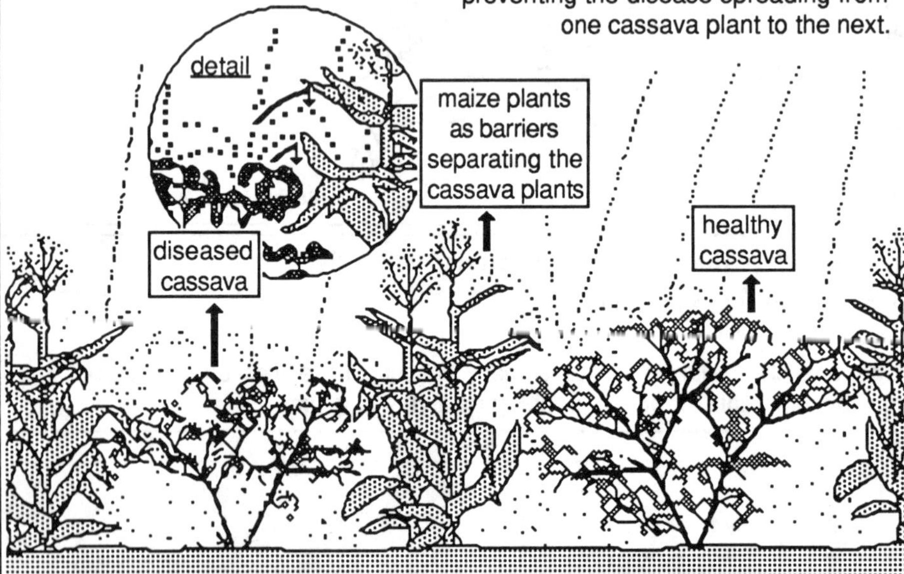

The bacteria of cassava wilt are capable of surviving in the soil. If the leaves of the mixed crop stop a certain number of bacteria from falling to the ground, the disease is prevented from being carried over into the following season.

The barrier effect arises precisely because **different plant species and families are not infected in the same way.**

Mixing different cultivated species is beneficial **for other reasons** too :

- Some of the intercropped species may harbour insects, spiders and small animals that prey on the pests of the other associated plants.

  For instance, infestation of maize by the hopper *Empoasca* **(figure 267)** is reduced when the crop is interplanted with bean. Ladybirds **(figure 333)**, find favorable living conditions in this intercrop mixture and are responsible for the reduction in the number of hoppers. There is nothing to stop the farmer from introducing ladybirds himself.

- Certain plants produce odours which repel pests and these plants can be grown in association with crops.

  Figure 285 shows how the diamond-back moth (*Plutella xylostella*) damages cabbage. However the pest is repelled by the smell of tomato and growing these between the cabbages will prevent the moth from landing.

  Experience shows that it is worthwhile cultivating aromatic plants like basil, citronella, lantana, Siam weed *(Eupatorium oderatum)*, marigolds (*Tagetes*) and tomato. Their smell wards off a number of injurious insects while other plants whose effects still need to be observed attract beneficial ones.

  Plants not only repel by smell. Some are able to emit **toxic substances** that poison pests.

Marigolds (*Tagetes*) are common garden flowers which discharge toxins through their roots. These affect nematodes *(Meloidogyne sp.)* on cabbage **(figure 287)**.

Crotalaria retusa is a seasonal herb belonging to the legume family **(figure 286)**. In Cameroun, the plant is believed to control scale insects on cassava with which it is often mixed.

284

285

Some spurge plants, such as *Euphorbia tirucalli* **(figure 337)**, apparently eject toxins into the soil. *Euphorbia tirucalli* is used in Rwanda to keep termites away from young trees. The species is also used as a quickset hedging plant round homes.

Careful mixing of cultivated or useful species in fields and gardens is a worthwhile practice. However, not **all cultural associations are beneficial**. Some may even encourage the spread of the pest to be eradicated. It is inadvisable, for instance, to mix marrow and potato because the marrow will encourage late blight of potato. Marrow keeps the soil very damp, thus creating ideal growth conditions for the fungus, *Phytophthora infestans*, which is the causal agent of late blight.

It is also unwise to mix plant species belonging to the same family because they are prone to attack by the same microorganisms. This means, for example, that it is inadvisable to mix potato and eggplant, cabbage and cauliflower, cucumber and courgettes **(table 288)**.

286

287

It is safer to mix species from different families, like tomato and pigeon pea, cabbage and onion, cucumber and maize.

This advice also holds for crop rotation. Plants from the same family should not be grown in succession.

Experience is the only sure guide to judicous crop associations. These must **weigh up local growing conditions including seasonal factors**. An association that is successful in a given district may be unsatisfactory elsewhere, and an association that turns out well at a particular time in the cropping season may be disappointing at other periods.

In any case, other control methods are always needed to complement intercropping.

288 Some vegetables and their families

Solanaceae

Tomato, potato, mock tomato, black nightshade,Solanum gilo Raddi, eggplant, bitter tomato, chillies.

Cucurbitaceae

Marrows and courgettes, cucumber and gherkin, bitter cucumber, gourd, pumpkin, citrullus and watermelon .

Zingiberaceae

Turmeric, ginger, grains of paradise, costus.

Leguminosae

Beans, Bambara groundnut, cowpea, pigeon pea.

Araceae

Taro, cocoyam.

Malvaceae

Okra, roselle, kenaf (Hibiscus cannabinus)

Cruciferae

White, red and green cabbage, African leaf cabbage, cauliflower, radishes and turnips, mustard greens.

Amaranthaceae

Amaranth, Celosia

Liliaceae

Onion, garlic and shallot, leek.

Gramineae

Sugar cane, maize, sorghum, millet.

Labiatae

Coleus, mint, basil

Plant density and pest control

Varieties which are susceptible to or, on the contrary, resistant to a disease can be found in the same plant species. Two varieties planted in a mixture may restrict the spread of disease in gardens and orchards. The resistant variety acts as a barrier preventing the spread of the disease from one host-plant to the next.

By mixing susceptible and resistant strains, the resistance of the variety is maintained. If, on the other hand, the resistant variety is grown in pure stand, the resistance may eventually break down because the pests, deprived of weaker plants on which to feed, will adapt to the strong variety and finally overcome its resistance.

Careful observation of pest life usually reveals the environmental factors that most affect pests, e.g. humidity, sunshine, wind, presence of other pests or plants. When you have a clear idea of the way a pest develops and of its preferences, you may be able to alter the habitat to the pest's detriment.

289 The effect of plant density on groundnut rosette virus

1 Groundnut close together

The aphids stay on the upper surface of the leaves.

2 Groundnut more widely spaced

The aphids pierce the underside of the leaves extensively.

The high humidity under densely planted groundnut does not suit *Aphis craccivora* ; the pest is attacked by pathogenic fungi. On the other hand, wider spacing means that the atmosphere under the plants is drier. The aphids multiply and inject large quantities of the virus into the underside of the leaves. Many plants contract the disease. Associated plants can also increase the humidity and be a hostil envionment for aphids.

Take the example of the aphid *Aphid craccivora* that transmits groundnut rosette virus. The pest attacks the underside of leaves but does not like deep shade. Thus, to reduce infestation a high planting density is good practice because it creates shade and humidity under the groundnut plants.

Conversely, for other pests, it may be worthwhile reducing seed density slightly, so that all plant parts are in full light **(figure 289)**.

290

291

Sources of infection

When a plant is diseased or infested, it acts as a reservoir which can transmit the agent, the disease or the pests. Pests are capable of travelling from plant to plant, or infection can be spread by wind and water, or by contact between plants, or carried by humans and animals.

Infection can take place in two ways :

- starting from the first diseased plant, **it spreads from plant to plant in the same season**,
- it spreads **from one season to the next when a reservoir of pests is allowed to survive in the field or garden.** This means inspecting the garden at regular intervals in order to prune, dig up or gather all diseased or infected plants or plant parts that might harbour insects, their larvae, fungal spores and other sources of infection.

During these cleaning-up operations you must take great care not to touch the healthy plant parts which you intend to keep. In this way, you avoid carrying infection from plant to plant.

Plants killed by disease or pests must be collected, because the infections they contain are capable of remaining alive in the soil for weeks or months, with subsequent transmission to seeds sown in the following seasons.

The collected waste - plant and plant parts chopped off, dug up or gathered - must be removed from the site and burnt. Adding them to compost, except in a hotbed, is not enough to guarantee the destruction of pests when these are insects still in the larval stage, or microorganisms able to survive in compost.

Figure 290 shows the damage done by the maize stalk-borer, larva of the moth *Busseola fusca* . The larva is not likely to survive the dry season unless it can take refuge in a maize stalk left standing in the field. Thus it is very important at harvest time to pull up all maize stalks particularly diseased ones.

The banana stem in **figure 291** was not cut back low enough. The stump left behind is a perfect habitat for weevils who are hiding there, until they can invade the replacement suckers. Proper inspection would have discovered this. As weevils appreciate the humid shelter provided by banana stumps, the stem should have been cut back to ground level; the removed part should then have been chopped up and the pieces split open to allow them to dry out. This practice reduces the number of places where weevils can shelter.

Figure 292 demonstrates why diseased, fallen fruits often have to be picked up. The example chosen is that of the Mediterranean fruit fly (*Ceratitis capitata*). It shows clearly why many insects remain in the garden from season to season.

Insects have different developmental stages which must be studied to discover at which stage they can best be destroyed. This may be as adults or larvae when stationary or migrating. Close observation of the life cycle of an insect is very important economically speaking because action can then be taken at exactly the right moment without wasting time or money.

292 The life cycle of the Mediterranean fruit fly and how to control the pest

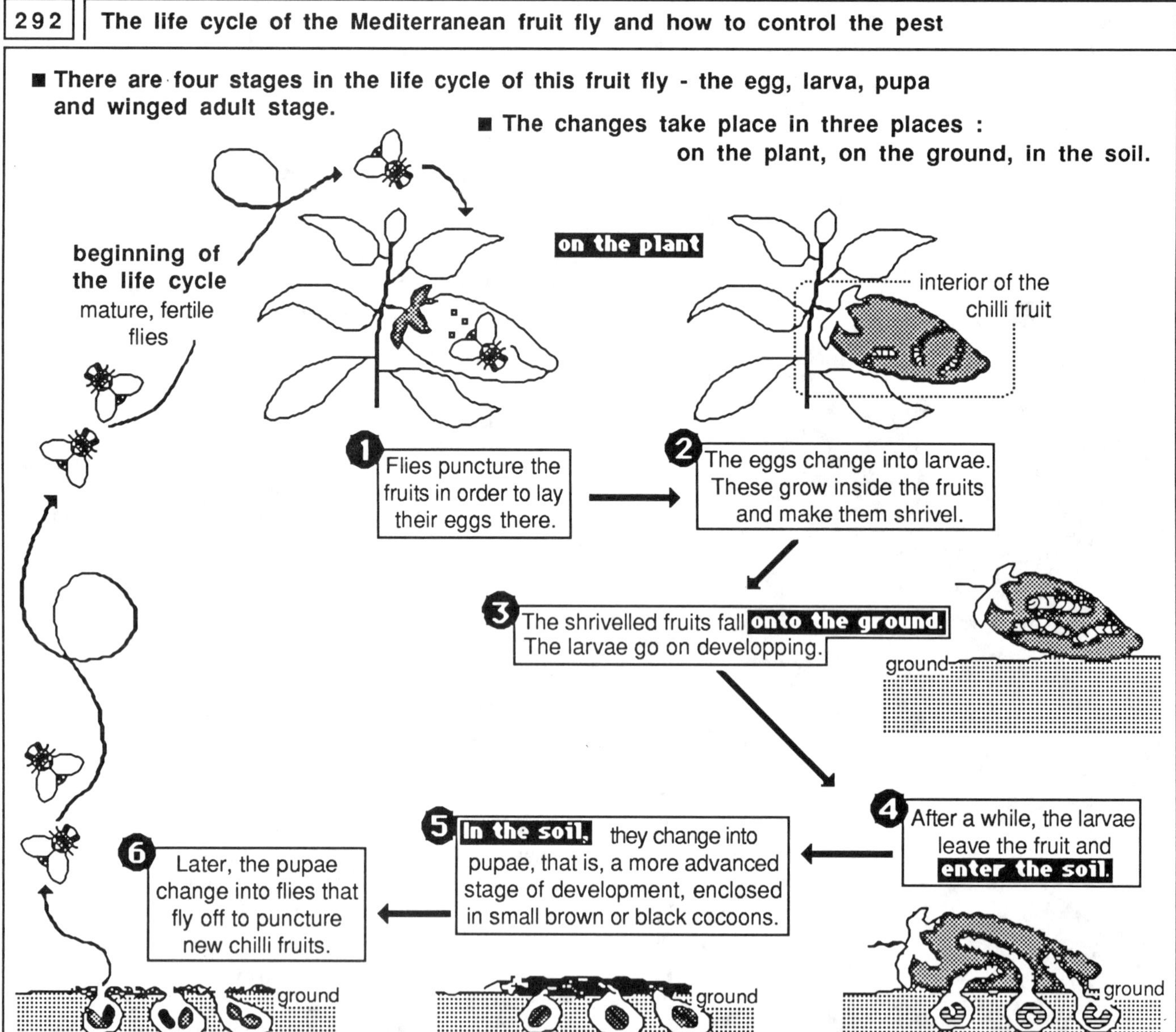

Pest control is most effective when applied **as soon as the shrivelled fruits fall off** and before the larvae disappear into the ground. Once the larvae have pupated, it is impossible to destroy them. It is also impossible to kill the winged flies except by repeated spraying with insecticides. This is costly and may not be very effective. Moreover, spraying kills all insects, good and bad, indiscriminately.

Let us suppose that a gardener has noticed the first fruit flies **(stage 6, figure 292)** and that he rushes out to spray the fruits with insecticide. The spray will cost him a lot of money whereas he could have asked his children to pick up the fallen fruits before the larvae had moved out to hide in the soil. In order to kill the fast-moving flies, the gardener will have to spray many times, because insecticide sprayed into the air one day has hardly any effect on flies that hatch out on the following days and, in any case, the spray cannot reach the pupae sealed up in their cocoons.

Pest control with no knowledge of life cycles is money thrown away

What happens to fruits can happen to entire plants especially in wet regions where infested plant shoots somehow manage to survive the dry season. These new shoots, from seeds shed at the end of rains, are a life-saving haven for pests that settle there and become active again with the next cropping season. Thus any new growth must be pulled up to get rid of hiding places for pests.

Cultural practices which limit the risk of infection

Avoid contact between cultivated plants and sources of infection

The sources of infection are found either in the diseased plants or in the soil.

Contact between healthy and diseased plants must always be avoided as was already explained in **figures 282 and 283**. If there is any risk of infection the plants must be pruned or pulled up quickly. This may even include diseased trees.

If you have to dig up a tree because the roots are suffering from root rot, remember that it is not enough to uproot the stump. You must **remove the diseased roots** right to the extremities using a pick or spade, and burn them. Otherwise, the source of infection remains in the soil and all the other trees are at risk.

The soil is a reservoir for pests and disease; it harbours fungi, bacteria, insects, slugs and small rodents. Many of these pests are not able to reach leaves, stems and fruits above ground level because they cannot climb up the stem.

When plants are staked, their aerial parts do not come into contact with the ground **(figure 293)**. If staking is not feasible, contact between fruits and soil can be avoided by spreading a layer of straw mulch. When it rains, water flows away through the straw, and in periods of drought, the straw dries up and the fruits do not touch the ground.

293 **Do not let fruits and leaves touch the ground.**

1 trailing plants

All the pests living on the ground have access to fruits and leaves.

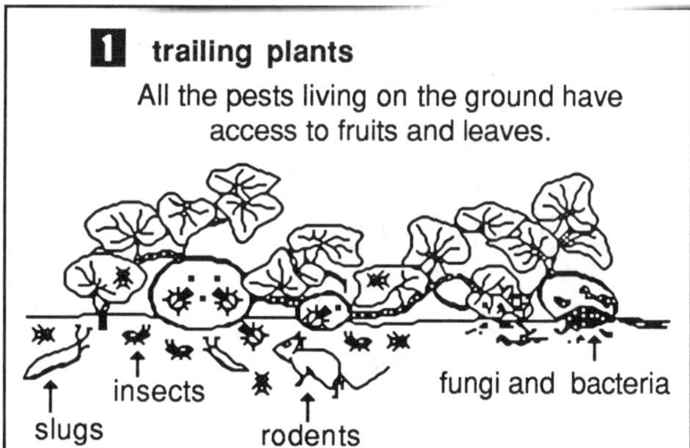

2 straw bedding under fruits

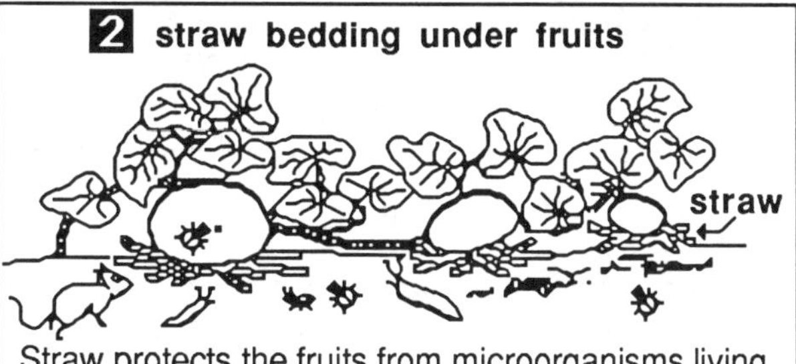

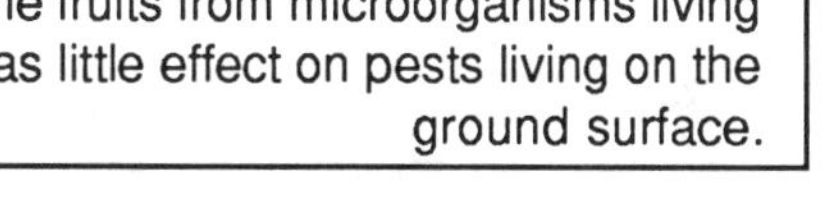

Straw protects the fruits from microorganisms living in the soil but has little effect on pests living on the ground surface.

3 staked plant

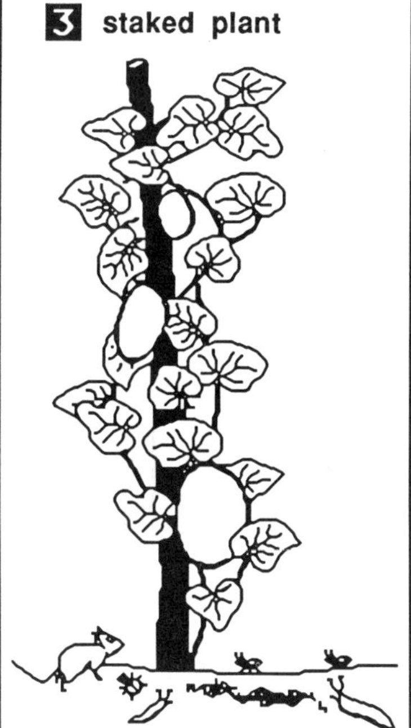

Pests that lives on and below the soil surface have no access to fruits and leaves.

294

Avoid practices and operations that transmit infection

- **Do not wound plants unnecessarily** by slashing them with knives and machetes, or by breaking off branches. Every wound is a gateway for pests. A canker developed on the soursop **(figure 294)** which was gashed by a machete. The tree may not die, but it will become less productive.
- **Clean or heat tools** used for pruning and cutting to avoid transmitting the spores of microorganisms clinging to the blades. This is particularly important for grafting and budding tools.
- **Handle healthy plants as little as possible**
- Some diseases caused by microorganisms are easily transmitted by contact. Fingers, clothes and tools can carry spores which are then deposited on healthy plants.

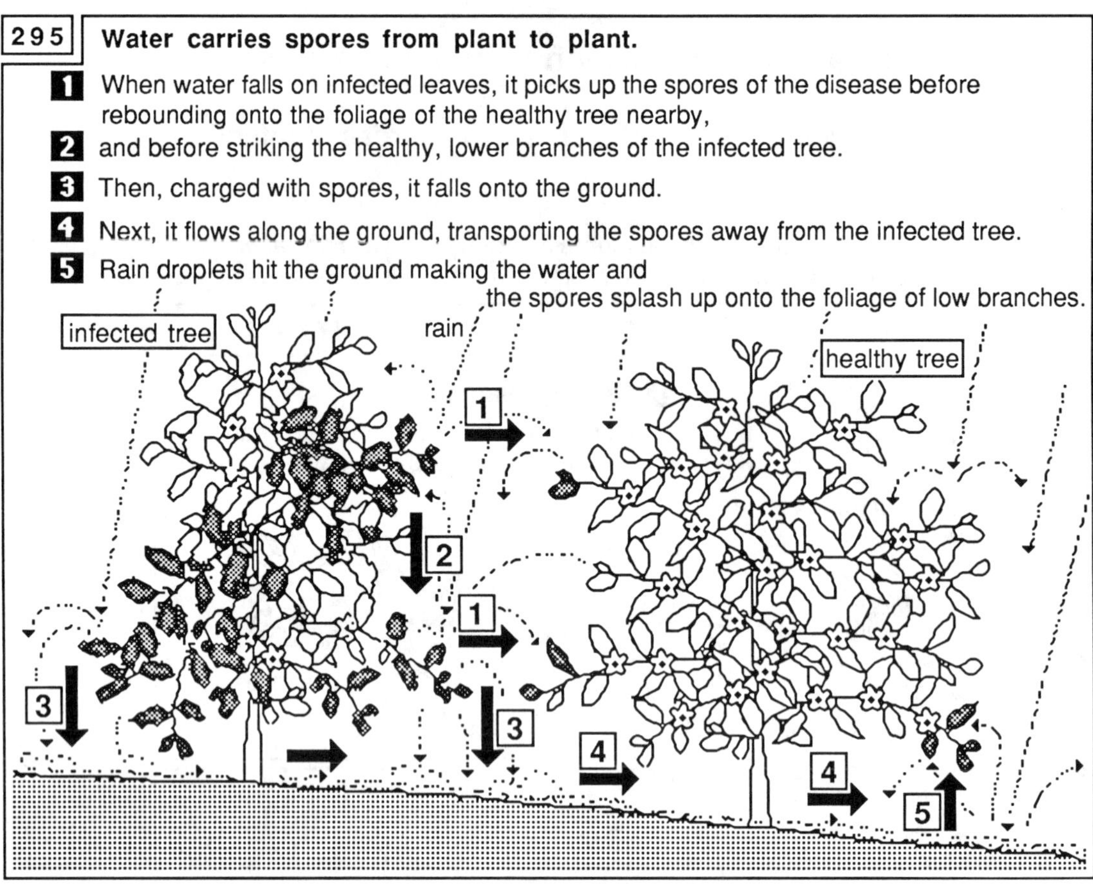

295 Water carries spores from plant to plant.

- **Beware of irrigation water**
- Water is an important factor in the transmission of disease in irrigated plants **(figure 295)**. Every effort must be made to **prevent water flow, runoff and splash from infected plant parts to healthy ones.**
- Use good soil cover to **avoid splash** (water hitting and bouncing off the ground); this is a most effective precaution. Also, try to irrigate at ground level rather than watering leaves from above.

Fire as a disinfectant

Fire destroys all life and is therefore a most efficient agent for pest control. Fire is used

- **to destroy** sources of infection when infected plant parts have been removed,
- **to disinfect tools,**
- **to heal** wounds.

Heating metal tools over a flame or plunging them briefly into boiling water eliminates most of the pathogens. But tools should not be overheated because the metal might be deformed.

Fire may sometimes be used as a healing agent. The canker in **figure 294** could be treated by applying a red-hot iron. You would have to remove the diseased parts with a knife and brand the wound with a red-hot iron in order to form a thin film of charcoal over the wound. The charcoal seals the cut and acts as a disinfectant barrier.

The rotation of cultivated plants

As well as helping to maintain soil fertility, crop rotation is an excellent way of controlling pests, especially those living in the soil.

Crop rotation is also practised to control the root-knot nematodes (*Meloïdogyne*) seen in **figure 236**. These microscopic worms often infest vegetable gardens and can cause considerable damage. However, they do not attack all vegetables so severely. Eggplant, tomato and cabbage are among their favourites and the worms cannot multiply without these vegetables. They are able to survive in the soil for several seasons before dying out for lack of food. **Table 296** is an example of rotation practised in Sahel regions in order to disinfect soil invaded by this pest.

If infestation is particularly bad, plants such as cotton, *Crotalaria* and marigolds (*Tagetes*) that are known to be harmful to nematodes can be introduced in pure stand or in mixture with resistant vegetables. Another possibility is to let the land rest during the driest season and to hoe it regularly so that the nematode cysts dry out and die.

Rotation is also used to eliminate *Pseudomonas*, the bacterium causing late potato blight **(figure 282)**. When a potato crop is sown year after year on the same patch, the bacterium multiplies so fast as to make potato cultivation impossible. On the other hand, when species resistant to *Pseudomonas,* for example, maize, then beans and peas, are planted, the bacterium has no food and dies out after a while.

Crop rotation is therefore a good way of **eradicating the spores and cysts of pests** which live in the soil and are not very mobile. Whatever pests are involved - microorganisms, specialised insects, nematodes or parasitic plants like striga - the rotation of cultivated plants and of cultural associations is always beneficial in the long run. This is particularly so when plants from different families are grown in succession **(table 288)** and when different types of plants are grown, for instance, leafy vegetables, fruits, roots, or tubers. The longer the rotation lasts, the more effective it is. The minimum rotation is three years.

296 **Crop rotation unfavorable to nematodes**

First season	
Eggplant *is grown in the bed.*	*Nematodes invade the eggplant and proliferate in the soil. Many cysts remain there after the harvest.*
Second season	
Cowpea, cat's whiskers *and* ***Jew's mallow*** *are cultivated in the bed.*	*The nematodes have no hosts on which to feed and some die.*
Third season	
Groundnut *is sown in the bed. This crop stimulates reproduction of the nematodes but does not nourish them.*	*Lured into activity by the groundnut but with no plants at their disposal, the nematodes die in large numbers.*
Fourth season	
Okra, onion, citrllus *and* ***sorghum*** *are sown in the bed.*	*The pest population is so severely reduced that a more susceptible plant such as tomato and potato can be grown again.*

Variations in sowing dates

Changing the planting time sometimes helps to confine pest outbreaks. For example, in regions where water melons tend to rot before ripening, late planting is sometimes advisable. Plants sown in the middle rather than at the start of the wet season make the most of the rains to develop stems and foliage. Their fruits enlarge and ripen at the beginning of the dry season when microorganisms causing fruit rot are less active and therefore cause less damage to crops.

In other cases, early planting may be necessary, for example, when aphid attacks are a hazard in crops such as beans, peas and groundnut, and particularly when drought periods break up the rainy season.

The population of these sucking insects builds up during the wet season and reaches a climax half-way through the rains, coinciding with flowering and fruit set (formation of fruitlets). When the aphids attack the fruit-bearing stems and branches, they cause fruit drop. But when plants are sown early the fruits are set before the build up of insect numbers.

Moving the planting season forwards or backwards is one of the weapons used in the fight against pests. Accurate timing calls for careful observation in order to determine the periods of pest activity. Here is another field where practical experience is an all-important factor.

Weeding and earthing up

Abundant weeds **(figure 297)** on cultivated land often encourage a rapid increase in pests.

- Weeds are **a refuge** for pests. Some plant pests find refuge in weeds or feed on them with the result that pests are harboured near cultivated crops;
- **Weeds make crop protection difficult**;
- **Weeds lower the resistance of cultivated species** by competing with them for food and light.

Weeding controls unwanted plants therefore promotes the health of cultivated plants. But controlling weeds does not mean getting rid of them altogether. Care must be taken not to leave bare earth which may lead to soil erosion.

297

Earthing up also helps to control pests especially when they attack the root-stem junction. Mounded earth protects this region. Another advantage is that some species when mounded, grow adventitious roots above the collar, thus strengthening the plants and making them less susceptible to damage by pests.

Banana weevils like to lay their eggs at the base of the stools. When the soil is earthed up, the weevils cannot reach the stumps, so that mounding is a way of inhibiting the spread of weevils in infested banana plantations **(figure 298)**.

298

The use of healthy seeds of good quality

Importance of choosing the right seeds

Successful cultivation depends to a great extent on how plants germinate and become established in seedbeds. Obviously, the quality and vigour of the seeds used is extremely important.

- **A seed contains** within itself most of the **characteristics** of the plant it will produce. These good and bad characters are inherited from its parents.
- **A seed can transmit diseases** especially viruses and bacteria. The parent plant may have passed these pathogens to the seed , or the seed itself may have been infected on the surface. In either case, the new plant will develop the infection.
- **The seeds may be attacked by pests** that either weaken the seedlings or prevent them from germinating **(figure 299)**. Seedlings show signs of poor growth when the **embryo** or **germ** is damaged, when the embryo's food reserves are inadequate, or when the seeds are attacked by a microorganism.
- **Vegetative parts** such as cuttings, shoots, scions and bulbs already contain the food reserves they need for growth (see Chapter 12).

299

If these stores are depleted, the new plant begins life with diminished vigour and suffers from lack of vitality.

For all these reasons, seeds and vegetative material need to be carefully checked before planting. Let us see how this is done, in practice, step by step.

300

Susceptibility and resistance to pests

Susceptibility and **resistance** to certain diseases or pests are among the qualities and faults attributed to plants. Different varieties of the same cultivated species can have different levels of susceptibility, and these differences can even be found in two plants of the same variety. The right choice of parent plants whose seeds are to be collected is an important measure in preventive pest control. Chapter 12 goes into the subject in detail.

In practice, you need to tie a piece of string to the plants that have proved the most pest-resistant during the growing season. These plants are the ones marked out for seed selection **(figure 300)**.

Diseased or pest-infested seeds

Many diseases caused by microorganisms (viruses, bacteria and fungi) are handed down, via the seeds, from the parent to the new plant. Sometimes the seed may show no signs of infection, yet the new plant quickly shows disease. This is why seeds must never be taken from plants that are obviously diseased. On the other hand, if a handful of healthy plants are found growing among a large number of diseased subjects, seeds should be taken from the vigorous strain.

This advice is all the more essential where vegetative material is concerned because it contains exactly the same characteristics as the parent plants, even to the pests living on them.

This careful attention to the parent plants of seeds is justified for **two major reasons :**

- **if the infected parent plant transmits the pest to its seeds, the daughter plant will also be diseased;**
- **carrying infected seeds from one place to another spreads the infestation.**

In some regions well-known for their banana production, the banana weevil causes extensive damage and severe loss in yield. Weevils rarely move outside the plantation where they occur. The pest is mainly spread by man himself because the suckers used for vegetative propagation are not thoroughly inspected. Checking and disinfecting every sucker one by one are basic steps to prevent the spread of this pest which causes considerable damage.

Bean anthracnose caused by the fungus *Colletotrichum* **(figure 241)** was mentioned earlier. There are two valid reasons why seeds from a diseased plant must not be used. First of all, the seeds themselves may contain the fungus that remains invisible. Secondly, handling can spread the fungus spores. These adhere to the seed coat and multiply on the seedlings.

Here are other examples where disregard for seed health and hygiene leads to the spread of pests.

Bacterial potato wilt increases season by season if diseased seed potatoes or pieces of tubers are removed from diseased plants, or even from nearby plants showing no symptoms of the disease. The bacterium causing this disease spreads within a radius of a metre or more from the infected plant, and may therefore have contaminated the tubers of nearby plants even if these seemed perfectly sound when harvested. The use of contaminated seed potatoes means that the disease is passed on to the next generation. This is why potatoes coming from infected patches must on no account be used for planting again.

Cassava mosaic **(figure 245)** is a viral disease mainly propagated by using stem cuttings from diseased plants. The best way of eradicating the infection is to choose cuttings every season from plants that show no trace of stunting or leaf discolouration. In order to avoid mosaic and other diseases, healthy parent plants must be selected every time new cuttings are needed.

301

Some seeds are labelled **uncertified** meaning that their exact origin is unknown. This is often true of seeds sold by traders or in urban markets as opposed to reputable firms and official seed stations. Introducing uncertified seeds into farms and gardens is always a risk because the purchaser has no guarantee that they are healthy. Uncertified seeds coming from other parts of the country or imported from abroad should first be tested to see that they are not contaminated and that there is no danger of introducing new pests onto the farm.

Cocoyam root rot caused by the fungus *Pythium* has spread quickly through farmlands in Cameroun because farmers exchange seeds without checking to make sure they are free from disease.

To prevent the risk of introducing uncertified seeds, some governments control importation, and uncertified seeds are refused entry. In certain cases, seeds are tested to see if they are clean. They are put **into quarantine**, that is, they are sown on quarantine farms away from cropping fields to make sure that no new disease appears during cultivation. Infested batches are destroyed.

Quarantine control would have been particularly useful for the mite, *Mononychellus tanajoa*, that attacked the cassava leaves in **figure 301**. The symptoms of infestation are similar to those of mosaic disease. This very dangerous mite was introduced into Uganda some years ago by a traveller from South America. When the cuttings were planted, the mites multiplied and spread. Now this pest is gradually spreading all over Africa and causing considerable damage.

Grading seeds

When seedlings are grown from damaged seeds like those in **figure 299**, they may not find enough stored food and, in common with all stunted plants, are an easy prey for pests. This is the reason for :

- **discarding,** without exception, **all stained, chewed, soft, discoloured seeds** from the batch to be sown;
- **selecting the most wholesome-looking seeds.**

In Central Africa, many varieties of bean are intercropped in the same field. Seed mixtures are justified because each variety reacts differently to pests. One variety is susceptible to anthracnose, the others, far less. Another variety is prone to downy mildew but withstands anthracnose. Aphids may multiply more on one variety than on another.

The woman in **figure 302** is sorting bean seeds in order to prepare a mixture for sowing. Because the woman knows every one of her fields and the diseases likely to occur there, she also knows the mixtures that suit each one best. She is demonstrating that there are **varietal mixtures resistant or tolerant** to the range of pests living on her land. If one variety in the mixture is attacked by a specialized pest, the other varieties go on developing and the whole harvest is not at risk.

If you have to buy uncertified seeds and cannot test them in quarantine, you must sort and disinfect them before mixing them for sowing. It is advisable to buy a small quantity of seed over and above what is needed for sowing so that there is enough to discard the inferior seeds. Then a small sum of money should be set aside to buy a fungicide and an insecticide to treat the grain seed.

Controlled, improved or selected seeds whose health and resistance to disease is obviously better than those of **uncertified batches** can be obtained from official bodies and specialized firms.

302

Selected or improved seeds are definitely worth using when growth conditions are fully under control, but they are rarely suitable for mixtures.

Seed treatment

Disinfecting seeds is fairly effective and inexpensive for insects and fungi. Disinfecting is not much used against bacteria and is completely ineffectual for viral diseases.

Grain and vegetative material which may be infected is treated by soaking or dusting.

Soaking cuttings in a special insecticide kills any larvae and insects in the propagating material. This treatment is effective, for instance, against banana weevils, scale insects on pineapple suckers and all other kinds of larvae and insects. Do not soak for more than a few minutes and make sure that the insecticide actually reaches the pest especially if it is lodged in holes or channels. Grain seeds must not be soaked too long, otherwise they swell up with water. After mixing with an insecticide or a fungicide, seeds must be dried.

303 Seed protection

- **Fungicides for protecting seed grain**

  Thiram, Demosan, Thioran, Thirasan

- **Insecticides for disinfecting seed grain and vegetative material**

  B.H.C., Dieldrex, Lindamul, DDT, Gammalin, Dedemul, Endosulfan, Zeidane, Thimul, Didimac, Thiodan, Pirimiphos, Dieldrine, Pirimicid.

Some of the names on the list denote an active substance, others are brand names.

They are powders for dusting or for mixing in water.

All these products are toxic for human beings and for animals. The World Health Organization has come out against their use and they are banned in some countries. Nonetheless, firms with little regard for the health of farmers and consumers, go on selling these pesticides in Africa without stating the precautions to be taken in those countries where regulations on toxic substances are inadequate.

Dusting consists in mixing the seeds with a powdery substance.

Disinfecting seeds before sowing must not be confused with disinfecting grains stored for consumption. The aims and treatment are different in both cases. Products used for seed grain are intended to **protect future seedlings** as well as dormant seeds. Grains for consumption are treated to prevent degradation of the produce itself for the duration of storage while avoiding any health risks to the consumer.

Table 303 gives a list of common products used for disinfecting seeds. Most of these products are **highly toxic for humans and animals**. They must be handled with the greatest caution and **never be used on grains destined for consumption**.

Cultivating resistant varieties

For every species and variety of cultivated plant, there are certain pests which are more harmful than others because of the amount of damage they cause. Pest **incidence** is said to be high or low depending on the degree of devastation.

When pest incidence is high year after year on a cultivated species, it may be worthwhile looking for **resistant varieties** of the same species that withstand the attacks of the pest in question.

There are, to be exact, two types of resistance: **mechanical** and **chemical.** These resistant traits are written into the genes transmitted from one plant generation to the next. (A **gene** is a unit of inherited material in the living cell).

Generally speaking, varietal resistance is related to a specific pest. Occasionally, when resistance is mechanical, it asserts itself with regard to a particular type of insect, for example, piercing insects of a particular size, small midges, butterflies with a wing span of more than two centimetres.

304

Mechanical resistance to pests

Figure 304 shows a variety of okra found in Burkina Faso. Its leaves are covered with long hairs that discourage aphids from feeding.

We can say therefore that the form and structure of the okra, its morphology, make it more resistant to insect attack.

Some varieties of millet and sorghum are known for their bristly spikelets that stop birds from eating the grains. Or again, thorns on certain trees and shrubs are most effective in preventing browsing animals from eating them. The fact that a variety is erect rather than creeping makes it less accessible to ground-level pests.

Glandular hairs produce sticky secretions which are sometimes noticeable on leaves and flowers. Tiny insects that come in contact with the secretions will stick to them.

Chemical resistance to pests

Chemical resistance in plants is due to the presence or absence of particular substances in the plant tissues. Among these chemical substances, some are pest-attractive, others are unattractive or toxic.

Chemical resistance in plants can be explained in many ways :

- Plants of the resistant variety do not contain some substances essential to the pest and are therefore unattractive;
- They contain a substance that disturbs or harms the pest, and consequently prevents attack;
- Sometimes, they produce substances specially designed to act as an alarm signal and repel the pest.

Most plant substances are produced in minute quantities. However some plants produce resins when damaged, and some react by abnormal growth of plant tissue forming galls **(figures 251, 252 and 253)**.

The point to remember is that **some plant varieties are better equipped than others to prevent or withstand attack by pests.** When pest damage becomes significant, it is advisable to look for resistant varieties or species.

Choice of cultivated varieties in relation to pests of economic importance

A cultivated plant is sometimes invaded, season after season, by the same pest. The first thing to do in this case is to look for immune, resistant or tolerant varieties.

- **Varieties are immune** when a pest has little or no effect on them.
- **Varieties are resistant** when they are able to withstand the pest by one of the mechanical or chemical means described above. Pests are present but do not cause significant damage.
- **Susceptible varieties,** on the other hand, are seriously damaged by the pest.
- **Tolerant varieties** are able to adjust to the pest or repair the injury, without undue loss of yield.

Immunity, resistance, susceptibility and tolerance are varietal characteristics usually shown towards specific pests and may depend on environmental variables such as climate or soil type. A variety may be immune or resistant in one region and susceptible in another.

Varietal characteristics including resistance is inherited. Plants propagated by vegetative reproduction, e.g. cuttings, will be identical to the parent. Plants grown from seed will show variability. Plant resistance is not permanent and the pest may adapt to the defenses.

The only way of discovering resistant varieties is to meticulously observe plants when attacked by pests.

Take, for example, the badly diseased bean crop suffering from anthracnose in **figure 241**. If you spot a few healthy or only slightly infected plants, these are the ones whose seeds should be used for the coming season. By selecting seed in this way for many successive seasons, you are almost sure of obtaining seeds more resistant to anthracnose. This strategy is called **mass selection.** But remember that not all plants free of anthracnose are necessarily resistant. Perhaps they merely escaped infestation during the growing season. Mistakes are easily made in this way.

Take maize as an example, **figure 307** shows how to make a mass selection of seeds resistant to streak. The symptoms of this viral disease are yellow and white streaks along the full length of the leaves alternating with lines of green. The virus responsible for the disease is transmitted by hoppers **(figure 267)** that pierce the young leaves. The streaks only appear on leaves growing after injection of the virus. The other leaves seem normal.

Another method of mass selection against streak is to remove the male spikelets from diseased plants, so that the pollen of plants susceptible to the virus does not fertilize the ovules of less susceptible plants.

Mass selection systems are not always as simple as in the case of viral maize streak and are more complicated when the pest is a fungus. However, it always pays to try mass selection before testing other, more expensive methods, or to try mass selection and other methods together.

Selection systems that can be carried out on farms are also undertaken by researchers at seed stations and are combined with methods of varietal improvement called **genetic selection or breeding for resistance.** Such methods are very complex and are beyond the scope of this book. In brief, the term **selected, improved seeds** should only apply to seeds that have been studied and **tested in the real growth conditions of small holdings**. Unfortunately, this is not always the case and it is not unusual for suppliers to sell so-called improved seeds that have never been tested on farms.

307 Mass selection of maize seeds resistant to streak disease

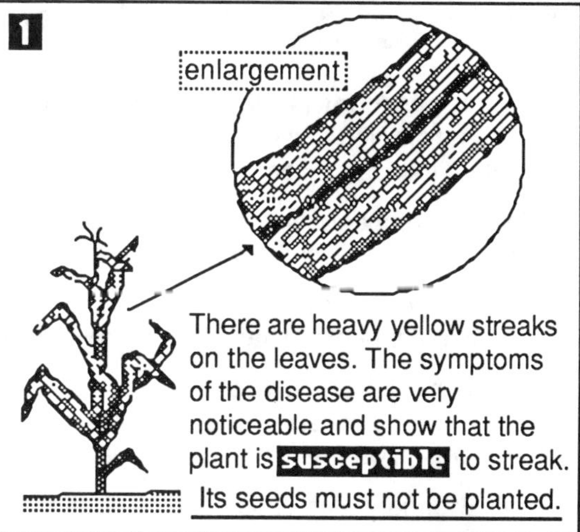

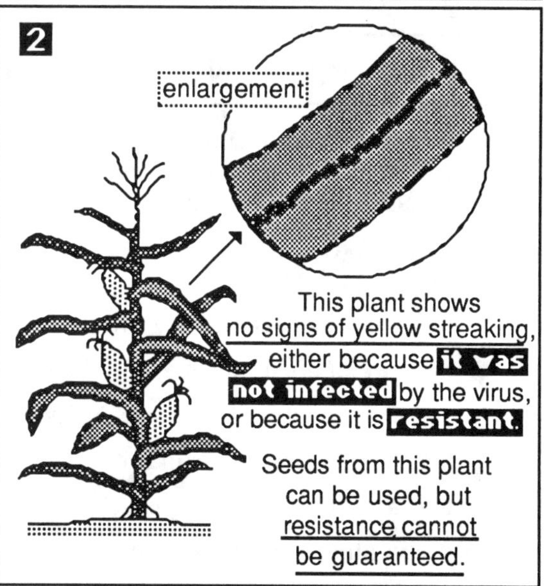

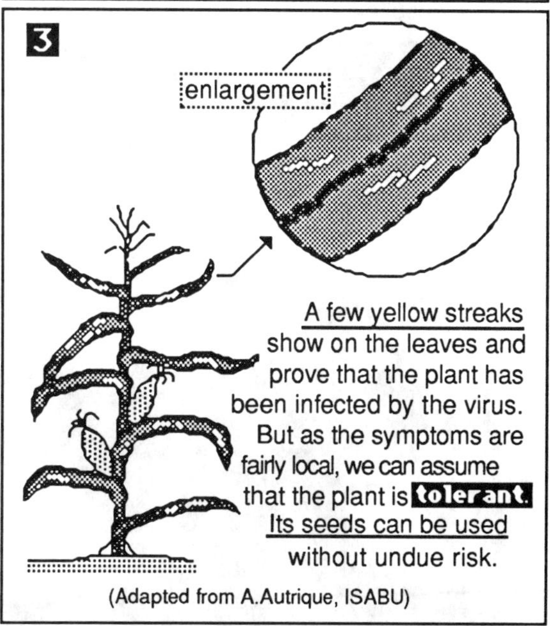

(Adapted from A.Autrique, ISABU)

Chapter 9

Natural methods of pest control

The aim of **preventive pest control** is to create unfavorable conditions for crop pests. **Direct control** attacks the pests themselves in order to kill them by poisoning, by using insecticides, by trapping, or by exposing them to attack by predators (biological control).

The poisons used for direct control are obtained either from **natural substances** such as plant extracts, urine, minerals and oils, or **artificial substances** manufactured by chemical industries.

Whatever is used, the aim of control is to reduce pest infestation to **an acceptable level**, for we cannot escape the fact that pests take some of the harvest, but their share should be as small as possible.

In some countries where agriculture relies heavily on chemical industries, farmers aim at eradicating all crop pests. Unfortunately, killing all pests may lead to a chain-reaction of destruction of all life ! - of insects, worms, birds, fungi and rodents. Even man himself can be poisoned in the process (see pages 162 and 163).

This chapter deals with natural methods of pest control, i.e. those based on the use of products found in nature.

Natural products used for pest control

On farmlands, nature supplies a fair number of vegetable, mineral and animal products that have useful properties for crop protection. Often neglected in favour of commercial products, these natural substances possess **certain useful qualities** :

- as a general rule, they are quite **specific and cause little disturbance to the natural balance** between living organisms,
- they are **cheap**, particularly when produced by the farmer from local resources,
- **they are often, or always, harmless to humans and animals.** They are rarely toxic to plants.

Compared with artificial pesticides, natural products have **certain drawbacks** :

- they tend to deter rather than eradicate pests,
- they are more effective against insects as opposed to fungal diseases,i.e. caused by microorganisms,
- **preparation often takes a lot of time** and calls for a certain amount of skill.

Yet, despite their disadvantages, these products deserve careful attention.

308

Quite a number of natural products are used in rural settlements and can be divided into three categories depending on their origin - mineral, vegetable or animal.

Natural products of mineral origin

Fine ashes are often used as a disinfectant or as an insect repellent and are sprinkled onto leaves or on the ground. **Figure 308** shows how ashes were used on cucurbit leaves in order to repel a chewing insect. The ashes should be carefully applied because handfuls of dust spread unevenly on foliage may burn the leaves or the buds.

Ashes are preventive, and their effectiveness depends to a great extent on their fine texture. It is advisable to dry them and pound them before application. They also improve soil fertility thus contributing to crop vigour.

309

In Central Africa, finely crushed **laterite** is often mixed with stored grains, and provides lasting and remarkably effective protection. **Figure 309** shows two lots of bean seeds that were stored in well-sealed earthen jars for many months. Only the batch on the right was mixed with laterite. After six months in store, the untreated batch contained many seeds punctured by beetles (*Zabrotes* and *Acanthoscelides*), whereas the batch dusted with laterite was virtually intact.

Researchers compared the effectiveness of laterite with that of Actellic, a pesticide commonly used for protecting grains in storage. Three series of six batches of bean seeds were stocked in identical baskets for periods from one to six months. The first series was not treated, the second was mixed with the pesticide Actellic, and the third with finely crushed laterite. Every month, each batch was examined and the number of beans punctured by beetles was counted. **Table 310** gives the results of the experiment. Actellic worked well for five months after which its effect began to wear off.

The crushed laterite was most effective because it kept beetle damage to less than 7 seeds per 1,000. The mechanism by which laterite protects seeds is not fully understood. The laterite probably acts as an abrasive which drives the pests away.

The effectiveness of laterite in protecting leaves has not yet been tested. It seems that farmers in many African countries manage to control aphids and other piercing insects by dusting laterite on foliage. Unfortunately, laterite in dust form is rapidly washed away by the rains, so that its protective powers are short-lived in the rainy season.

310 **Experiments to protect bean seeds from beetle infestation ***

The figures refer to the number of damaged seeds out of the thousand seeds in each batch. There were a total of eighteen batches divided into three series of six. Eachseries of six batches was treated differently and, in each series, the batches were stored for periods varying from 1 to 6 months as indicated.

duration of storage	**Ist series,** batch untreated (figure 309, left side)	**2nd series,** batch treated with Actellic	**3rd series** batch treated with laterite (figure 309 right side)
1 month	7	4	less than 7
2 months	144	6	less than 7
3 months	523	8	less than 7
4 month	746	11	less than 7
5 months	817	12	less than 7
6 months	767	76	less than 7

Kaolin and other rock dusts are sometimes applied like laterite with unreliable results in the field but more positive effects in granaries.

Fuel oil and **kerosene** are also used to control pests but because they are phytotoxic (toxic to plants), direct application is ruled out. These substances are used when the insects to be destroyed are massed together, for instance, nests of leaf-curling ants or termites. The nests hanging from branches are dipped in kerosene, petrol or fuel oil for a few seconds so that the ants are completely coated in the liquid.

Good control of slugs in nurseries may be achieved by spreading **quick or unslaked lime** on the ground. Lime is also used to paint the trunks of fruit trees in order to kill the larvae or the eggs of insects.

Natural products of vegetable origin

Both cultivated and wild plants supply a number of effective anti-pest products.

- The juice of tobacco stems and leaves contains the insecticide, **nicotine**. This is a remarkable poison against aphids. Because nicotine acts by contact, it must actually touch the bodies of the target insects.

* In a study published by P. LYAMUGEMA, *Tests d'efficacité et de rémanence de trois formulations de Pyrimiphos-méthyl et de la latérite contre les ravageurs du haricot et du maïs entreposés*, (ISABU, Burundi, 1984).

311

Tobacco plants also repel certain pests. Farmers in Burkina Faso and Burundi have noticed that maize is less susceptible to attacks by borers when it is intercropped with tobacco **(figure 311)**.

- The herb **hyptis** (*Hyptis spicigera*, **figure 312)** is very common in Africa and usually grows wild. It is a seasonal herb of medium height (50 centimetres to 1 metre) and, like basil, belongs to the same family *Labiatae*. It is distinguished by its pungent smell and its minute white flowers 1 or 2 millimetres in size. Like other *Labiatae*, its stem is quadrangular, that is, it has four sides.

  This herb is often used in granaries to protect food stores from weevils and other beetles. It is spread in layers between stored grains and pulses. Farmers tend not to pull the herb when weeding because they believe it helps to control chewing and piercing insects that may be deterred by its strong smell.

  It is quite likely that the sap of this plant contains insecticidal substances. The juice could be tested in infusions and decoctions, see page 151.

- **Tevetia** nuts (*Thevetia neriifolia*) are used to make a **rodenticide,** i.e. a product that kills rodents. The plant is illustrated in **figure 326**.

- Some plants are said to be effective because of the smoke they release when burnt. Senufu people in Senegal burn branches of **Guiera** (*Guiera senegalensis*), a bush often found in dry savanna, in order to drive away locusts, ants or winged insects likely to attack gardens **(figures 313 and 314)**. Fires are lighted between the vegetable patches at the time of the day when the insects are most active. In Rwanda and Burundi, certain kinds of **Coleus** (*Coleus amboinicus*, *umuravumba* in Rwandan) is used in much the same way. The species is also popular as a hedging plant.

- **Vegetable oil** can be used against harmful insects. The oil mixed with water forms a frothy solution called an **emulsion**. When insects, which breathe through pores (spiracles) in their cuticle, are covered in the emulsion, they suffocate. **Fatty soaps** made from vegetable oil act in the same way. They are effective in varying degrees against aphids and other fairly stationary insects such as caterpillars and larvae.

312

Table 315 gives a list of some plant species extracts which are reputed for their deterrent effects on pests.

Even if they do not kill pests, the juice of many plants or their extracts can help to **drive away or to discourage pests**.

313

Neem leaves and flowers and many species of basil are supposed to drive away pests. The plant juices are sprinkled on the leaves of the species to be protected, so that the pests no longer recognize the cultivated plants on which they usually feed. Other strong-smelling plants are also worth testing in this way.

Some agricultural byproducts may also prove effective. For example, the water in which shea butter is washed during extraction is a powerful insect repellent and is used to control termites.

Our knowledge of the plants used in direct pest control and the best way of exploiting them is still very limited. Growers who are keen on diversifying pest control can do so by looking for useful plants on their farms and then testing them out. They could set about the task as follows :

- In fields and the surrounding countryside, look for and collect plants whose smell, taste or any other characteristic might be an asset in pest control Plant extracts are then obtained by **macerating, infusing** or **decocting** the plants, as described below. Next, the resulting liquid is sprayed on the plants to be protected and its effects ascertained;

314

315 **Some plant insecticides** (This list is far from complete)

Names of species	Extracts obtained and plant parts used
Derris spp., Lonchocarpus (cube)	*Two species are used in laboratories to produce the insecticide, rotenone. An insecticide powder is prepared from the dried roots.*
Lantana spp., Eucalyptus spp., Tephrosia spp., tobacco	*Insecticides are extracted from the leaves and seeds.*
Pyrethrum	*An insecticide is obtained from the inflorescences, pyrethrin is extracted from the flowers on an industrial scale.*
Citronella and basil	*Their leaves, either fresh or dried, are crushed to a powder, and used to repel insects.*
Entada africana, Psorospernum febrifugum	*Insecticides are extracted from the bark.*
Cashew	*An insecticide is extracted from the nut shells, and an insect repellent from the gum exhuded by the trunk.*
Neem	*Its leaves, flowers and fruits are insect repellent. Insecticides are sometimes obtained from the plant.*
Combretum micranthum, Hyptis spicigera and *Hyptis suaveolens*	*The leafy branches repel insects. They are used in granaries in layers between the grains (Hyptis) or in the form of matting woven to cover the inside walls (Combretum).*
Euphorbia balsamifera	*The leaves and latex are insecticides.*
Wild custard apple *(Annona senegalense)*	*An insecticide is obtained from the macerated bark.*
Sweetsop	*An insecticide is obtained by macerating the fresh seeds.*

- When dealing with bacterial and fungal diseases, it is worth trying all the plant substances used as disinfectants by medicine men and healers. Village elders who often know a great deal about plants might be consulted to advantage.

Growers who dislike being overdependent on chemical pesticides that often cost a lot of money, would benefit from testing the effectiveness of toxic plants - those used for hunting, for example, arrow and bait poisons, those used for fishing, e.g. substances that daze fish, and finally those used for human and animal health, especially plants used as disinfectants or as remedies for worm infestation.

Great care must be taken with poisonous substances particularly on food plants. People who appreciate the value of exploring pest control in this direction and put effort into it should be backed by intense agricultural research programmes.

How to prepare plant extracts for spraying

If you want to use plants for pest control, there are many ways of extracting the toxins and making it suitable for spraying, for instance :

- **The fresh juice is extracted** by pressing the plants vigorously and then diluting the liquid in small quantities of clean water;
- **The leaves, flowers, stems and fruits are macerated** for a comparatively long time - from a few hours to a few days. Macerat-

ing means prolonged steeping in cold water. You can help release the plant juices into the water by chopping up the plant or pounding it beforehand. Extracts left to macerate for several days often start fermenting, a process that reinforces their toxic effects;

- **Infusions** are another way of extracting active plant substances. Water is brought to the boil and then removed from the fire; the plant parts are immersed in the water and left to stand like tea and herbal infusions. The infusion is allowed to get cold before use;

Decoctions are made by throwing plant parts into boiling water and leaving them to boil for several minutes.

316

In order to make the extracts pest-effective, water and plants must be added in proportions that are different for every preparation. Since the active substance must not be overdiluted, you will have to proceed by trial and error so as to obtain the most efficient mixture.

After extraction, the liquid is filtered through a clean cloth to get rid of solid impurities such as plant waste and fibres. It is then ready for use - for painting on plant parts, for watering or for spraying **(figure 316)**.

A small quantity of fatty soap or starch (cassava or millet flour) can be added to the mixture to make it adhere more easily to the vegetation treated and to the bodies of undesirable insects.

Animal substances

There are two types of animal substances used for pest control. They are

- **solid manures and droppings,**
- liquid **slurry and urine.**

Excrements are known for their fertilizing properties. They are active agents in combatting deficiency diseases and, generally speaking, make plants more vigorous and increase their resistance to fungal and bacterial infections.

Like solid manures, urine contributes to soil fertility (see Chapter 4).

In some parts of the world, urine is collected and stored in containers or in pits dug for that purpose. Storing urine with exposure to light - in bottles, in demijohns or in open pits - seems to give better results than storage in the dark. After two weeks, the urine is ready to be diluted in water and sprayed in gardens to combat insects preying on vegetables - on beans, cucurbits, tomatoes and okra, for example. Some people maintain that urine also helps control certain types of mites, and keeps down thrips, vectors of viral diseases. Before spraying, the urine must be diluted six times, that is, 1 dose of urine to 6 doses of water; the solution is then tested to make sure that it does not scald foliage. If it does, a little more water is added. Spraying is carried out when insects are vulnerable and preferably on a warm day.

317

Diluted urine can be mixed with extracts from plants known for their insecticidal powers, for example, turmeric juice, neem and tobacco leaves. The plant solution is filtered through a clean cloth just before it is poured into the sprayer.

Apart from the harmful effects it can have on pests, urine has a positive, if indirect, influence on plant health due to its nitrogen content.

A farmer with stabled cattle should consider building a urine pit. At night, the cattle are left on gently sloping flagstones so that the urine flows down into the pit while solid dung remains where it falls. Simpler still, urine can be collected in drums, cans and demijohns. Finally, **vegetables sprayed with urine must be thoroughly washed; this is particularly important if they are to be eaten raw.**

Mechanical methods of pest control

318

Fencing : live and dead hedging

When domestic animals - cattle, goats, sheep, pigs and poultry - are left untended, they can cause an enormous amount of damage in fields and gardens. The situation is so bad in some regions that wandering cattle destroy every attempt to start gardens. Cattle cause arguments between growers and stock owners because herds are allowed to stray.

Negociation between farmers and cattle owners is the first step towards settling clashes of this kind. Rules must be drawn up to prevent encroachment by cattle while at the same time making provision for enough grazing.

After that, the most effective measure is to put up fencing or make enclosures. Either the cultivated plot is enclosed, or the animals are fenced in.

Figures 317 to 320 illustrate four different types of enclosures, each one adapted to particular circumstances. They include live or quickset hedges so called because they are made of live poles or cuttings, and dead hedges made of dead wood.

320

319

Closely-planted *Dracaena* cuttings were used to make the quickset hedge in **figure 317**. Species suitable for live hedging can be found in every region. Live hedges have an advantage over dead wood; they last longer if they are looked after regularly and if cattle do not eat the species chosen. Live hedges can also be productive and supply fruit, forage, wood and vegetable compost. Sometimes they need to be strengthened with horizontal laths or with wire as in **figures 317 and 318**.

Two types of dead-wood fencing are shown in **Figures 318 and 320**. The first example, very common in West Cameroun, is made of raffia palm or bamboo. The second, typical of Sudan and

321

322

Sahel, is made of thorn branches placed side by side and criss-crossed.

The drawback with fences made from dead wood is that they are attacked by termites and have to be renewed frequently.

There is a major drawback to thorn-tree fencing in those parts of Africa where trees and shrubs are disappearing; it hastens the destruction of trees at the very time when a cover of trees and forage shrubs should be restored to these lands.

When wood is scarce, wire fencing is suitable but it is fairly expensive. The meshes must be adapted to the kinds of animals to be enclosed or to be kept out **(figure 319)**. Sometimes, wire mesh is available locally.

Where possible, it is worth establishing hedges and enclosures with a two-fold aim in mind : keep cattle out of cropping fields and give them forage plants. For example, the lower storey of the hedge can be made of thorn bushes that stop the cattle from getting in, and the upper stories can produce foliage. In a similar way live hedging made of trees and shrubs can be used to support wire or a wire-mesh fencing.

Another solution is to build stone or dried-brick walls. Much hard work is needed but the result usually lasts longer. They are useful for enclosures and pens for small animals.

Enclosures are also a way of keeping wild animals away from plants or out of gardens.

Palm midribs were used to make the small nursery enclosure designed to keep out small rodents **(figure 321)**.The smooth side of the stakes was turned to the outside so that the rodents cannot climb up.

The young palm in **figure 322** is protected from rodents by a sheet of corrugated iron. Wire netting serves the same purpose.

A large cylinder of plastic sheeting is used to keep insects away from the banana bunches in **figure 323**.

323

324

Scarecrows

Scarecrows sometimes manage to scare away birds and monkeys who are frightened by what seems threatening **(figure 324)**. The most efficient scarecrows are those looking more or less like a person; parts of the figure flash in the sun, or move and make a noise when the weather is windy.

At certain times of the year, scarecrows can be placed in the fields and manipulated regularly by a watchman. For example, when an onslaught of *Quelea quelea* birds is expected, a string can be stretched between two trees and noisy objects tied to it in pairs, for example, empty cans, scraps of iron, old metal lids. The string is jerked systematically to make a noise and scare away the invaders, whether they be birds, monkeys, or small rodents. Scarecrows are installed when predators first arrive on the scene.

325

Control of bird pests

So long as birds are in small numbers and of different species, they are beneficial to farmers. But they can cause catastrophic damage when they begin to multiply rapidly and whole flocks descend upon crops, for example, *Quelea quelea* and **weaver birds (figure 325)**.

Birds damage crops in three ways :

- they eat standing crops by attacking cereal heads,
- they peck seeds that have just been sown,
- they strip trees of their foliage in order to build their nests.

Preventing damage from large flocks of birds is not an easy matter. Immobile scarecrows and attempts at driving them away are ineffective.

Here are some measures that might be tried.

- **Driving the birds away** from the fields by scaring them at regular intervals, approaching them and making them fly off. The use of noisy objects already described is also a possibility or special shot-guns that fire rounds every two or three minutes.

  But these measures merely shift the problem : chased from one place, the birds move to other sources of food.

- **Destroying bird-nests** is another possibility. Gregarious birds nest communally in trees and the crowns are completely colonized. The nests must be destroyed after the eggs hatch out and before the fledglings take wing.

  Both children and adults can be mobilized to dislodge the nests during the breeding season and catch the birds. To encourage participation, people should be paid a small sum every time they hand in a **bird, a fledgling or an egg of the pest species.** The sum of money must be enough to incite people to take part in the bird-hunt, and cover the cost of their catapults and snares. This is a way of spending money for the good of the local population.

- The nests are destroyed by knocking them to the ground with a long stick or by setting them on fire with a burning torch.

326

Baits, traps and snares

Once the habits of pests are known, baits and snares can be laid, either to capture or kill them. **Bait** is food that entices pests, it is poisoned or attached to a snare.

The banana weevil shows a preference for fresh or fermented banana sap. When the pest is first detected, pieces of banana stem 50 centimetres long can be cut and split in two to form traps. The pieces are laid on the ground, cut side down. The weevils in the plantation bore their way into the chopped sections in order to eat the sap. After a few days, traps and weevils are collected and burnt together. Fresh traps are prepared.

In Cameroun, *Thevetia* fruits are used to lure rodents **(figure 326)**. The fruits are pounded, mixed with urine and sugar cane juice. The preparation is smeared at the base of the stems likely to be attacked; more of it, mixed with a little flour, is made into small balls left lying round the plant. The rodents are attracted by the sugary bait which dopes them on the spot so that they are easily captured next day.

If you want to make poisoned bait for a particular pest, you must observe its eating habits down to the last detail. The poison must be lethal, but smell and taste must not deter the animal from eating the bait. Baits and traps or snares are often combined. The bait attracts the pest, the trap captures him. Trapping devices call for a little skillful ingenuity.

- Light **nets** and **fine wire netting** provide protection from birds on a small scale. They are suitable for spreading over seed-boxes, nurseries or bushes when an attack seems imminent. This type of protection is only adapted for use over very limited areas.
- When there is a risk of damage by grain-eating birds, the farmer should consider sowing **varieties** with barbed ears that make the grain less tempting.

Generally speaking, bird pests are controlled by natural control. Birds of prey hunt and kill other birds and rodents, and are in no way harmful to crops. Killing these useful birds unnecessarily is against the farmer's interest.

Remember too that flocks of *Quelea quelea* are a much greater hazard for millet and sorghum when neighbouring pastures do not provide them with enough food. When plenty of varied grasses are available, the birds do not all attack the grain crops. Thus, preserving and improving grasslands is a way of limiting the damage done to farmed land in the vicinity, provided that overgrazing does not prevent grasses from fruiting.

327

328

329 Some traps for rodents

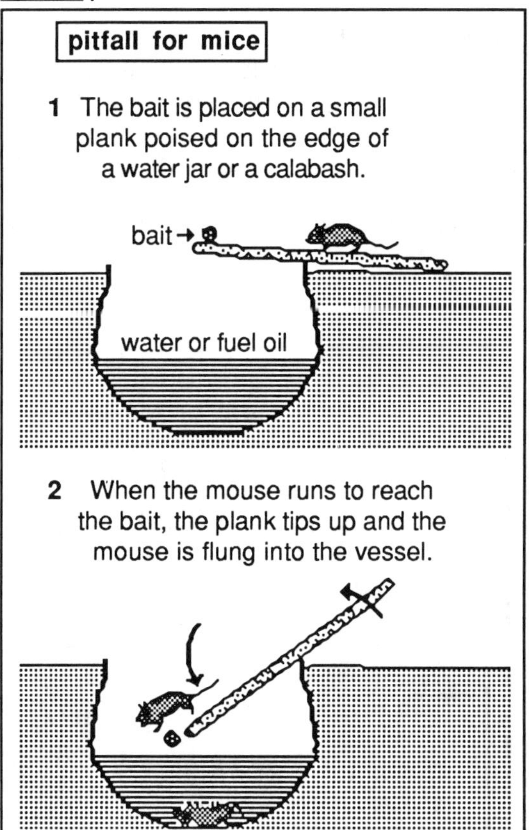

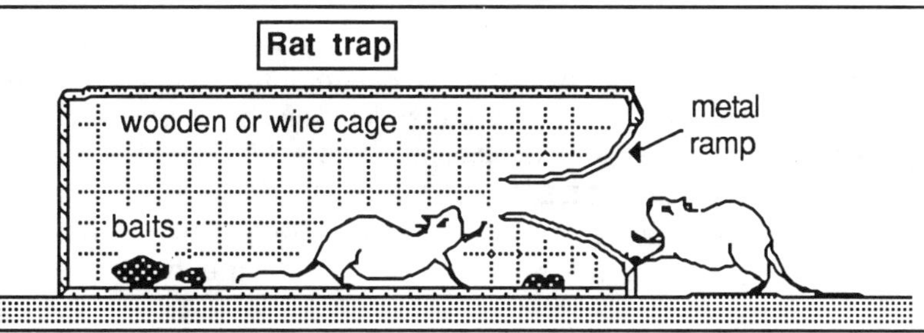

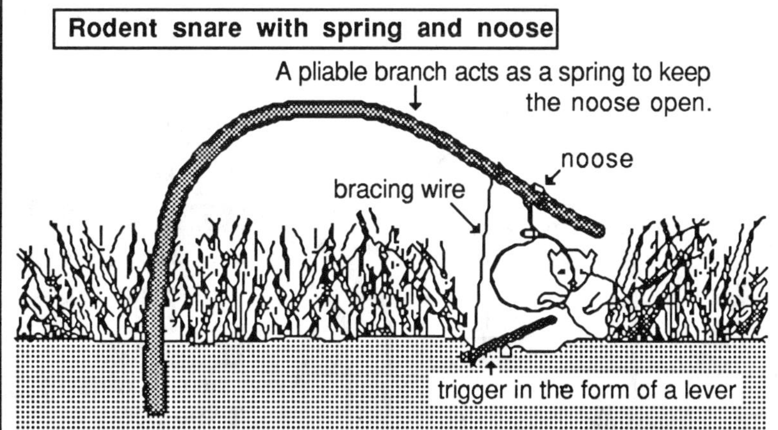

As the animal goes through the noose, it moves the trigger and releases the bracing wire. The spring, i.e. the bent branch, is suddenly released ; the noose jerks tight and captures the animal.

Figure 327 shows a metal trap for catching small game such as gazelles, monkeys and aguties. Such traps are common in Africa but they are most undesirable and often banned. They are dangerous for people and for all animals.

Trappers have a long tradition of laying many kinds of useful snares for protecting gardens. The man in **figure 328** is laying a mole snare. The spring of the snare consists of a pliable branch pushed into the ground and bent back sharply towards the pit. A small bracing wire keeps the wooden spring under tension. The animal is captured by a noose or running knot that jerks tight when the bent branch, acting like a spring, is released. The mole itself operates the release mechanism by knocking against the trigger. This type of snare can also be used on the ground but the animal must approach the noose by a sort of enclosed ramp shaped like a funnel.

Figures 329, 330 and 331 sketch resourceful ways of catching small, warm-blooded pests, insects and slugs.

330 Fly trap

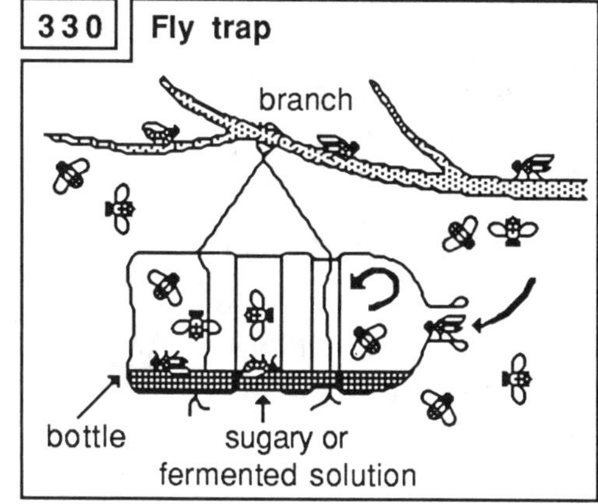

331 Slug trap

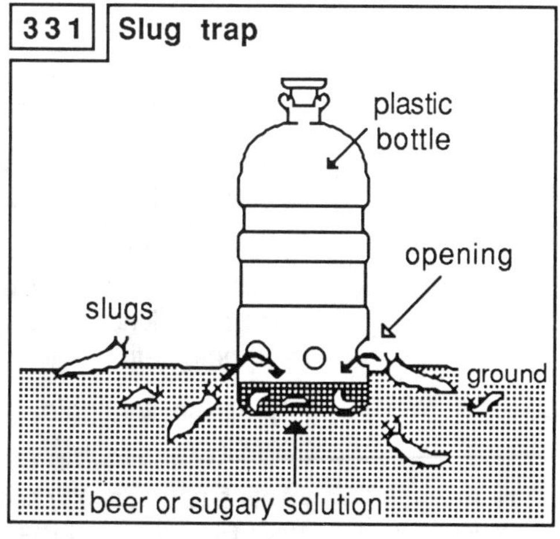

Food chains

The living world is composed of a multitude of interdependent living beings. There are millions and millions of species : higher plants, ferns, algae, mosses, fungi, bacteria, viruses, insects, worms, spiders, frogs, reptiles, fishes, warm-blooded animals, human beings. They are connected by complex links. They may compete for food or prey on one another.

Table 332 sets out in simplified form what is called a **food chain**. Every living being is at the centre of a food chain; he eats and is eaten. Some living beings

332 Examples of food chains

Any living being can be taken as the starting point for observing a food chain. In this table, the sweet potato and the aphid have each been placed at the centre of a food chain, but these chains are not independent of one another. The blacks arrows point to the dependent links between the living beings. The dotted arrows remind us that other dependencies exist, for example, monkeys eat fruits, cats eat mice.

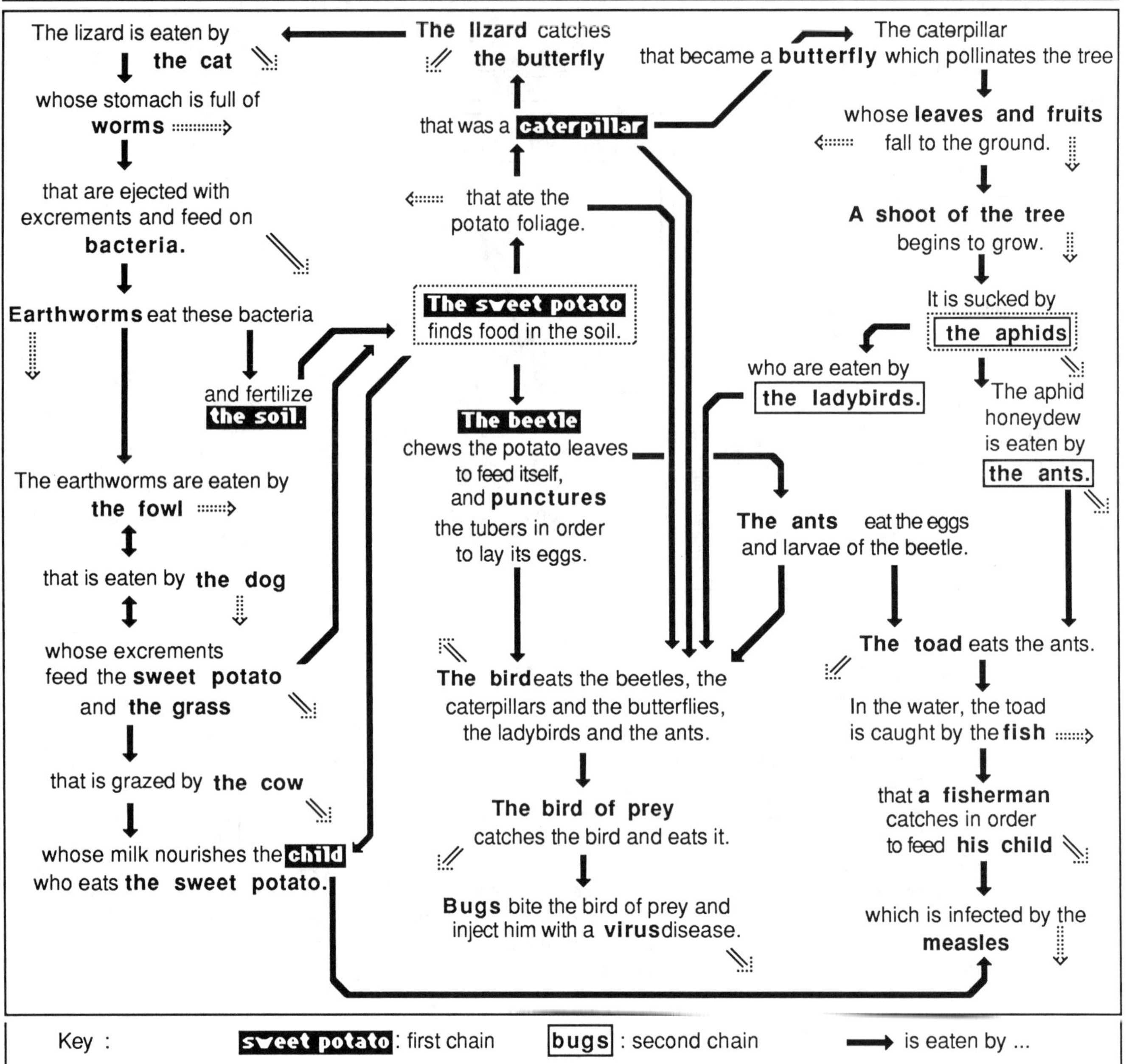

are very large, others are tiny, or even invisible to the naked eye. The smallest living beings attack the biggest just as much as the big attacks the small.

The sweet potato is at the centre of one of the food chains. It finds food in soil enriched by earthworms, soil bacteria, animal excrements, vegetable waste, and so on. The sweet potato, in turn, is a source of food for all kinds of living beings - caterpillars, beetles, fungi, rodents, not forgetting human beings who are the potato's main consumer.

Apart from the aphid, the fowl, the tree and the child, for example, are each at the centre of another food chain.

Ants and toads may seem of no particular interest to human beings who prefer eating sweet potato and fish. But what would happen if ants were completely wiped out? Beetle larvae would no longer be attacked and would consequently inflict much more damage on the sweet potato. The toads would have less to eat, and so would the fish. The fisherman would catch fewer fish. Children would have smaller rations of sweet potato and fish. They would be undernourished and more liable to severe attacks of the measles that might cause their death..

But ants also eat certain aphids. If the ants disappeared, the aphids would increase. They would suck the sap of more cultivated plants and yields would decline.

Suppose we follow the third food chain in **table 332.** If all the beetles and butterflies are killed to preserve the sweet potato tubers there will be less food for the birds, which may decrease in numbers thus affecting the numbersof birds of prey. It can be seen that there is a balance between all living organisms in nature. When the amount of food available for one species is decreased, it is also decreased for another. Consequently, total elimination of one species will affect the numbers of other species and sometimes even man.

Controlling a sweet potato pest amounts to severing the food chain that links the pest and the potato. If the disruption in the food chain is temporary and does not affect the other food chains too badly, control is beneficial because it protects the potato harvest to man's advantage without jeopardizing the living environment.

Imagine, for the sake of argument, that a farmer uses a general insecticide, meaning one that kill insects and spiders indiscriminately, i.e. without making any distinction between useful and injurious pests. By looking back at **table 332**, we can pick out the missing links in the food chains after this insecticide has been sprayed. What is left of the chain when caterpillars, butterflies, beetles, aphids, ladybirds and ants have been eliminated ?

These reflections on food chains prompt us to spell out the basic principles to be respected when undertaking pest control :

- **Total elimination** of a crop pest is **never desirable**. Its indirect effects on food chains are negative on the whole, and are not compensated for by the value of increased harvests;
- **The repeated use of toxic substances** that kill many living species indiscriminately leads to the **deterioration of the environment**. **Soil fertility** may decline due to reduction in microorganisms and must be restored at considerable expense. The **fertilization** of certain plant species is reduced by the absence of pollinating insects. **Animals that prey on plant pests** disappear;
- **Eradicating pests and the repeated use of toxic substances cause ever-increasing imbalances in the food chains**. These disturbances can only be cancelled out by spending more money on the purchase of new pesticides. This extra outlay means that growers come to rely more and more heavily on industrial and commercial firms.
- After a certain length of time, **plant pests acquire resistance to the toxic substances** used against them. When this stage is reached, they begin to multiply much faster than ever before. This build-up in population is explained by the fact that the pest's natural enemies, i.e. its predators, did not get used to the pesticide or have all died. When this happens, growers have to buy other pesticides, thus spending more money and becoming more dependent on chemicals;
- As a general rule, the control methods that deserve first consideration are **those which nature puts at our disposal**.
- Every cultivated plant is beset by a small number of pests that cause really worrying damage. But the farmer himself can line up **a large number of natural allies**. In the fight against pests, **it is vital not to kill the helpers that nature provides**.

Chapter 10

Biological control of crop pests

In the food chains displayed in **table 332**, we find some insects and animals which deserve to be called the farmer's **allies :** ladybirds eat aphids, lizards catch caterpillars and butterflies, spiders eat caterpillars, ants attack beetle larvae, birds eat beetles. Again, there are bacteria and viruses that attack caterpillars and beetles. All these are the farmer's active allies because they lower the population of sweet potato pests without any risk to the potato itself or to other cultivated plants.

Biological control is characterized by the use of parasites or predators of the crop pests themselves,.

Biological control can be exercised directly and indirectly.

Direct biological control means introducing the enemies of the crop pest into the field.

Indirect biological control means changing the environment of the crop so that as many major pest-enemies as possible find shelter there.

Direct biological control

In Central African countries, for example the South Cameroun, gardeners introduce species of **carniverous ants** that attack caterpillars of, for example, the cabbage leaf moth. In order to encourage the ants, their nests must be placed in the shade of trees and include a queen and some of the eggs, otherwise the colony quickly dies out.

Some gardeners introduce **ladybirds (figure 333)**. These insects, and particularly the larvae, feed on aphids. Collecting ladybirds and bringing them into the garden encourages them and reduces the aphids.

333

334 **Carnivorous spiders**

A **small wasp** by the name of *Encarsia lutea* specializes in attacking the *Bemisia* fly that transmits viruses to tobacco, groundnut, sweet potato, cotton and cassava.

Introducing **carniverous spiders** may also prove effective particularly where flies, caterpillars and other larvae are concerned **(figure 334)**.

Many African countries are beginning to use a **bacterium** called *Bacillus thuringiensis* to attack caterpillars. The spores of this bacterium are sold in powder-form under trade names such as Bactospeine, Dipel, Thuricide. When caterpillars become a hazard, the powder is diluted in water and sprayed on the infested plants so that the pest rapidly contracts a fatal disease. This method has the advantage of using natural means that are harmless to human beings and animals.

In Nigeria, biological control of the cassava mite (*Mononychellus*, see **figure 301**) is practised by introducing two species of small insects, *Oligota* and *Typhodromalus*. Both insects have a marked preference for cassava mites

In Africa today, too little is known about **direct biological control**. Remember that this control which is usually less hazardous to man and the living environment would not be expensive if it were adopted on a large scale. Scientific research programmes should be much more concerned with the subject than they have been up until now.

Indirect biological control

Indirect biological control means increasing the number of pest enemies. This is done by organizing the environment and fields so that they provide habitats for a great variety of the farmer's natural allies.

Some aspects of indirect pest control were reviewed in Chapter 8 in the section on preventive measures - the need for balanced plant nutrients, altering spacing patterns, establishing plant barriers, associating different species, practising crop rotations and timely planting.

Trees, hedges and thickets near fields encourage the presence of birds that eat insects. The cover of plant waste that builds up at the base of hedges is an ideal habitat for a wide range of living organisms of whom many are a real help to the grower.

Two landscapes photographed in Rwanda illustrate this point. The landscape in **figure 335** is one of mixed woodland and pastures; the fields are divided by hedges and dotted with trees. All kinds of birds, insects and spiders, many of them farmers' allies, find shelter here. However the fields are also a haven for crop pests that have to be dealt with specificially if they do too much harm.

Admittedly, in this environment, a limited portion of the harvests may have to be surrendered to the living beings that are part of the food chains. It may be better to sacrifice this than incur the expense of saving it.

The second landscape **(figure 336)** is in a nearby region, but the land is stripped bare; most of the trees have been removed and the number of plant species reduced to make way for permanent cultivation. The main crops here are maize, beans and peas. First, the bean plants are attacked by a fly. Then the remaining plants are infested by aphids. Flies and aphids multiply because the environment does not allow a wide variety of predator species to flourish. Indeed, the fewer the plants living in a given area, the greater the risk of pest proliferation.

335

336

337

When trees and beneficial insects who shelter there, disappear from rural settlements, when fallow periods are shortened, when nature is overexploited, farmers pay the price in the form of pest infestations that become more and more unmanageable. They are then forced to undertake, at their own expense and by their own toil, the protective work that their allies carried out for nothing.

This shows the importance of checking wild plants for the useful insects they may harbour.

Some farmers in Central Africa have found that *Euphorbia tirucalli* **(figure 337)**, a plant also found in West Africa, provides a good habitat for insects that prey on pests (see page 127).

Other plant species offer sanctuary to certain pests. Growers must stop growing these plants, or eliminate them, as the case may be. Here too, careful observation.should guide the farmer. *Prosopis*, for instance, is said to encourage eelworm infestation in gardens. Consequently, sowing it near vegetables is to be avoided.

Cultural practices influence the environment to the benefit or detriment of predators. The soil protects many predatory insects that feed on the insects which infest cultivated or uncultivated plants. We can understand, therefore, why certain cultural methods are harmful. For example, uncontrolled, unselective fires in fields destroy or drive away all life and must be used with caution and for limited areas **(figure 338)**.

Weeding operations should be carefully carried out. During germination and the early stages of growth, root competition between crops and unwanted plants must be kept within bounds. But, later on, when the crops are well established, weeding should be more specific and not so thorough. Only the weeds whose fast growth makes them a real hindrance need be eliminated, for instance, those that cause crowding, have rhizomes, or very many seeds. Other weeds should be left or simply flattened because they give cover to beneficial insects, or because they are pest barriers or act as repellents by their odour (Chapter 8).

338

When weeding, the farmer must try to offset the advantages and disadvantages of undesirable plants. Every weeding operation calls for a great deal of thought because of its consequences on the balance between crop pests and their predators.

Biological pest control is not a recipe for miracles, but it is undeniably effective. Chemical control, on the contrary, often has immediate effects, but it can lead to deterioration of the natural environment.

Chapter 11

Pesticides

Pesticides are chemical substances that kill plant pests.

There is a wide range of pesticides, each one with its own formulation and characteristics. Pesticides are manufactured from **mineral** substances such as oil, or **organic** substances such as plant extracts. The toxic substances they contain are found in nature (**natural** substances), or are invented and manufactured by man (**artificial** substances).

Pesticides are divided into eight categories :

- **insecticides** effective against insects and spiders,
- **fungicides** effective against fungi,
- **rodenticides** against rodents,
- **acaricides** against mites,
- **nematicides** against nematodes,
- **molluscides** against molluscs, slugs and snails,
- **herbicides** against unwanted plants, i.e. weeds,
- **bactericides** widely used in treating humans and animals, but rarely in agriculture because most bacteria are protected by the tissues of the diseased plants.

There are no active pesticides to combat viruses.

Growers who believe that weeds in fields are not farm allies to be managed but plants to be eradicated like pests put **herbicides** on the same footing as pesticides. There are **total herbicides** that poison a great number of plants, and **selective herbicides** that attack one or more particular species. Applications of both general and selective herbicides always entail serious risks. They may also have injurious consequences on soil structure and fertility.

Pesticides come in **liquid, solid** or **gaseous** form. Liquids and solids are most commonly used in farming. They are applied by spraying and dusting on plants or by spreading on the ground. Pesticides in gas form, are used for stored grain in silos or other well-sealed containers.

Pesticides usually contain many substances, each added for a different reason. They contain :

- a toxic substance called the **active ingredient** designed to attack the pest;
- a substance that **suspends** the active ingredient and lends volume to the pesticide. The **suspension** can take the form of water, fuel oil, or substances especially designed by the manufacturer for liquid formulations, or various powders in the case of solid pesticides. The active agent is present in varying proportions depending on the mixture;
- other substances are sometimes added. Wetters are substances that help water to spread on a surface rather than form droplets - soap is a **wetter**, but there are many others. **Adhesives** help the poisons to stick to the plants or insects on which they are sprayed.

All pesticides have a fixed range of action referred to as their **spectrum**, for example, insecticides do not kill fungi and fungicides are ineffective against nematodes. The rule of specificity also applies to pesticides in the same category. Insecticdes effective against insects, aphids, for example, may not necessarily act against caterpillars. Fungicides active against blight are not necessarily effective against root rot or gummosis.

So, when you have decided to use a particular pesticide, check first to see if it is right for the pest you want to control.

Remember, however, that the specificity of pesticides does not stop them from affecting other living beings. Man and warm-blooded animals can be poisoned by these products.

Insecticides

Insecticides act in many ways.

- **Contact insecticides** act by contact with the body of the target insect and are absorbed through the skin or cuticle. The toxic substance must therefore be deposited on the insect by spraying or dusting, or come in contact with it when it moves over a surface on which the chemical has been spread.

  This means that contact insecticides are barely active or not active at all against insects and larvae deep in galleries tunnelled in branches, or lying in cocoons buried in the ground.

  Contact insecticides must be applied when the insect is vulnerable, that is to say, when moving on an exposed surfaces (figure 339).

  We must also remember that if two or three different kinds of insects are involved, control is only effective if spraying is carried out precisely when each insect is vulnerable. This will mean spraying at different stages in the agricultural calendar in order to catch each pest at the right time.

  In many cases, eggs and larvae cannot be reached by insecticides. The adult insect may only move in the open air for a few days and then it begins to lay its eggs in places inaccessible to the insecticides.

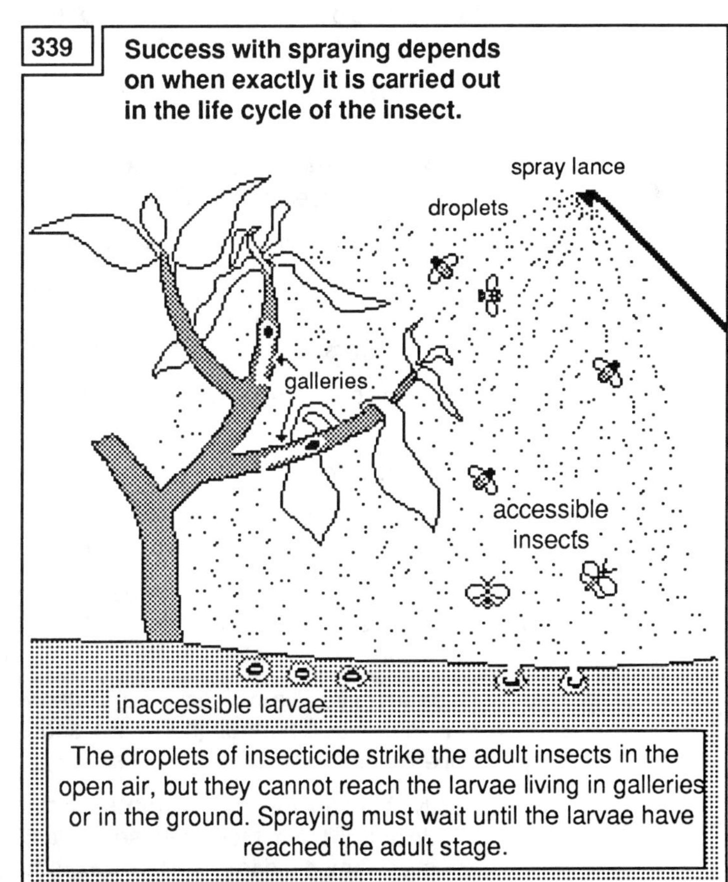

339 Success with spraying depends on when exactly it is carried out in the life cycle of the insect.

The droplets of insecticide strike the adult insects in the open air, but they cannot reach the larvae living in galleries or in the ground. Spraying must wait until the larvae have reached the adult stage.

340 **Observing the insect's life history to discover the best time for spraying**

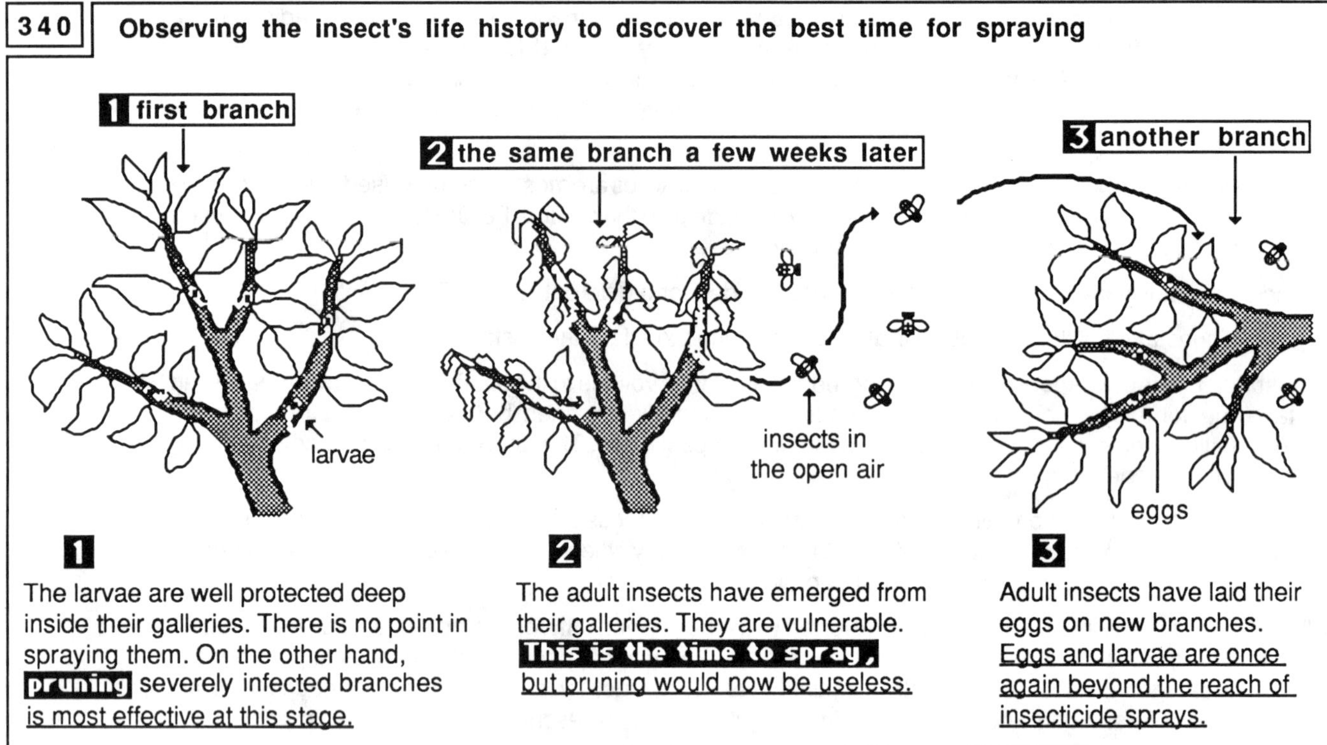

1 The larvae are well protected deep inside their galleries. There is no point in spraying them. On the other hand, **pruning** severely infected branches is most effective at this stage.

2 The adult insects have emerged from their galleries. They are vulnerable. **This is the time to spray,** but pruning would now be useless.

3 Adult insects have laid their eggs on new branches. Eggs and larvae are once again beyond the reach of insecticide sprays.

Spraying carried out the very moment the egg-laying insect emerges from its retreat is effective; it is useless at any other time because the pest has had time to lay its eggs.

The timely application of a contact insecticide means pinpointing the exact time when the insect causes damage and when it is vulnerable to sprays or dusts **(figure 340)**. For example,

- if a larva or a caterpillar chews vegetables on the outside, a contact insecticide is used to attack the pest at that stage in its development,
- alternately if it feeds on the stems or fruits from the inside, control measures must be taken before the adult insect has laid its eggs.

- Other insecticides called **stomach poisons** must be eaten at some stage in the development of the pest. These insecticides fall into two groups :
  - the more usual are **sprayed on the plants** or mixed with bait;
  - **systemic insecticides** which are less common and more difficult to use **act inside the infected plants**. They mix intimately with the sap. When insects like aphids begin to suck the sap, or weevils and borers begin burrowing, they swallow the substance and are killed.

Stomach poisons must be applied at definite times, that is, when the insects are about to eat the plant tissue.

- Some insecticides act **by inhalation.** Insects **breathe in** their toxic vapours.

  These insecticides are sometimes applied by dusting, or by spraying after dilution in water. They gradually evaporate and are breathed in by pest insects.

  These insecticides are also prepared in liquid form and evaporate on being released into the air by aerosol dispensers. The system only works in closed premises with little air circulation during the operation. It is a waste of money to fumigate in the open air.

  Gaseous or volatile insecticides are often very effective in granaries or well-sealed silos because they circulate easily all through the silo and are capable of penetrating inside the beetle and weevil galleries burrowed in the stored seed.

- Lastly, there are **insect repellents**, products that drive away or deviate insects from their usual host but do not kill them. Most of these products are natural and are not classed as pesticides. As a rule, chemical firms tend to manufacture products with more direct effects.

Insecticides have other distinguishing features that are important when it comes to deciding on an application.

- There are **all-purpose insecticides** that act as both contact and stomach poisons on all insects indiscriminately - piercing and sucking insects, borers, caterpillars, butterflies, ants, and so forth. These products are also called **broad-spectrum insecticides**. They are very harmful to the environment when they are used repeatedly because they destroy a great many links in the food chains. **Specific insecticides** only poison particular insect species or families, and for that reason are called **narrow-spectrum insecticides.**

- The duration of insecticidal effects varies. Some insecticides produce **immediate effects**, their action is instantaneous and devastating, but after a few hours, the toxic ingredient becomes inactive.

  Other insecticides are **persistent**, meaning that the active substance remains effective for days, weeks or months. The advantage of these products lies in their residual effects. They are available during the insect's most vulnerable phase, in contrast to insecticides with immediate effects which must be applied at exactly the right time which is limited to a few hours or a few days.

- Insecticides are also distinguished according to the stage in the insect's life when they are most effective. There are insecticides designed to attack the eggs, or the larvae, and those which eliminate adult insects. It is useless substituting one for the other.

It is understandable that the use of insecticides for crop protection is complex. The user must consider

- the risks which the insecticide poses to the **food chains**,
- the risk of **wastage** when applications are untimely,
- the risk of **killing useful insects**, especially the allies of crop protection,
- the risk of **poisoning humans and animals**.

It follows that instructions for using these products should always be carefully followed. This is why purchasers must have the information they need printed on the insecticide packs.

All too often, because agricultural agents and pesticide dealers do not know enough about the pest to be treated, they suggest buying all-purpose, broad-spectrum products rather than specific, narrow-spectrum substances. They are sure the injurious pest will be destroyed but do not consider the serious risks to the natural environment. This sort of salesmanship means that dealers keep their customers : the dealers' bad advice leads to more pest problems, and the farmer is only able to cope with them by buying more chemical products.

Fungicides

The aim of fungicides is to protect crops from fungal diseases. On the whole, these products are of little use in killing fungi already established on plants. However, they are able to stop fungi from developing and prevent fungal spores from germinating.

Generally speaking, fungicides must be used preventively or at the beginning of the infection. They cannot be used as a cure after infection because the tissues have already been destroyed by the time the symptoms of the disease become apparent.

Many fungi live in the soil and infect plants by being carried on splashing raindrops. It is a waste of time trying to control them in the soil where they are well protected. What you can do, however, is protect the leaves and fruits at the base of the plant by spraying a fungi-

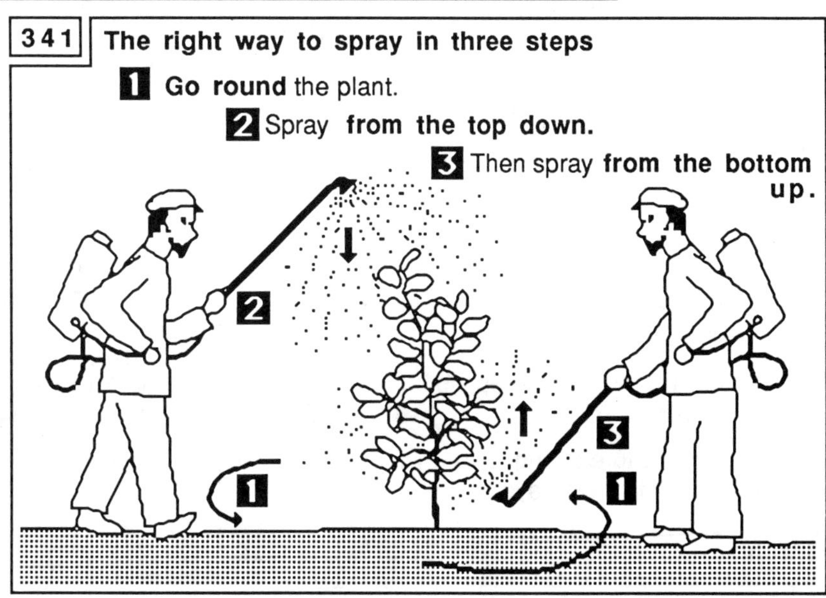

341 **The right way to spray in three steps**

1 **Go round** the plant.

2 Spray **from the top down.**

3 Then spray **from the bottom up.**

cide from the bottom up, thus depositing the toxic substance just where the fungi will attack the plant.

Il is always helpful to observe how a fungus spreads in a garden or a field. Is it scattered here and there because it is transported by the wind, by insects, by man ? Does it spread by contact from plant to plant, working its way from the ground to the top of the plant as a result of rain splash ? Or does it travel from the top to the bottom of the plant because of water runoff on the leaves ?

These observations allow the gardener to decide the kind of control he must initiate. If transmission is from the ground level upwards, he will leave the area fallow. If transmission is by rainwater, the diseased plants can be removed by harvesting or by pruning away diseased parts.

Whatever the gardener decides to do, he must always make sure that the fungicidal sprays reach all the plant parts likely to be attacked - under and upper side of leaves, stems and fruit **(figure 341)**.

Fungicides play an important role in protecting seeds and seedlings. Young plants which have just germinated are particularly susceptible to fungal attack; they have no protective bark and are not strong enough to resist invasion.

Like insecticides, fungicides have broad or narrow spectrums and persistent effects of varying degree.

Bordeaux mixture is an example of a well-known fungicide that can be prepared on the farm with low-cost ingredients **(table 342)**.

Rodenticides

Rodenticides are poisons for rodents - mice, rats, field-mice, etc. They are usually mixed with baits and laid in places frequented by the pests. The rodents are first fed for a few days with unpoisoned baits which they like eating. When they have grown accustomed to eating the bait, poison is added.

Chlorophacinon, Coumachlor, Coumafene, Warfarin and phosphide poisons are among the chemical rodenticides on the market. All these poisons are **extremely poisonous to man** and animals and **must be used with the greatest vigilance**. Children, poultry and animals must be kept away from poisoned sites; anyone in contact with these poisons must wash thoroughly.

Natural poisons also exist. The use of *Thevetia* nuts was mentioned in this connection (see page 156).

Some rodenticides act by contact. They are spread on the routes usually taken by the pests.

342 Bordeaux mixture

Bordeaux mixture is a water-based solution with lime and copper salts in given proportions; a wetter or soap is sometimes added. It is an efficient fungicidal spray **against blights** in plants like potato, tomato, eggplant, cocoa, tobacco, and against gummosis and fruit-tree cankers. It has no effect on wilts and mildews.

To prepare ten litres of Bordeaux mixture

- dilute 150 grammes of copper sulphate in 2 litres of water;
- dilute100 grammes of lime, also in 2 litres of water;
- mix the two solutions thoroughly and then add 6 more litres of water;
- melt a lump of fatty soap, about 100 grammes, in the mixture.

Filter the mixture through a clean cloth just before pouring it into the sprayer.

Other pesticides

Growers can get information on pesticides from government departments and chemical firms. Many products are available and are adapted to deal with every kind of pest*.

Some common pesticides

The best advice we can give is never to buy or use a pesticide before you know everything about its characteristics and modes of action. **Table 344** gives the vital information you need. Regrettably, most African countries have not enacted legislation to deal adequately with pesticides. In the absence of proper regulations and control, products that are strictly prohibited in industrialized countries are dumped on African markets. Some retailers go so far as to repack the pesticides without even bothering to mark the names of the products on the bags for sale.

Table 343 gives information on common pesticides with an apparently low toxicity levels for humans.

* See the bibliography for useful references.

Safety in the use of pesticides

When pesticides are used properly, they offer advantages such as ease of preparation, efficiency, rapid effect and, in some cases, precision. But their technical advantages cannont hide their disadvantages.

- **As the name implies, all pesticides are poisons, they kill living organisms. Very few pesticides are completely non-toxic for man and warm-blooded animals.** Many of them are definitely dangerous when they are absorbed via the skin, the mouth or the lungs. This is true of most insecticides and rodenticides and of some fungicides designed to protect seeds.

  Some pesticides cause immediate poisoning leading to headaches, respiratory problems and allergies. Sometimes, they may even prove fatal, and are then said to be **acutely toxic**.

  Other substances cause **slow or chronic poisoning** with similar symptoms, or they -may cause cancers. Sometimes, the symptoms are only observed when the victim loses weight, contracts a disease, is weak due to worm infestation, or has some other health problem. The reason for this sudden manifestation of poisoning is explained by the fact that toxic substances accumulate in human and animal fatty tissues and are not decomposed. When a person loses weight, the amount of fat available for storing toxins decreases and, as a result, they spread through the blood, the muscles, the bones, the nerves or vital organs, causing delayed, unexpected damage.

- In some, fortunately very rare, instances, women contaminated by the toxic substance transmit its injurious effects to the children they bear, and certain malformations in infants are attributed to this fact. These substances are said to be **mutagenic**.

- **The wrong pesticides applied at the wrong times are ineffective against the pests the grower wants to eliminate, but they sometimes destroy food chains and affect microorganisms in the soil.**

- **Pesticides are sometimes harmful for cultivated plants,** and are said to be **phytotoxic** (toxic for plants). At times, abnormal leaf scalding is observed after chemical dressings have been applied. The damage is caused by pesticides that are ill-adapted, are used in excessive doses, or are applied in the wrong conditions. Pesticides may also affect the plant's capacity to resist pathogens. Treatment of a field can make the plants sensitive to attack from other pests or diseases which they had withstood in the past. When this happens, the farmer begins to wonder if he shouldn't have left his crops untreated in the first place.

- Most pesticides are **expensive**. When they are applied incorrectly, their cost is high for two reasons :
  - the outlay on pesticidal applications is not compensated for by adequate returns,
  - the **ecological cost** of the damage caused is added to the financial outlay.

344 **What you need to know about pesticides**

You need to know

- tho namc of the product,
- the name of the active ingredient
  - so that you can compare the pesticide with other available products,
  - so that you can give first aid and arrange for medical treatment in the event of human poisoning,
- the health hazard,
- mode of application - spraying or dusting
- dosage rate
  - to ensure that application is effective,
  - to avoid wasting the product and your money,
- the solvent to be used - water, fuel oil, kerosene,
- the target pest for which the pesticide is intended.

You must also ask these questions :

- Has the substance a broad or a narrow spectrum ?
  - Does it need a broad spectrum, or is this characteristic dangerous for the environment ?
  - In the case of a narrow spectrum, is the target pest included ?
- When precisely must the pesticide be applied ?
- How long does it persist ?
- Does it act by contact, as a stomach poison, or by inhalation ?
- Are the components natural or artificial ?
- What is the minimum interval between the last application and the moment when fruits and vegetables can be eaten without risk ?
- How much does its application cost ?
- Are there other efficient products for the same target pest that cost less and are not so harmful to the natural environment ?

Buying a pesticide is not like buying a pound of sugar or a packet of washing powder. Dealers who cannot answer all your questions are exposing people to very serious health hazards.

343 Characteristics of some common pesticides with moderate toxicity

Name of product (active ingredient in boldface; trade name in lightface)	Origin	Spectrum	Formulation and dosage rates (1)
Fungicides			
❑ **copper** derivatives : sulphate (Bordeaux mixture,...), hydrochloride (Cupravit Cuprosan, Cuproxol,...)	mineral	all-purpose, but ineffective against mildews and wilting agents	85 to 100 grammes powder diluted in 10 litres water
❑ **sulphur** (Microlux, ...)	mineral	particularly effective against mildews	50 grammes powder diluted in 10 litres water
❑ **benomyl** (Benlate, ...)	synthetic	all-purpose, but ineffective against mildews	4 to 8 grammes powder in 10 litres water
❑ **captafol** (Difolatan, ...)	synthetic	all-purpose, but ineffective against mildews	20 to 25 grammes powder in 10 litres water
❑ **maneb** (Manate, Dithame, ...)	synthetic	anthracnose and Cercospora leafspots	20 to 25 grammes powder in 10 litres water
❑ **zineb** (Zinocan, ...)	synthetic	fungal diseases of leaves and fruits	20 to 25 grammes powder in 10 litres water
❑ **dinocap** (Karathane, ...)	synthetic	particularly effective against mildews	10 grams powder in 10 litres water (not to be used in very hot weather)
Insecticides			
❑ **pyrethrin**	plant extract	aphids, white flies, caterpillars, some mites	dry powder dusted on the pests (the powder becomes rapidly inactive on exposure to sunlight)
❑ **rotenone**	plant extract	aphids, homoptera, some caterpillars	dry powder dusted on the pest
❑ **nicotine**	plant extract	aphids	dry powder dusted on the pest or diluted in water
❑ **bromophos** (Nexion, ...)	synthetic	flies, aphids, some bugs, caterpillars, insects living on the ground	5 to 8 grammes powder in 10 litres water. Also used in granule form against insects living in the ground
❑ **carbaryl** (Sevin, ...)	synthetic	caterpillars	10 to 20 grammes powder in 10 litres water
❑ **fenitrothion** (Sumithion, Folithion,...)	synthetic	leaf piercing and chewing insects, some mites	5 to 8 grammes powder in 10 litres water
❑ **malathion** (Sumitox, L25, Cerathion, Zithion,...)	synthetic	aphids, scale insects, caterpillars, some mites	between 25 and 30 ml of concentrated liquid in 10 litres water

(1) if there are no instructions on the insecticide pack (2) Insecticides must not be applied when cultivated species are in flower

Mode of action	persistence	Interval from last application to harvest	Health hazard to man	Toxicity to fauna, flora and crops
preventive action (fungi)	low	2 to 3 days	low	low for fauna phytotoxic for foliage
preventive action (fungi)	low	2 to 3 days	low	low
systemic action	-	15 days	fairly low	low
preventive action, poor curative powers	-	21 days	fairly low	low
preventive action, poor curative powers	-	between 15 and 30 days	fairly low	low
-	-	between 15 and 30 days	fairly low	low
-	1 to 2 days	15 days	fairly low	low
acts by contact (paralyzing effect)	2 to 3 days	2 days	none	low
contact, stomach poison	1 to 2 days	7 days	powder irritating to the eyes and mucus membrane	toxic to bees and fish (2)
contact	long duration	15 days	relatively high	fairly low except to bees (2)
contact and stomach poison	long duration	between 6 and 8 weeks	relatively low	toxic to pollinating insects (2)
contact and stomach poison	2 to 3 days	15 days	relatively high	very toxic to bees (2)
contact and stomach poison		20 days	relatively high	toxic to bees (2)
particularly effective by contact and stomach poison, to a small extent by inhalation		10 days	relatively high	toxic to pollinating insects (2)

- **A first application of pesticides can trigger off a chain-reaction that creates more needs.** A single pesticide is rarely sufficient Since a pesticide destabilizes the natural environment, it may lead to the rapid multiplication of other pests that need more pesticides. Moreover, after a few seasons, the **pest can become immune to the pesticide supposed to control the infestation.**
- The farmer who builds his pest-control strategies on the constant, exclusive use of chemical pesticides will be **dependent on suppliers** who do not know his environment and care nothing about preserving it.
- **Pesticides are injurious to useful fauna.** They do not distinguish between useful organisms and crop pests. The good and the bad are killed indiscriminately. Endrin and Lindane, for instance, are all-purpose insecticides efficient against many crop pests, but they also destroy bees, ants, carniverous spiders and other animals that prey on crop pests, or are needed for pollinating plants. After an application of Endrin or Lindane, insects that were innocuous in the past may become serious pests because the insects that controlled them have disappeared.
- **Many products are tested in foreign countries outside the tropics,** and no particular attention is paid to the conditions prevailing in the importing country which is not usually equipped to carry out its own research programmes. Through lack of information the farmer may not be able to obtain pesticides at the right time and his spray programme will be affected by delays in delivery.
- Finally, we must not forget that the effects of the toxic substances contained in pesticides are not limited to the area where they are deposited (see **table 347**). They go on circulating, carried by vectors like wind, water, and insects, while man is oblivious to what is going on.

Strict precautions must always be observed when handling pesticides **(table 345).**

345 Precautions to be taken when handling pesticides

- **do not buy products sold without instructions for use,**
- **follow the instructions** given by the chemical firm, and apply the recommended **dosages**,
- leave a **long interval** between the last application and the moment when vegetables are eaten - at least three to four weeks so that applied chemicals will decompose and become harmless. **Figure 346** shows nightshade; its leaves were sprayed with a fungicide designed to control brown rot in cocoa pods and coffee anthracnose. Traces of fungicide can be seen on the leaves about to be picked and will probably be present in the food unless the housewife washes the leaves very carefully, not once but many times.
- **wear protective clothing,**
- wear a protective cloth **mask** to cover the nose and mouth when spraying or fumigating,
- **wash** thoroughly after applying pesticides,
- avoid **unnecessary applications**,
- **wash vegetables repeatedly in plenty of water** before eating,
- **destroy** all used containers by burying or burning,
- **do not reuse containers** for any other purpose,
- do not leave chemical substances within reach of **children and animals**,
- **in cases of poisoning, consult a doctor, and take the label on the pesticide bag or the bag itself with you .**

346

347 **Pesticides are harmful to man and nature.**

Pesticides are poisons. They can poison indirectly, so that the victims do not know what is affecting their health.

1 The man who sprays a pesticide without taking safety precautions breathes in the toxic substance.

2 The insects that are killed by spraying contain the poison in their bodies. The poison contaminates the fish that eat these insects.

3 Water that runs off the surface of the field towards the river may also contain some pesticide.

4 People who drink water from the river, even if it is filtered beforehand, can swallow a little pesticide.

5 The pesticide contained in the fish passes into the body of the person who eats it.

348

It is sometimes necessary to use pesticides to avoid the devastation of crops but it must never be forgotten that they are toxic and must be handled with care.

Pesticides are not miraculous remedies. Chemical pest control in gardens and orchards must be carefully considered and thought given to the possible consequences on the living environment, on soil fertility, on human health, and on the user's pocket-book. It would be best to practise chemical control only when all other means, preventive and natural, have been correctly applied and have not given adequate results.

Summary of chapters 8, 9, 10 and 11

The choice of control measures

The contents of these chapters make it obvious that pest attack does not inevitably lead to a disaster about which the farmer can do nothing. We have seen, on the contrary, the extent to which the farmer's decisions - the choice of crops, of cultural practices and sowing and harvesting patterns - all influence the presence of pests.

Preventive measures have the most impact on crop protection, that is to say, those measures that are directly linked to farm work, and more especially to the farmer's know-how and experience.

Therefore, when pest infestation starts, you must first and foremost check all the cultural methods you used :

- ❑ were the varieties chosen suitable to soil fertility, to the location of the plots, etc. ?
- ❑ were the seeds properly treated and sorted ?
- ❑ was the seedbed preparation carried out properly ? Was the seedbed damaged by fire ? Was enough manure and compost applied ?
- ❑ were the crops sown at the best time ?
- ❑ were species and varieties mixed wisely ?
- ❑ were the plots weeded at the right time and in the right way ?
- ❑ were the plots inspected regularly during the growing season ?
- ❑ were the different species given the best maintenance - staking, pruning, shading, earthing up ?
- ❑ does the field environment encourage beneficial insects ? For instance, are there hedges and trees on or near the cultivated land ?

The answers to these and other questions will help you find out which factors favoured the onset of pest attacks, and enable the right measures to be taken for the coming seasons.

When there is a risk of considerable damage, you may consider falling back on direct control, but the outcome is always more of a gamble. Natural products and biological control, when this is feasible, are the first weapons at the farmer's disposal. Pesticides and especially synthetic insecticides must be used as a last resort in order to avert a catastrophe. In no circumstances must pesticides be the cornerstone on which crop protection rests, although this is what some people advise, either through ignorance or because pesticides are easily applied.

Agronomic research has an important role to play in both preventive and curative control methods. Too many questions in many fields remain unanswered. The mutual protection provided by associating plant species and varieties, the selection of resistant varieties, the search for insect-repellent or insecticidal plants, biological control on the farm and the rural settlement, these are some of the research programmes on which farmers are relying to give them a better solution to crop protection problems.

Indeed, research is most likely to succeed if it is based on farming in small holdings, if it forges ahead with the cooperation of farmers, if it uses their experience, and makes allowance for the production constraints which they face.

Chapters 12 to 16 Seeds, sowing and planting

349 The parts of a flower

1 **inflorescence of the tomato plant**
(cluster of flowers)

flower section

pistil

stamen (yellow)

petal (yellow)

sepal (green)

ovary and ovules

- The **stamens** contain the **pollen** or **male** seed of the plant.
- The **ovules** contained in the ovary are the **female** seeds of the plant.
- The **ovules** fertilized by the pollen produce the **seeds**
- The **ovary** that contains fertilized **ovules** develop into a **fruit**.

2 Marrows have **male and female flowers.**

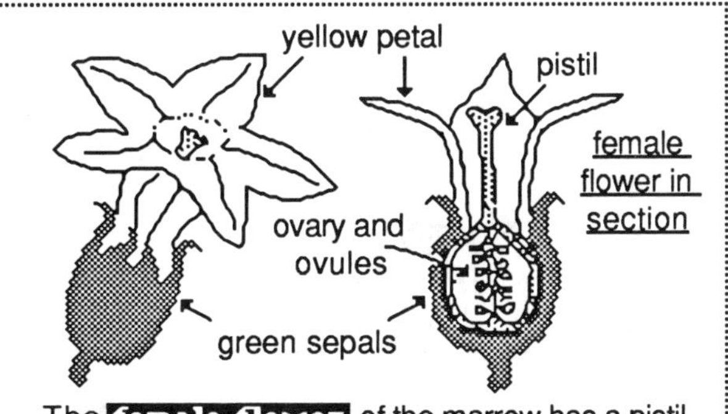

The **female flower** of the marrow has a pistil and ovary, but no stamens

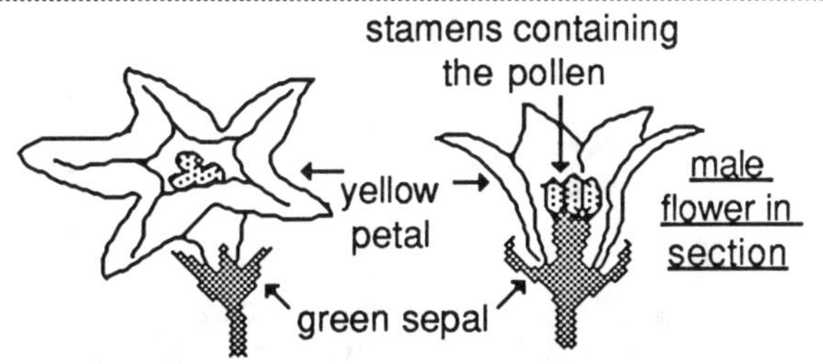

The **male flower** has stamens that produce pollen, but it has no pistil or ovary.

In some species, male and female flowers appear on the same plant. In other species, they grow on different plants.

Chapter 12

Propagation by seed and by vegetative material

The seed is that part of a plant from which a new plant is propagated. There are two main types of propagating material : **seeds and vegetative material.**

Seeds are produced by the flowers that are sexual organs. The seeds develop when an **ovule** is fertilized by a **pollen grain**. The pollen grains can travel from flower to flower, carried by the wind, by insects, by water or sometimes by man, whereas the ovules, fixed in an **ovary,** remain attached to the plant until such time as they have grown into ripe seeds. Depending on the plant species, the ovary contains one or more ovules. The ovary becomes **a fruit**; the fertilized ovules become seeds **(figure 349)**.

Pollen can be compared to the sperm in man, the fertilized ovule to the egg in the woman's womb that becomes the foetus. The fruit of a plant can then be compared to the female uterus and the placenta that enlarges as the foetus grows, and nourishes it.

The role of fertilization in flowers must be emphasized. Without it, there are neither fruits nor flowers. Some plants are **self-fertilizing** or **self-pollinating**, that is to say, their ovules are fertilized by their own pollen. Others are not self-pollinating. The intervention of outside agents, especially in the form of honey-gathering insects, is necessary **(figure 278)**. This explains the important function of these insects for those plants whose fruits and seeds are to be harvested.

The need to fertilize as many flowers as possible also explains why **artificial fertilization** is practised; it consists of providing flowers on a plant with pollen gathered from another plant of a different variety.

When fertilization takes place, the good qualities and defects of the male and female parent plants are combined. This is why, under natural conditions, the daughter plant produced from a seed is never an exact replica of the mother or the father plants; the offspring resembles its parents but is not identical with them.

Consequently, seeds collected from a very productive plant may produce plants that are quite unproductive. And a plant which is resistant to a particular disease may produce susceptible progeny.

All plants are capable of producing seeds, but some species have evolved a simpler way of self-propagation without seeds. Banana plants are one example. They have many flowers, fruits and seeds, but the seeds are mostly sterile and are hardly noticeable in the fruits. This species usually propagates itself by developing suckers, i.e. vegetative propagation.

Vegetative material for propagation may come from any portion of the plant except the seed; portions such as stem cuttings, roots, leaves and tubers.

Vegetative propagation produces plants with exactly the same qualities and defects as the parent plant. If the parent is resistant to a disease, the progeny are too. If the parent is productive, the progeny are also fruitful.

There are many forms of vegetative propagation, some of which are produced naturally by plants, others exist solely by man's intervention.

Natural methods of vegetative propagation

- **Figure 350** shows **two stem suckers** at the base of sugar cane. They have all the parts they need to produce new plants - buds, leaves and roots. If they are cut off with some of their roots attached and transplanted, they will develop quickly.

  Root-suckers are shoots that grow on the roots some distance from the main underground stem of a plant.

- **Bulbs** are also vegetative organs. Before the stem dries up, the plant accumulates food stores in the special (scale) leaves that adhere to it underground. These stores allow the plant to wait for a new season with good growing conditions.

  After one season a bulb can be subdivided. A garlic bulb is formed of many segments called cloves **(figure 351)**. Each clove contains the parts needed to form a new plant.

- **A stolon or runner** is an underground stem capable of producing a full plant from the bud at its extremity. Runners stretch from a few centimetres to a metre away from the parent plant. When the offspring is established, the runner dries up. Strawberry runners are seen in **figure 352**.

- The yam **bulbils** in **figure 353** look like small tubers attached to the creeping stems. No roots or young shoots are visible but they appear when the bulbils fall on the ground. Agaves also grow from bulbils that form on the tip of the floral stem.

350

351 **Bulb**

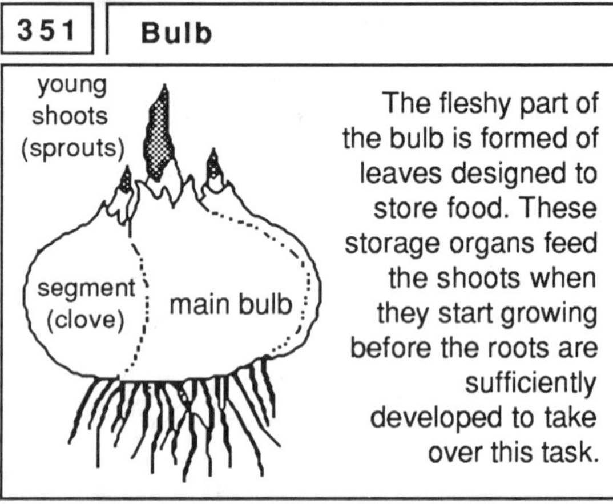

The fleshy part of the bulb is formed of leaves designed to store food. These storage organs feed the shoots when they start growing before the roots are sufficiently developed to take over this task.

352

Secondly, there are **vegetative forms of propagation developed by man's intervention**. They are called **cuttings**.

- A **cutting** is a portion of the parent plant which is removed in order to create a new plant. It can be a portion taken from the stem, from the roots, the tubers, the leaves, or a section taken from the top of the tuber with some basal stem attached. When the piece is planted, it reproduces a complete plant. In order to make propagation by cuttings possible, the parent plant must be capable of reproducing a complete plant from a specialized portion. For example, a cassava stem planted in the ground should be able to produce roots; a piece of a banana corm should be able to produce a stem bud, etc. Some plants are unable to perform these functions and the planted cuttings wilt.

- **Layering** is the technique of developing roots on a branch called a **layer**. When the roots are established, the layer is cut and transplanted.
- **Eye-cuttings** are made from tubers. Potato, sweet potato and some yams are among the plants propagated in this way. The cuttings must have, on or under the skin, buds or eyes which are capable of developing into stems and roots.

Grafting is a special form of vegetative propagation. As a rule, it consists in uniting a section of stem with a bud to a plant grown from a seed (Chapter 17).

353

354 Ways of multiplying some horticultural plants

Most cultivated species are propagated by seed. A few of the many plants that cultivators reproduce in this way are bush greens, nightshade, Jew's mallow, basil, avocado and pawpaw.

In some cases, however, vegetative propagation is easier and more efficient.This explains why some plants, **when cultivated**, are never, or hardly ever, reproduced from seed. They include garlic, banana, citronella, turmeric, *Gnetum sp.*, ginger, yam, grains of paradise, cassava, sweet potato, potato

These plant species are multiplied by cuttings, pieces of underground stem, bulbs, bulbils, root-suckers, etc. Exceptionally, they are multiplied by seed, for example, for work on improving plant varieties.

- **Propagation by seed or by stem cuttings**

  Giant granadilla, basil, some figs, guava, waterleaf, Indian jujube, grains of paradise, mint, black nightshade, horseradish, chillies, pigeon pea, *Triumphetta*, tamarind, bitter leaf.

- **Propagation by seed or bulbs**

  Garlic, shallot and bulb-forming onions

  Layering is successful with cashew, breadfruit, giant granadilla,carambola, Indian jujube, dika *(Irvingia gabonensis)*, sapodilla, bush butter, aidon tree *(Tetrapleura tetraptera)*, tamarind.

  Bauhinia, shea butter, African locust bean, guava, sugar cane, grains of paradise and breadfruit can be propagated from **root-suckers**.

- **Propagation by vegetative means only**

  Pineapple - shoots, root-suckers, crowns; banana - shoots, pieces of corm; citronella - by root division; *Costus* - rhizomes; turmeric - rhizomes, pieces of tuber; gnetum - shoots, rhizomes; ginger - root-suckers, rhizomes; yam - sets from the top of the tuber, pieces of tuber, bulbils; cocoyam - sets from the top of the tuber, pieces of tuber; sweet potato - stem cuttings, sets from the top of the tuber, pieces of tuber; potato - pieces of tuber; taro - sets from the top of the tuber, pieces of tuber

Table 354 gives the usual ways of propagating some of the plants mentioned in this book.

The cultivator's **choice** of propagating material - seed or vegetative part - depends on many factors :

- **the chararacteristics of the plant.** Some plants are only propagated by seed, others by seed and vegetative structures, still others have sterile seeds and must therefore be propagated by vegetative parts;
- **the quantity of seeds produced** by the cultivated plants and the amount of seed required. The seeds produced may not be enough, in which case the grower will have to use cuttings or, on the other hand, the number of cuttings available may not meet requirements and seeds will have to be obtained;
- **the qualities looked for** in the crop being grown. Do these have to be exact copies of the parent plants or can they be different ? If the progeny must have the same characteristics as the parent plants, the planter will prefer vegetative reproduction; If identical characteristics are not needed, propagation by seed is more appropriate;
- **ease** of transport and handling. Vegetatively propagated plants are bulkier than seeds. They are also more susceptible to deterioration - drying out, pest attacks and rots. The risks are in proportion to the time and distance between preparation and planting.

Choice of quality planting material

What is a good seed ? This is an important question because successful cultivation depends on good seeds; **a good seed has the following characteristics :**

- **it produces a vigorous seedling that is capable of developing and establishing itself quickly;**
- **the resulting plant has all the qualities that the cultivators and consumers demand;**
- **it is well adapted to the cultural methods** of the farmers who sow it and **to the climate** of the region. Seeds that produce good plants in one region can produce low-quality, unfruitful, intolerant plants in another region;
- **it is healthy and produces healthy offspring;**
- **it has a high germination capacity.** This means that when a batch of seeds is sown, almost all the seeds have the potential to germinate.

355

The quality of seeds depends to a large extent on how the seeds are produced, harvested and stored before being sown. Basic precautions must be taken, such as :

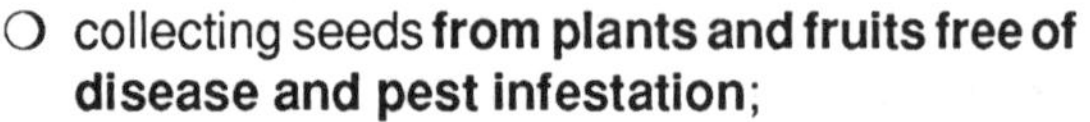

- collecting seeds **from plants and fruits free of disease and pest infestation**;
- looking for plants with the **qualities** one wants to find in the harvested produce - quality of the fruits, tender leaves, aromatic barks or roots, etc.;
- **picking out plants with high quality seeds**. When these plants have been selected, you must earmark them exclusively for seed production. For example, if the plant is a leafy vegetable, you must stop gathering the leaves. This is good practice because such plants produce more seed and should receive special attention.

  The practice of picking out high quality seed plants is well suited to species such as bush greens, bitter leaf and Jew's mallow, but with cucurbits, okra and tomato, it is better to take the seed from the best fruits of one or more plants;
- **picking fully ripe seeds**. Only well-ripened fruits produce seeds that will mature. Immature seeds do not store well, they often fail to germinate or produce puny plants;
- **selecting seeds.** You must only keep well-filled seeds with no visible defects. Large seeds contain more food reserves than small ones. For that reason, they are worth selecting because the germination and growth of seedlings, two stages in plant life that are so important for successful cultivation, depend very much on the amount of food stored in the seeds;
- **selecting vegetative material.** This should be chosen just as carefully as the seeds. You should only take vegetative portions from healthy plants that produce plenty of good fruits. The structures must be vigorous and contain enough food reserves.

As with seeds, it is a good idea to set aside for vegetative propagation, the plants that display the characteristics you want to find in the harvested produce.

The vigour of cuttings is judged by the diameter of the shoots, the distance between the internodes and the appearance of the buds. You must not retain plants with thin stems, with nodes too widely or too closely spaced, or with poorly developed buds. Avoid taking leafy cuttings from branches with deformed, undersized leaves of unusually dark or pale shades of green.

Figure 355 shows three basil stem-cuttings. The vigorous cutting in the centre was well chosen. The bottom one is weakly and will not grow well when planted.

The branches reserved for cuttings must have accumulated enough nutritive reserves in their tissues, and must therefore be at least one season old. As a rule, the bark of woody species (trees and shrubs) must be well-

356 **When a tree is propagated by seed, the habit of its stem and roots is different from that of a tree propagated by a cutting.**

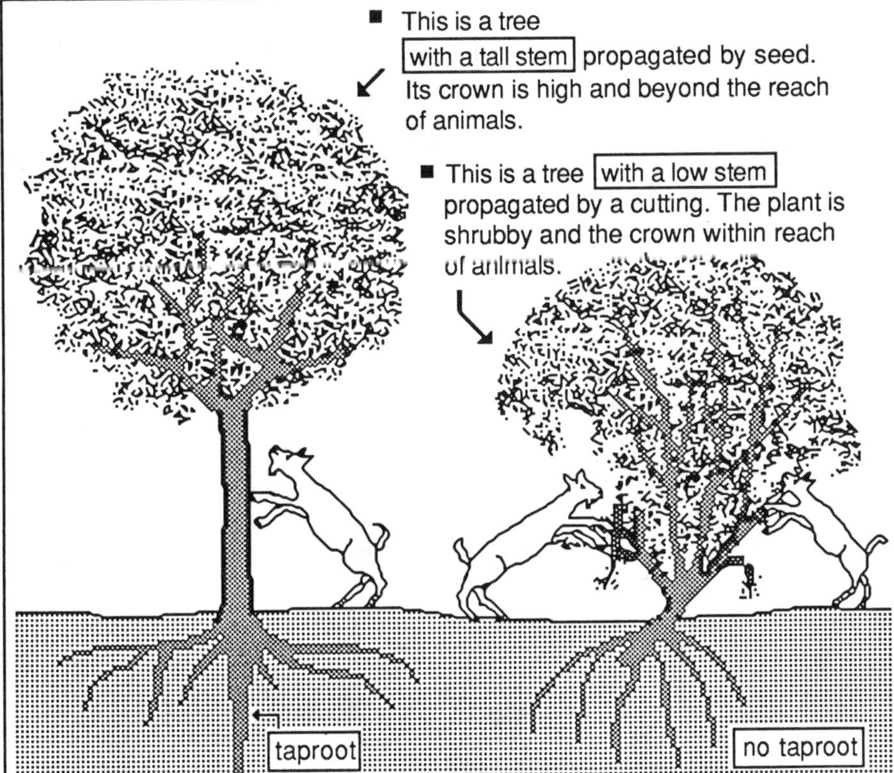

A taproot system is only obtained by using seed for propagation, and never by planting a cutting. The habit of the stem is also influenced by the way the tree is pruned in the early stages of growth.

formed but not hard. The branches are said to be **ripe**.

The same criteria are applied to layers and rhizomes.

The appearance of the eye-buds is what matters when selecting tubers. When the eyes are black and dried up, the tubers germinate badly. When the eyes are too small, the plants are less fruitful.

The selection of shoots, pieces of underground stem, stolons and root-suckers depends on the diameter of the stem at ground level. Long, thin shoots and any that look abnormal should be rejected. Weight is another yardstick. Heavy shoots are a sign of ample nutritive reserves and are therefore more promising than light, frail shoots.

When you are looking for vigorous root-suckers or shoots, you can single out some for special attention while they are still on the parent plant. For example, you can decide to keep only a few vigorous shoots and cut off all the others so that they do not compete for sap with the shoots destined for propagation.

Selecting seeds for specific conditions

A choice has to be made when the species to be cultivated can be reproduced by seed and by vegetative structures. The choice may be unimportant, but sometimes it will influence the end-result. Some examples illustrate this point.

If you sow a **tamarind seed**, it will normally grow into an erect plant, with a well-established stem, a collar and a taproot. The crown is fairly well developed. On the other hand, when a cutting is used, the tamarind has no taproot and is more like a shrub. There is no collar. The crown is not so high and livestock can reach it rather easily. The fruits are larger and the leaves are easier to gather **(figure 356)**.

This example shows that the mode of reproduction of a tree is an important factor, since it influences :

- the **habit** of the tree;
- the **rate at which it grows**;
- the **type of root system**;
- its **fruitfulness**,
- its **precocity** or early maturity where fruit-bearing is concerned.

Another example is pineapple that can be reproduced by various kinds of vegetative structures **(figure 357)**. Shoots appear on the plant at several levels.

357

- Shoots called **ratoons or basal suckers** appear on the underground part of the stem, and **root-suckers** on the roots;
- **Stem suckers** grow in the axils of leaves;
- **The crown shoot** is the single shoot at the apex of the fruit;
- **Crown slips** are also found round the base of the fruits.

Depending on the type of shoot used for propagation, you get different results affecting the duration of cropping, the way the pineapple grows and the quality of the fruit. The supply of vegetative cuttings also varies. While there is obviously only one crown to each plant, the plant itself produces many different kinds of suckers suitable for propagation.

358 Different kinds of pineapple suckers influence their offspring in different ways

	Kinds of suckers			
	Ratoons	**Stem suckers**	**Crowns**	**Crown slips**
Length of production cycle	18 months	15 to 16 months	22 to 24 months	20 months
Growth rate of batches	fast, uniform	fast but varies from plant to plant	slow, erratic	slow but regular
Resistance to drought	good	good	average	poor at the beginning
Availability of propagating material	available all the year round	practically all the year round (22 to 24 months)	one shoot per cultural season, at harvest	several crown slips per cultural season, at harvest

359

Table 358 shows that the differences in propagation methods cannot be overlooked and that the cultivator can choose between several ways of planting .

- If he wants to harvest the whole crop at a particular time in the season, he will decide to plant one type of pineapple sucker. For example, if he decides to plant stem suckers, all the fruits will be ready for harvesting after fifteen to sixteen months and will have to be sold within a month.
- On the other hand, if he wants to stagger sales and vary the quality of his produce, he can use various types of suckers. In this case, the first fruits will be picked from plants propagated by stem suckers from the sixteenth month after planting; the last fruits, propagated by crown slips, will be gathered twenty-four months after planting. Thus, the farmer is able to spread the harvest over a period of eight months.

This is a case where a range of propagating material from the same plant allows the farmer to alter the cultural calendar and change the economic aspects of his production.

Take another example, that of sugar cane for chewing. The best quality is obtained by taking cuttings (sets) from the central part of the stem. However, this part of the stem is also in great demand and fetches the highest price. Here, part of the plant required for reproduction is the part most prized by the consumer.

For some smallholders, the loss of income that results from taking sets from the central part of the stem is too costly. Consequently, they take cuttings from the tops of the cane that are fibrous and are not highly rated by consumers. After some weeks, shoots develop on the transplanted tops and on the stumps left in the field at harvest time. These shoots are cut off and planted. The transplanted cane tops are also cut back, leaving only one side shoot or tiller that thrives well **(figure 360)**. This cultural method lengthens the production cycle, but it means that all the best sugar cane can be used for consumption or for sale.

Green cabbage (*Brassica oleracea var. capitata)* is usually multiplied by seed but some varieties produce shoots from the cut stems **(figure 359)**. By letting these shoots develop after the harvest and then transplanting them, the hard work associated with nursery beds is eliminated and the quality of the vegetable maintained. However, this mode of propagation limits the number of plants, since there are only a small number of shoots. Multiplying cabbage in this way is useful when there is a shortage of seeds, and also when a variety of cabbage sells particularly well but the farmer does not know its name, and seeds are not available.

These examples of tamarind, pineapple, sugar cane and cabbage propagation show how numerous factors affect the choice of propagation methods. We have already mentioned the question of transport, the growth rate, the root system, and the early maturing of the crop. Other factors are :

- **the farmer's aims** when he chooses to cultivate a particular crop - for self-sufficiency or sale;
- **the wish to stagger harvests or, on the contrary, to concentrate them in time;**
- **the availability** of particular types of seed or propagating material at planting time;
- **the mode of cultivation** : cropping in pure stands or in association, manual or mechanized cultivation, use of chemical fertilizers, etc.

The best choice is determined by the farmer's personal experience.

360 **One way of reproducing sugar cane for chewing without losing the best cane**

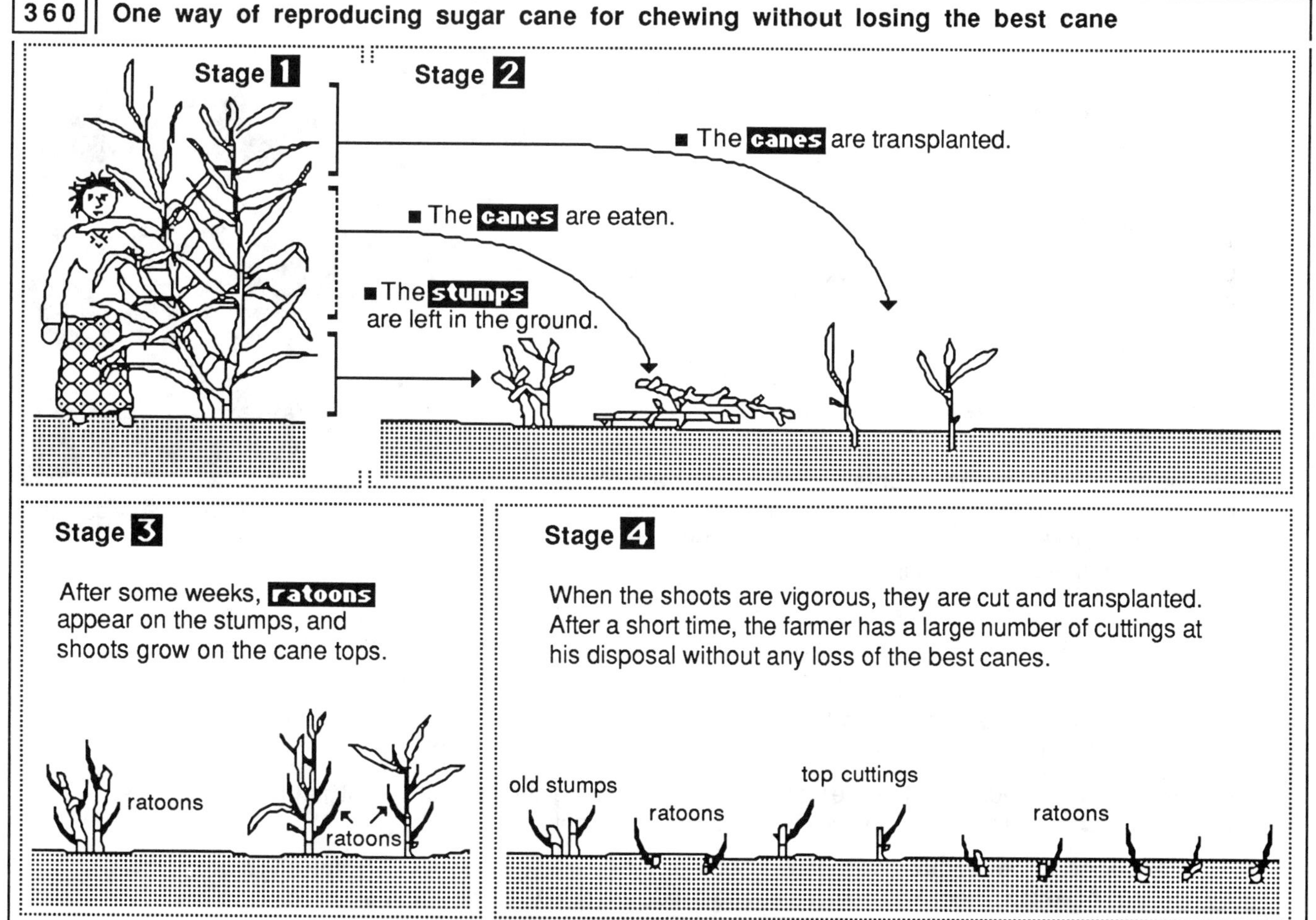

Harvesting and storing seeds and cuttings

Harvesting and storing seeds

All too often, farmers are not careful enough when it comes to harvesting and storing seeds, although this is an important farming activity that can have a decisive effect on successful cropping. Here are some of the points that must be kept in mind during these cultural operations :

- **Collect seeds from the healthiest plants.** Start by picking out the plants that seem likely to produce good seeds, and mark them with a piece of string **(figure 300);**
- Pick **really ripe fruits when production is at its peak.** Full maturity is needed to let the seeds accumulate large reserves of food;
- The pulp is removed from moist fruits such as tomato, eggplant and marrow. As pulp is a source of pest infestation, **the seeds are then washed to get rid of any pulp clinging to the seed coats.** Clean water, e.g. well water or tap water, must be used, because dirty water may carry microorganisms capable of settling on the seeds and attacking them.

  After they have been washed, the seeds are **dried in the shade** in a well-aired place. They must, on no account, be overheated in full sunshine, because overheating damages the vitality of seeds, that is, their germination power, and may even kill them. Notice that the procedure for drying seeds for planting is different from that for food grains. These can be exposed without harm to the sun, because there is no need to preserve their germination capacity.
- Dry fruits fall into two groups. Some dry fruits such as groundnut, rice and sorghum remain enclosed in their pericarps (fruit coats) that serve to protect the seeds. These grains are also dried in the sun but **the fruit coats are not removed**.

  Other fruits are **dehiscent**. This means that they split as they dry and release their seeds such as okra and Jew's mallow. These fruits must be picked as soon as they are ripe but before the seed coats burst. The fruits are first dried in the shade and then the seeds are removed from the pods with a view to storage. They are winnowed to remove the waste from the husks.
- Whatever seeds are being stored, dry fruits, seeds or whole cereal heads, **impurities** in the form of wood, shells, husks, pebbles, earth and straw **are always removed**. Impurities expose the seeds to pest infestation.
- Seeds and dry fruits are stored in **containers that are as airtight as possible**. The less air, the better. In the first place, pests are reduced due to a lack of air, and secondly, the dry seeds respire less, a condition that prolongs their life.

  361

  It is a good idea to store small seeds in bottles **(figure 361)**. The bottles must be filled to the brim and carefully sealed. If there are not enough seeds to fill the bottle, you may add dry sand, heated and sterilized on a metal sheet placed over a fire. Storage by bottling only suits perfectly dry seeds.
- **Do not store seeds for too long a period.** When seed storage is prolonged, some seeds **lose their germination capacity**. They may look normal but, in fact, they are dead.

  The longer a batch of seeds is kept before planting, the greater is the number that will not germinate. The duration of germination capacity varies with species and variety.
- With some species, however, there is an interval between the time when the seeds are ripe and the time when they have the potential to germinate. The seeds are said to be **dormant** until such time as dormancy is over.

(Chapter 8 has already dealt with some ways of protecting seeds from pest infestation.)

Harvesting and storing other propagating material

Seeds have to be dried for storage whereas vegetative material must be kept damp.

When plants are to be propagated by **stem cuttings, the stock plants are simply left standing until it is time to take the cuttings**. If weather conditions are favorable, the parent plants are maintained in the open field or in the garden. However, if the weather is dry, the plants must be kept in plots specially reserved for reproducing plants. A corner of a village in the Sahel savanna was set aside for sweet potato cuttings **(figure 362)**. Waste water from a shower is discharged there, so the potatoes are watered regularly all through the dry season, and the gardener can take any cuttings needed as soon as the rains start.

In regions with a long dry season, the production of cuttings is **an off-season activity**. This means that the reproducing plants must thrive at a time when all other plants are resting. By the end of the dry season, the stock plants must have developed enough to provide all the cuttings that are needed. You must therefore start looking in good time for sites which can be watered during the dry season and establish the parent plants there. Choose fertile, wet sites, a valley bottom, for instance, or a place with a watering point or a pond nearby.

There are many different methods of propagating trees. Cuttings can be taken from parent plants at the onset of the rains and can be planted at once. In this case, the problem of conservation does not arise.

362

Usually, though, cuttings are made when the rains have begun and they are placed in bags or baskets kept in a shaded nursery and watered regularly. The cuttings that have rooted are transplanted to their permanent place the following year, again when the rains begin.

When cuttings are taken from tubers, roots or rhizomes, the best method is to store them in dry soil, preferably in special pits. If pits are used, the tubers or sets taken from the tuber tops are piled up carefully in the pit and covered with fine, clean, dry sand from which any waste likely to cause disease has been removed. The cuttings develop slowly in the pit, and their moisture content is more or less constant. The pit is dug in dry ground where there is no risk of water flow, and it is covered to stop rainwater from infiltrating between the tubers **(figure 363)**.

363 How to store tubers and tuber tops for seed

Dig a pit in dry ground and put in the tubers in even layers. Pour sand into the empty spaces between the tubers and fill the pit with sand to the top. Now cover the pit with straw, and then with plastic sheeting or a metal sheet.

plastic sheeting

stones

straw

fine, dry sand

pit

tubers

dry ground

Preparing for planting

Seed preparation

Seeds must be ready just when the farmer plans to sow and plant. Apart from this basic rule, the rest depends on the grower's observations and experience.

Normally, seeds that are harvested and stored in good conditions do not need to be specially prepared for planting. They are simply sown in a seedbed with well-loosened soil.

At times, however, preparation is useful or even necessary to promote germination and the growth of seedlings. Such cultural methods fall under three headings :

- **practices that speed up the absorption of water by the seeds** - soaking, scarification and scalding;
- practices designed to **nourish the seedlings** - puddling and inoculation;
- practices that **encourage germination** - germinators and pregerminators (Chapter 14).

When a seed is left to germinate in the ground, it begins by imbibing or absorbing water from the soil surrounding it. If the soil is dry, nothing happens. If the soil is moist, absorption can take place. The wetter the soil, the faster moisture is absorbed.

Bean, maize, cucumber, pea and okra are examples of seeds that imbibe fairly quickly because the seed skins are permeable to water. But other plants such as mango, oil palm and coconut have seeds sealed in hard coats impervious to water. Consequently, absorption takes place very slowly.

364 Water absorption by seeds

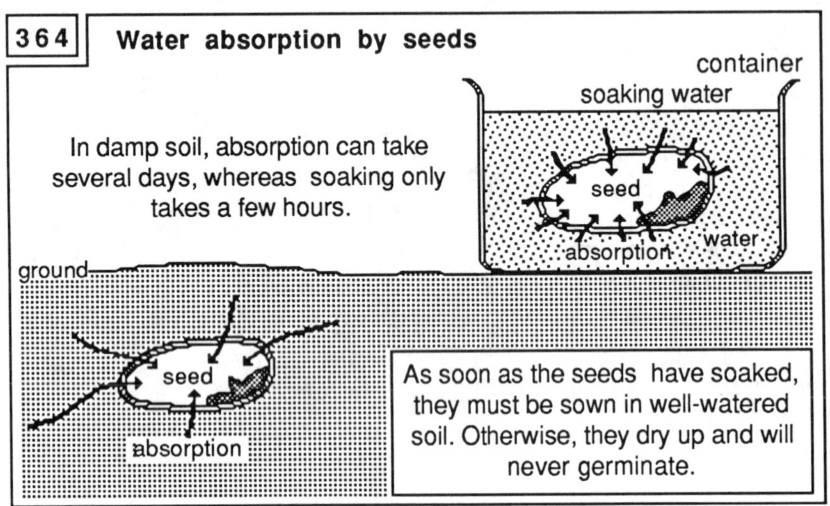

There are ways of hastening absorption before germination. **Soaking** is the most usual procedure. The dry seeds are soaked in water for some hours just before sowing time. This practice lets the seeds absorb the water they need much faster than if they were left to absorb it the water in the ground, where it can take several days **(figure 364)**.

When soaked, the seed and its contents swell. When a white speck appears where the primary root will grow, the seeds are taken out of the water and sown immediately. If the seeds are soaked too long, the primary roots emerge and are liable to break when the seeds are sown. A seed with a broken primary root or a broken tiny stem will never develop.

A little soluble fertilizer can be used to encourage the growth of the seedlings.

Soaked seeds must be sown at once in a well-watered seedbed and, under no circumstances, must be allowed to dry out. If the seeds dry out, germination cannot take place because the primary stem and root, once wilted, are unable to develop.

The **scarification of seeds** involves scratching the seed coats deeply to allow water to penetrate the seeds. The seed coats can even be cracked provided no harm is done to the actual seeds.

There are many ways of scarifying seeds. For example, you can rub them on stones or remove the coats if this is possible. You can also use a chemical solution to dissolve the outer layer or testa, provided you do not damage the kernels. A common practice is to feed some types of seed to livestock. The seeds pass into the intestines, where the skins are attacked by the gastric juices and become more permeable. However, the seed kernels are not damaged by this short passage through the intestines. This method is well known in West Africa and is used, for instance, for desert date, tamarind, *Acacia albida*, *Bauhinia* and *Lannea acida*. This practice involves penning the animals until such time as the seeds have been retrieved from the dung.

Scalding also helps speed up the germination of certain kinds of hard seeds. The process aims at softening the skins and making them more permeable to water. The seeds or nuts are thrown into very hot or boiling water for a few seconds and then removed. When they are cold, they are sown immediately or they can be soaked in water. They can also be stratified in a crate or box as explained in Chapter 14. **Figure 365** shows a nut in section.

Scalding is a delicate operation because it involves heating the seed skins without killing the kernels. This is why you must do some preliminary testing on a few seeds at a time in order to find out the exact scalding times.

365 A nut seen in section

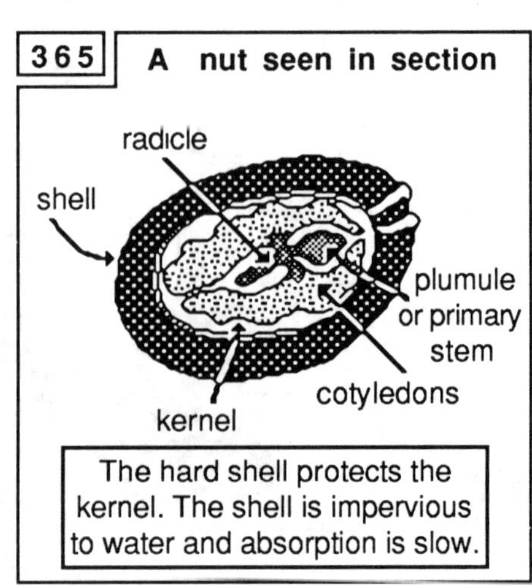

The hard shell protects the kernel. The shell is impervious to water and absorption is slow.

The seeds of the following species tolerate scaling:

- *Lannea acida*, tamarind and desert date - plunge briefly into very hot, but not boiling, water;
- baobab, African locust bean and njansan *(Ricinodendron heudelotii)* - four or five minutes in boiling water;
- *Acacia albida* - up to fifteen minutes in boiling water.

After they have germinated, the seeds **must become established in the ground**. Here, the primary root must gradually find the nutrients it needs to nourish the tiny shoot before the stores contained in the seed are all used up. Coating the seeds beforehand with a little food helps them to get established. **Pelleting** or **puddling** is the name given to this cultural practice. A few days or hours before planting, the seeds are thickly coated in animal dung, clay, manure or a mixture of these materials **(figure 366)**. A little fungicide can be added to prevent fungal diseases. The puddled seeds are dried before they are sown.

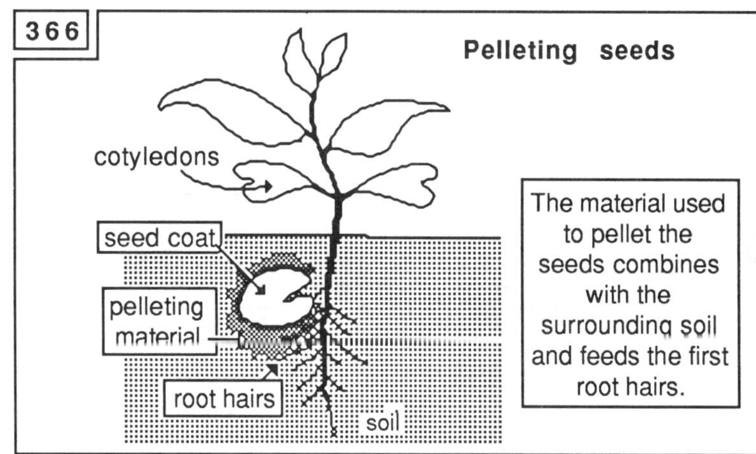

In some parts of Central Africa, cucurbit seeds are covered in fresh cow dung and then dried before being stored. As soon as the seeds are sown, the dung becomes impregnated with water and fertilizes the soil directly in contact with the seeds.

The yields from leguminous plants can be increased by **seed inoculation.** Many legume plants use certain soil bacteria to fix atmospheric nitrogen. These bacteria called *Rhizobium* spp. or **nitrogen-fixing bacteria** live in nodules that grow on the roots **(figure 367)**.

However, some cultivated legumes do not find the type of *Rhizobium* they need. As a result, the plants do not form nodules and do not benefit from the nitrogen in the atmosphere which the *Rhizobium* could make available to them.

Inoculation is carried out just before planting and consists of soaking the legume seeds in a solution containing *Rhizobium* spp. This practice is particularly useful when a legume species is sown in a field for the first time. The most economical method is to look in the vicinity of the farm for plants with an abundance of nodules. The plant roots are crushed and carefully worked into a mixture of dung and clay which is then used to coat the seeds.

Powders containing dried bacteria are sometimes on sale, but there is no guarantee that the bacteria incorporated are adapted to the needs of specific varieties of legume.

Vegetative propagation

Stem cutting preparation

Stem cuttings are portions of trees or herbaceous plants with one or several active or dormant buds. When these cuttings are placed in moist soil, they develop roots and grow into new plants.

369 Various kinds of stem cuttings

a a cassava cutting

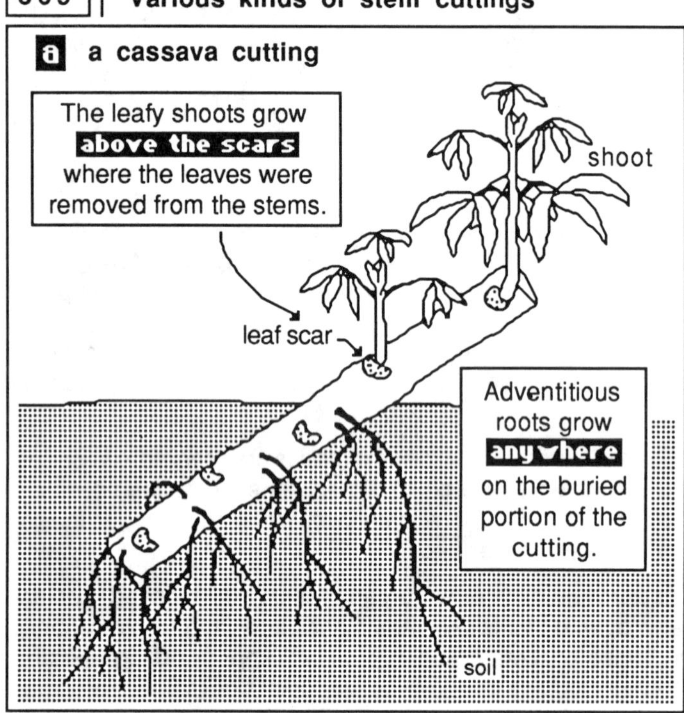

b a sugar cane cutting

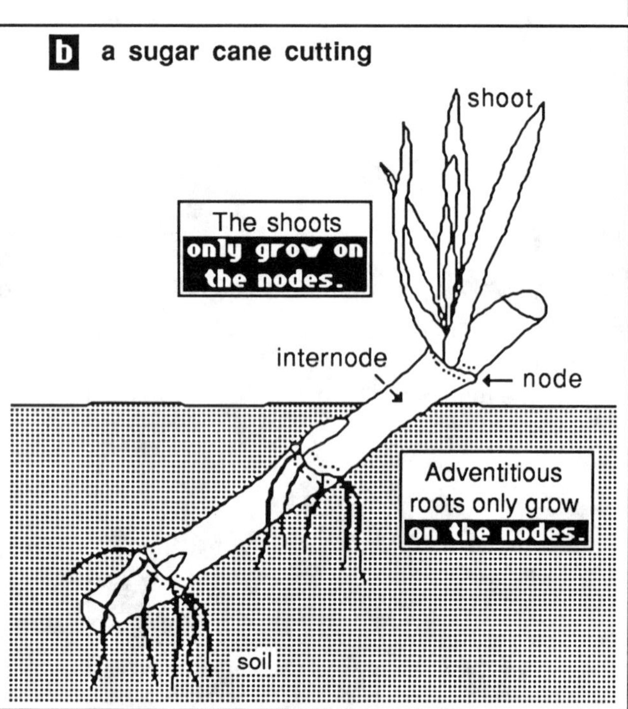

c a cutting split in half

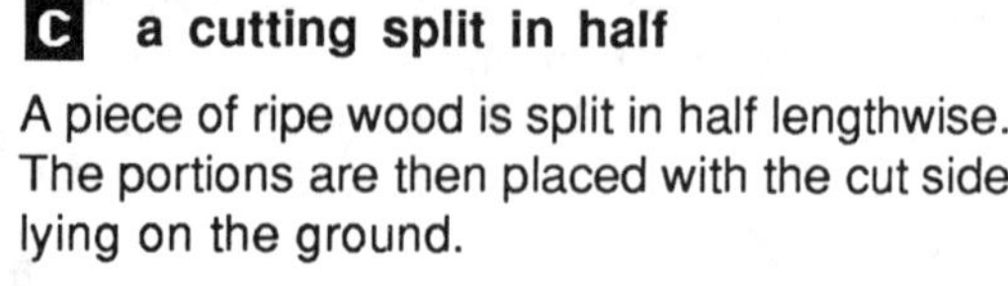

A piece of ripe wood is split in half lengthwise. The portions are then placed with the cut side lying on the ground.

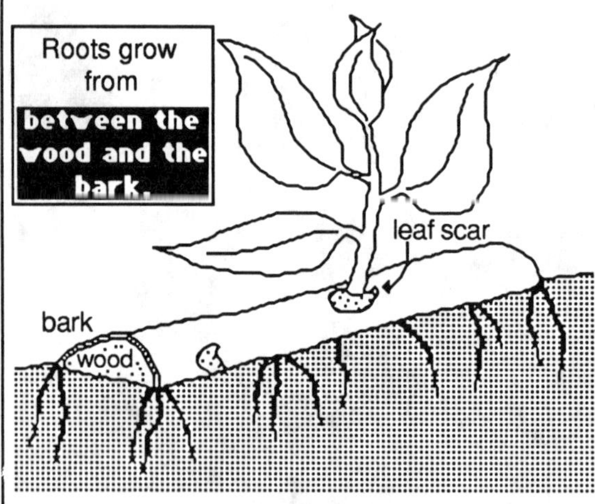

If it can produce two new plants, a cutting split lengthwise will double the supply of propagative material.

d unusual cuttings

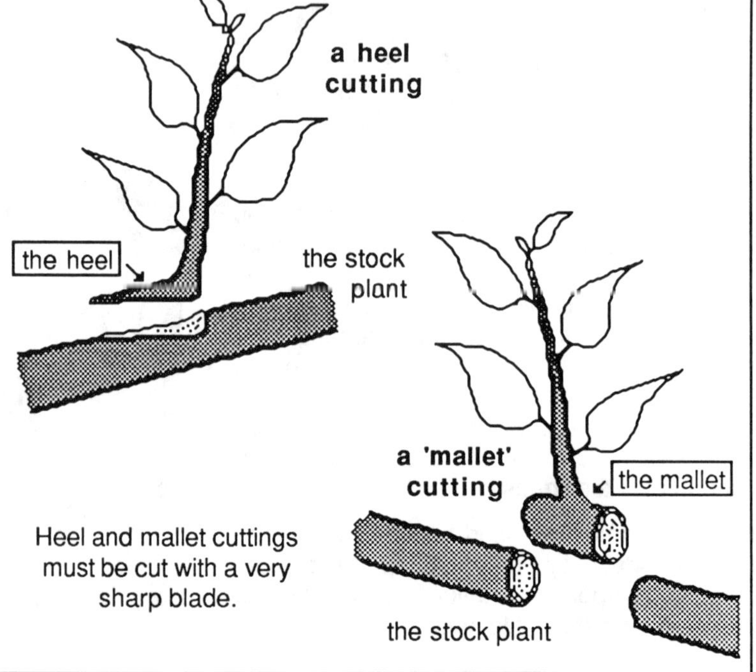

Heel and mallet cuttings must be cut with a very sharp blade.

In some plants such as cassava, sweet potato, certain varieties of bitter leaf, cabbage and drumstick, rootlets appear all over the underground part of the cutting, both on the nodes and on the internodes, while woody shoots only produce roots from the nodes or above the leaf scars **(figure 369a)**.

In other plants, roots only grow in certain places, for instance, near leaf axils. This is true of sugar cane cuttings taken from stems, rather than from stumps. Consequently, the portion of the cutting that is inserted into the ground must have at least one or two nodes **(figure 369b)**.

Figure 368 shows a potherb, *Diodia scandens*, used in Central Africa. Here, the plant has been layered and the new roots are only growing on the nodes.

In other cases, the roots grow right at the bottom of the cutting.

Propagation by cuttings is usually carried out by placing the cuttings on or in the ground. But a cutting can also be induced to grow roots by putting the base in water or in a nutritive rooting solution **(figure 370)**. This is the method used in agricultural stations that produce cuttings in large quantities. These nutritive solutions have admixtures of substances that encourage root growth.

370 Placing a cutting in water or in a nutrient solution

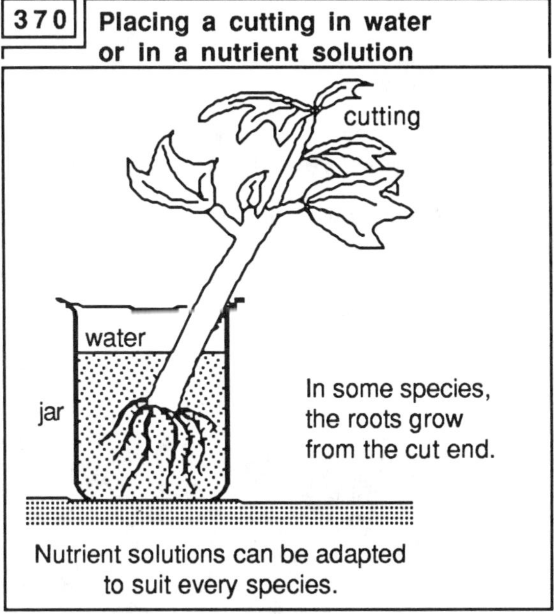

Nutrient solutions can be adapted to suit every species.

The branches or sections of creeping stems removed for cuttings must have reached maturity. The bark must be well formed and be clearly distinguishable from the underlying tissues. In ligneous, i.e. woody species, the bark must be mature but still fairly soft. The tip of growing shoots is sometimes too soft and may therefore dry up or rot when planted. On the other hand, the bark on the base of the shoots is sometimes too thick for the new buds to break through it easily. The central part of the stem is usually best for stem cuttings. **Ripe wood** is taken from woody plants. As a rule, this is wood from the previous year's growth **(figure 371)**. The tips of branches can only be used if they are well ripened.

The following points should be kept in mind when making cuttings :

- **Stem cuttings vary in length** depending on the species, the number of cuttings you want to obtain from the same stem, and the method of planting you have in mind;
- **If the crown of the mother tree from which the cuttings are taken is relatively thin**, the cuttings tend to be shorter - seven, ten or fifteen centimetres long. On the other hand, if the crown is dense or you only need a small number of cuttings, they can be longer - between twenty and fifty centimetres in length;
- The length of the cuttings also depends on **what you want to achieve** - the establishment of a hedge, of an orchard or an individual tree, the production of leaves or fruits, or the shape of the tree **(figure 356)**. As a rule, hedges are planted with cuttings sixty to eighty centimetres long, even longer. Cuttings from trees that root easily can be between one and one and a half metres long;
- Every cutting must have **a few buds** from which new stems will grow and a rather long piece of stem that is buried in the ground and develops adventitious roots. When these roots grow only from the nodes as with sugar cane, at least one or two nodes must be buried, and one or two nodes left above the ground.

  Cuttings must contain enough stored food to nourish the roots and the new stems but, at the same time, they should not be too long **(figure 372)**;

371 Stem cuttings are taken from ripe wood.

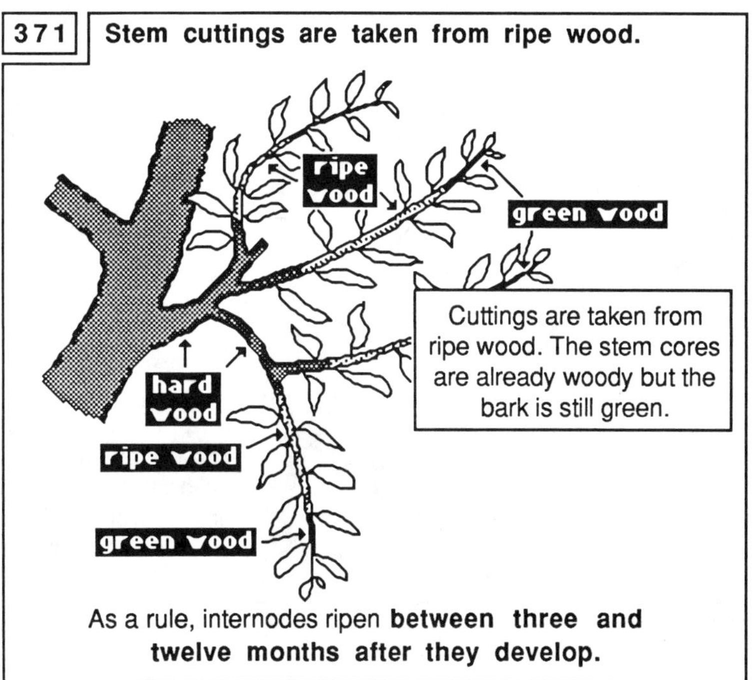

As a rule, internodes ripen **between three and twelve months after they develop.**

372 How to take cuttings

Wrong : two wrong ways of propagating cuttings from plants similar to sugar cane
■ No node was buried. No adventitious roots can develop. The buried portion rots.
■ A stem portion without a node was buried. It begins to rot. The rot spreads to the top of the cutting.
soil
Right : the right way of propagating cuttings from plants similar to sugar
■ One or more nodes are buried.
■ The superfluous parts have been removed.
soil

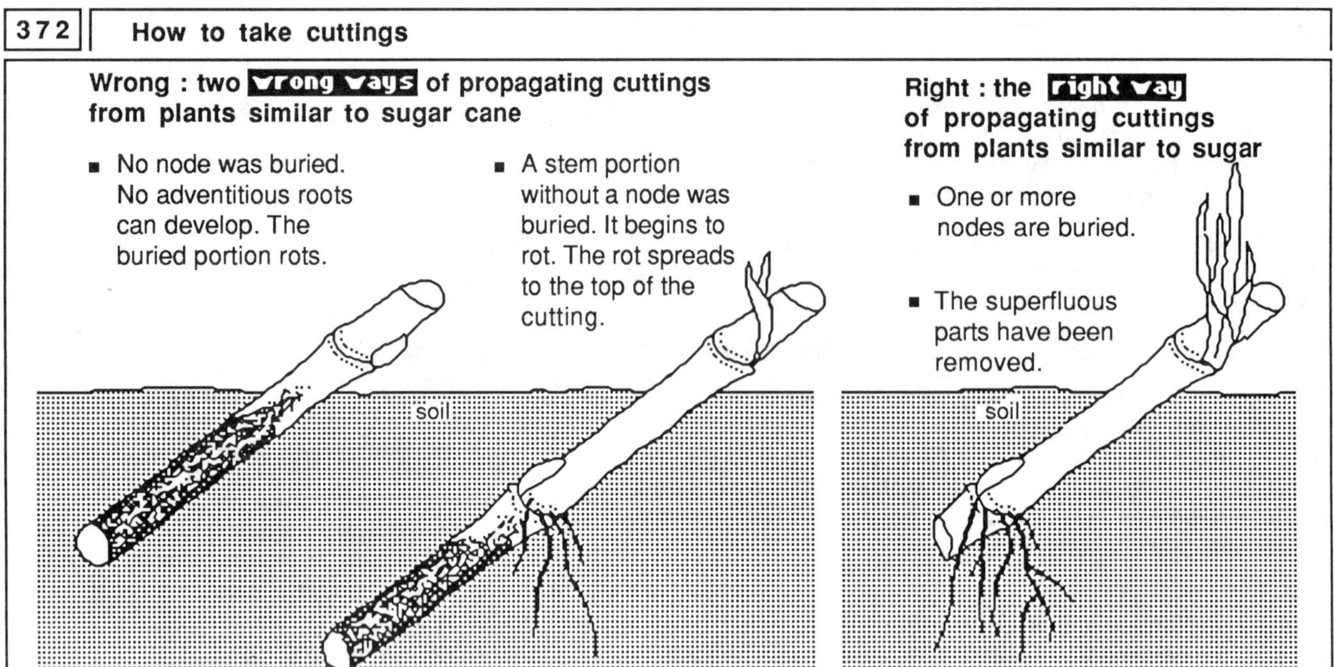

373 Cutting and trimming branches for propagation

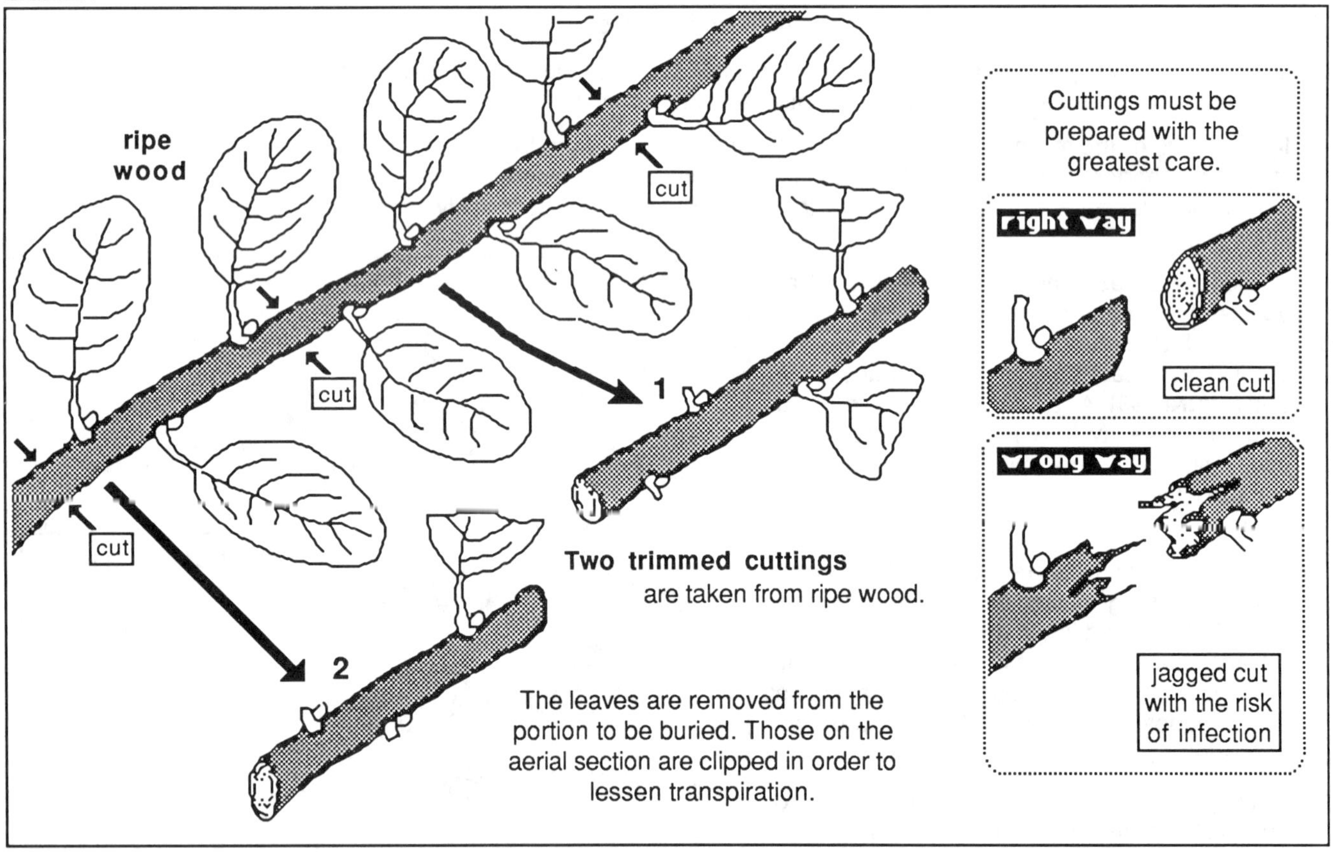

ripe wood
cut
cut
cut
1
2
Two trimmed cuttings
are taken from ripe wood.
The leaves are removed from the portion to be buried. Those on the aerial section are clipped in order to lessen transpiration.
Cuttings must be prepared with the greatest care.
right way
clean cut
wrong way
jagged cut with the risk of infection

- It is worth checking to see if there are **dormant buds** which are likely to develop after the cuttings have been planted. Even a few buds will be adequate. If more than two or three shoots seem likely to develop, some buds are removed to allow the cutting to devote all its sap to the remaining buds. This practice is called **bud excision** and must be done without wounding the cuttings.
- Cuttings must be taken **with a very sharp knife** in order **to avoid splitting**. A neat, clean cut makes healing easier and lessens the risk of infection. The exposed cuts can be coated in ashes that have disinfectant properties and which quicken the healing process **(figure 373)**.
- If leaves are left on the new cuttings, the leaves transpire and use up the sap in the cuttings that are still without roots. A practice called **trimming** is carried out to prevent the leaves from exhausting the cuttings to the detriment of root formation.

  Trimming consists of removing all the leaves on the portion to be buried and leaving no more than two clipped leaves on the aerial part.

Practical experience is the only way of discovering the method that suits each plant best. Some species whose propagation was deemed impossible in the past are now multiplied by cuttings in great numbers thanks to the patient efforts of farmers and researchers.

Here are some tips for success with cuttings:

- **Heel** and **'mallet'** cuttings are cuttings with a portion of the main stem attached to their base **(figure 369d)**. Root growth is often very active at the intersection of the main stem and the side-shoot.
- In some plants that are hard to propagate, for instance, shea butter, eggplant and chillies, adventitious roots can be induced by ringing the branch to be cut. **Girdling** or **ringing** means cutting and removing a narrow ring of bark one or two centimetres wide from the point at which you intend taking the cutting. Some days later, a small swelling appears at the lower end of the future cutting. This is now the time for cutting and planting, because the swelling proves that the wood and bark have entered a phase of intense activity that will assist root growth **(figure 374a)**.

374 Ringing and air layering

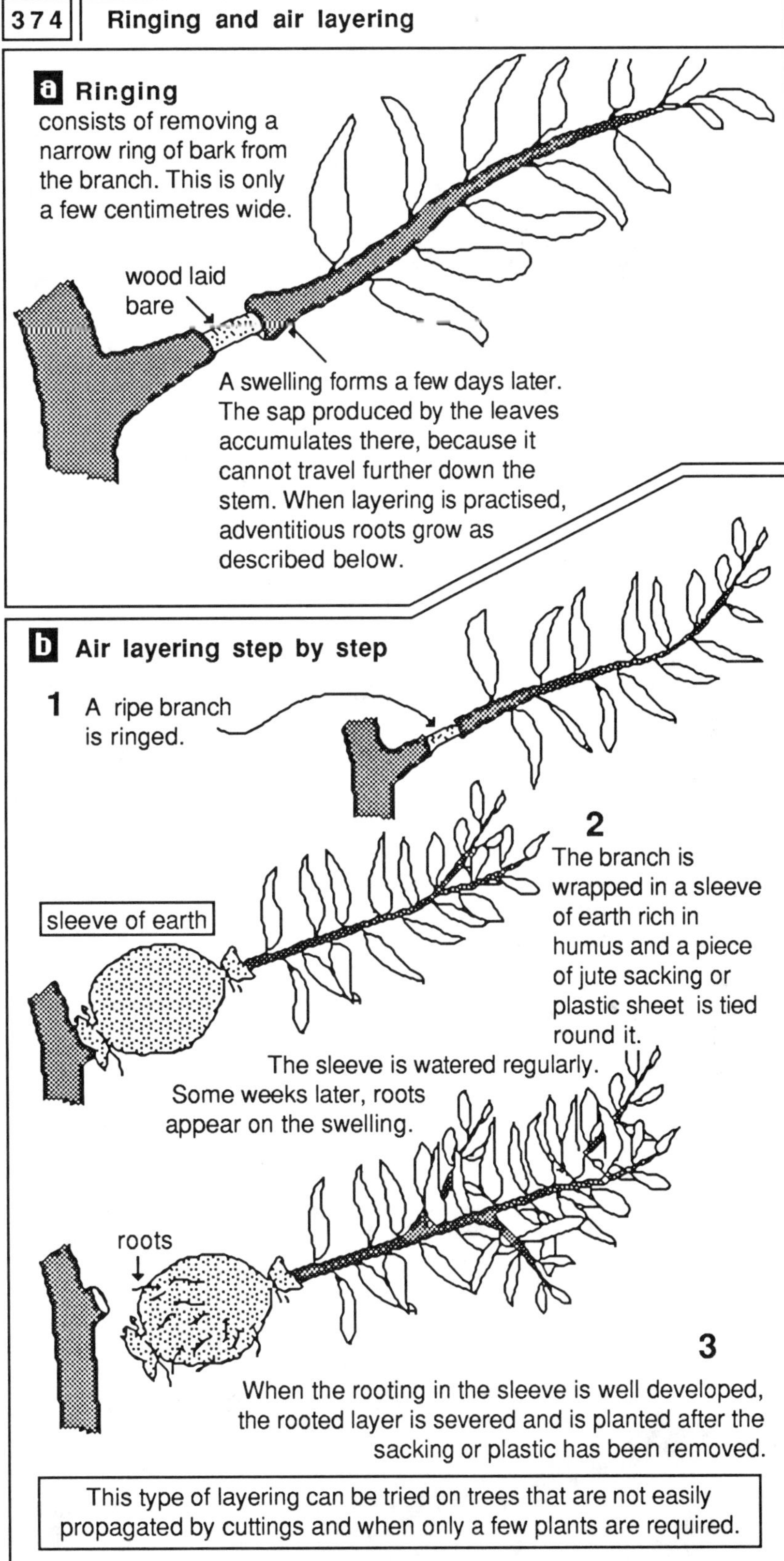

This type of layering can be tried on trees that are not easily propagated by cuttings and when only a few plants are required.

Notes

375 Layering on the ground

stake

A low branch is bent and covered with soil. The end is staked to keep it in place.

stake

layer

Some weeks later, adventitious roots have appeared on the layer that is ready to be cut and transplanted to its permanent site.

- Ringing is also used for the air layers shown in **figure 374b**.

  Another, more usual form of **layering** is practised at ground level. It consists of pegging a branch or stem to the ground and covering it with soil. After some time, it may take months, roots grow on the buried part **(figure 375)**. Ringing can also be used with this method.

  The soil surrounding all layered plants must be watered regularly, because moisture is vital for the development of adventitious roots.

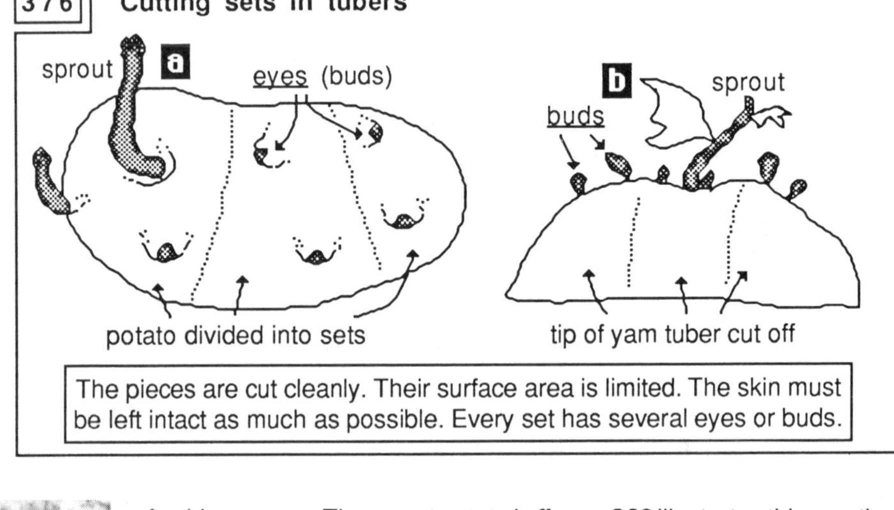

When a number of cuttings are required, plants should be kept specially for this purpose. The sweet potato in **figure 362** illustrates this practice. When many cuttings are required to reproduce trees, these should be grown separately and pruned to encourage the growth of shoots rather than fruit (Chapter 6). A plantation of these trees is called a **tree nursery**.

377

Cuttings from rhizomes and tubers

Rhizomes are shoots that grow underground like roots. They differ from roots because they have leaf buds as well as root buds, normally roots only have root buds.

It is very easy to take cuttings from rhizomes. You need only cut the horizontal stems into lengths and plant them.

A potato is a tuber full of starch. It has many **eyes** with both leaf and root buds. The potato is cut into pieces or **sets** for planting. Every set has some eyes and a certain amount of stored food **(figure 376)**.

Tubers are modified stems packed with nutritive reserves. As a rule, new shoots only sprout near the top which was attached to the main stem as shown in **figure 377**, but sometimes pieces of tuber can be made to grow.

It is common practice to let yams sprout. Shortly before the rainy season, the tip of the yam tubers are cut off and placed in a shallow pit. They are covered with straw and watered frequently. The sprouted tips are planted when the sprouts are between twenty and thirty centimetres long, or even longer **(figure 378)**.

Bananas can also be multiplied by sets. The rhizomes are cut into pieces, each one with one or two eyes; they are left to sprout.

378 The sprouting of yam tuber tips

The tips are placed in the bottom of a pit and covered with straw. The straw is watered from time to time to keep it moist. When the sprouts are 20 to 50 cm high, they can be transplanted.

Shoots, root-suckers and underground stems

Roots are already growing on the sugar cane **shoots** in **figure 350**. In this case, the shoots are simply cut off and replanted; the roots are handled carefully. Sometimes, however, the shoots have not yet rooted as in the case of the pineapple in **figure 357**. Here the shoot is treated like a stem cutting and must be cut off close to the main stem. The base of the shoot is then trimmed of its leaves so that it can come into direct contact with the soil.

Root-suckers need only be cut with a sharp knife and transplanted. They are often transplanted with a ball of earth attached.

Cuttings from pieces of underground stem are harder to prepare because the base of the root stock must be cut lengthwise so that each cutting has a portion of stem and some roots **(figure 379)**.

These examples illustrate the need to prepare cuttings in time :

- If yam tops take three weeks to sprout, they will have to be placed in the pit just three weeks before the time scheduled for planting. If planting is less than three weeks away, the sprouts will be too short for planting. If planting is more than three weeks away, the sprouts will be difficult to separate.
- Sweet potato cuttings must be planted as soon as they are large enough. This means that, if you want to ensure a plentiful supply of cuttings, you will have to establish the stock plants three or four months before you plan to take cuttings.
- Fruit tree seedlings are transplanted to the main field at the start of the rainy season. The seedlings are only ready for permanent planting when they have rooted and have produced fairly long shoots. Hence the need to start raising them in nursery beds one or two seasons before transplanting.

Planning ahead is therefore vital for all propagation operations.

379 How to split underground stems

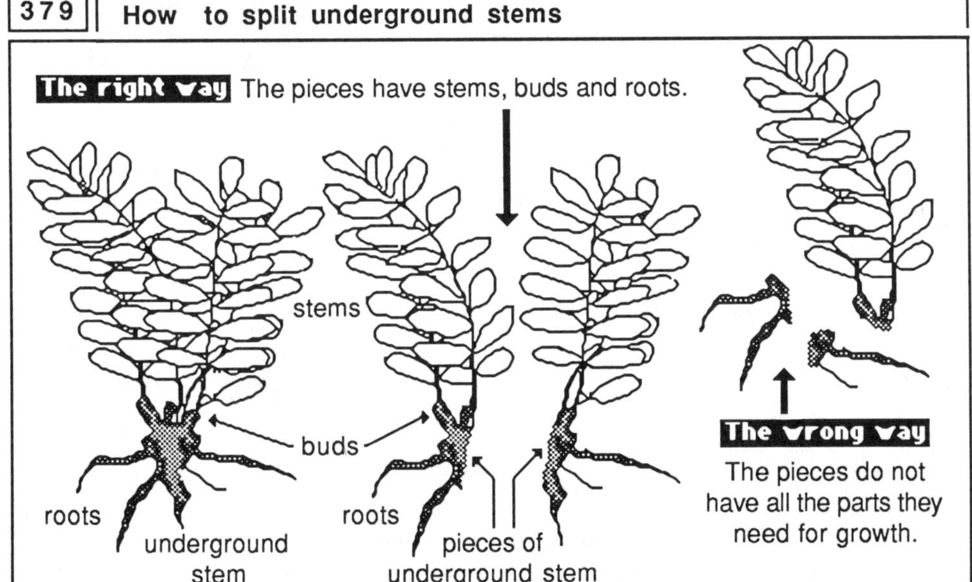

Chapter 13

Sowing and planting

Good sowing and planting arrangements allow for the way plants are going to develop both above and below the ground, during the whole of their life cycle. This spatial arrangement of plants must be examined in three dimensions :

- the **ground surface** occupied;
- the **aerial space** that the foliage of the plants will need in order to make the most of the light and air;
- the **underground space** in which the roots will develop.

The whole volume of the field or garden must be occupied to the best advantage while, at the same time, minimising competition between plants. A balance of the produce grown must also be considered.

The space that plants occupy varies all through their life cycle. Sowing schedules and patterns must therefore anticipate how the plants are going to fill the space at each phase of their life cycle.

Many elements have to be taken into account in deciding the methods used in sowing and planting :

- the **cropping pattern** - a crop in pure stand or crops in mixtures;
- the **species and varieties** that are sown : seasonal or perennial, early or late-maturing plants;
- the **habits** of the associated plants : herbaceous, shrubby, arborescent, erect, spreading, creeping, etc.;
- the **surface and volume occupied by the roots** of each interplanted species and variety;
- the differences between the **lengths of the vegetative cycles** of the intercropped plants - some plants mature in three months, others take six months or more. One of the associated plants may have reached the end of its cycle when the other is only at the the first phase;
- plants can be sown direct **in the field.** This means that plants grow to maturity on the site where they germinate;
- they can be sown **in nurseries**. This implies that when the plants reach a certain stage of growth, they are transferred to the site where they will mature.

380

381 **Thinning gives each plant the space it needs to thrive.**

Thinning is carried out in the early stages of growth.

1 Shortly after germination

2 Some weeks after thinning

3 If thinning is not carried out

Carrots are sown very densely. When the seedlings are allowed to grow without being thinned, the roots compete for food and the leaves for light. The roots do not develop properly. Production is poor and erratic. Thinning is practised to remove interplant competition. The weaker plants are pulled up, and care is taken to give all the remaining plants an adequate volume of soil and light. With certain species, but not for carrot, the plants removed can be transplanted if their roots are intact.

Direct sowing in the field

Plants sown **in the field** can be broadcast, or drilled, or sown in holes, following the patterns described in Chapter 5.

Only fairly large seeds are **sown in holes** because they can be counted one by one. Seeds such as okra, cucurbits, beans and maize suit this planting method. Small seeds are always broadcast or sown in drills.

When you sow directly in the field, seed density cannot be fully controlled. In **figure 380**, for example, the seedlings are overcrowded in places, whereas elsewhere there are empty spaces.

When seeds are sown in holes, some holes may contain more than two or three plants. When plants are overcrowded, they compete with each other.

Thinning is a way of regulating plant density in rows and in holes **(figure 381)**. It consists of pulling up some seedlings in order to leave enough room for others to thrive. When sown in holes, two or three very vigorous plants, sometimes more, are left standing. When rows of seedlings are thinned, **overcrowding is reduced** so that the remaining plantlets are properly spaced.

382

383

384

During thinning operations, weak, distorted seedlings are pulled up to let healthy plants reach maturity without competition.

Figure 382 shows a drill of Swedish turnip thinned for the first time in the growing season. Later on, when the plants have developed, they will be thinned for the second time. The young plants pulled up at this stage can be eaten.

During the thinning operation, seedlings are sometimes transplanted to fill the gaps. Only plants carefully pulled with their roots intact can be used to transplant.

Sowing in the field calls for well-loosened soils in which the tiny rootlets can penetrate with ease. **Crusting of the soil** caused by raindrop splash

must be avoided at all costs. Soil becomes crusted when rain strikes the soil and compacts the soil particles. After the rain, the clay in the soil forms a thin layer that hardens as it dries in the sun. It is difficult for tiny seedlings to penetrate this hard layer. Crusting can be prevented by mulching as in **figure 383**, or shading as in **figure 384**.

Mulches must not hinder plant growth and must therefore be removed as soon as the seedling emerges, particularly if a thick layer of mulch was applied as in the foreground of **figure 383**. Rice and millet chaff and sawdust all provide excellent mulch for germinating beds.

Mulching and shading are also valuable because they retain moisture in the superficial soil layers where the seedlings germinate.

In some regions, seeds are broadcast in grasslands. This system is used for sesame and elephant grass in Northern Zaire and Southern Sudan. Sowing takes place at the onset of the rains on grassy fallows that are burnt prior to broadcasting. Sometimes, the fallow is burnt after sowing. The tiny sesame and elephant seeds fall between the tufts of grass, under the layer of mulch, and germinate there. This cultural practice associated with fallows needs hardly any labour. The wild herbs and grasses prepare the seedbed by loosening the soil, and in so doing, provide small seeds with a good germination bed.

385

386

387

Establishment of cuttings and tubers

Seasonal plants produced by vegetative propagation are usually planted directly into the field, i.e. in their permanent site - on mounds (also called hills) or ridges, in plots or in sunken beds, as described

388

in Chapter 3. The soil must be tilled and well loosened to a depth of at least 15 to 20 centimetres.

As a rule, tubers are planted on mounds and ridges. This is because they thrive in soil well-loosened to a good depth. These soil conditions are more easily created by mounding and ridging than by flat tillage.

Figure 385 shows a yam hill. The tuber tip is planted on the top of the hill. It is covered with straw to prevent erosion and retain moisture.

Figure 386 shows a more unusual mound designed for a cassava cutting. The top of the mound is depressed to form a little hollow where the cutting is planted. Some rain runs into the hollow and covers the cutting. Normally, cassava is planted without forming this hollow, with the result that water runs off the mound and tends to erode the soil from the buried portion of the cutting.

This system of shallow depressions can also be used in land tilled on the flat to help retain moisture in the immediate vicinity of the plant.

The way cuttings and shoots are positioned, in or on the soil, affects the speed with which they root. It also influences the development of the root system, and the shape of the future plant **(figure 389)**.

Cuttings are usually inserted slantwise because the plants obtained are bushier than when the cuttings are planted in an upright position.

If long cuttings are placed horizontally, a larger number of shoots may be obtained which can be useful if the shoots are to be harvested.

389 **Three ways of planting cuttings**

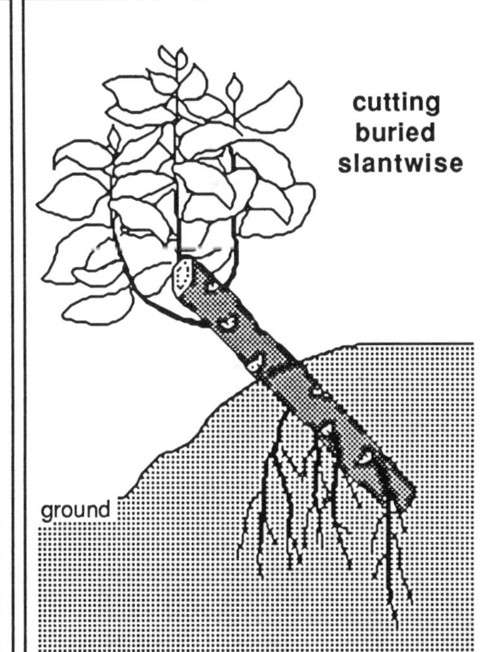

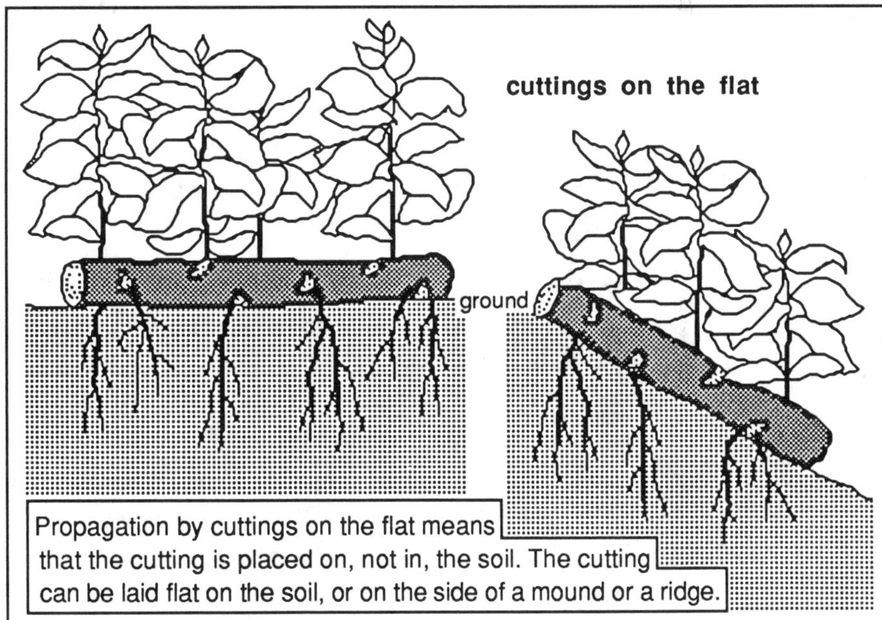

Propagation by cuttings on the flat means that the cutting is placed on, not in, the soil. The cutting can be laid flat on the soil, or on the side of a mound or a ridge.

The bitter leaf plants in **figures 387 and 388** were propagated by cuttings. The first shrub developed from a cutting placed horizontally, the second from an upright cutting.

Generally speaking, tuber tops , shoots and pieces of underground stem must be placed vertical rather than slantwise, but there are exceptions to this rule. In the main, upright planting is best when you want to develop one productive head, as in the case of banana, cabbage and pineapple.

Personal experience is the best guide when it comes to planting cuttings. There can be no hard and fast rules without an intimate knowledge of the local environment and of soil conditions.

Planting depth for seeds

The depth at which seeds should be planted depends on three main factors.

- **Small seeds** have limited food reserves. They must grow quickly and produce a seedling capable of feeding itself by photosynthesis. If they are sown too deep, seeds will exhaust their food stores before emerging above the ground. They also need constant moisture in the soil surface. **Larger seeds** can be sown deeper. They give rise to more vigorous seedlings that must be firmly rooted in the soil if they are to thrive.

  The **size of the seeds** is therefore the first factor which determines planting depth.

- The second factor is **the type of germination**. If we examine a bean seedling we see that the cotyledons which break out of the seed casing are carried above the soil to spread out, and form the first green leaves **(figure 390)**. Before emergence the cotyledons are responsible for taking in soil water.

  This type of germination is called **epigeal (figure 390)**. To reduce the amount of effort required by the germination seed, it is important not to bury the seed too deep, and not to let the surface soil crust over.

  Germination can also be **hypogeal**, that is, under the soil **(figure 391)**. The cotyledons remain below the soil transmitting food to the growing root and shoot. Gramineae - for example, maize, rice, millet, sorghum and sugar cane - germinate in this way. The energy these plants need to break through the superifical soil crust is less than that required for epigeal germination.

  We can now see why the ideal planting depth varies with each species and with each variety. While the grower must be guided by personal experience, it is true to say that **a seed must never be sown at a depth which is more than two or three times its diameter.**

- The **nature of the soil** is the third major factor in planting depth. The primary stem can force a passage through sandy soil more easily than through clay. On the other hand, sandy soil is more susceptible to drought, with the result that seeds should be sown deeper in sand than in clay.

390 **Epigeal germination**

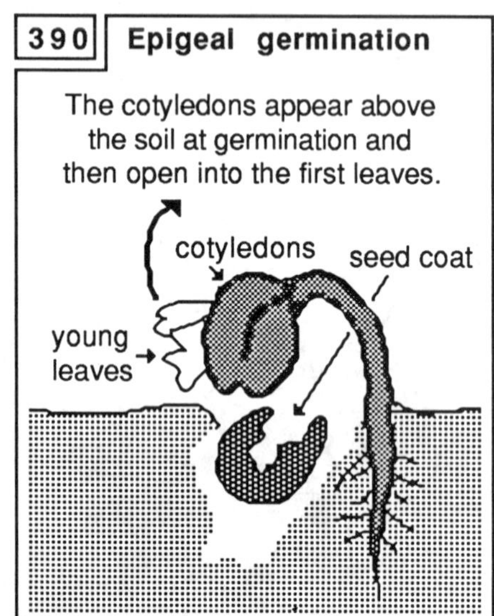

391 **Hypogeal germination**

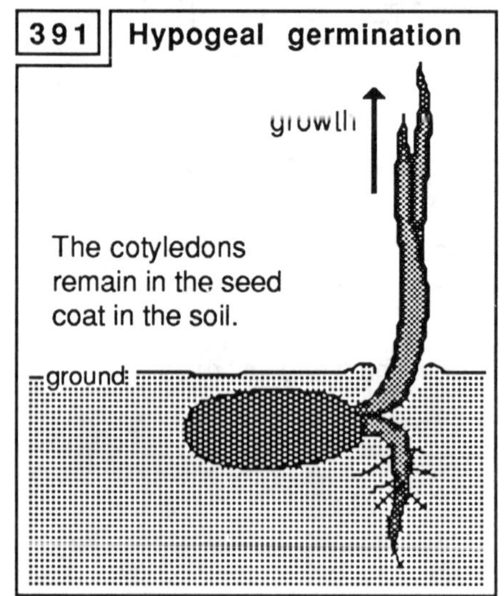

Good sowing practices

This is how vegetable beds should be sown :

- **work the seedbed to a fine tilth.** If you intend sowing in rows, mark the rows by depressing them lightly;
- broadcast or drill in tiny handfuls. Work out the approximate number of seeds you must sow in order to obtain the right seed density for one square metre or for one metre in the row; then **keep to this density**. Planting too densely is a waste of seed and demands much more work at the thinning stage;
- **cover the seeds with a thin layer of fine, dry soil;**
- with big seeds, press the soil slightly to ensure **good contact between the seeds and the soil** . The soil can be lightly compressed with a flat instrument or a board. Small seeds may not need firming;
- **cover the seed bed** with fine straw free of weed seeds, or use millet, rice or sorghum chaff or sawdust, or a temporary shading framework;
- water the drill or soil before sowing and keep **the surface soil moist at all times,. Avoid the formation of a crusted layer**.

Planting depth for vegetative material

The ideal planting depth is determined by the type of cutting, its length, the planting site, soil moisture, and how you want to position the cutting.

The best way of planting cuttings is to **bury them to about half their length**. If they are not buried deep enough, they will topple over under the weight of the new shoots. On the other hand, if they are buried too deep, there may be too few buds present above the soil to produce enough shoots; the deepest part of the cutting will not root and will start rotting.

The moisture content of the soil will also affect the way cuttings are planted. The soil must be kept damp to the depth to which the roots penetrate as illustrated in **(figure 392)**.

392 | Planting cuttings in the field

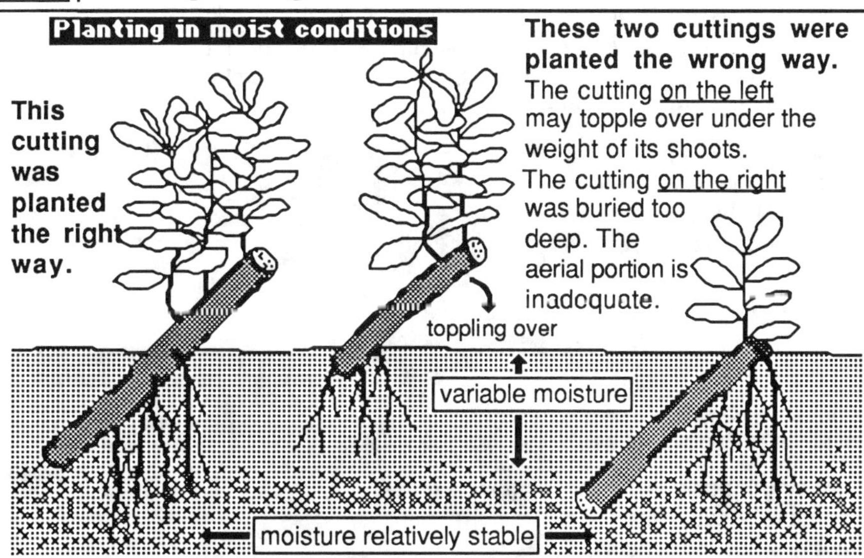

Cuttings have to grow roots in the superficial soil layers where the moisture content is much more variable than it is in deeper soil. The superficial rooting layers must therefore be well loosened, watered very regularly, and protected from excessive evaporation.

Planting in dry conditions

When the soil is moistened by rainwater or by irrigation, the depth of the damp layer must be at least equivalent to the length of the buried portion of the cutting. Later, when the roots grow, the damp layer must be as deep as the roots themselves.

depth of the roots

This is the dry, hard soil that is not irrigated. It is an obstacle to root development.

These are general recommendations and cannot replace practical experience.

Sowing varietal mixtures

Sowing mixtures of species and varieties is common practice in fields and gardens. **Mixing seeds of different varieties of the same species is particularly recommended.** This practice is popular and there is a wide choice of mixtures - of bean, pea, Bambara groundnut **(figure 394)**, okra, maize, sweet potato, bitter leaf, bush greens, fruit trees and banana.

Sowing varieties in a mixture is justified for two main reasons. One has to do with **cultural hazards**. The other is linked with the **need to**

If watering, either by irrigation or rain, is irregular young roots may be damaged by drying out. There is a greater risk of this occurring when the soil is not protected from the drying effects of wind and sun.

Figure 393 compares the right and wrong way of inserting shoots removed from such plants as pineapple, cabbage and agave. The basal shoot is prepared by trimming off the leaves. Trimming is essential because it allows the firmed soil to come into direct contact with the planted cutting.

Bulbils are also planted by being pressed firmly into the surface of the soil.

Bulbs - onions, garlic, shallot, etc. - are planted so that the tops are almost level with the soil surface.

Root-suckers and **pieces of underground stem** are buried at about the same depth as that from which they were taken.

393 | Transplanting shoots

The right way

The base of the cutting must be buried in the soil. The soil is firmed and comes in contact with the base of the shoot.

Wrong ways

Planting is too shallow. Contact between the base of the shoot and the soil is inadequate. Rooting will be poor and the plantlet may topple over.

1

The shoot was not properly trimmed. It was buried too deep. Leaves prevent the surrounding soil from pressing against the base of the shoot. The leaves may rot and infect the shoot.

2

maximize the small holding's resources (mainly soil and water), and **improve agricultural returns.**

A visit to a Rwandan farm, where bean seeds in mixtures are being prepared, illustrates the value of this cultural practice **(figure 395)**. The farmer has eighteen varieties with which to make up the mixtures that will be planted in different plots. Apart from a banana grove, the family has two plots of land, one fertile, one less productive. **Table 396** gives the names and some characteristics of the varieties that will be sown on the three plots.

A mixture of the seventeen varieties listed is sown in the banana grove along with the variety called *Nyirabunwabuta yibika* in Rwandan (n° 18 in **figure 395**) because it thrives remarkably well under bananas. As a rule, varieties with tiny seeds are sown at the base of the bananas and in the shade, while large seeds are sown in areas with more light.

Many other varietal characteristics are connected with the size and colour of the seeds : long and short vegetative cycles, early and late maturing, short and staggered harvests, climbing and creeping habits, resistance to drought and moisture and resistance to this or that pest.

The varietal mixtures respond to the specific growing conditions of each plot. If one of the varieties in the mixture is in trouble because the rains are inadequate or it is diseased, another variety steps in to maintain yields. In fact, one of the varieties (*Nyiragihura*) is only seeded on the poor soil to forestall total crop failure. Normally, this variety is overrun by every imaginable pest and, when harvested, it yields about the amount of seed that was sown to reproduce it. On the other hand, in drought conditions and when all the other varieties have wilted, the *Nyiraghihura* crop survives. Such a calamity only happens every five, ten or fifteen years, but it is precisely for those disaster years that it is worth seeding the variety every year on dry lands.

The practice of sowing varietal mixtures aims at lessening cultural hazards which are related to

- **weather conditions,**
- **pest attacks,**
- **economic factors** - supplies of adapted seeds are not always available at planting time.

But the practice is also dictated by the characteristics of the seed varieties themselves. Some varieties and species are **cross-pollinated :** their ovules **(figure 349)** must be cross-fertilized by the pollen of other plants of the same species. The varieties responsible for cross-fertilization must therefore be growing nearby and must flower at the same time as the cross-pollinated plants. This planting pattern is of significant importance in all orchards because the **presence of varieties capable of fertilizing each other is an essential feature of arboriculture.** So many orchards are unproductive because they were established with cuttings all taken from the same tree or from the same variety of trees.

Figure 398 shows a mixture of two varieties of peas growing together. These peas, one with white flowers, the other with red, are found at high altitudes in Central Africa. The women know there is no point in cultivating these varieties separately because, although there would be plenty of flowers, there would be few full pods. On the other hand, both plants established in a mixture are very productive. Local experience has proved that about twenty percent of the mixture should be the red variety.

This example shows the extent to which the discovery of the right varietal mixture can lead to improved yields.

394

395

396 **The composition of varietal mixtures of beans sown on three plots on a farm in Rwanda**

0 1 2cm

Plot A : fertile, damp soil

	Varieties*	Colour of the seeds
1	*kinyamanza*	*light beige with black streaks*
2	*Rubero*	*pale speckled beige with red streaks*
3	*Mulinga*	*mauve*
4	*Mutiki*	*red with white spots*
5	*Icyivuzo*	*greyish*
6	*Rwasamanzi*	*yellow with black streaks*
7	*Jbikara*	*black*
8	*Muhundo*	*reddish-yellow*

Plot B : poor, dry soil

	Varieties*	Colour of the seeds
9	*Nyriamacumu I*	*shiny black*
10	*Nyiramacumu II*	*dull black*
11	*Gitsimbayjjogi*	*beige with black spots*
12	*Nyirakavundeli*	*light brown*
13	*Ubunyange*	*white*
14	*Nyiragahomb*	*pinky beige*
15	*Karolina*	*purply red*
16	*Ubudida*	*white, hilum ringed in brown*
17	*Nyiragihura*	*grey*

Plot C : the banana grove

The seventeen varieties listed above and *Nyirabunwabuta Yibika* **(18)** are sown here.

* The numbers refer to **figure 395.**

However, it takes a long time to achieve a good mixture. Its merits are only proven when there are regular improvements of yield over a number of years. The choice of varieties and the proportions in the mixtures can only be determined by testing again and again.

Unfortunately, at the present time, we are witnessing a decline in knowledge about varietal mixtures. So-called 'selected' seeds oust traditional mixtures but do not meet the farmer's needs as satisfactorily as the old system. It is not easy to obtain good varietal mixtures, but it is not any easier to obtain 'wonder' varieties, especially when these varieties are produced by firms and seed stations unfamiliar with the environment where the seeds will be sown.

The answer is to go on picking and choosing different seeds and testing them in gardens. Admittedly, for some species, it is profitable to sow selected varieties without mixing them. The seeds are of good quality and cheap, and there is no point in mixing them. This is true, for example, of lettuce plants, onion, carrot, tomato and cabbages, and generally of vegetables of European origin. On the other hand varietal mixes are essential for almost all other species, particularly until such time as specialists get down to studying tropical vegetables and African farming practices in earnest, and use means consistent with the economic and social role of market gardening.

When composing a mixture of varieties adapted to local farming conditions, you should keep the following aspects in mind :

- **the varieties must be compatible**
  - in their **morphology** - shape of leaves, shape of their root systems, etc.,
  - **in their vegetative cycles**,
  - in the **hazards that can be anticipated** - different levels of tolerance to pests, to weather conditions, etc.,
  - in the **farm labour** involved - cultural practices, tillage, etc.,
  - in the **way their flowers are fertilized**;
- the **right proportion** of each variety in the mixture must be determined;
- with some species such as tomato, cucurbits and chillies, **seed plants must be cultivated separately** in order to preserve the original characteristics of the varieties;
- **sowing patterns have to be adapted** to suit the characteristics of the different varieties.

398

All this means that combining suitable varietal mixtures calls for lengthy testing. It also explains why it is not easy to introduce new varieties into established mixtures, especially when the new seeds have not been tested for sowing in mixtures.

Chapter 14

Nurseries

Nurseries are places used for germinating seeds and propagating plants by vegetative means. The plants raised there are then transplanted to their permanent site.

Objectives in nursery construction

There are many good reasons for establishing nurseries :

- **Some plants in the nursery need to be tended very carefully.** Take fruit tree cuttings, for example. They must be left in the shade and watered every day. One can imagine how difficult it would be to water them in the field. It is easier to watch out for the first signs of pest attack and to deal with it in nursery conditions;
- **During the first phase in their life cycle, seedlings do not take up much space.** When they are sown in a nursery, only a small surface area is needed for the germination bed. So, preparing such a small bed is labour-saving;
- **Seedlings cannot withstand drought** because their tiny roots are not yet anchored in the deep, moister soil layers. Sowing them in a nursery **makes it easier to regulate watering** and to control the moisture in the superficial soil layer;

- **Many plants flourish with renewed vigour when they are transplanted.** Beds with plants which have been moved usually look more impressive than beds with direct-sown seedlings. There are two reasons why transplants do much better :

  - transplanting properly carried out invigorates the plant and accelerates its growth;
  - **as he transplants, the gardener selects the hardiest plants** and eliminates the weakest. This means that the number of seeds sown in the nursery is usually greater than the number of seedlings the gardener wants to transfer to the beds. The cost of the few seeds sown in excess is definitely compensated for by the increased productivity obtained by being able to pick out young, healthy seedlings for transplanting;

  By establishing nurseries. the gardener often **gains time during the growing season**. Suppose he decides to sow bush greens on a plot where cabbage was previously cultivated, he can choose between two sowing strategies :

- He can pull up the cabbage and prepare the bed for sowing with bush greens. In this case the bush greens will take ten or fifteen days to germinate and become established.

  Alternately, he can decide to sow the bush greens in a nursery two or three weeks before the cabbage harvest, after which the bush greens are immediately transplanted. In this way, the farmer gains two or three weeks in the cycle of farm production.

  Nurseries are established on **relatively small plots of land where the soil can be thoroughly fertilized**. Any plants raised there will benefit enormously from this fertility all through their life cycle even if, later on, they are transplanted to less fertile soil.

- By way of comparison, these well-fed plants can be contrasted with a sheep that was badly nourished during the first months of his life and was sickly as a result. No matter how the animal is fed at a later stage, he will never be as strong as an animal properly nourished from birth. Plants growing in a nursery are like the well-fed sheep.

Plants raised in nurseries must not be left there too long. There comes a time when they have not enough room to develop normally. If transplanting is delayed, the seedlings suffer : they become deformed and leggy, they compete for food, their roots get tangled and are hard to separate for transplanting. Dwarfed and twisted plants must not be transplanted.

Methods of nursery establishment

Whatever kind of nursery is established, the following rules must be applied :

- make **a germination bed with loose, fertile soil** at least 10 to 15 centimetres deep;
- **use clean soil.** Do not take soil from sites where fungal or bacterial diseases are prevalent. You can, if you like, sterilize the soil by heating it on a metal sheet;
- do not take soil from sites likely to harbour the **seeds of undesirable plants**;
- **get rid of everything that might hinder growth or deform the roots.** This includes leaves, stones, pebbles, and hard clods of soil **(figure 399)**;
- **fertilize with well-decayed organic matter and ashes.** Break up any lumps of manure that might burn the seedlings;
- **level the ground** to prevent runoff that would carry away seeds;
- use mulches, a nursery shed or a roof of some kind to **protect the soil surface from rain splash** and from crusting over;
- protect the nursery from **predators**;
- establish the nursery **near a water point** - this will make watering easier;

399 The germination bed in a nursery must be worked to a fine tilth.

Pebbles and stones in the bed cause root deformation. Distorted plants do not thrive well and are hard to transplant.

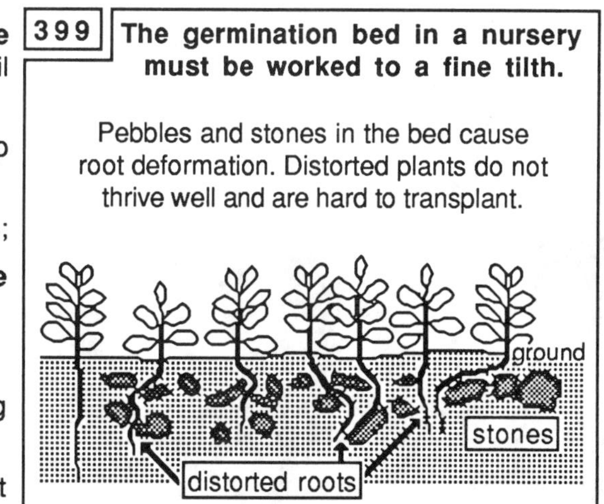

A well-established nursery will last for many years. The labour spent setting up the nursery and then looking after it is usually worth the trouble, especially if the fertility of the germination beds is maintained and any unwanted weeds are eliminated.

Weeds cause more trouble in nurseries than they do in plots or in orchards. You must work to keep the soil clean and, to achieve this, it is vital to pull up weeds regularly, season after season, as soon as they emerge. You must never let weeds propagate by seeds, shoots or rhizomes. Also, if you want to keep the soil clean for the coming seasons, you must not neglect the nursery after you have transplanted its contents.

401

402

400

Sterilization by heat is a way of treating the soil in nurseries and of killing unwanted seeds. However, there are other ways of eliminating weeds.

There are many, more or less efficient ways of establishing nurseries. Here are some examples of the methods used.

The most elementary but the least reliable method is shown in **(figure 400)**. The soil, raked and loosened, is left bare, exposed to sun and rain. A few bush green seeds are scattered there and are watered twice a day in dry weather.

Some of the seedling roots manage to penetrate the soil and find the water they need for growth. Others fail to do so and wilt. The gardener is satisfied with this limited success because only a few plants are needed and there are plenty of seeds available. If this were not so, the sowing method would obviously be unacceptable.

The tobacco nursery in **figure 401** was placed in the shade of a tree on a spot where crop trash and ashes had been collected. Here too, the preparation of the nursery was minimal and the number of seedlings raised small.

On another site, fruits or nuts were left in a pile at the foot of a tree and covered with plant waste **(figure 402)**. Moisture and heat speed up the germination of the nuts. However, the drawback to piling the nuts in this haphazard fashion is that the young stems and roots may become distorted or tangled.

The methods described above are simple and quite adequate when the gardener only wants to obtain a few plants and has a good supply of seeds at his disposal. More elaborate methods are necessary when large areas have to be sown, when many plants need transplanting, or when seeds are expensive.

Figures 403 and 404 illustrate two types of nurseries, one on the ground, the other on a table.

The one at ground level consists of beds worked to a very fine, loose tilth. The stones and large clods of earth were heaped up all round the edge of the beds to prevent rain or irrigation water from flowing away.

The area in the garden reserved for the nursery has lighter, sandy soil with a good structure. It was enriched by animal manure that was well-crumbled to remove lumps. The beds were sown and covered with straw which will be removed after the emergence of the seedlings. **Figures 383 and 384** also illustrate the use of mulch.

403

In West Africa, it is common to find nursery beds on tables made of wood and straw **(figure 404)**. A germination bed 15 to 20 centimetres deep is placed on the straw top. The bed consists of a mixturo of light soil and plant compost or animal manure; it is sieved and a little fertilizer is sometimes added. The bed is watered morning and evening, and the soil is always well drained because excess water seeps away through the straw. One advantage of this system is that the seedlings are safe from pests moving at ground level.

Nurseries are also established in trenches in order to promote moisture retention **(figure 405)**. The trenches are 30 to 50 centimetres deep. They are covered with straw roofing that protects them from rain.

When seeds are protected by a hard coat or shell, germination is sometimes quite slow. The seeds need certain conditions of humidity and temperature, and react badly to fluctuations. **The stratification** of seeds is a way of placing seeds in layers and of maintaining an even level of moisture and constant temperatures round them **(figure 406)**. As soon as the primary root becomes visible as a white spot on the growing point, the seeds are removed and planted in bags in a nursery **(figure 410)**. Germination by stratification can take many weeks or months during which the seeds must be checked frequently.

404

405 A nursery in a trench

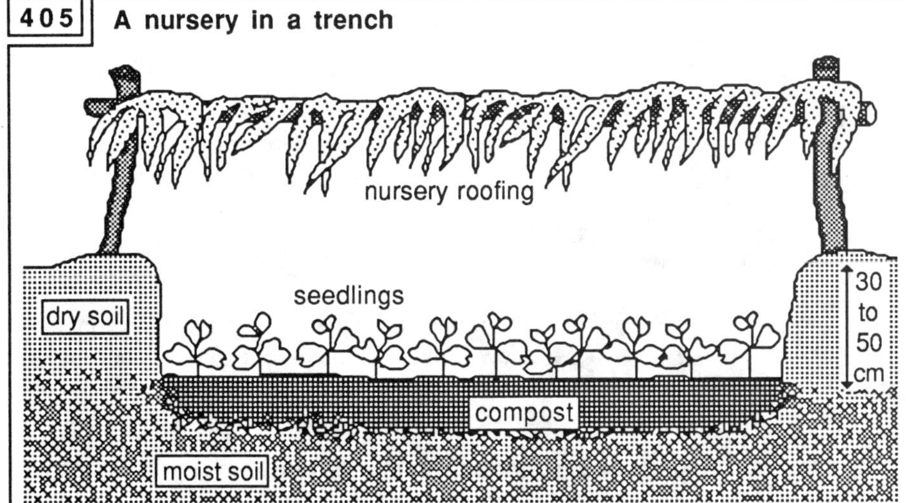

The layer of compost in the bottom of the trench helps to maintain moisture in the lower layers. These withstand evaporation better than the superficial layers. At the beginning, the roofing also helps to retain moisture in the germination bed. It can be removed later on.

Protecting nurseries

Nurseries must be protected from pests - birds, slugs, piercing and chewing insects and marauding domestic and wild animals.

All the methods of preventive control described in Chapter 8 can be applied to nurseries :

- they can be surrounded by **hedges or enclosures** to keep out domestic animals;
- they can be surrounded by **a strip of bare land** one or two metres wide. This space without vegetation keeps away a number of pests that move at ground level;
- protection from rodents can be provided by putting the germination beds on **tables (figure 404)**,

or by building a **low wall** round the nursery **(figure 321)** or by putting up fine-meshed **wire netting**;

- **thorny branches** give protection from birds, crickets and domestic animals **(figure 407)**.

Emerging seeds are generally very sensitive to heat. That is why nurseries are established in the shade of a tree or, better still, in nursery sheds, or under temporary roofing as shown in **figures 409 and 384**. Roofing creates cool conditions at ground level and stops the direct, beating action of raindrops.

The most satisfactory shaded areas are created by roofing made from mats and palm fronds. It should be possible to regulate shade intensity depending on the stage of plant growth : deeper shade at the time of sowing, lighter shade when the seedlings are established.

Ideally, roofing for shaded areas should be **adaptable and permeable**. Shade is regulated by adding or removing matting or palms or by raising them up if you have a covered nursery similar to the one in **figure 409**.

The roofing shown in **figure 408** is made of metal sheets and gives the **wrong kind of shade**. These are the drawbacks to this kind of structure :

- the shade under the roofing is too dense for the seedlings just when they need a lot of light for photosynthesis;
- rainwater cannot reach the seedbed : yet the seedlings need a lot of moisture;
- the metal gets very hot when it is exposed to the sun. Ambient temperature under the roofing rises and the seedlings wilt;
- watering is made difficult. It has to be done from the sides, or the roof has to be removed.

The roofing in **figure 409** is placed high enough to allow workers to move round easily underneath it. Notice how the seeds were placed in **plastic bags** and not in a bed.

406 The stratification of hard seeds

The germinator is made of a wooden crate with holes in the bottom to let excess irrigation water drain away. It is roofed for protection.

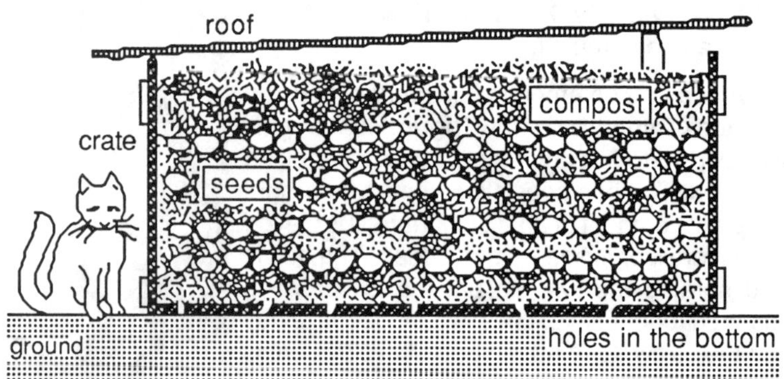

Start by filling the bottom of the crate with a layer of **compost** . This is prepared by sifting sand and compost. The seeds are then placed, in a single layer on the soil. Place big seeds on their side so that the stem and the root do not have to twist and turn in order to face the direction in which they will grow.

Now, fill the crate with **alternate layers** of compost and seeds. **Water generously** morning and evening.

<u>Remove the seeds as soon as you notice the white spot that signals the appearance of the primary root.</u>

Next, the seeds are transferred to a nursery where they will remain until it is time to transplant them.

407

The bag technique is very common for propagating trees both from seed and from vegetative material.

The bags are filled with light, rich compost, prepared as for a nursery. A few holes are made in the bottom of the bag to let excess water drain away. One seed or one cutting is placed in each bag **(figure 410)**. By proceeding in this way, each seedling will be protected by its own ball of soil when it is transplanted.

The size of the bags depends on the extent of the root system that the young plants will develop by the time they are ready for transplanting. Root volume can vary from 0.5 kilograms for small plants to 10 or 15 kilograms for very large plants.

If the seedlings are left too long in the bags, the main root becomes twisted, and the other roots develop in circles, for lack of room. In these circumstances and if transplanting has to be delayed, the seedlings can be moved to bigger bags. Pruning the shoots is another possibility.

Plastic bags are easy to use and are fairly cheap but other containers such as raffia baskets, pieces of bamboo and earthen pots can be used. Whatever the container, water must be able to drain through the bottom. Otherwise the roots run the risk of asphyxiation and plants may wilt permanently.

408

410

409

Chapter 15 Transplanting

Transplanting means removing a young plant from a nursery in order to plant it in its permanent place. Transplanting is done, either with exposed roots, or by transferring the plant with the root ball intact. (The root ball is the ball of earth adhering to the roots).

Transplanting techniques

The advice that follows holds for small plants that are transplanted **with their roots exposed**. This means that most of the soil clinging to the roots is removed **(figure 411)**. The rules for transplanting bigger plants, trees, for example, are described on page 210.

- Most vegetable transplants should have **two to six true leaves**, without counting their cotyledons. They should have **several well-developed roots** and the **epidermis** on the stem should be **firm**.
- The seedlings must be **sturdy and erect**. Sickly, dwarfed or distorted plants which would not thrive are rejected.
- **The young plants are removed from the nursery bed with the help of a suitable implement** such as a trowel that makes the soil crumble and disintegrate as the plants are lifted. This method ensures that all the roots remain intact. Seedlings should be transplanted when the soil is damp but still friable. If it is heavy and sticky, the roots may get damaged when the plants are separated **(figure 412)**.

  It is very bad practice to pull up the young plants because too many roots are broken, especially the taproot in plants with taproot systems.

411

412 How to uproot plants for transplanting

- If you pull up plants roughly, the roots and especially the taproot will get broken. This is bad gardening practice.
- Dig up seedlings with a knife, a machete or a trowel. Be sure to free all the roots including the taproot, but leave a little soil on them.

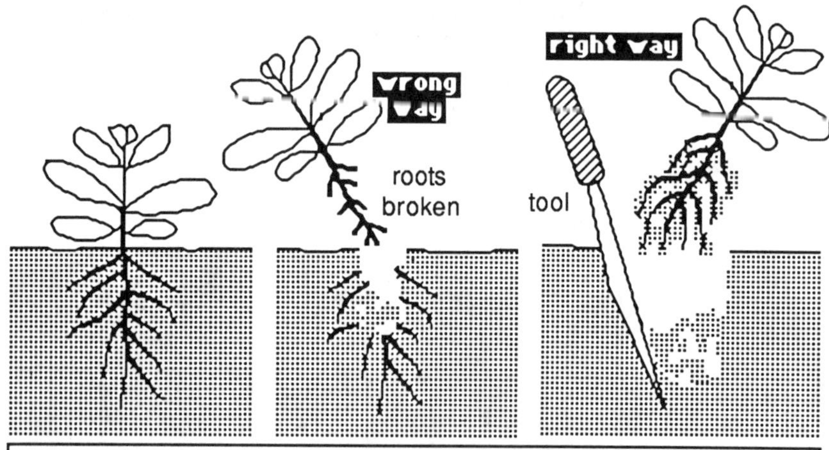

If there are too many roots, cut some off, using scissors or a knife. Trimming means cutting off, not pulling or tearing.

- Once removed from the nursery, **young plants should be transplanted immediately**. Seedlings are very sensitive to drought. **Avoid leaving them in the sun**, and wrap them in a wet cloth if they have to be transported.
- **Transplants have to be trimmed.** If the roots are long and extensive, shorten them a little with a sharp knife, and out off some of the leaves. When the roots are too long, they do not fit properly into the transplanting or planting hole **(figure 416)**. Again, if there are too many leaves, transpiration may be too great at a time when the seedling is short of water.

  The young pawpaw in **figure 413** was trimmed and then placed in the planting hole . Trimming is particularly important when there is a long interval between the time when the plant is removed from the nursery and is actually transplanted.

Transplant into **well-loosened soil** which the rootlets can penetrate easily.

- When transplanting small plants, begin by digging a hole with a knife or a dibber. A dibber is a pointed wooden or metal tool with a handle that is pushed into the ground to make the **transplanting holes.** When larger plants are transplanted, a spade is used to dig the **planting holes**.

The depth of transplanting and planting holes must be greater than the length of the transplanted roots.

- **The collar**, i.e. the transition link between the stem and the roots, **is positioned to be exactly level with the ground surface when the soil has been compacted round the plant (figure 414)**. If the collar is below the ground surface, the stem may rot. If the collar is above the surface, loosening or toppling may occur.
- Take great care to **position the roots properly when the plant is placed in the hole**. Since the roots must never be bent upwards, the hole must be deep enough to start with. When the roots are being covered with soil, **pull the plant gently upwards** - about half a centimetre - so that the rootlets fall into place, that is, facing downwards. Now, firm the earth round the seedling.
- Transplants with exposed roots are sensitive to soil and atmospheric moisture, and wilt in the heat. Consequently, it is better to transplant **at the end of the day** to give the seedlings the cool night hours that will let the roots recover and allow them to take up enough soil moisture during the coming hot weather.
- Transplants are delicate and **shading is advisable**. This can always be removed when the plants have quite recovered.
- As soon as transplanting in a particular bed is finished, **each plant is watered generously** so that the soil becomes even more compacted round the roots.
- **Puddling** is a technique that consists of dipping the exposed transplant roots into a **soft mixture made of water, clay, dung, and, if possible, fertilizer**. This sticky paste or **puddle** feeds the rootlets and protects them from disease. A pesticide is sometimes added, or rhizobium in the case of legumes. Puddling roots has the same effects as pelleting seeds, a practice that was described in Chapter 12 and illustrated in **figure 366**.

414 How to transplant seedlings

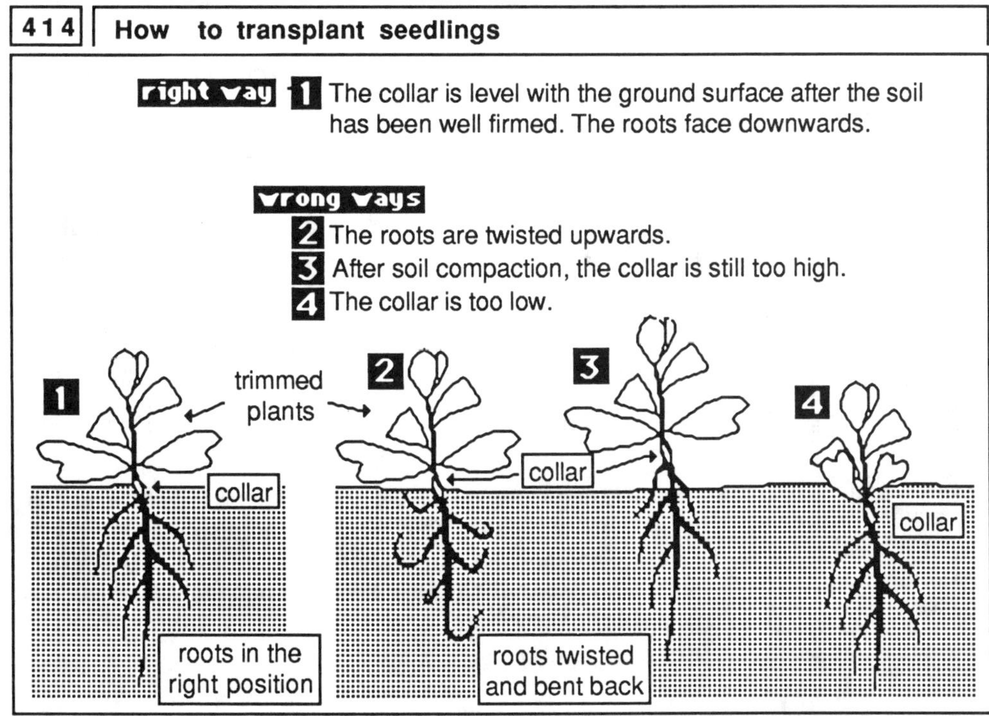

The rules for transplanting with exposed roots can be applied to **transplanting with a root ball**, the method that leaves the roots protected in a lump of soil. The soil round the plant may be contained in a plastic bag **(figure 415)**, in a basket or a flower-pot.

Transplanting with a root ball is not as risky as the method with exposed roots. Roots in the root ball are not trimmed, and the collar is easily positioned level with the ground. The only problem is transport because a lot of soil has to be transferred from the nursery to the plantation.

There is one basic rule for root-ball transplanting : the roots must be freed when the transplant is inserted into the planting hole. The protective bag or pot is removed at the last minute or, alternately the bottom is slit with a knife.

Plants transferred with the root ball intact do not need as much shade as those with exposed roots. However, the soil must be pressed firmly into the hole and the plant watered well.

Planting trees

Planting trees involves digging **special planting holes** that are filled with loose, fertile soil at the time of planting **(figure 416)**. It is in the planting hole that the new roots of the tree start growing. The hole must therefore be wide and deep. Making the planting hole too small retards plant growth and must be avoided.

Planting holes are 60 to 70 centimetres in width and in depth. They are prepared some weeks before the transplanting period so that the surrounding earth is well aerated. The end of the rainy season is a good time because the soil is still soft enough for digging and the holes will be ready at the onset of the rains. The excavated soil is piled up round the holes; this technique stops rain runoff from filling the holes.

You need well-structured soil to fill the holes when it comes to transplanting. Sand, clay and organic matter must be thoroughly mixed and the clods broken up.

This is the way to transplant a tree :

- Hold the plant in the empty hole so that **the collar is exactly level with the ground surface**;
- Pour in fine soil all round the plant and press it lightly as the filling proceeds. Be sure that the **side roots, if there are any, are well spread** and that the **stem is erect**;
- As you firm the soil, **align the collar keeping it level with the ground**;
- When the hole is full, **press the soil firmly** with your heel while holding the plant so that it does not slip down;
- Add more soil to keep water away from the root collar. Place **a thick layer of mulch** round the seedling.

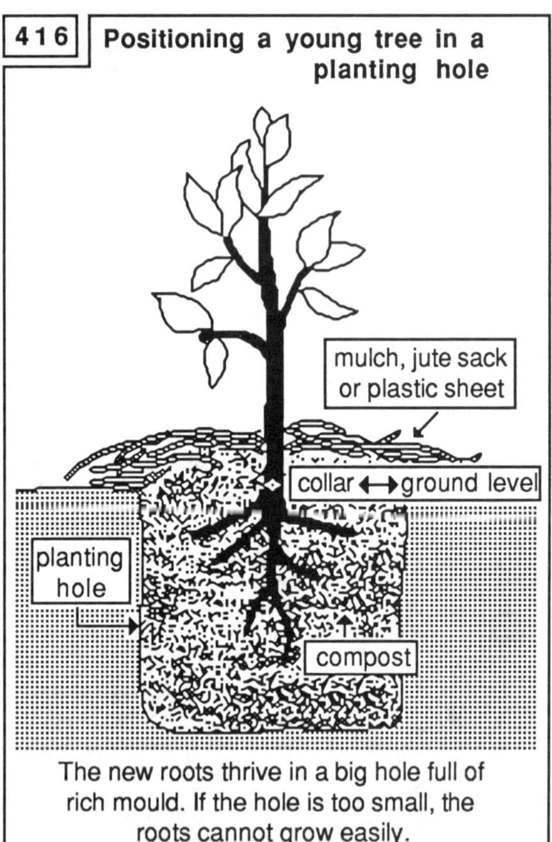

416 Positioning a young tree in a planting hole

The new roots thrive in a big hole full of rich mould. If the hole is too small, the roots cannot grow easily.

When transplanting with a root ball in a bag, pot or basket, start by filling the hole so that when you place the ball inside it, the collar of the tree is level with the ground surface. Press the soil lightly. Then, place the tree in the hole and go on filling as before. When the root ball is protected by a bag or a basket, make wide slits in the bottom to let the roots through and increase the moisture available to them.

Some young trees, when transplanted, adapt easily to their new environment but most seedlings need special attention.

- **Shade** is often required and is usually supplied by palm fronds or other leafy branches. Young plants can also be placed in the shade of another tree, like the young *Fagara* tree that was planted under the banana in **figure 417**. The banana will be cut down when the sapling has reached a good height and can stand exposure to full light.

- Small fences must be used to **protect young trees from browsing animals and rodents**. Thorny species enclose the young trees in **figure 418** and ward off animals. **Figure 322** shows a type of rodent guard for seedlings.
- Do not let **weeds** compete with young trees. Undesirable plants, if any, must be pulled up at regular intervals.
- Straw and other mulches, sacking or plastic **(figure 101)** protect the base of the trees. This is a way of **maintaining good soil structure** and preserving moisture in the planting hole. It also stops weeds from growing near the collar.
- If the seedling is in danger of bending, **it should be staked**.

Trees are always planted **as early as possible in the rainy season**, and they are watered abundantly if rainfall is low. When the planting hole is the right size and it contains well structured soil, water infiltration is better and the benefits of irrigation are greater. **Figures 78 to 82** illustrate ways of encouraging the infiltration of rain and irrigation water; they can be studied again in this connection.

417

418

Some trees do not withstand transplanting. The African fan palm and the silk cotton tree are good examples of this. Before the stem appears, the seeds grow a long, thick root thirty to forty centimetres long. It is hard to avoid breaking or damaging this root when trying to transplant the tree. Consequently, it is better to sow these and similar species in their permanent sites.

As a rule, drought-resistant trees have very deep roots. Hence the importance of giving them deep holes and of breaking up the bottom layer of soil with a spade or with a metal bar.

Chapter 16

Timing of sowing and transplanting

Two further aspects of the sowing and planting patterns that were discussed in Chapter 5 need to be examined :

- how plants can be arrranged so that they occupy **field space** as fully as possible;
- how plants can be arranged to take account of their development over the time of their growing season.

419

Planting patterns

There are so many ways of arranging plants in space and of staggering their cultural cycles that it would be impossible to mention all of them. It is more instructive to look at examples of planting patterns and to understand their advantages and disadvantages.

420

The bush greens were transplanted fairly densely in a pure stand **(figure 419)**. The plants occupy only one cultural layer of the field space available and it will take a month for them to provide complete ground cover. The ground will be exposed again when the leaves are picked and until other plants have developed. Here, we observe successive phases of soil cover and bare earth.

In the bed shown in **figure 420**, the tomatoes on the outside and the lettuce in the centre were transplanted at the same time. The tomatoes will be staked when they develop. Notice that they were properly spaced and that it will take about eight weeks for them to cover the entire surface. As for the transplanted lettuce plants, they will be ready for harvesting after four to six weeks. In the meantime, their leaves will spread and complete the cover provided by the young tomato plants. The gardener will have sold the lettuce plants by the time the first tomatoes start to ripen.

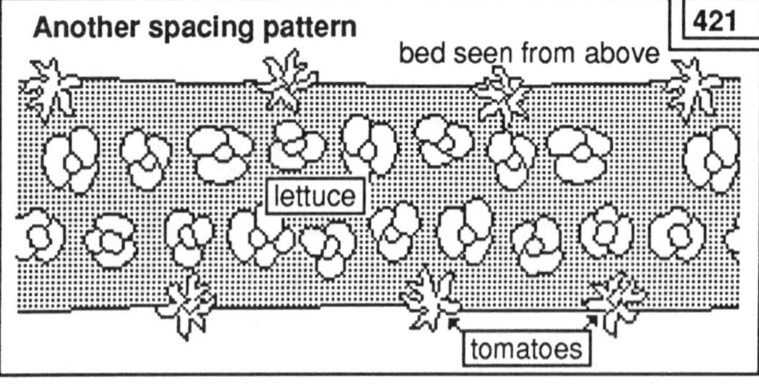

It is doubtful whether the plant density in this bed was the best that could be achieved. More lettuce plants might have been transplanted and arranged in two staggered rows as suggested in **figure 421**. If the gardener had adopted this pattern, the bed would have been more fully occupied giving a larger crop and better cover from rain splash.

The arrangement of the lettuce and bush greens growing in association **(figure 422)** is similar to the pattern for the lettuce and tomato **(figure 420)**. However, the density of the associated plants and the timing of transplantation were miscalculated because the bush green foliage covers and smothers the lettuce underneath.

This interplant competition could have been avoided

- **by altering plant density** if both species must be transplanted at the same time, or
- by **staggering transplant operations** and not transplanting the lettuce plants until the bush greens have almost reached maturity.

The way things are, the lettuce plants can only be saved from suffocatllon by thinning the bush greens although these are not yet ready to be pulled.

The association of plants shown in **figure 423** was more carefully planned. Eggplant, an erect plant, is growing in the centre of the bed while cowpea, cultivated as a leaf vegetable, is growing on the outside. The cowpea will spread along the sides of the bed, while the eggplant will occupy more space in the middle.

Here are the advantages of this arrangement :

- the sides of the bed are covered with vegetation from the beginning of the growing season, and are consequently **protected from erosion**;
- when the plants are fully developed, they occupy two quite different **cultural layers** : a spreading layer for the cowpea, an erect layer for the eggplant. The volume of air and light available above the bed is occupied to advantage;
- **the roots also exploit several soil layers** : the cowpea roots penetrate deeper than those of the eggplant;
- cowpea is a **legume that fertilizes the soil**. As soon as it starts to grow and **produce seeds, the eggplant will benefit from the fertilizing capacity of the cowpea**;
- the cowpea leaves can be gathered some time before the eggplant fruits are ready for picking. Thanks to the cowpea, **money from the garden comes in sooner** than if the eggplant had been grown in a pure stand.

Figure 424 shows a sowing pattern designed to protect taro mounds. The black nightshade was sown to stop heavy rainfall from eroding the hills and exposing the taros. Two or three days later, the nightshade had already provided protective cover. The tender nightshade can be picked as it grows, although care must be taken not to leave the ground without cover. After four to six weeks, the taro covers the whole mound.

This arrangement uses a plant, black nightshade, to **control erosion on the taro mounds and to make this control productive in the form of a pot-herb**.

The garden in **figure 425** appears to have been sown in an unplanned way. Yet, every plant growing there serves a purpose and has its own cultural calendar. Some of the plants were propagated by seed (maize, marrows, beans), the others by cuttings and shoots (cassava, taro, banana). The arrangement is such that the plants are free to occupy their natural level. The effectiveness of the plan is judged by weighing up the following factors :

- **the amount of foodstuff** produced and its diversity,
- **the way the harvest is staggered** in time,
- the amount of **plant manure** which is returned to the soil,
- **soil protection** against rain splash,
- **the number and severity of pest attacks** on each of the species growing in this associaton.

425

The plant association in **figure 426** is more intimate and the cultural calendar needs to be carefully planned. If the association is to be productive, the bean shoots must manage to hook themselves onto the maize stems. But if these are too young and too short, they are in danger of being overrun by the bean plants. On the other hand, if the stems remain lying on the ground because of lack of good supports, they will wither. This is why the beans must be sown two or three weeks after the maize. In addition, the bean has direct and indirect effects on soil fertility due to the nitrogen-fixing bacteria present in root nodules. It also protects the soil from erosion and is therefore of direct benefit to the maize, and feeds the soil with organic matter that will be very useful during the coming cultural seasons.

426

Personal experience of local conditions is the guide for timing the sowing of each plant, and for deciding how these should be staggered for each crop to allow for the associated plants. Apart from the aspects mentioned above, two other elements determine the effectiveness of the arrangement :

- **the advantages and disadvantages of the interaction of the plants in the mixture;**
- **the cost of a living support** (maize, in this example) compared to that of a dead stake.

The temporary garden in **figure 427** was established under an *Acacia albida* tree, in a groundnut field. Groundnut does not thrive under acacia, in contrast to other cereals like millet and sorghum and certain legumes. To avoid wasting the space at the foot of the tree, the farmer sowed okra and roselle. In the previous season, this had been a field of sorghum, which grew right under the acacia tree whose shade actually benefits the cereal.

427

Apart from the return obtained from the land, this arrangement has its merits because

428

429

430

- instead of cultivating the whole area in the same way, the farmer **makes the most of the diversified potential of his land**;
- **the space** under the acacia **is used as part of the field** when cropped with cereals, **and like a garden** when groundnut is the main crop.

In West Africa, the space under acacia and other trees is often used in the way described. Yam, for example, is frequently cultivated in the shade of shea butter and other trees.

The garden in **figure 428** is situated in a valley bottom. Every year, flood waters flatten the beds laid out during the previous season, and add their share of fertilizing silt and clay to the soil. Observe how some fruit trees form a **permanent upper storey.** They are scattered rather widely apart and give limited shade to the vegetable beds. As the flooding does not last long, the trees are unharmed.

Figure 429 shows how cultivators in West Cameroun lay out their orchards and grow many species of trees and herbs there. Coffee trees occupy the lowest tree storey. They are pruned to a man's height in order to make berry picking easier. Planting density is such that their crowns overlap. The layer above the coffee plants is occupied by many species - banana, avocado, native pear, orange and palm. They are not closely spaced; their crowns are rather far apart and allow enough light to reach the coffee plants. Here and there, coffee shrubs were removed and replaced by bitter leaf plants grown for their leaves.

This planting arrangement reflects the pattern of natural forests. Nonetheless, we are looking at an orchard in which all the plants play a cohesive part in the agricultural production that is diversified and spread out in time.

Economists usually make a distinction between crops for sale (cash crops) and food or subsistence crops. But nature does not make this distinction, and farmers in West Cameroun show how the cultivation of the two sets of crops can be combined.

The cultural pattern of the semi-arid garden in **figure 430** is similar to that of the Cameroun orchard. The gardener has a well which he could not do without during the rainy season and part of the dry season. He wants to build up a tree cover round his house, and cultivate seasonal vegetables at the same time. The trees benefit from the regular watering of the garden and, during the dry season, they get just enough water to survive the drought period. After three or four years, their deep roots will have reached the soil layers moistened by the water table. By that time, the trees will be well established and able to survive on their own resources throughout the year.

There are positive aspects to this planting arrangement :

- When the trees are young, **they are treated like vegetables**, and are watered regularly. At a later stage, irrigation is not so necessary because the tree roots will have penetrated the moister soil layers;
- The trees in this garden fulfil several **important functions** :
  - they **produce** wood, fodder, fruits, leaves and plant manure;
  - they **keep the soil cool** during the day and prevent it from becoming too cold during the night;
  - they **screen the house** from sand storms.

The planting patterns we have mentioned aim at **restoring and making the most of village lands.** In semi-arid regions like the Sahel, just as in wetter parts of Africa, forests are being destroyed with incalculable effects on the climate, on precipitation, runoff, erosion, and agricultural and pastoral production. The cultivators whose practices have been described adopted ways of restoring the fertility of rural settlements. Their practices are based on the **concept of diversified agriculture** that can answer all the needs of home consumption and the demands of the national economy.

The layout of the neem plantation in **figure 431** does not conform to the same strategy. The neems were planted for the production of building poles. **The return in terms of wood is fairly high.** This is undoubtedly a major advantage, but notice that the sloping soil under the trees is bare : there are no vegetables or forage plants, not a trace of any herb or grass that might encourage water infiltration which this part of the Sahel needs so badly. Here is a clear-cut example of how the **pursuit of maximum return from a single product** - wood, in this case, **can sometimes jeopardize other aspects of land management that are just as important, for instance, the infiltration of rainwater and the preservation of soil structure.**

431

It is obvious from the gardens we have shown that the choice of sowing and planting patterns is an essential feature of proper management. The choice gardeners make demonstrates

- their ability to **produce without ruining the land** - to produce fruits, vegetables, wood, and so on, while treating the land with due regard and improving its structure;
- and also their ability to **produce without being overdependent** on chemical firms whose aim is to sell goods rather than preserve the farming environment.

Sowing calendars

Sowing patterns and timing for seasonal crops

The **sowing or planting calendar** in a garden or a farm means the way sowing and planting are planned in time and follow one another. **The sowing pattern determines plant arrangement and spacing in the garden; the sowing calendar arranges the plants in time.**

The sowing calendar depends on :

- the characteristics of the cultivated plant and, particularly, **the length of its cultural cycle** (the interval between sowing and harvesting) : some varieties are **early**, others are **late-maturing**;
- **the availability of soil water**. The plant must be able to take up enough water in the soil for the duration of its vegetative cycle. Therefore, the cultural calendar depends to a large extent on the rainfall calendar, except where the soil is watered or irrigated;
- **the type of produce** required. For leafy vegetables, the harvest will be earlier than for fruits or seeds. If seeds are desired, the gardener must sow in good time so that the cultural cycle of the plant will be over by the end of the rainy season;

- the sowing or planting **pattern**, not forgetting the **cultural associations** the gardener has in mind. This is important because the associated plants can be sown at the same time or they may be spread out in time;
- **the amount of produce needed for home consumption and for sale**. The beds are sown one after the other in order to **make the harvest time last longer,** if the climate or water for irrigation makes this possible. This helps to **stagger the gardener's work load**. The first fruits or vegetables on the market always fetch higher prices just because they are **early in the season**. The gardener who, by clever planning, can get this early produce to market a week or ten days before anyone else usually makes a lot of money, whereas, later in the season when vegetables and fruits are plentiful prices are lower.

How should we go about drawing up a good cultural calendar for garden produce ?

We can experiment with six beds of a late variety of okra with a vegetative cycle of four and a half months. The beds are labelled A, B, C, D, E and F. They receive natural rainfall from May to September and because there is **a drainage pit**, watering can be extended to the end of October.

432 **Key to the signs in tables 433, 434 and 435**

This line represents the annual calendar. It indicates the time of the year when the farming operations to which the tables refer take place.

This line shows the length of the rainy season during which the beds are mainly irrigated by rainwater.

This line shows the period when the beds have to be watered from a catchpit.

This line shows the extent of soil cover. When the ground is well covered, the line is black. When soil cover is poor, the line is broken.

Drawings like the one here represent the okra plants in the beds and show the stage of growth they have reached.

Figures 433, 434 and 435 show ways of arranging the six beds in order to increase production and stagger the harvests. **Figure 432** explains the signs used.

Three different sowing patterns and cultural calendars are set out :

- In the first example, okra is sown in pure stand in the six beds, on the same day **(figure 433);**
- In the second example, the okra sowing is staggered **(figure 434)**. Beds A and B are sown simultaneously, beds C and F are sown later, beds E and F are sown last of all;
- In the third example, okra sowing is staggered, while lettuce, bush greens and black nightshade are grown in association **(figure 435)**.

First example : the whole okra crop in pure stand is sown at the same time (figure 433)

433 **First example : the okra crop is sown at the same time in six beds.**

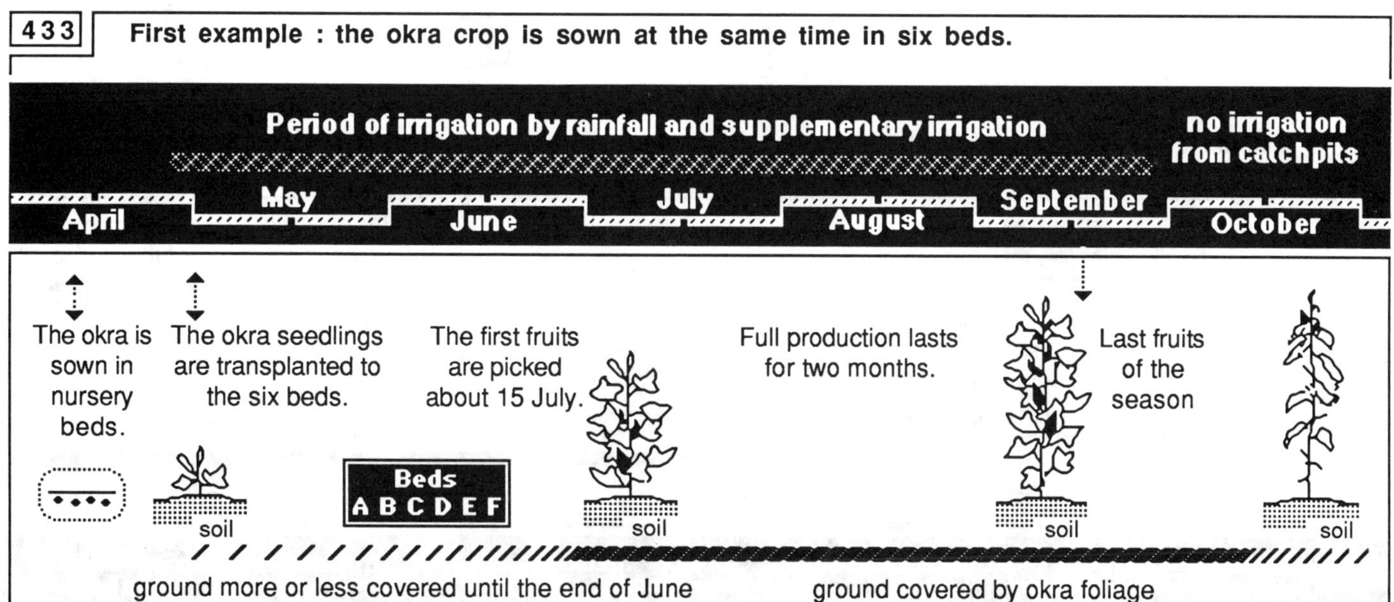

The okra is sown in the nursery about 10 April. It is transplanted to the six beds on 1st May, by which date irrigation by rain water can be relied on. All the beds are harvested at the same time - from about 15 July to 15 September.

If you observe the beds during the season, you notice that the ground is completely or partially bare into the second half of June. Then, it has good cover until October when it becomes bare again.

The fruits are picked, in all the beds, between 15 July and 15 September.

Second example : the okra crop is in a pure stand but sowing is staggered (figure 434).

Okra sowing is staggered in order to **spread the harvest** over a longer period than in the first example.

434 Second example : the okra crop is in a pure stand but sowing is staggered.

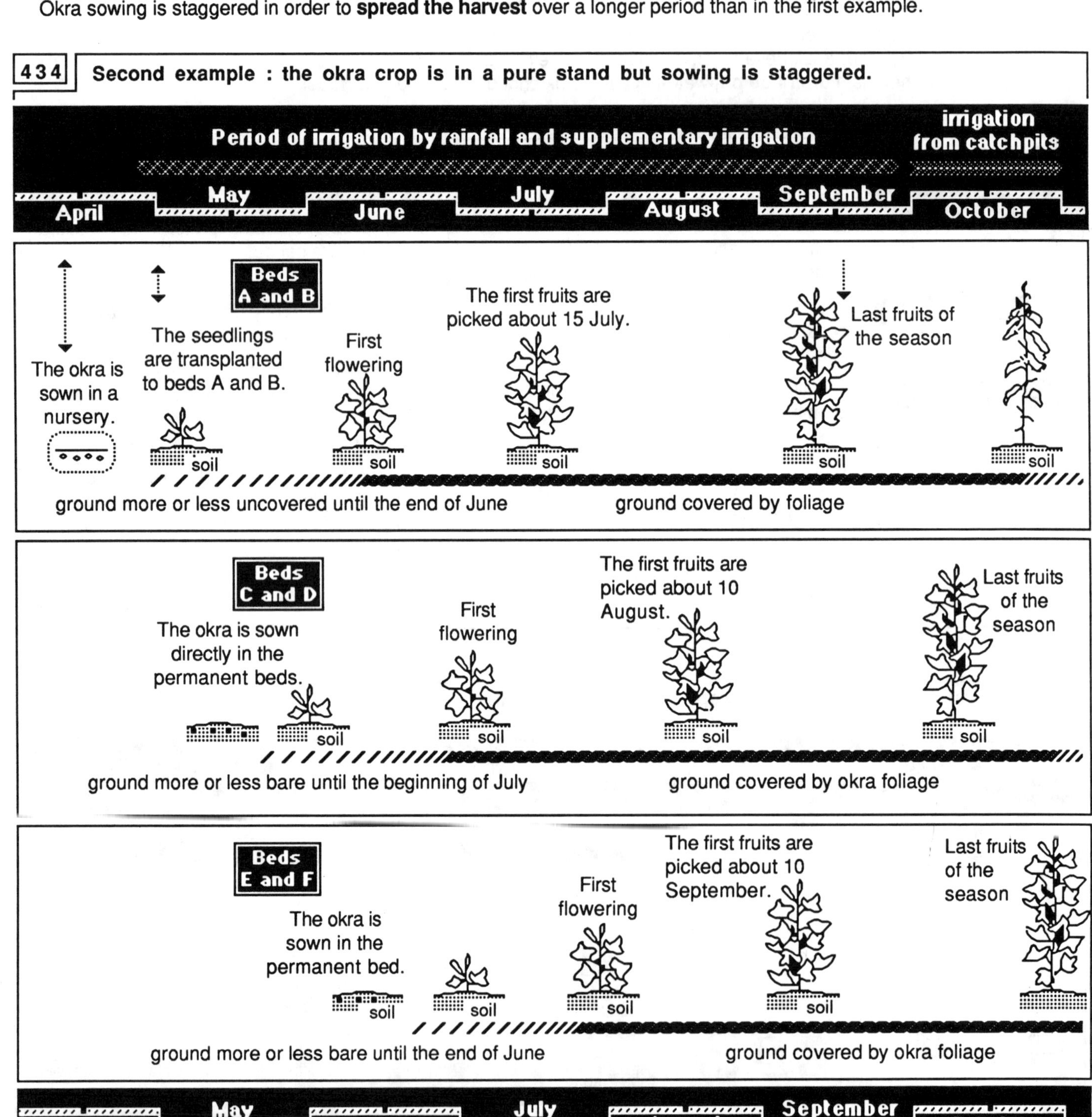

- The six beds are divided into three groups of two : AB, CD, EF. Beds AB are sown first, about 10 April, and the seedlings are transplanted 1st May. By this date, watering by rainfall is guaranteed. The ground is barely covered until roughly 15 June. From then until 30 September, it enjoys more or less full cover. The okra leaves have dried out, but the risk of erosion by rainfall is limited because the rains have slackened.
- Beds CD are occupied from 15 May when the okra is sown straight into its permanent site rather than in a nursery. The ground is bare until the beginning of July. The first fruits are picked about 10 August and the last fruits are harvested about 10 October. From the end of September to the beginning of October, supplementary irrigation is needed to let the last fruits ripen.
- Beds EF are sown later still - between 10 and 15 June. The last fruits will be picked at the end of October. Irrigation from the drainage pit is needed for the whole month of October. The ground is bare until about the end of June, and only has full cover from about 20 June. Consequently, the risk of erosion is very high on these beds left without cover at the very time when rainfall is at its heaviest and most damaging.

435 **Third example : the okra sowing is staggered and other plants are grown in association.**

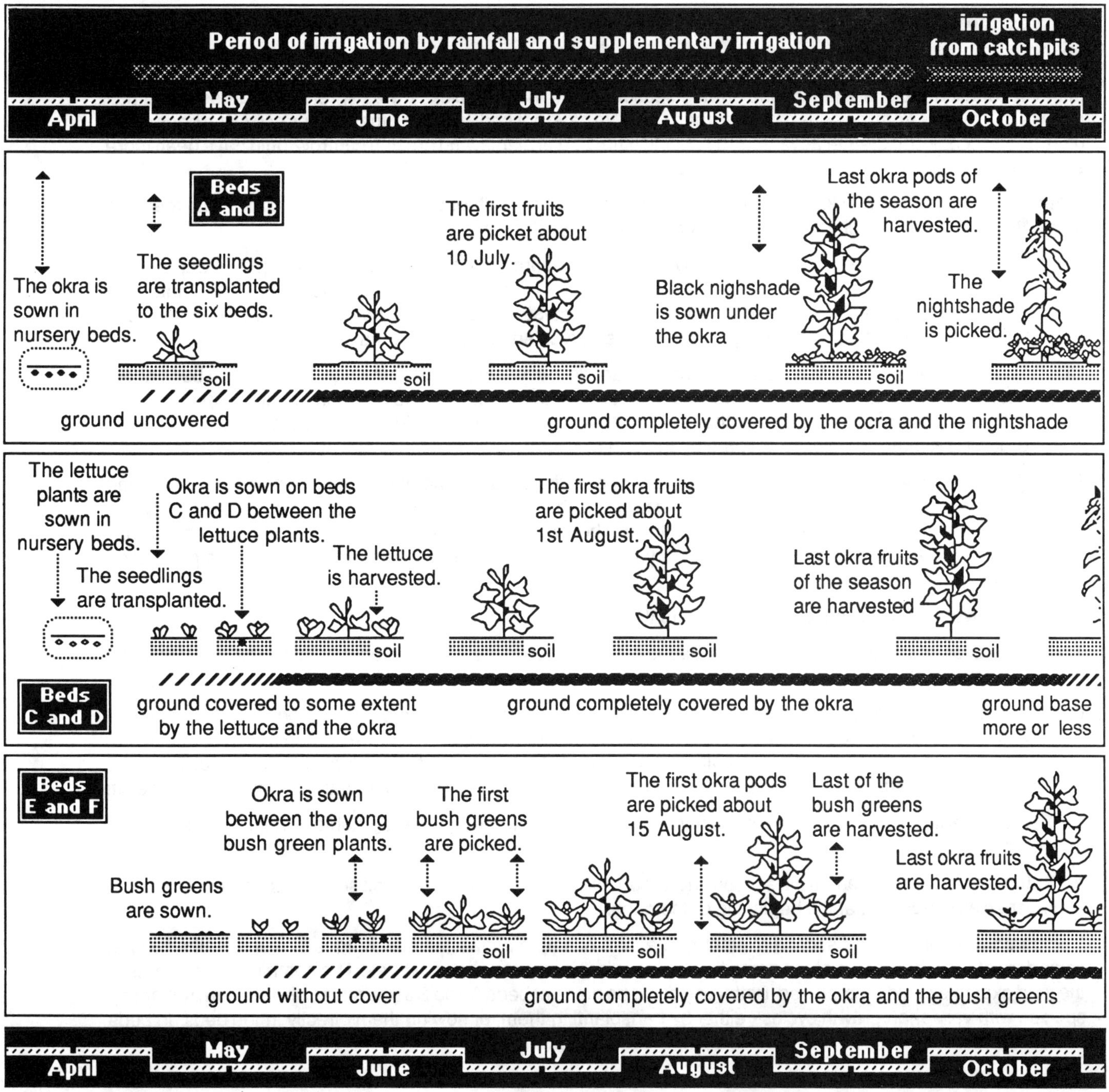

Period of irrigation by rainfall and supplementary irrigation | irrigation from catchpits

April | May | June | July | August | September | October

Beds A and B

The okra is sown in nursery beds.
The seedlings are transplanted to the six beds.
soil
The first fruits are picket about 10 July.
Black nighshade is sown under the okra
Last okra pods of the season are harvested.
The nightshade is picked.
ground uncovered
ground completely covered by the ocra and the nightshade

The lettuce plants are sown in nursery beds.
Okra is sown on beds C and D between the lettuce plants.
The seedlings are transplanted.
The lettuce is harvested.
The first okra fruits are picked about 1st August.
Last okra fruits of the season are harvested
soil
Beds C and D
ground covered to some extent by the lettuce and the okra
ground completely covered by the okra
ground base more or less

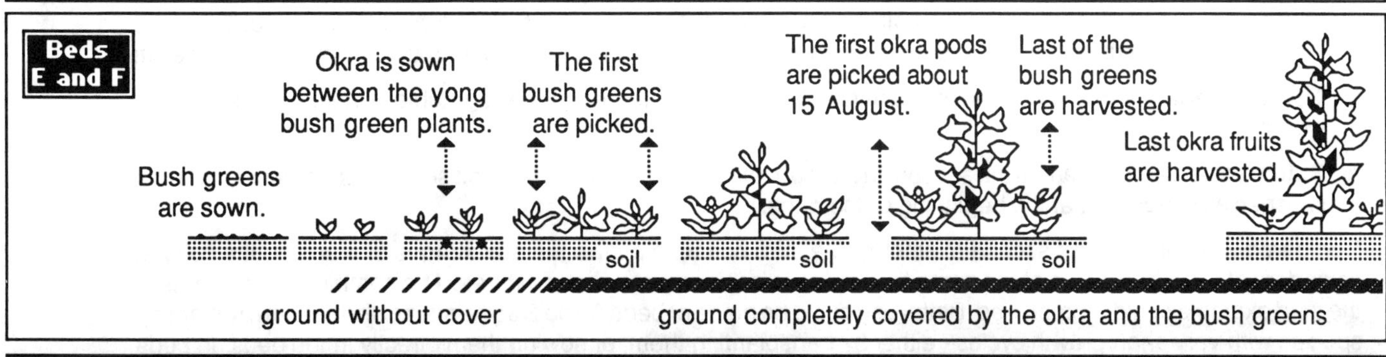

The advantages of this cultural calendar, compared with that of the first example, are as follows :

- **The total production** of fruits from the six beds is **comparable** to that obtained in the first example. On the other hand, fruit picking and income from sale are spread out over three and a half months as opposed to two;
- The longer harvest period means that the **overproduction** or **glut** that occurs in the first example in August is avoided. Gluts increase the demands on labour and on transport facilities, and cause prices to slump;
- The **work** of seedbed preparation, sowing, maintenance and picking is spread more evenly in time when sowing is staggered.

These are the drawbacks of the prolonged sowing season :

- **The ground is bare** on beds C, D, E and F at the onset of the rains and may be liable to erosion;
- The okra nursery beds, A and B, **have to be watered** for three weeks in April, and beds E and F during the month of October. Watering means extra work but it is coincides with times when other gardening activities are fairly slack.

Third example : the okra sowing is staggered and other vegetables are grown in association (figure 435).

In the second example, staggering the sowing season meant that fruit picking was spread over three and a half months, but returns from the beds remained the same. We have noticed, however, that the surface of the beds could have been occupied to greater advantage by adding other useful plants, and erosion control would have been more satisfactory.

Figure 435 shows how the okra sowing can be staggered, and then other plants can be associated with the main crop. What happens in each of the three sets of beds ?

AB Okra seedlings are transplanted to beds A and B from about 1st May, as in the first example. In September, when the last fruits of the season are almost ripe, black nightshade is sown between the okra plants, and is watered from the drainage pit during the month of October. If necessary, the unproductive okra plants can be cut back to give light to the nightshade that is harvested in the second half of October.

CD The okra is sown on 15 May as in the second example, but lettuce plants transplanted to the two beds about 1st May are already growing there. This meant sowing the lettuce in nursery beds about 10 April. In June, the lettuce is removed from under the okra plants which are now at a fairly advanced stage of growth. The ground is almost completely covered by the end of May.

EF The okra is sown about 15 June as for the same beds in the second example, but it is sown between the young bush green plants that were sown about 1st May. The bush greens reach maturity in the first half of July and go on developing under the growing okra plants. The ground is completely covered by the beginning of July. Watering from the drainage pit is necessary in October so that the okra crop can complete its production cycle.

Table 436 gives the work schedule applicable to the third example.

The advantages of staggering the sowing seasons of the okra crop are therefore enhanced by the benefits of the cultural association :

- **A second crop of vegetables** - lettuce, bush greens and nightshade - can be harvested as well as the okra crop. If we take the six beds as a whole and the four plants cultivated, harvests are spread over a period of four months as opposed to three and a half months. The first heads of lettuce are harvested about 20 June; nightshade and okra are still being picked at the end of October with the use of irrigation from the drainage pit;
- **The maintenance of the beds** involves thinning, topping and fertilizing the vegetables rather than controlling weeds;
- **Soil cover** is ensured early in the season and is more extensive than in the first and second examples. This factor is especially important at the beginning of the rains.

Compared with the first and second examples, the third example shows the advantages of planning the cultural calendars of each bed, while at the same time trying to achieve good crop mixtures. The combination of plants in the third example could be improved. Better use could be made of beds A and B at the start of the season by planting species with very short growth cycles - either by transplanting them, or sowing them directly in the beds. In beds

436 **Work to be done in the beds**

Dates	Beds A and B	Beds C and D	Beds E and F
1st April	nursery seedbed prepared	nursery seedbed prepared	
10 April	okra sown in the nursery	lettuce sown in the nursery	
15 April	permanent beds prepared	permanent beds prepared	permanent beds prepared
1st May	okra transplanted	lettuce transplanted	bush greens sown
20 May		okra sown	
10 June			okra sown
20 June		first lettuce harvested	
10 July	first fresh okra pods picked	last lettuce harvested	first bush greens picked
1st August		first okra picked	bush greens harvested
15 August			first okra picked
20 August	black nightshade sown		
15 September	last fresh okra picked		
1st October	nightshade picked		
10 October		end of fresh okra season, irrigation now over	
30 October	last nightshade picked		last of the okra harvested, irrigation now over

E and F, bush greens could be established in nursery beds in order to gain time and bring the harvest forward. Each of the beds could have its own sowing pattern as opposed to planning for two beds at a time.

We could go on discussing all sorts of plant associations and overlook what we have learnt - that **it is possible to increase and stagger the production from beds in a garden by skillful planning of cultural calendars and plant associations.**

We only examined the six beds which were planted with okra as their main crop. Other beds in the same garden were full of toma-

437 **Cultural calendar for the garden**

Dates	Beds							
	AB	CD	EF	G	H	IJ	KL	M
1st April								
10 April								
20 April								
etc.								

The work to be done on the beds on the dates marked in the first column is written down in the appropriate square.

toes, eggplants, Jew's mallow, basil and cabbage. A calendar like the one in **figure 436** can be drawn up for each bed, and then all the calendars combined to form a general calendar for the whole garden **(figure 437)**.

Establishing an accurate cultural calendar for all the beds in a garden increases the return from market gardening, because the available space is occupied to the best advantage in the growing season and because the duration of the life cycle of all the plants cultivated is taken into account. Of course, the work schedule cannot be expected to run with the precision of a stop-watch, but the very fact of planning a calendar mentally or in writing saves time and space, and leads to the best use of rain and irrigation water.

438 A planting calendar based on a fixed point in time

Operation	Date
Plantation of young trees required	1st June 1991
The planting holes are prepared at the end of the rainy season.	September-October 1990
The scions are grafted, in the nursery, onto rootstocks which are about two years old.	June 1990
The seeds for stock plants are planted in nursery beds.	July 1988
The seeds for the stock plants are placed in nursery beds.	May 1988

Gardeners may find the explanations about cultural calendars too theoretical; in fact, they merely express in writing what gardeners do spontaneously during the vegetable season. The calendars discussed should help agricultural officers to think about the practical suggestions they make to vegetable and fruit growers and to establish their own work schedules.

Timing for tree and perennial crop planting

An accurate calendar is also a necessity for tree plantations. One point in time on this calendar is always fixed in advance : **a tree is always planted as early as possible at the beginning of a rainy season** in order to encourage the young roots to become well established and extensive. before the beginning of the dry season.

So, if you want to draw up a planting calendar, you must work backwards from that fixed point in time - the start of the rainy season. Suppose you intend planting orange trees **(figure 438)** and that the planting date is fixed for 1st June 1991, the start of the rainy season. You need about three years to get a grafted scion ready for transplanting to its permanent site. Since your work calendar has to allow for this interval, seeds for the stock plants must be available in May 1988.

If the seeds are not sown in May 1988, the permanent planting will almost certainly be postponed for a year, from 1st June 1991 to June 1992.

The timetable in **table 439** is worked out differently. The calendar starts from the day when the cuttings are first inserted, for example, 1st June 1988. Working forward from there, the approximate time of permanent planting can be decided.

439 Planting calendar from the date of the first operation onwards

Operation	Date
The cuttings are placed in bags in	June 1988
They will be 60 centimetres high and.ready for planting after 18 months but this coincides with the dry season when young trees cannot be planted.	December 1989
Planting will have to be postponed until the onset of the rains.	May 1990
The planting holes must be prepared at the end of the previous rainy season.	October 1989

Chapter 17
Grafting

Reasons for grafting

Grafting is a form of vegetative propagation which involves the union of two separate, usually woody, structures, commonly stems. The upper part is the **scion** which combines with the **stock**. The scion and the stock must belong to the same species or to the same family. Grafting means that the qualities of the two parent plants are united in one plant **(figure 440)**.

440 **The parts of a grafted plant**

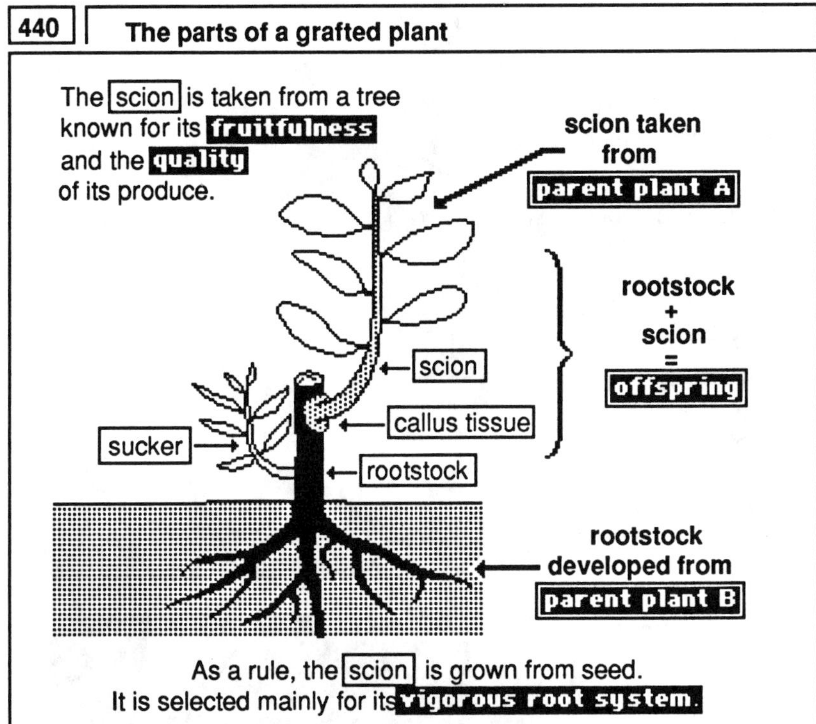

Generally speaking, when grafting is successsful, the qualities of the plant from which the scion is taken are enhanced by the vigour of the plant which serves as the rootstock.

There are many reasons for grafting. A fruit grower may wish to multiply particular trees which produce an abundance of specially good, early maturing fruit and which withstand certain pests. If propagated by seed there is no guarantee as to which characters will appear in the offspring. These trees must therefore be propagated vegetatively. However if these trees, in spite of their outstanding qualities have some shortcomings affecting their root system such as unsuitability to some soils, this can be overcome by grafting on to adapted stocks.

It should be noted that some varieties of trees with only moderately vigorous growth produce large quantities of good quality seedless fruits; it is therefore worth multiplying them vegetatively in order to increase their vigour.

All the branches of the grafted plant will grow from the **scion** which is the source of characteristics such as :

- quality of the fruits,
- productivity,
- early or late maturity,
- resistance to diseases and pests of the aerial parts,
- shape of the tree canopy.

The **stock plant** determines :

- the vigour of the plant,
- the development of the root system,
- resistance to diseases and to pests of the stem and roots.

Grafting is carried out in three stages : first the rootstock and then the scion are prepared; then the stock and the scion are bound together and finally, any leaves or suckers are cut off the stock plant.

The **separation** of the scion consists in gradually cutting back the tissue of the rootstock when the scion has become firmly united.

Some plant structures related to grafting

Plant anatomy is the study of internal plant structure, the characteristics of their tissues, their shape, etc. It is necessary to know a little about basic anatomy before attempting to graft plants.

If you take a branch one or two centimetres in diameter and make a slanting cut as in **figure 441**, you will see :

- A layer of brown or green **bark**. The bark is tender and immature on young branches, it is harder and drier on older branches and stems. Under the bark is the phloem which transports the food from the leaves **(figure 149)**;
- An area right in the centre of the branch is made of hard wood called the **heartwood**. This part is for support and no longer functions for water conduction;
- Outside this there is an area of **sapwood** which is moister than the heartwood and which carries the water and mineral salts from the roots;
- The **cambium** is between the sapwood and the bark. The cambium is not easy to detect with the naked eye because it forms a very thin layer of tissue whose function is to produce wood on the inner side and phloem on the outer side. When the bark of the wood is lifted, the cambium is seen immediately below it **(figure 442)**.

It is vitally important for the grafter to identify the cambium layer both in the rootstock and in the scion. **All grafting techniques depend for success on bringing together the cambium layers of the stock and scion so that they can unite allowing water and mineral salts to ascend from the stock to the leaves and manufactured food to pass down from the leaves**. The tissues which form the union are called the **callus**. Grafted trees can be identified by the presence of the thickened callus tissues.

441

442 **The parts of a ripe branch**

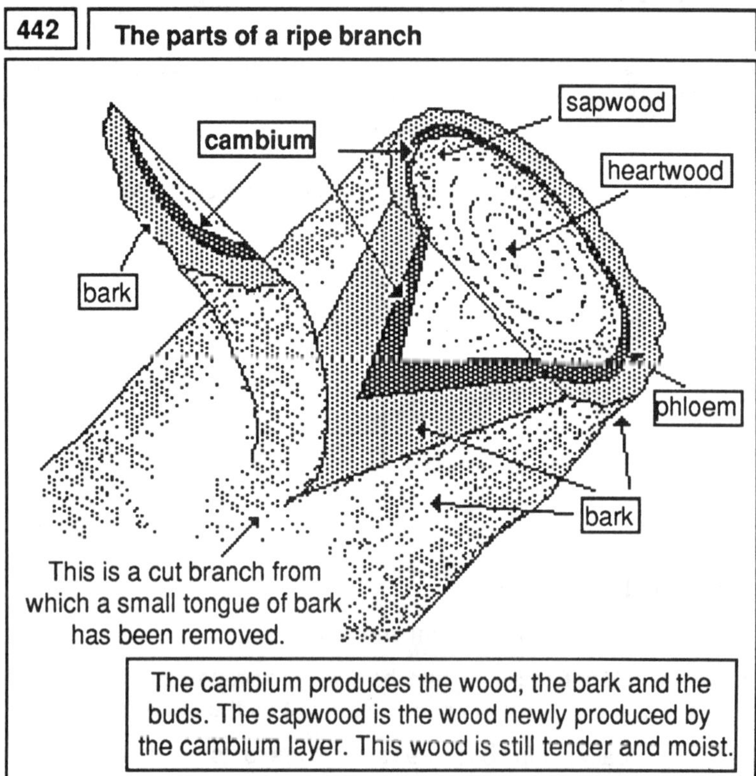

The cambium produces the wood, the bark and the buds. The sapwood is the wood newly produced by the cambium layer. This wood is still tender and moist.

443

Figure 443 shows two of the components of a graft : the rootstock with the tip removed, and the scion that is beginning to unite with the stock. The callus tissue which grows between the stock and the scion is hidden by the plastic tape that was used to bind the two plants tightly together.

Once the callus has formed and the scion bud starts growing, the union between the stock and the scion may be considered to be permanent. Buds below the callus may sometimes develop. All these buds, called **suckers**, must be removed because they will have the characteristics of the rootstock and do not possess the qualities required in the grafted tree.

Selecting stock plants and scions

At the beginning of the chapter, we mentioned the qualities required of the stock plants and the scions, and it is obvious that these qualities must be present in the parent plants. Personal observation and experience will help the grafter to choose the right plants and achieve the best possible unions.

How should the grafter select stock plants and scions ?

The **stock plants** can be raised from seed and must be from a variety well adapted to the soil and the environment where the grafted tree will be planted; for example, the stock plant must withstand drought in dry areas or tolerate waterlogged soil in valley bottoms. The stock plants should be two or three years old with a well developed root system and straight stem.

There should be no trace of disease or pest infestation.

The scions are preferably obtained from the outermost branches of the donor tree the terminal parts of which are well ripened **(figure 448b)**. The branches selected should be vigorous with no pest infestation and there must be several well developed buds. The buds should ideally be swelling slightly, but not actually bursting. The diameter of the scion should be about the same, or slightly smaller than that of the stock to which it is going to be grafted. For budding, take a central section of wood with buds that will grow into shoots not fruiting buds. Dormant buds can be stimulated by removing the leaves from the budwood branch a few days before the buds are excised.

Always graft in the rainy season when the trees are full of sap and the bark of the stock plants and the scions can be lifted easily. The rainy season is also the time when the cambium layer is most active.

Compatibility between stock plants and scions

As a general rule, the rootstock and the scion come from two trees of the same species but of different varieties. Occasionally, trees of different species but of the same family can be grafted successfully. For instance, orange and lemon can be grafted on to sweet lime and grapefruit. These fruits belong to different species but are very like one another and all belong to the Rutaceae family. On the other hand, an avocado cannot be grafted to a mango, nor a guava to a lemon, because these fruits come from different families.

The graft will only take if the two varieties are **compatible**. This means that :

- the rootstock and the scion must be able to complete their union by the **formation of callus tissue**. This process can only take place when the two sets of cambium cells are closely related;
- **the qualities of the rootstock and the scion must be complementary, not incompatible.**

Sound judgement on the compatibility of plant varieties is a matter of experience. All sorts of grafting techniques on different varieties can be tested, but only successful grafts are worth repeating, and it may be several years before the tree can be fully assessed for quality and quantity of produce..

Incompatibility may even exist after successful grafting. For example, the scions of some varieties of sweet orange may occasionally produce bitter fruits when they are grafted onto some types of stock. Sometimes, too, a grafted tree may be slow-growing and unproductive.

- **If the new trees are completely successful** and the grafting is to be repeated, **the same two varieties** as those used for the original experiments must be used. Also they must be in the same 'direction', i.e. if variety A was grafted on variety B and proved satisfactory, the opposite, B grafted on A, might give totally different results.
- If you want to avoid mistakes, mark the origins of the grafted plants on an indelible label; note accurately the variety of the two parent plants.

Grafting tools

Only a few tools **(figure 444)** and some simple materials are needed for grafting :

- a **knife with a very sharp cutting blade;**
- **lengths of pliable binding material** - raffia, string, or plastic tape;
- a little birdlime, resin or a recommended form of **wax** for sealing, if you use binding material made of raffia or twine;
- a **whetstone** for sharpening the blade;
- a **pair of secateurs**, useful for cutting scions from branches and for topping stock plants;
- a **budding knife**. This is a knife with a curved, sharp-pointed blade that grafting specialists use to make clean incisions in the bark of the rootstock.

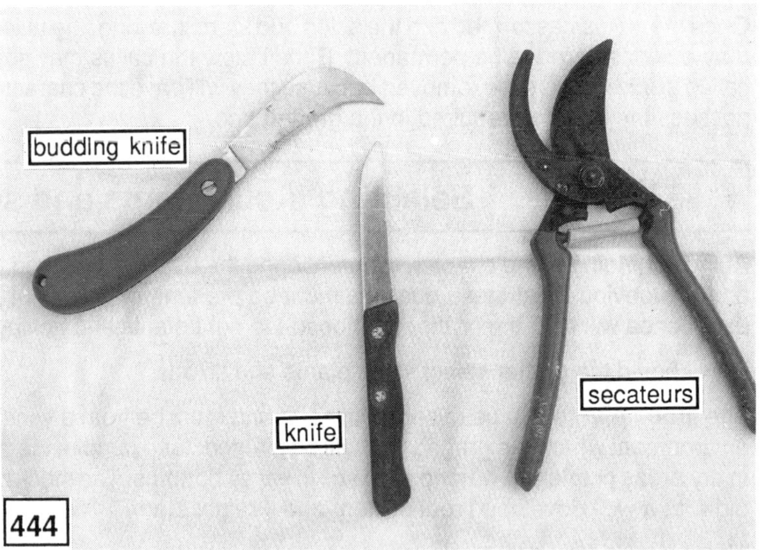

444

The success of grafting operations depends very much on the sharpness and cleanliness of the knife blade. Neat incisions are essential : plant material for grafting must never be snapped or pulled off, or damaged unnecessarily in any way. The grafter's hands and tools must be clean at all times and knives should be sterilized between each grafting operation by being washed in a disinfectant solution of sodium hypochlorite (household bleach).

Positioning the graft

The height at which the scion is grafted will depend on the type of tree required. For a low tree like the grafted mango shown in **figure 445** the scion is inserted at the base of the stem. Low trees make picking, pruning and general maintenance easier but they will restrict the vegetation growing below and could interfere with mechanical cultivation.

445

Taller trees can be either **standard** or **half standard**. For standard trees the scion is inserted at a height of 1.80 metres giving branches at shoulder height or higher. **Figure 446** shows a tall mango tree and the younger grafted trees in the centre which are all standard trees, while to the left there is a batch of half-standard trees with branching at about 1 metre.

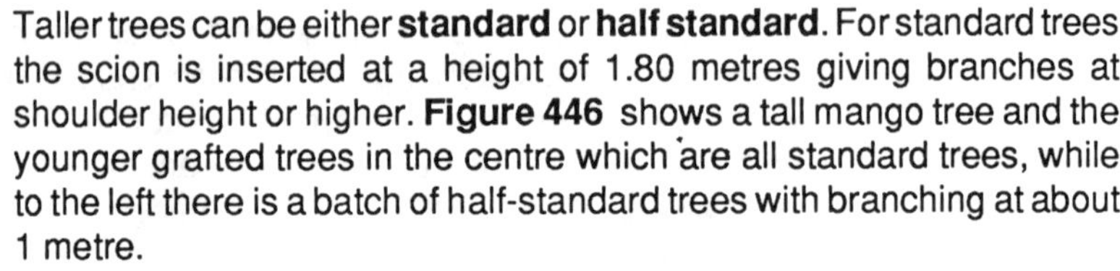

Standard trees should be grown in fields or on grazing land as they do not restrict the vegetation below, their crowns are beyond the reach of livestock, and they do not hamper machinery.

Trees can be grafted **in their permanent positions** or **in a nursery**. **Grafting in the permanent position** means that the stock plants are already established on a particular site. This would be an unusual way of grafting young stock plants, but it is common when a gardener wants to rejuvenate old stems by **topworking (figures 456 and 457)**. Topworking is the technique of replacing the crown of an old tree by a young crown with improved characteristics.

Grafting in the nursery is the more usual procedure. The young stock plants are taken from the germinator and are either transplanted in a seedbed 20 or 30 centimetres apart, or placed in large plastic pots or bags or baskets so that the roots can develop well. Grafting is carried out when the stock plants are two or three years old. When the scions have taken and the callus tissues are well formed, the grafted trees are removed from the nursery and planted in the field.

The nursery should be shaded and the plants must be watered frequently. Whatever happens, do not let the scions dry out before the callus tissues, produced by the scion and the stock, have united. You may also protect the scions with transparent plastic bags in which you have made a few air holes **(figure 447)**. The bags help to prevent desiccation but cannot be left in place for too long because they might smother the scion or encourage the formation of moulds.

447

446

Methods of grafting and budding

Methods of grafting can be classified under four headings, depending on the type of grafting material used and its position on the stock plant:

- **Grafting with scions**, which uses pieces of stem joined to the stock by
  - **cleft (wedge) grafting,** or
  - **whip or tongue grafting;**
- **Budding (bud grafting)** uses buds as propagating material;
- **Approach grafting** when two rooted plants are united. When the graft has taken, the plants are separated.

The choice of a grafting method depends on the plant species, on the gardener's personal experience and on the diameters of the material. If you cannot get detailed information, it is best to try several methods and see which one is the most successful.

Cleft grafting

Cleft grafting consists in slitting the stock lengthwise and inserting the tapered scion into the cleft. This operation involves making **a slit in the top** or **in the side** of the stock and may also be referred to as **top grafting**.

The illustrations in **figure 448** show how **cleft grafting** is carried out. Start by **preparing the stock (448a)** by cutting off the tip of the stock at the desired height. Leave one or more leaves to draw the sap **(figure 460)**. Next, with a very sharp, thin blade, split the stock down the centre, making a vertical cut about three centimetres long. Hold the stock very tightly between your fingers **(figure 448a)** to avoid making the cut too deep. The cut must be neat and absolutely straight.

Next prepare the scion. Taper it at the lower end on both sides, the length of this tail should be slightly shorter than the slit made in the stock. The sides of the tapered scion should be perfectly smooth **(figures 448b and c)**. As soon as the scion is ready, slip it into the cut made in the stock **(figure 448d)** making sure that, at least on one side, the cambial tissues are in close contact over a maximum length **(448e)**. Then, bind the two parts tightly together **(figure 448f)**. The tape can be removed after the scion and the stock have been united.

Side grafting can be compared with top grafting, except that the tip of the rootstock is not cut off. A slanting incision is made from the bark towards the centre **(figures 449a and b)**. There is no need to keep any leaves below the incision because the tip of the stock will draw up the sap.

448 Cleft grafting

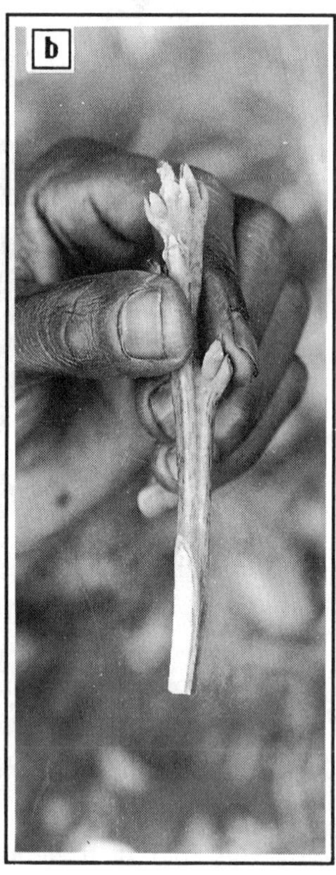

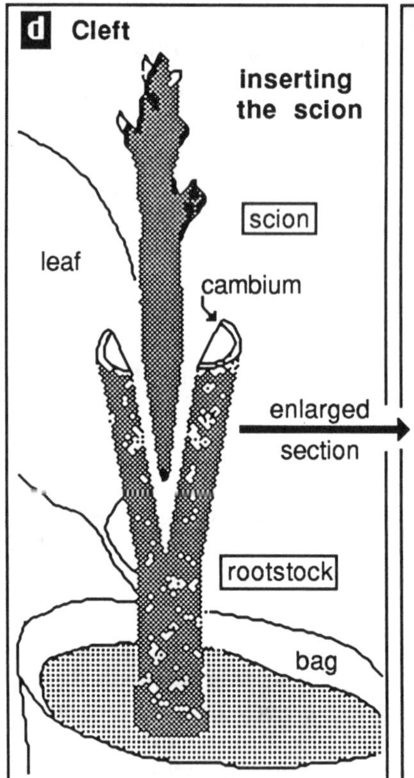

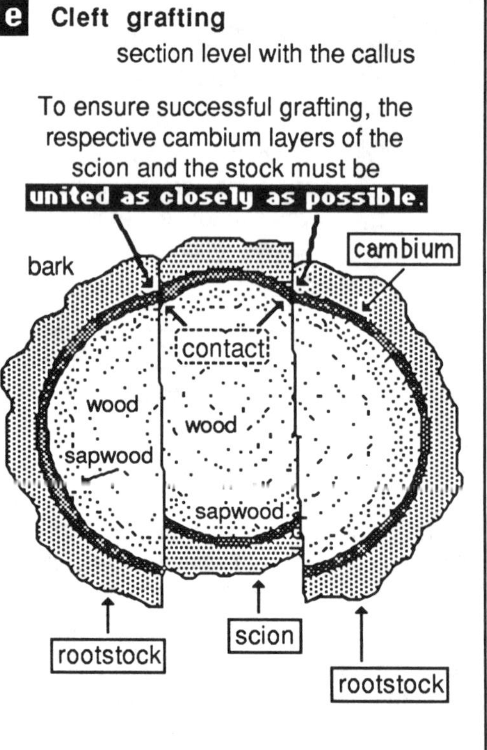

Here, too, it is very important to keep your fingers in the right position when you are making the incision, **(figure 449a)** because it would be fatal if you severed the tip of the stock by cutting right through the stem.

The scion is prepared as in **figure 448 b and c**, inserted with the same care **(figure 448e)** and bound **(figure 449c)**.

Figure 447 shows the grafted plant protected by a plastic bag.

449 **Side grafting**

Whip grafting

Whip or tongue grafting unites the scion to the stock without making an incision into the stock. A slice of bark is cut from the side of the stock to expose the wood and the cambium **(figure 450a)**. The scion is tapered on one side and is then placed against the stock so that the two cambium layers are united as closely as possible **(figure 450 b and c)**. When the stock and the scion have been fitted to ensure maximum contact, bind the two parts together with plastic or any suitable tape. Begin taping from the bottom to stop the scion from slipping out of place - this can happen if you bind from the top down. Be especially careful to stop water from infiltrating the union by sealing it with birdlime, resin or wax.

Budding

Budding is the technique of inserting a scion in the shape of a shield under the bark of the stock. The shield is a small slice of shoot with a bud in the centre **(figure 452 b and d)**. The shield is cut in such a way that it bears a bud, a piece of bark and cambium, and a small tongue of sapwood. **Figure 452** shows how to proceed for this method of grafting called T-budding :

450 Whip grafting

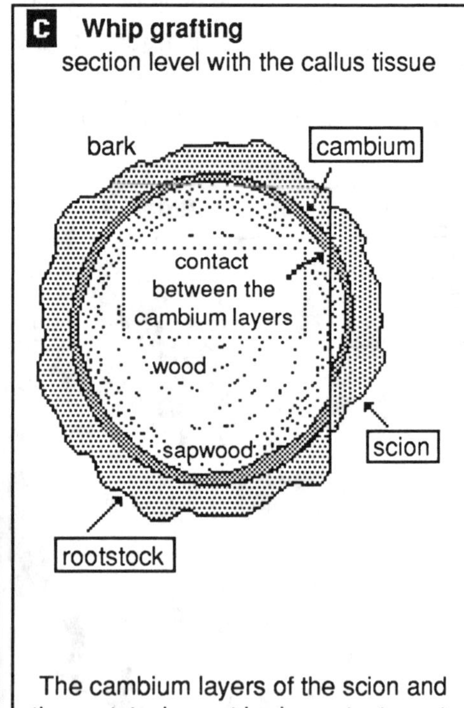

The cambium layers of the scion and the rootstock must be in contact on at least one and, if possible, both sides.

- Make a T-shaped incision, first a cross-cut, then a vertical slit, in the bark of the rootstock **(figure 452.1)**. Use a very sharp blade making sure that it only cuts the bark and does not penetrate the sapwood;
- Using a sharp blade, cut the shields from portions of shoots with at least one bud. Bud shields are usually taken from leaf nodes; the leaves are cut off but a stub of stalk is left on each one **(figure 452.2 and 3)** to protect the bud and facilitate the handling of the shield;
- Only remove the buds from the bearing shoots when you have incised the stock plants. On no account must the buds be allowed to dry out;
- With the point of the knife, gently lift the edges of the incised bark;
- Now insert the bud shield between the sapwood and the bark so that the two cambium layers are in close contact. If a tiny strip of sapwood remains attached to the shield, try to detach it before inserting the shield; this increases the surface contact between the cambium layers **(figures 451 and 452.4)**. Never touch either cambium layer with your fingers, use the stub of the petiole to ease the shield into position;
- Bind the union firmly, but leave the bud uncovered so that it is free to develop.
- During wet weather it is usual to use the 'inverted T' method to reduce the risk of water penetrating the cut surfaces. The technique is as described except that the T-shaped incision is reversed.

The bud should have united with the stock in ten to fourteen days. The bud will have started to swell by then, and the leaf stalk will come away between the fingers. Remove the tape some weeks later when the callus tissue is well developed.

Figure 453 shows the result of budding an orange tree. Notice how the shoots tend to spread sideways. They need to be trained upwards to prevent the tree from developing an unstable framework. In this case, the new branches could be tied to the top of the stock.

451 Budding

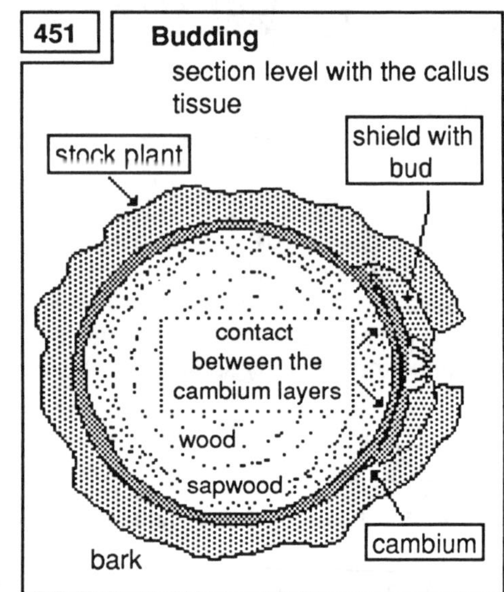

452 Budding

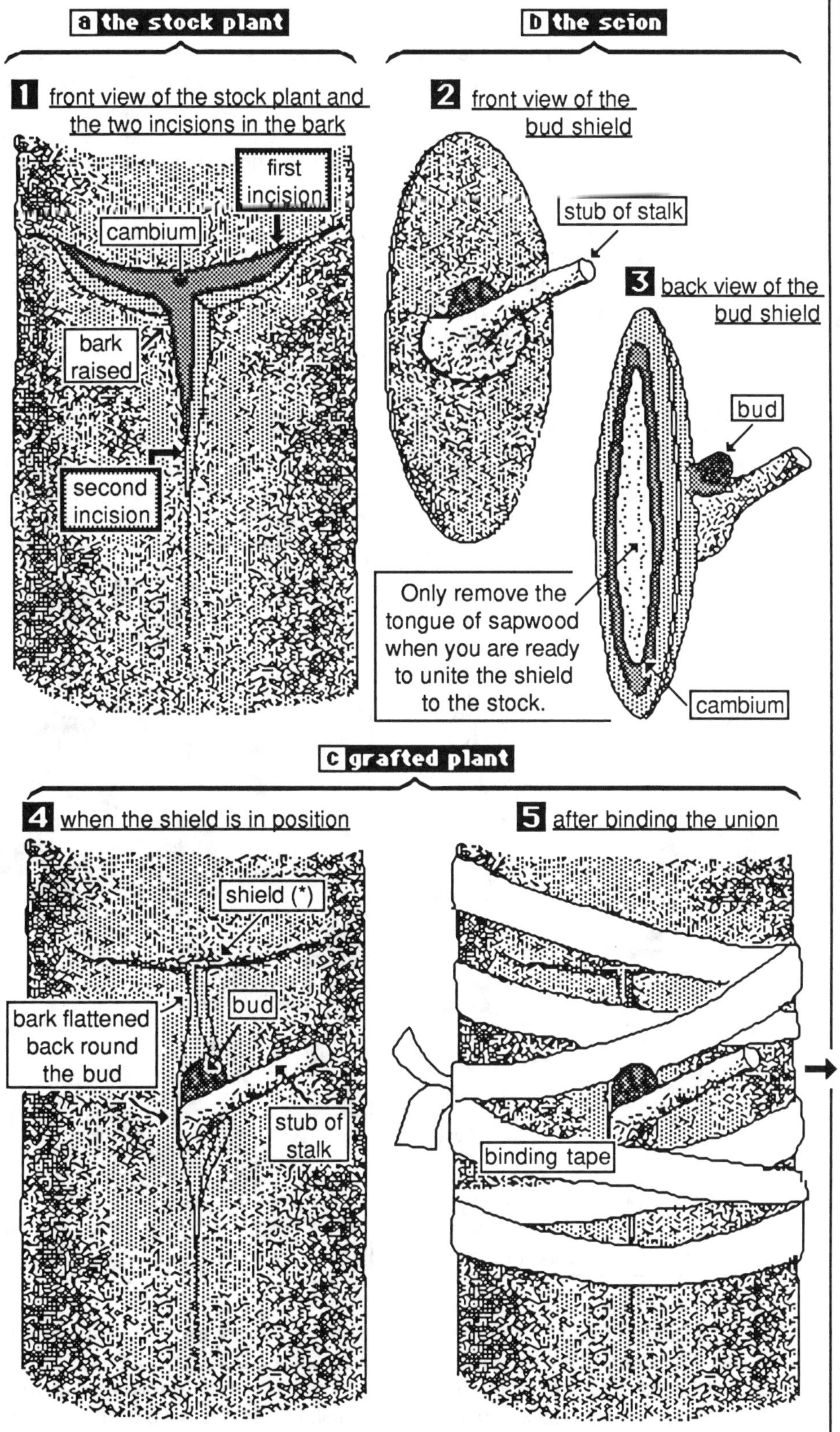

a the stock plant

1 front view of the stock plant and the two incisions in the bark

b the scion

2 front view of the bud shield

3 back view of the bud shield

Only remove the tongue of sapwood when you are ready to unite the shield to the stock.

c grafted plant

4 when the shield is in position

5 after binding the union

(*) The top of the shield must not protrude above the slit. If it does, it means that contact between the cambium layers is unsatisfactory.

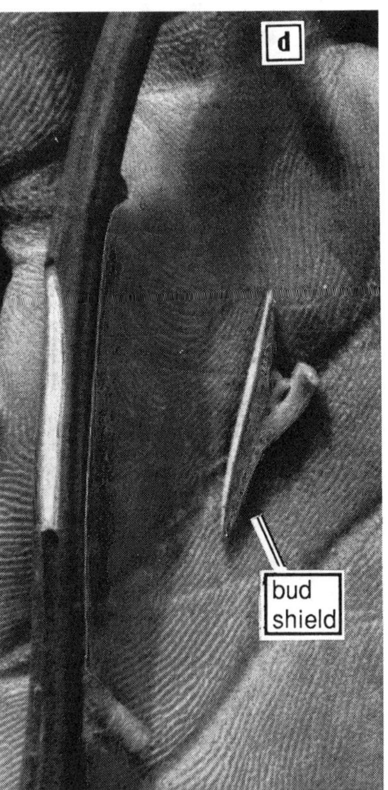

Notes

453

Approach grafting

Approach grafting consists in taking a scion, still attached to the parent plant, and uniting it with a young stock plant. **Figures 454 and 455** illustrate this technique with a guava.

The stock is planted in a bag or basket, close to the young shoot which will produce the scion. The two stems are placed side by side, and the bark on one side of the stock is sliced away for a distance of five or six centimeters. A similar cut is made on the side of the scion. The two cut surfaces are then pressed closely together so that their cambiums match each other as closely as possible; the union is then bound tightly.

The next step is **separation**. This involves gradually separating the parent shoot from the scion. A small cut is made in the shoot just below the graft union and is gradually deepened at intervals of about two weeks. First cut a quarter of the way through the stem, then half-way, then three-quarters, then sever it completely. For some species the separation may take months. The state of the callus union and the appearance of the scion will tell you how frequently to cut.

Topworking

Topworking is a grafting method that enables the branch system of an old tree to be replaced by grafting onto it a more productive variety. The stock plant therefore consists of the trunk and the frame of a mature tree. Side and splice grafting and budding are suitable. The method adopted depends on the species and the gardener's preference.

454 Approach grafting

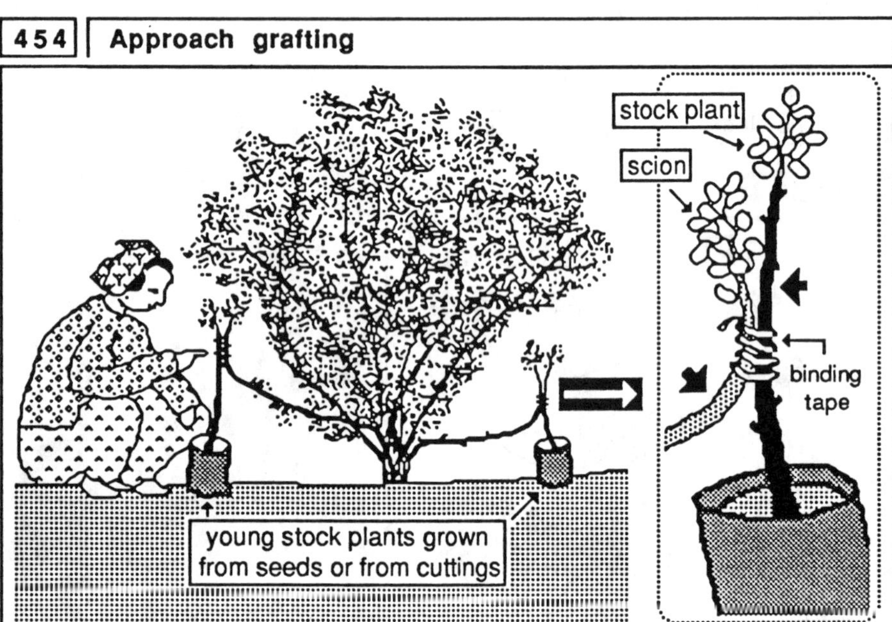

A cut, five to six centimetres long, is made on the respective stems of the stock and the scion. The stems are then united so that their cambium layers are in close contact. When the graft has taken, the scion and the stock are cut as shown by the black arrows. The separation of the scion is carried out in stages.

455

The old mango trunk in **figure 456** has been topworked. The original framework was kept but the crown was completely rejuvenated. The operation was carried out in two phases. During the first season, the branches were cut off and all the leaves were removed. New shoots grew on the framework. During the second season, some of these shoots were selected as 'stock plants', and scions were grafted on them **(figure 457)**. All the other shoots were cut back.

456

457

When adult trees are topworked, they can be in full production after three or four years. This is an appreciable advantage because a grafted tree developed from a seedling stock takes seven or eight years to reach maturity.

The scions used for topworking a tree can belong to one or to several varieties. For example, the old lemon tree in **figure 459** was topworked and now produces oranges (left) and mandarins (right). The gardener could have grafted different varieties of orange onto the original lemon, if he had wished.

Be particularly careful at two stages in this grafting method :

- Place hoops of pliable wood a**round the newly-grafted scions (figure 458) to stop birds from alighting on them** and breaking the unions;
- When the scions have taken, **remove all the suckers** growing below the grafted unions.

Topworking trees and trying to arrange combinations of different plant varieties for grafting on the same stock is rewarding, because, on a single adult stem which would normally only bear one variety, you will get results from grafting many varieties.

458 How to keep the birds away from topworked trees

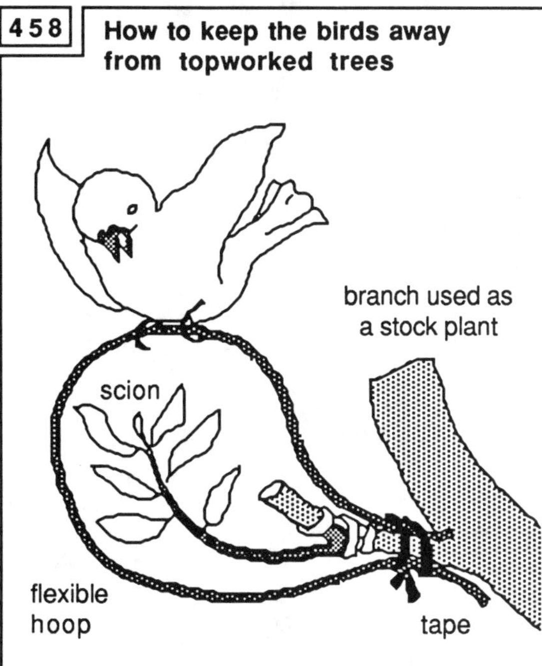

459

Notes

Precautions required in grafting

Whatever the method chosen, you must take a series of precautions before and after grafting operations.

Budding

- The stock plants and the scions must be **trimmed** before any budding operation. **Trimming a bud shield** means cutting off the leaf of the node from which a bud is removed. The leaf is cut level with the stalk **(figure 452b)**; sometimes a piece of the leaf blade, a few centimetres long, is left behind; this can be used to position the shield within the incision.

Grafting

- The **scions** used in grafting contain a little more food than the shields used in budding and they do not dry out so rapidly. Here, trimming means eliminating almost all the leaves by cutting the stalks. You must cut the leaves, never pull them off.The way the **stock plants** are trimmed depends on the grafting method you intend using - side or top grafting, splice grafting or topworking. For side grafting, one or two leaves are left intact on the stock plant, underneath the section. In other cases, a few leaves are left above the grafting union **(figure 460)**. The shoot that draws the sap is topped and pinched out so that, as it grows, it does not compete with the development of the scion.

  The cambium layers which will be in contact with each other must be as fresh as possible and only exposed at the last minute. This is why the incisions should be made when everything is ready for the grafting operation. Do not touch the incised pieces or leave them on the ground. Work in the shade so that the incisions are not dried by the sun, and keep flies away. Always keep scion material covered with a wet cloth until it is actually being used.

- Bind the **graft unions** very carefully. Make quite sure that water cannot infiltrate into the slits and, if necessary, coat them with wax, resin or birdlime. Tape the unions leaving the buds uncovered with room to swell and develop.

  When the graft has taken, gradually loosen the binding so that the stem can thicken. Otherwise, a swelling will form just below the constricting tape because the sap is unable to flow through and accumulates there **(figure 461)**.

- **Separation** is the next step. It involves removing the shoot or shoots that attract the sap and, at the same time, gradually loosening the binding. You should start undoing the tape when the callus is thick and the buds on the scion have begun to swell. Bud enlargement is the sign that the sap of the stock plant is feeding the scion; the shoot drawing the sap has served its purpose and can be cut back.

  However, the fact that the sap is moving through the thin layer of newly formed sapwood and bark does not mean that the graft union has healed perfectly. The process may take many months. Hence the need to loosen the binding very gradually; the shoot drawing the sap or the leaves remaining on the stock plant are also removed by degrees.

- Grafted plants must be **shaded** and watered until the scions have taken completely, by which time transplanting to the permanent site is feasible.

- When the scion has starting growing, it must be trained and pruned to **give it a good framework**. Maintenance will depend on the structure and habit you wish to obtain (Chapter 6).

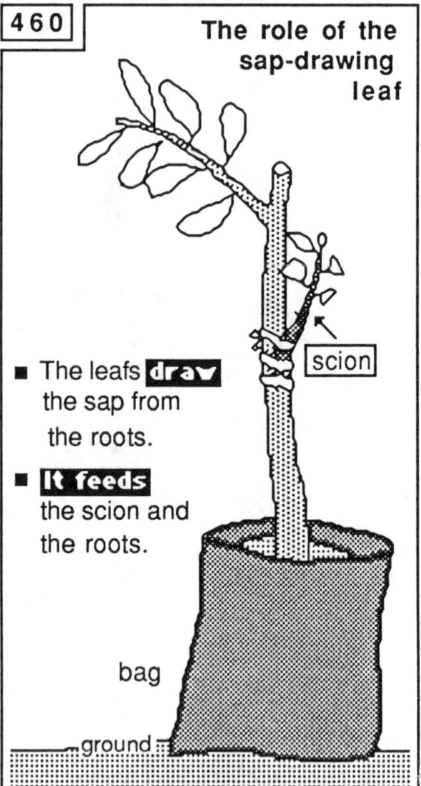

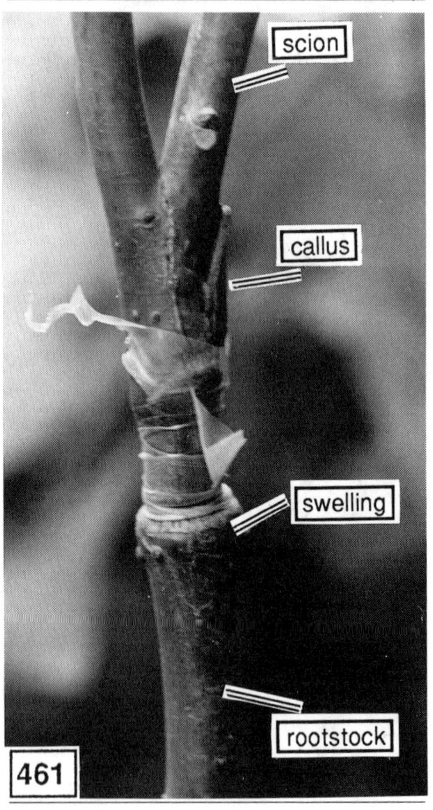

- **Systematically remove all the shoots growing below the graft union**, i.e. shoots, suckers, branches and flowers. These plant parts do not possess the qualities you want to obtain by grafting; they only possess those of the stock plant.

Chapter 18

The domestication of wild species of annual and perennial plants

We are surrounded by many spontaneous and subspontaneous species whose leaves, fruits and seeds can be used as food.

The term **spontaneous plants** describes wild plants growing naturally and freely in a wild state. **Subspontaneous plants** are also wild but man indirectly encourages their growth and spread. These plants are plentiful near compounds, by the roadside and in orchards, although they are not planted there deliberately. Some of these plants are well-known to women and medicine men who pick them regularly, or occasionally as the need arises when there is a shortage of other vegetables.

462

The expansion in market gardening in Africa today is largely based on the introduction of foreign species, the so-called European vegetables - leek, carrot, Chinese cabbage, etc. There is perhaps insufficient emphasis on the very great potential of plants from the African environment itself. There are more than 2,500 plant species which are regularly or occasionally eaten in different regions of the continent.

It may be well worthwhile trying to domesticate some of the wild plant species which could benefit man's diet, and this is within reach of every cultivator. Take, for example, the plateau field **(figure 462)** that belongs to a Cameroun farmer. This experienced planter decided to grow some raffia palms close to his home. Naturally this species of raffia grows in wet valley bottoms. Here the plant is on drier ground but, thanks to

463

African *Gnetum* is widely sold in Central African markets **(figure 463)**. The leaves of this creeper, which is in the process of becoming a domesticated crop, are very popular. *Gnetum* was originally found in thickets on forest lands, but it is fast becoming a subspontaneous plant in cultivated fields. Farmers do not pull up its rhizomes when they clean the fields.

464

466

465

Another example is Zamena *(Acacia macrostachya)* **(figure 465)**. In parts of Burkina Faso, the pods of this shrubby acacia are gathered in the dry season. The seeds, rich in proteins, are used in sauces. *Crassocephalum crepidioides* is found in wetter regions; this is a creeper with edible, pale green leaves **(figure 466)**.

Foetid cassia is a bushy legume cultivated for its leafy shoots **(figure 467)**. It usually grows wild in savannas or as a weed in fields. However, in some places, it is domesticated on the edges of fields or in compounds.

There are many more woody and herbaceous species which would be worth studying to see to what extent they could be domesticated on a wider scale. The following is a list of plants which could potentially be domesticated : acacias, Indian jujube, various peppers, hog plum and red mombin *(Spondias mombin and Spondias purpurea)*, dika *(Irvingia gabonensis)*, njansan *(Ricinodendron heudelotii)*, the garlic tree *(Scorodophleus zenkeri)*, the aidon tree *(Tetrapleura tetraptera)*, *Lannea acide*, true indigo, grains of paradise, *Costus afer* and *Hilleria latifolia* **(figure 468)**.

Rural dwellers all know where to look for edible and medicinal plants and when to pick them. Yet collecting these plants often gives meagre results. The plants may be destroyed by cattle or pests, simply because they are not protected or looked after. Since the plants grow wild, people pick them indiscriminately. The more popular the plants, the more liable they are to thoughtless destruction, with the result that, not infrequently, useful spontaneous and subspontaneous species die out. This is why, in some parts of Africa, there are farming traditions aimed at protecting useful plants and ensuring that all members of the community get a fair share of them.

An example of these traditions is found among the Mossis in Burkina Faso. Local societies decide when the locust bean pods are ready for picking and, in order to prevent a disorderly scramble for the fruits, they fix the exact dates of the harvest.

In many other parts of the world, the hunting and fishing seasons are regulated in order to preserve game and fish resources. In the same spirit of conservation, farmers preserve the tree stumps of useful species during slash-and-burn operations.

467

468

In West Africa, many trees such as the African locust bean, tamarind, shea butter, baobab and the silk cotton tree grow in association with the main crops. From time immemorial, the wild seedlings of these plants have been respected by farmers who wish to preserve them. In fact, these plants are subspontaneous species which man has gone

470

Generally speaking, the utilization of spontaneous and subspontaneous plants should be encouraged because these plants often provide food or extra income. Unfortunately, the produce is unreliable, especially when the population of a region increases. The amount harvested is never constant, and commercialization is often restricted. Again, the quality of the produce tends to be unsatisfactory because no attempt is made to improve it by such cultural practices as seed selection, fertilization and maintenance.

How can spontaneous species be domesticated?

The **domestication** of a spontaneous species involves planting it in a field or a garden and treating it like a cultivated plant. Simpler still, the plant can be tended and exploited where it grows.

Two plants are growing side by side in **figure 469** : *Vernonia calvoana* on the left, *Vernonia amygdalina* (bitter leaf) on the right. *Vernonia calvoana* was domesticated in recent years, first in Nigeria, then in Cameroun. Its leaves are larger, more tender and less bitter than those of *Vernonia amygdalina* . Bitter leaf is propagated by cuttings, but *Vernonia calvoana* can be grown from seed, a characteristic that makes cultivation easier.

469

to the trouble of conserving, although they are rarely sown in nurseries with a view to permanent planting. Their multiplication in this way, however, is quite feasible and would be profitable for the farming community. It would mean that, instead of letting the trees grow at random, plantations on settlements would be established on a planned basis.

The locust beans sown in plastic bags **(figure 470)** are ready to be transplanted. These particular seedlings have been raised with a view to producing fruits. Later on, some of the young plants could easily be propagated by cuttings or by grafting if they show signs of the qualities particularly desirable in seeds for human consumption or for forage.

The domestication of woody species is to be particularly recommended in the dry zones where the great natural forests are being destroyed through overexploitation. These depleted resources could be restored, while taking the foreseeable needs and changes in agriculture into account.

In Cameroun and Nigeria, the small dry fruits of the fagara tree *(Fagara heitzii* and *macrophylla)* are in much demand because they are a choice ingredient of sauces. **Figure 471** shows a fagara tree growing in a compound. The owner domesticated it by letting it germinate in the shade, in very moist soil, similar to that of forest areas. The tree was planted in its permanent place when it was 1.5 metres high.

If you want to domesticate a wild species, you must start by carefully observing the plant in its natural environment. This means:

- **observing the environment**: Does the plant grow in shade or in full light ? Some plants prefer shade when they are young and full light when they are mature. What kind of soil does it grow in - wet or dry, rich or poor, light or heavy ? Does it grow best in the dry or in the wet season ?
- **observing the plant's characteristics**: What is its habit ? Is it a herb, a shrub, a tree or a creeper ? Is the foliage well developed ? Is it too prolific ? If it is a creeper, how does it scramble onto other plants in order to thrive ? How does the root system occupy the soil ? Does it need a deep soil or will a thin layer of soil suffice ?
- **observing its vegetative cycle**: Is it a seasonal, annual, semi-perennial or perennial plant ? Is it fast- or slow-growing ? If it is slow-growing, could it be cultivated in association with more rapid growing plants ? Is the produce you are looking for in regular supply ? How quickly is it produced ? At what times of the year ?
- **finding out its modes of propagation**: Does the plant produce seeds ? How can it be propagated by vegetative means (cuttings abd tubers) ? Does it produce shoots ? Can seedlings from wild plants be transplanted ? Can it be grafted ?

Working from these observations, the next step is to determine the most favorable growth conditions for the species you want to domesticate. As a rule, it is best to recreate the plant's natural environment as closely as possible. A creeper that always grows in the shade of undergrowth must be domesticated in a thicket, a hedge or an orchard. A plant that usually grows in light soil, rich in organic matter, should be domesticated in a place with well-loosened, well-fertilized soil. If the plant comes from a valley bottom, it should be domesticated in beds of moist, clayey soil.

471

You may decide to start domesticating plants simply by **preserving spontaneous or subspontaneous species and encouraging their growth in their own environment. This means:**

- **removing the plants or harvesting the produce and, at the same time, remembering how they will survive this treatment.** This implies only gathering the produce that will be consumed, leaving part of the stem or the rhizomes in the ground, not removing all the plants from the same place, (leaving plants is essential for producing fresh seeds for the coming harvests), encouraging the growth of naturally-seeded plants and of basal shoots. The quality and abundance of later harvests depends, to a large extent, on your careful husbandry;
- **spacing out the harvests in order to avoid over-exploiting the plants;**
- **taking care not to damage the exploited plants unnecessarily** because every wound is a gateway for disease. Always use a sharp-cutting tool;
- **applying cultural methods that promote plant growth**: clearing scrub to reduce competition from other wild plants, weeding, cutting back diseased branches, tilling, adding fertilizers or manure, staking vines and creepers.

Domesticating a plant species is not always an easy operation. Difficulties may arise when it comes to sowing or maintaining the plant. When there is a choice between several varieties, it may be hard to decide which is the best variety for domestication. You must also decide on the best way of including the plant into crop rotations and into associations of cultivated plants. In a word, domesticating plants demands a great deal of experimentation and plenty of perseverance.

Chapter 19

Gardens and water availability

Water requirements and the irrigation of cultivated plants

Market gardening can give high yields when it is based on good horticultural practices. To produce high yields one of the essential features is the **adequate availability of water**.

Plants need a **global amount of water** for their life cycle. This water is required for transpiration by the leaves and for the absorption by the plant roots of mineral salts essential for its proper growth. Water is also needed for growth and fruit formation.

A plant will remain alive when it has **a minimum supply of water** but it will not be productive. Perennial plants can survive the dry season but when they are growing actively and producing new roots, leaves and fruit they need a lot of water.

On the other hand the soil round the roots must not have too much water for then the roots cannot take in oxygen for respiration and have difficulty in transpiring excess water.

Basically, **gardens must provide soil water in quantities which allow plants to take in as much as they need at every phase of their life cycle and support the active growth of their roots and aerial parts.**

In order to determine the water requirements of cultivated plants and the times when rain or irrigation water must be available, two aspects of plant growth must be **carefully observed** :

- **the production cycle** and the way in which water requirements vary throughout this cycle. If the gardener wants to produce leafy shoots or leaves, then water must be in plentiful supply when the plant produces these shoots and leaves. If the gardener wants fruit, the time between flowering and fruit set is the growth phase when abundant watering is most essential. But even this watering will be wasted if the plant has not already developed enough fruit-bearing branches;
- **the position of the roots at every stage of the productive cycle (figure 472).** If the roots are shallow, for example at the germination phase, it is useless watering in depth. What is needed at this time are repeated waterings to prevent the superficial soil layer from drying out and to avoid even a brief disruption in growth.

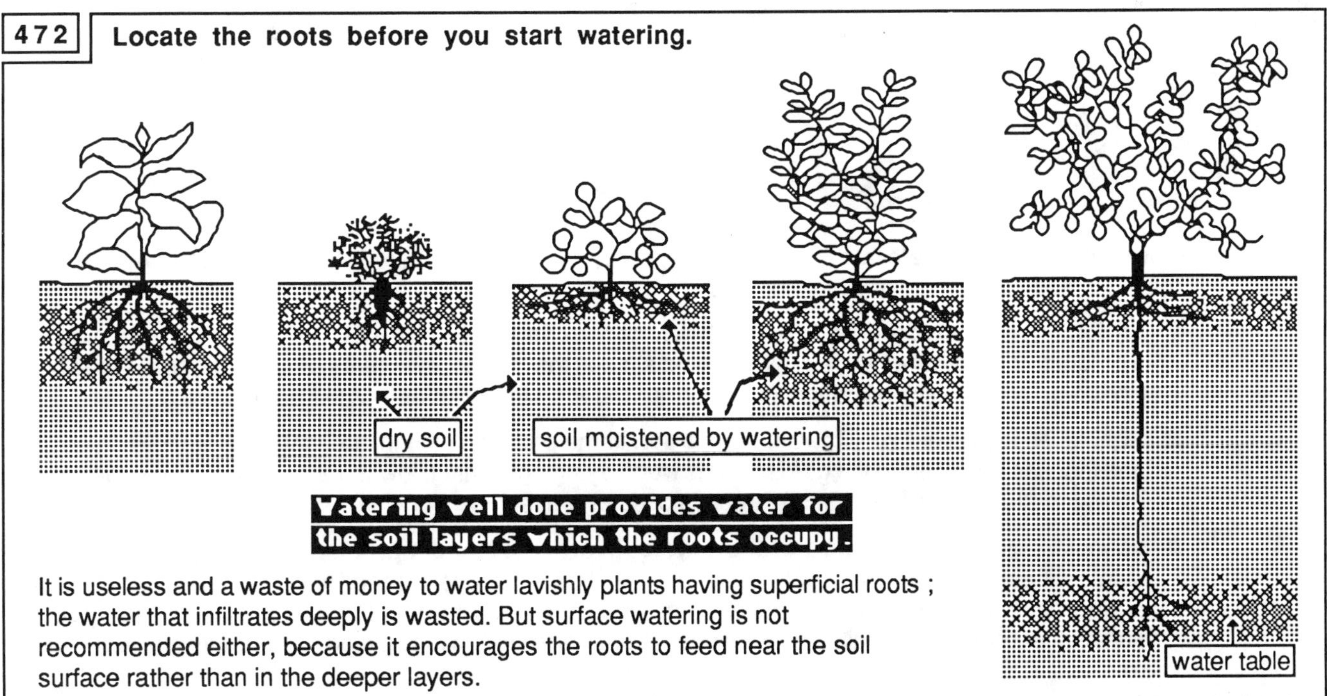

472 Locate the roots before you start watering.

It is useless and a waste of money to water lavishly plants having superficial roots ; the water that infiltrates deeply is wasted. But surface watering is not recommended either, because it encourages the roots to feed near the soil surface rather than in the deeper layers.

If rooting is extensive, water must be available in the deeper soil layers. Every time plants with deeply-penetrating roots are watered by natural or by artificial precipitation, they require more water than plants with shallow roots, but, on the other hand, the deeper soil layers retain moisture for longer periods because the rate of water loss is slower. Consequently, deep-rooting plants do not need to be watered as often as shallow-rooting species but they require more water. Some plants have roots that penetrate to a depth of several metres and reach down to **the water table**. Here, shallow irrigation is irrelevant. Only abundant rainfall can replenish these deep stores.

Gardeners must know the rate of growth of root systems in order to **water their plants efficiently and without wastage**. Water is often in short supply, and watering must be regular and carefully planned. Watering too much and wetting the soil layers not utilized by root systems is therefore useless.

Remember too that plants do not tolerate waterlogged soil. The roots are deprived of air and cannot thrive. Some very heavy, clayey soils are not suitable for growing vegetables unless they are drained. But, at times, gardeners themselves are responsible for killing the roots by suffocation; they believe they are doing the right thing by watering too generously.

From the point of view of market gardening and water supplies, cultivators may be confronted by any one of three situations :

- **market gardening that relies entirely on rainfall** because the cultivated plots are situated on plateaus and hillsides far from water supplies;
- **market gardening near a water supply** - a stream, a river, a well or a spring. The plants can be watered or irrigated regularly or occasionally;
- **valley bottom cultivation sometimes subject to seasonal flooding**, which growers sometimes exploit for irrigating their crops. This system is called **flood irrigation**.

473

Rainfed market gardening

Rainfed cultures are those crops that are only watered by natural rainfall. The plants are totally dependent on unpredictable rainfall cycles for their water requirements. Most market garden crops come to maturity in the dry season; only perennial plants that are able to withstand some months of drought can survive.

During the rainy season, erratic precipitation is also a hazard : the absence of rain at a crucial stage in the production cycle can destroy an entire crop. This is why, as far as possible, gardens and nurseries are established near a water supply or in valley bottoms so that a shortfall in rainwater can be compensated for by **supplementary irrigation**.

However, if there is no water at hand for an emergency, you can still take steps to maximize the available water, that is, in addition to mulching or using suitable crop associations. Such steps include :

- **protecting gardens from the drying effects of the climate. Figure 473** shows a garden surrounded by a productive, protective hedge. Its vegetation shades the ground, intercepts winds and lessens their drying effects. It also creates infiltration zones for rainwater on the perimeter of the garden;
- techniques to **prevent runoff from the garden** or the beds. Any technique that stops water running away and induces it to infiltrate the garden soil is worth trying - mulching, low terraces, partitioned ridges at right angles to the slope, rows of herbs, trees, stones or gravel;
- **associating plants with long and short cycles in order to stagger production in the garden.** Seasonal plants with a productive cycle of three or four months can be intercropped with other species with a cycle of six or seven months, or with perennial crops. Trees producing their fruits, seeds or leaves in the dry season are another possibility. Finally, there are many plants that build up ample food stores during the rainy season

and carry over their productive cycle into the first weeks or months of the dry season : mock tomato *(Solanum aethiopicum)*, foetid cassia *(Cassia tora)*, cassava, some vernonias, sweet potato, *Celosia*, *Solanum gilo Raddii*, bitter tomato, cowpea, late okra and watermelon;

- **establishing cultivated beds on sites where rainwater or waste domestic water accumulates** - in little hollows, or near dwellings where waste water is available;
- mounding the soil so that **rainwater is directed towards the base of trees (figure 78)** where it can infiltrate the soil and accumulate near the roots.

Nonetheless, however wide the range of cultural practices, rainfed market gardening is too dependent on precipitation. Supplies of fruit and vegetables cannot be guaranteed; there will be marked fluctuations in the amount of produce harvested, in market price, and in earned income.

Irrigated gardens

Hand methods

Artificial watering and irrigating can be carried out in both dry and wet seasons. Watering or irrigating in a wet season is called **supplementary irrigation**, that is, when crops need extra water, they are watered artificially in addition to natural irrigation by rainfall.

When consideration is given to the large quantities of water needed to water a garden, and the back-breaking work of carrying all that water by hand, it is obvious why gardens and water supplies must be situated close to one another *.

474

Figure 474 shows gardens established round shallow pits. These are dug and deepened until the water table is reached. **Shallow wells** into which watering cans are lowered are easily dug when the water table is high - between one and five metres below the ground surface. The deeper the hole, the wider its diameter and the more room it takes up in the garden. These shallow wells, however, are convenient because digging them calls for no special skills, and they are easily excavated when extra water is needed.

When the water table is deeper, it can only be tapped by digging proper **wells** which is the job of a skilled well digger. The size of the garden which can be watered and its cultural calendar are determined by the capacity of the well **(figure 475)**.

475

The greater the depth of the water table, the greater will be the energy required for lifting water, and this will influence the size of the area which can be watered. It is always an advantage to reduce the distance you have to carry the watering cans. This can be done by building small cement **tanks (figure 476)** or using drums or barrels that are filled with water piped from the well. Make sure that the pipe slopes gently in the direction of the tank, and fit it at the well end, with a metal or cement funnel into which you pour the water lifted from the well. These improvements cost very little and are labour-saving because the gardener is spared the work of doing what the water does of itself by flowing from the source to the tank.

(*) For methods of water lifting, e.g., shaduf, see Vanishing Land and Water, Jean-Louis Chleq, Hugues Dupriez. Macmillan Publishers, 1988, p. 129.

The tank in **figure 477** is filled in the rainy season by rainwater flowing from the hard ground nearby (the area is used as a drying floor). The water is channelled through a hole in the side of the tank. The hole is covered with wire mesh to keep out trash. Catchment tanks of this kind are handy for supplementary irrigation during the rainy season but usually the amount of water stored is not sufficient to last over the dry season. They are common near houses that have gutters for collecting rainwater from the rooftops.

If the garden is near a pool or a stream, you can make a water point nearer the beds by digging a channel that carries the water to a shallow well where the watering cans are filled **(figure 478)**. However this may result in a loss of water due to seepage and evaporation in the channel.

476

477

478

The method of watering is very important. Watering is not just providing plants with a certain amount of water; it must be done at the right time and in such a way that the plants and the beds are not damaged.

Take the example of the gardener in **figure 479**. He fills a bucket from the well where he is standing, and throws its contents as far away as possible on the nearby beds. This method saves carrying the water, but it has its drawbacks : first, the water is not spread evenly over the beds and, secondly, compact masses of water land violently on the plants and the soil. The soil suffers from compaction and the plants topple under the impact of the water.

479

The gardener can spread the water evenly in droplets with the help of a watering can, but this method is more laborious because the waterer has to lift the water, carry it some distance, and then empty the can walking up and down the bed **(figure 480)**.

This Senegalese garden **(figure 481)** is on sandy soil. The gardener has built a series of small, level beds, bounded by edges 15 centimetres high. Each time he waters, he gives each bed a bucketful of water, regardless of the growth stage of the plants.

481

480

This method has its advantages :

- **the work is well organized** : as every bed gets the same amount of water, anybody - even a child - can do the watering;
- **all the water infiltrates into the soil** because the raised sides of the beds prevent runoff;
- **If the surface of the bed is really level, the layer of water spreads evenly over the whole surface.**

However, the method has its disadvantages :

- **by pouring the water** directly into a corner of the bed, the gardener **makes little channels and moves the soil**;
- by pouring the same amount of water onto the beds from the beginning to the end of the vegetative cycle of his plants, the gardener **wastes an enormous amount of water**. The important thing is to ensure that moisture is present in the soil layer exploited by the roots at a given phase of growth. Watering constantly at the same rate may result in more water than is necessary going to the deeper soil layers.

This method of watering could be improved : the gardener could spray the plants with the help of a watering can or a tin can with holes in the bottom, and vary the amounts of water used daily, depending on the development of the root system and leaf development.

When the water point is far away and it is impossible to lay pipes and set up permanent tanks, water transport is made easier by making a mobile tank. The one in **figure 482** consists of a drum mounted on a push-cart. A length of flexible hose, fixed like a siphon or attached to an outlet welded in the bottom of the drum, could be used to carry the water to the plants. The gardener could also fit a watering can rose to the end of the hose in order to break the stream of water into droplets.

482

Figure 483 illustrates a method of watering that is useful in very dry regions. Porous (unglazed) clay

483

jars are half buried in the ground, regularly filled with water and covered to prevent evaporation. In this instance, watermelons were sown in the soil which is kept moist by water oozing from the earthen pots. This method of watering individual plants is very economical because their roots soak up the soil water and, in so doing, encourages the water to seep through the porous walls of the jar.

Gravity irrigation

Irrigation by this method consists in allowing water to flow through a garden from a higher to a lower level. Some of the water will infiltrate the soil and is taken up by the cultivated plants; the remainder flows through the garden and comes out at the lowest point.

Figure 486 shows the various ways in which water moves in the soil. When water is allowed to flow into a garden from higher up, most of it is absorbed by the soil or by the plants. The amount of water which is allowed to flow down at regular intervals from the source is determined by the water requirements of the crops.

Figure 484 gives an overall view of an irrigated garden created by a group of small farmers in Cameroun. Notice the central inlet channel and the beds which are irrigated by gravity. The outlet channel runs alongside the trees. This is a very simple system which required little or no investment or preliminary study.

484

The water is pumped by a small motor from a well situated to the left (not in the photograph), and discharges into the main channel over which the gardener is standing. Each day, the gardener diverts the water towards the beds which need irrigating. He uses lumps of earth to make diversion blocks, either in the main drain or in the side drains **(figure 485)**. The gardener can make the water flow where he wants, by the use of these mud blocks. When enough water has been allowed to flow into a drain, the entrance is obstructed and the gardener then diverts the flow elsewhere.

This system of irrigation is also very simple and has the advantage that market gardeners can install it with the means at their disposal. Large irrigation projects work on the same principle, except that the materials and the installations are on a much bigger scale with cemented channels, metal sluice-gates, more powerful motor pumps and larger reservoirs.

A motor pump is not always required. When the garden is on low ground near a stream, the water can be diverted from the stream to the main channel in the garden. A water intake is built by making a small weir : stones, wood, cement or even sandbags raise the level of the water in the stream so that some of it flows into the channel.

485

486 Irrigation by gravity

The top half of this figure **(a)** represents the layout of a small garden irrigated by gravity. The garden is seen from above. The bottom half of this figure **(b)** represents the garden seen in section.

a The layout of the garden (the arrows show the direction of water flow).

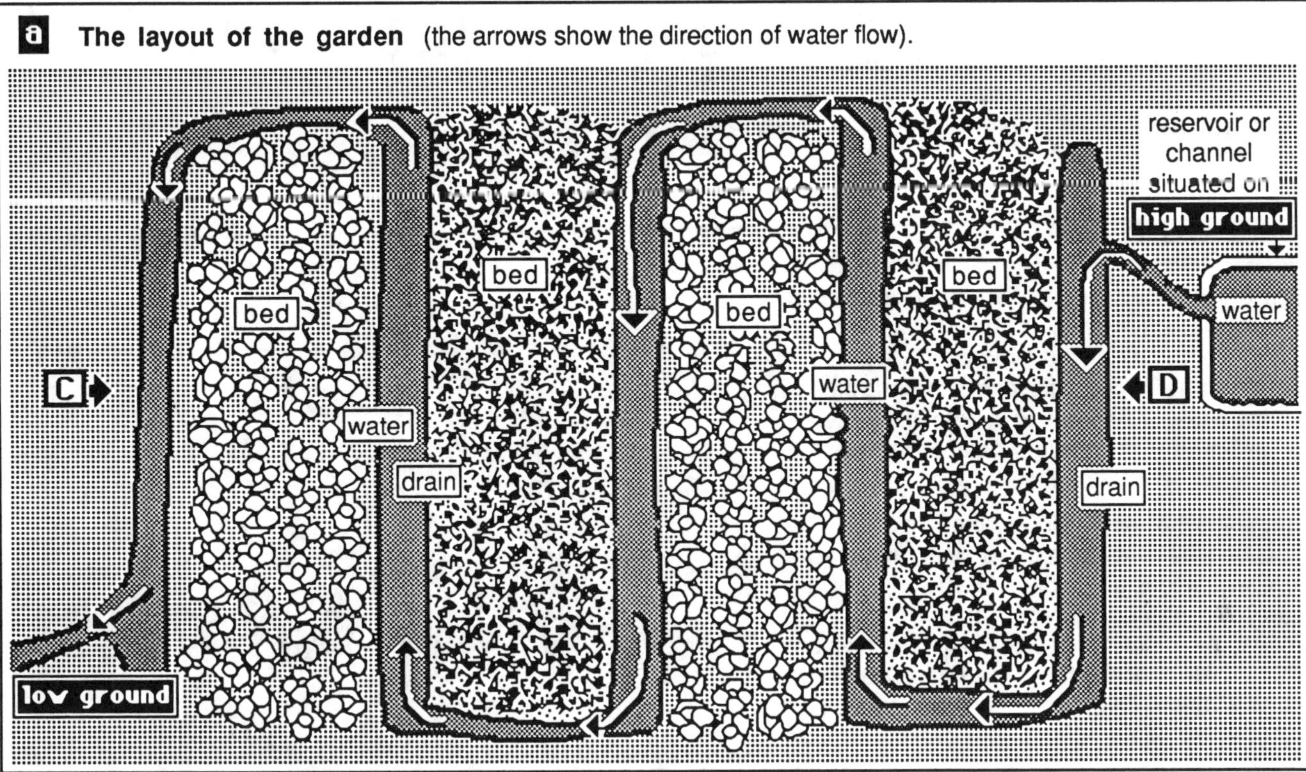

b The garden seen in section between points C and D

Water movements during irrigation by gravity :

- **in the drains,** the water flows in the direction of the slope ;
- **in the soil,** the water can :
  - **infiltrate vertically** into the deep soil layers ;
  - **infiltrate laterally towards the collecting drain** ;
  - **be retained** within the soil structure ;
  - **evaporate** from the ground surface ;
  - **be taken up** by the plants.

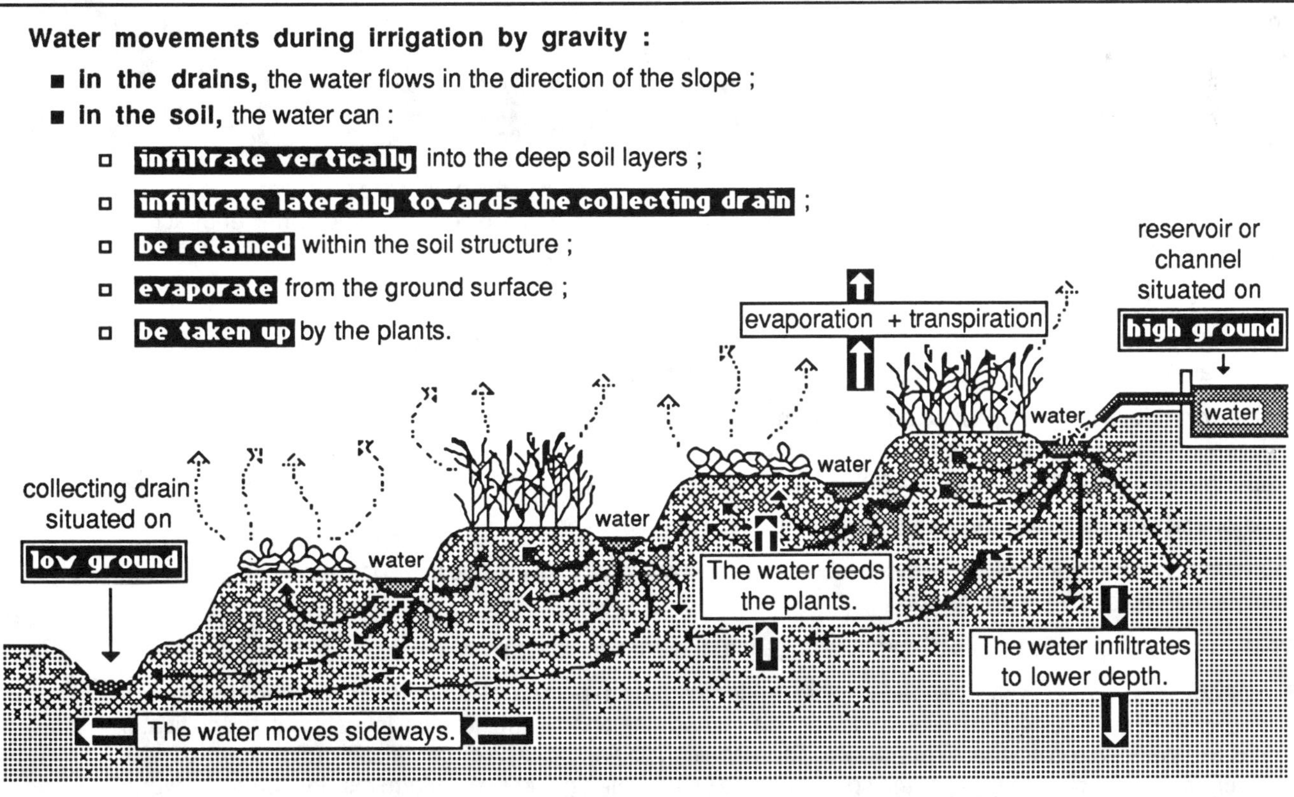

Irrigation must carry water to the soil layers where the roots develop.

In regions where water is very scarce, **drip irrigation** systems that release water drop by drop around the plants are used. The main pipe is laid on the ground and fitted with small lateral pipes, each with a nozzle that regulates the flow of water and directs the water exactly to the base of the plants.

The nozzles are sometimes difficult to adjust and it may take a lot of time to get the system running perfectly, but it has the advantage of distributing the water very accurately.

487

Sprinkler irrigation

Figure 487 shows a simplified sprinkler irrigation system. Water from a well is pumped back through a pipe (the pump is in the foreground). A watering rose or nozzle is fixed to the end of the long pipe so that the water is discharged in droplets. Watering like this with a motorpump means that workers must be present all the time.

Figure 488, however, shows a method of sprinkler irrigation where hardly any workmen are needed while watering is going on. A main supply pipe is laid on the ground from one end of the banana grove to the other; erect pipes called stand-pipes or 'risers' are attached to the main supply at regular intervals, and a revolving sprinkler is fixed on the top of each stand-pipe. Water pressure in the supply pipe and in the stand-pipes makes the sprinklers rotate rapidly. The pressure is obtained by using a powerful pump, or by taking water from a reservoir situated much higher than the sprinklers, for example, on a nearby hill or on a tower. The higher the pressure, the more evenly the sprinklers distribute the water on the plants (**figure 489**).

488

In some cases, the sprinkler installation is left permanently in the garden or the orchard to be irrigated. In others, however, the pipes are portable and can be moved to other places when necessary. One sprinkler attached to a flexible pipe and moved regularly often suffices for a small garden.

Gardeners who favour sprinkler irrigation must remember three factors :

- when the air is hot and dry, **the drops of water have a high evaporation rate** while they are airborne and when they are deposited on the leaves; this may lead to significant water losses;
- the **sprinklers** must be positioned so that the whole surface to be irrigated receives the water it needs. Because the water is scattered in circles round the sprinklers, it is distributed unevenly so that parts of the garden get too much water, others get too little. Hence the need to move the sprinklers at regular intervals;
- when the weather is **windy**, water distribution is still more uneven.

This is why, in small gardens with enough labour, a sprinkler system like the one in **figure 487** is more effective than the method shown in **figure 488**.

What are the comparative costs of sprinkler irrigation and irrigation by gravity ?

- **Specific equipment** is always needed for **sprinkler irrigation** - pumps, tanks, watertight piping, sprinklers, - and it has to be renewed on a regular basis. This means that, apart from the initial investment, the cultivator has to allow for **fixed annual expenditure**. The technical problems can be quite difficult - adjustment of water discharge rates, maintenance of the sprinklers and of the watertight joints, uniform distribution of the water on the ground round the sprinklers, etc.;

489 **Sprinkler irrigation**

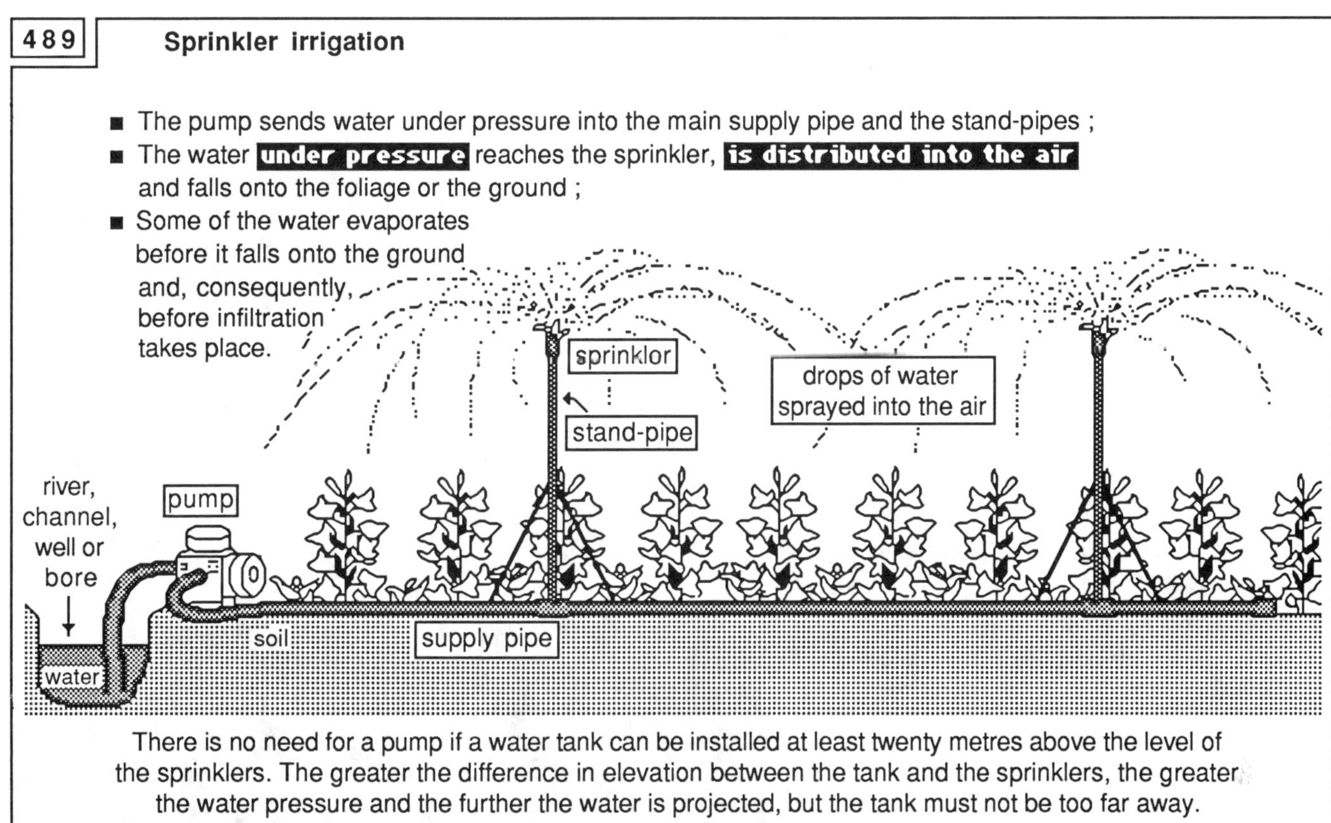

There is no need for a pump if a water tank can be installed at least twenty metres above the level of the sprinklers. The greater the difference in elevation between the tank and the sprinklers, the greater the water pressure and the further the water is projected, but the tank must not be too far away.

■ On the whole, **channel irrigation by gravity** is simpler, but **the cost of labour is higher than the cost of bought equipment**. To begin with, the system can be installed on small plots and extended by degrees depending on the available labour. Once the canals and drains have been laid out, the annual labour input consists mainly of regular maintenance and repair. Here again, it is a question of labour costs rather than of equipment.

These considerations apply mainly to small holdings. Major irrigation works for large tracts of land are another matter, since the requirements and operation are very different in scale.

490

Valley bottom cultivation and drainage

Crops may be at risk from too much water, especially in valley bottoms and swamps where flooding can be temporary or permanent, and at times so extensive as to prevent access to the land.

Drainage consists in drawing off excess water and diverting it to a water course. The soil layer in which the roots of cultivated plants develop is drained but not dried out, because the roots need moist, well-aerated soil. Methods of draining include techniques such as :

■ **Digging channels** in the land to be drained so that the water flows slowly away from a level surface. Drainage channels remove the water to the lowest point in the field from where it may be discharged into a river **(figures 490 and 491)**;

■ Making **cambered (raised) beds** and ditches to allow water to drain from the beds to the ditches **(figure 492)**;

■ Burying concrete, clay or PVC drainage pipes **in the ground**. These drainage pipes are punctured with holes to let ground water seep in and are connected to a main pipe lower down that distributes the collected water; the drainage pipes have to be laid at a slight slope and discharge outside the drained area;

■ **Mole ploughing** is sometimes carried out and consists in working the soil with a mole plough. This implement is pulled through the ground and makes underground drainage tunnels at a depth of 50 to 80 centimetres.

Good drainage is more difficult to achieve than good irrigation. Basically, irrigation depends on the amount of water available, the crops cultivated and the type of soil. Drainage, however, depends on factors that can scarcely be brought under control - the rain calendar, the characteristics of the catchment basin that supplies water to the valley bottom, the situation of the drained plot in relation to other plots higher up the valley, and the soil structure.

491

Efficient drainage depends on a detailed knowledge of the wet land. These are the questions you must ask yourself :

492

- When does flooding take place ? How long does it last ? How many times is the land flooded every year ? Does the floodwater stagnate for a long time in the valley bottom or does it flow away in a few hours ?
- When is the valley bottom wet - in the rainy season, in the dry season, during short intervening periods of rain or drought ? What is the best time for growing crops ?
- Is the soil clayey, peaty or sandy ?
- Are there noticeable variations in the level of the water table ? Do you have to drain at certain times in the year and irrigate at others ?
- What is the topography of the area ? Is the land relief high in places, low-lying in others ? Where does water stagnate ? Where does it flow away by itself ?
- What are you aiming at ? Do you want to drain in order to grow crops all the year round ? Or only at a particular time in the year when other farms and gardens cannot be cultivated ?

The answers to all these questions will help you choose an efficient method of drainage. But remember that, very often, drainage and irrigation must, or can, go hand in hand. A plot flooded at some periods of the year may have to be irrigated at other times.

Finally, some plants can contribute very effectively to drainage schemes. Notice how fodder herbs known for their high water requirements were planted along the ditches in **figure 491**, . These herbs help stabilize the banks while producing large quantities of leafy fodder. They also take up considerable quantities of soil water which is evaporated into the atmosphere. Plants that are efficient water absorbers are found everywhere in Africa and can be planted in water-saturated land as a means of reducing the soil water content.

Water management in perspective

Watering, irrigation and drainage are three aspects of water management that need to be examined, but they must not be allowed to obscure other factors of equal importance which were mentioned earlier on. These factors include techniques for encouraging water infiltration near cultivated plants, setting up windbreaks to protect gardens, associating plants that take up soil water in different ways, shading plants, and mulching. An overall water management in gardens is essential.

Part II

Vegetables, fruits and condiments

Part I of this book examines the cultural practices typical of gardens and orchards. Part II deals with the plants growing there, and gives systematic presentations (abbrev **SP**) of 86 plant species, including their environment and growth needs, uses, modes of propagation, husbandry, and specific cultural practices.

Not all the species cultivated or harvested in Africa are covered here. Some species are too well-known to justify their detailed study. It was decided to pick out species that are common in rural or urban food markets but are less familiar to researchers, technicians, writers and teachers.

Few of the species described have been researched individually, and quite often more knowledge about the appropriate methods of cultivation and the best varieties is needed. Readers are invited to make their own field notes, to complete or correct the presentation, and to send in their comments.

The plants are grouped in chapters as follows :

- Chapter 20 : plants grown mainly for their leaf vegetables and shoots;
- Chapter 21 : plants grown mainly for their vegetable and condiment fruits;
- Chapter 22 : cucurbits;
- Chapter 23 : plants grown mainly for their sweet and sour fruits;
- Chapter 24 : plants grown mainly for their nuts or kernels;
- Chapter 25 : palms;
- Chapter 26 : plants grown mainly for their bulbs and roots;
- Chapter 27 : plants grown mainly for their flowers and bark.

This classification is for convenience. Everyone knows that many plants are exploited for a variety of products : the baobab, for instance, is exploited for its leaves, flowers, fruits and bark; the cucumber is exploited for its seeds and leaves, and these are but two examples. It was decided to classify the plants according to their main use (as a fruit for example or a nut). They are presented in alphabetical order in each chapter.

The English names of the plants in are not absolutely reliable for identification purposes. In many cases, villagers do not use either these English names or their botanic equivalents in Latin. This explains why the names are given in some of the vernacular languages. The lists are obviously incomplete but they are included for the reader's guidance, although the spelling or the pronunciation of the plant names cannot be vouched for.

A glossary on page 324 defines some of the botanical terms used in this part of the book.

Chapter 20

Leaf vegetables and potherbs

SP1 Amaranths and Celosia

Amaranths are seasonal plants of the family Amaranthaceae. Their vegetative cycle lasts for two to three months. There are many species of amaranths that are not easy to identify because they cross-fertilize readily. **Bush greens** *(Amaranthus hybridus)* is the most common garden species. **Figure 494** shows part of a bed ready to be picked for the first time.

493

The main stem of this plant can be as much as two metres long **(figure 493)**. The pale green leaves are 20 to 30 centimetres long; they are lanceolate (lance-shaped) with long stalks. The white-yellow flowers are very small (2 millimetres). They form long terminal clusters 30 to 40 centimetres in length. The black, glossy seeds, produced in great quantities, are very tiny (1 millimetre).

Figure 495 shows other species that are often consumed; some are exploited in their wild state :

- ***Amaranthus viridis* (a)** a low plant, with a short terminal inflorescence sometimes involute;
- ***Amaranthus cruentus***, of which the two varieties, **(b) and (c)**, are characterized by their purple leaves, flowers and stems. It is like *Amaranthus hybridus* but with shorter inflorescences and leaves;
- ***Amaranthus dubius* (d)** has small, rounded leaves, and a foliaceous (leaf-like) terminal inflorescence;
- ***Amaranthus spinosus*** is distinguished by the spikes on the leaf axils and in the inflorescences.

Scientific Name	*Amaranthus spp.*
English	**Bush greens** *(Amaranthus hybridus)* **Red amaranth** *(Amaranthus cruentus)*
French	Amarante
Swahili	mchicha
Yoruba	tete, olorungbin

494

495

496

Scientific Name	Celosia argentea and C. trigyna
English	The scientific name is used.
French	célosie

Celosia spp. are vegetables of the same family **(figure 496)**. They are easily identified by their terminal flowers, scaly, silvery to purple in colour *(Celosia argentea)*, sometimes in clusters of three *(Celosia trigyna)*. They are seasonal plants and are 0.5 to 1.5 metres tall when mature.

Uses : The leaves and young shoots are used in sauces and soups, or are eaten with the main course. Matured, seeding plants make good food for poultry and other farmyard animals.

Environment : Amaranths and *Celosia* grow in full light. No particular soil is needed, but they are most productive on soils rich in organic matter.

Propagation : By seed from seed plants stored at harvest time, and by insertion of lateral shoots as cuttings.

Husbandry : One of the firsxt plants to colonise newly-cleared or eroded land. They grow well when associated with species that give little shade.

They are sown broadcast, sometimes with other leaf vegetables. Density recommended 10 centimetres by 10 centimetres. Thinning after two or three weeks. The unconsumed thinned plants are preferably transplanted with a ball of soil. The plant is cut back to ground level after three or four harvests when it begins to age. Topping stimulates flowering in some varieties of amaranths **(figure 155)**.

The plants are harvested in three ways : the whole plant is pulled three or four weeks after sowing; the longest shoots are removed, or whole leaves are individually harvested with the leaf-stalk attached.

SP2 Baobab

The **baobab** belongs to the family Bombacaceae, and is widespread in West Africa. The habit of the tree is characteristic : the trunk is shaped like a very wide cone, with a diameter of up to 6 metres and a height of between 10 and 20 metres or more **(figure 497)**.

The leaves are palmate, dark green and glossy. They are about 15 centimetres long **(figure 498)**. The white flowers, 15 to 20 centimetres wide, are pendulous on long stalks. The oblong fruits, 15 to 30 centimetres long, or even longer, are covered with downy hairs **(figure 499)**. They have brown seeds and a white-pink pulp called 'monkey bread'. The roots of the baobab are deeply penetrating. The tree sheds its leaves during the dry season.

497

Scientific Name	Adansonia digitata
English	**Baobab**
French	baobab
Swahili	mbuyu
Yoruba	oshé

498

Environment : The baobab adapts well to poor soils, and withstands drought and fires. The tree forms the uppermost storey in fields and savannas.

Propagation : Only by seed. When sowing, seed dormancy can be broken by plunging the seeds into boiling water for five minutes.

Uses : The produce of the baobab is used in many ways as a food, and for craft and medicinal purposes.

- As a food : the leaves, flowers, fruit pulp and peeled roots are cooked and eaten. The fresh flowers are sometimes eaten raw. All the produce is treated as a vegetable or as a seasoning for sauces. Flour, rich in protein and oil, is made from the seeds. It contains as much as 50% protein for dry weight, and about 15% oil;
- For handicrafts : the bark fibres are used for rope-making, and the roots produce a red dye;
- As a medicine : concoctions made from the leaves, the bark, the roots and the fruits are recommended for colic, asthma, and intestinal infections.

Husbandry : The produce is gathered from spontaneous and subspontaneous trees. The baobab is also planted in farms because it provides welcome shade and also fertilizes and conserves the soil. If it is pollarded or pruned to produce poles, the tree can be exploited for its leaves from the first or second year onwards. When the baobab grows in rich soil and its leaves and young shoots are not exploited to any extent, the tree bears its first fruits when it is six or seven years old. **Figures 497, 161** and **162** show mature baobab trees in full production.

499

Storage : The dried leaves ground into powder can be kept for several months.

SP3 Indian spinach

Indian spinach is included in the family Basellaceae. Its long stems branch densely whether lying on the ground or trained on supports **(figure 500);** they are sometimes many metres long.

The fleshy leaves are dark green or purple. They are cordate (heart-shaped) and lightly crimped, between 10 and 15 centimetres long. The leaf stalk is fleshy, green or dark red depending on the variety. The stem section is square. The small flowers are pale green to pink. They hang in small clusters in axillary spikes. The fruits are small berries 4 or 5 millimetres wide which are mauve at maturity.

Uses : The whole leaves or young shoots are eaten as a vegetable, or used in sauces.

Environment: Indian spinach demands full sunshine and is sensitive to drought. It responds to permanently moist soil, rich in humus.

Propagation : By seed or by cuttings from shoots two or three months old **(figure 355)**.

The plant is **cultivated intensively** in two ways :

- the shoots are trained on stakes or on fences and trellises; the secondary and tertiary shoots are harvested regularly from the primary stems;
- the plant is cut back to the ground after every harvest. Whole stems are pruned back, and the stump produces new shoots **(figure 207)**.

500

Both these systems mean that the plants are renewed each season. However, Indian spinach can also be exploited as a pluriseasonal plant, in which case production is less abundant.

Husbandry : The seeds are usually sown in planting holes. They are manured with compost or organic waste and watered frequently. Mulching and all the practices that encourage the retention of soil moisture are recommended.

Scientific Name	*Basella rubra and B. alba*
English	**Indian spinach**
French	baselle, épinard indien
Yoruba	amuntutu funfun, amuntutu pupa

SP4 Basil

Scientific Name	*Ocimum spp. and Basilicum spp.*
English	**Basil**
French	basilic
Yoruba	eferi

Basil plants of the family Labiatae belong to two closely related genera called *Basilicum* and *Ocimum* . Some are native to Africa, others to Europe.

Basilicum americanum **(figure 501)** is widely distributely in West Africa. It is a low-growing plant with small fruits. *Ocimum viride* has large, lightly serrate leaves. They are rough in texture and 8 to 10 centimetres long. This is a bushy plant as much as 2 metres high. The small flowers are arranged in terminal spikes **(figure 503)**. Both these species originated in Africa.

Two species of cultivated basil are natives of Europe. *Ocimum gratissimum* **(figure 502)** is a low bushy plant with large leaves between 60 and 80 centimetres high. *Ocimum basilicum* is smaller, 25 to 40 centimetres high, with glossy leaves 3 to 5 centimetres long **(figure 504)**.

All these plants have a strong, fragrant smell and are slightly pungent. Their leaves are more or less lanceolate, sometimes serrate. They are opposite, that is, borne in pairs on each side of the stem nodes that are square in cross section. The small white, pink or yellow flowers are arranged in terminal spikes **(figure 501)**. The seeds are small (about 1 millimetre) and dark.

501

502

503

504

Uses : The leaves and young shoots are used to flavour sauces. They are also made into remedies such as infusions for coughs and headaches.

Environment: Basil plants thrive in full sunshine. The African species withstand drought and poor soil. The species native to Europe demand better growth conditions.

Propagation : By seed, sometimes by cuttings or layering.

Husbandry : In kitchen gardens, one or two perennial bushes, from which shoots are occasionally gathered, are quite enough for cooking purposes. Plants for commercial production are sown every year; perennial species are cut back regularly to ground level.

The plant is sown in a nursery. The seedlings are transplanted with a root ball when they have 4 to 6 leaves. When the plantlets have 6 to 10 nodes, the tips are pinched out in order to induce lateral branching and to stop the flowers from opening too rapidly (controlled flowering). When basil is grown on a commercial scale, the plant is pruned drastically at regular intervals in order to encourage branching.

Storage : The leaves are first dried in the sun and, if desired, crushed and ground into powder. They can then be kept in dry containers.

505

SP5 Foetid cassia and negro coffee

Scientific Name	Cassia tora	Cassia occidentalis
English	**Foetid cassia**	**Negro coffee**
French	casse fétide	casse puant, café nègre

Foetid cassia is a herb of the family Leguminosae . It is a stout bushy plant, 50 centimetres to 1 metre high. Its leaves are composed of three pairs of oval leaflets, 1 to 3 centimetres long, and 1 to 2 centimetres wide, with a slender tip **(figures 505 and 506)**. The yellow flowers are borne in the leaf axils. The fruits are pods about 10 centimetres long, tapering to a point. They contain angular seeds of irregular shape.

Negro coffee *(Cassia occidentalis)* is a semi-perennial plant and has a bushy habit similar to that of foetid cassia to which it is closely related. It can grow to a height of 1.5 metres **(figure 507)**. However, its leaves, composed of three to five pairs of leaflets, are considerably larger and can be as much as 25 centimetres long. The yellow flowers have open petals which open, one above the other, along a terminal axis. The pods are about fifteen centimetres long and noticeably indented. The seeds are round and irregularly shaped.

506

507

Uses : The young leaves and shoots are used for flavouring sauces. Negro coffee is found in many remedies for treating viral hepatitis, neuralgia and eye complaints, and as a poultice for sprains. The roasted seeds are used to make black dyes, and are used in the preparation of a bitter drink, hence the name 'negro coffee'. The stems of foetid cassia are used for making fences and matting.

Environment : These cassias are light-demanding. They are drought-resistant and can survive on poor soils but the edible leaves are then of inferior quality.

Propagation : By seed.

Husbandry : The produce of these cassia plants is gathered wherever they grow in savannas, as a weed in farms or by the wayside. The plant is in the process of domestication in parts of Africa **(figure 467)**. The mildest varieties of these bitter-tasting plants are selected; the leaflets must be tender and separate readily from the stalks.

SP6 Cabbages

Cabbages belong to the family Cruciferae are are generally referred to as Brassicas. There are many species and varieties of which various parts are consumed :

- the leaves : African leaf cabbage **(figure 508)**, Indian mustard, Chinese cabbage, etc.;
- the heads : white, red and green cabbages, Savoy cabbage **(figure 509)**;

508

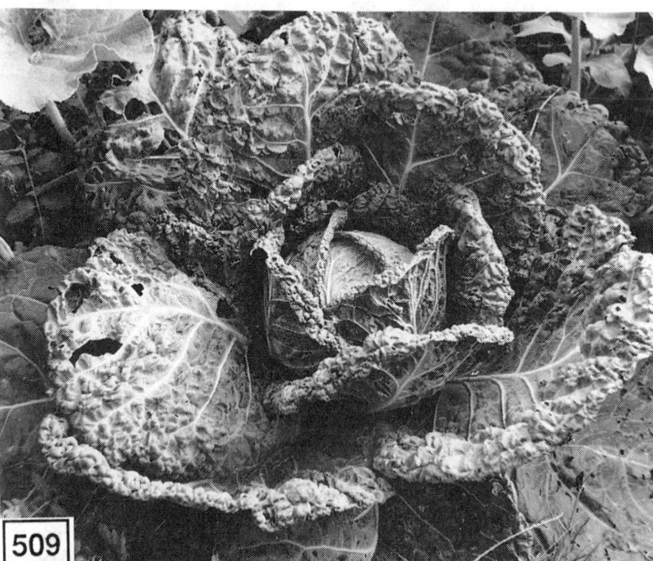

509

- the lateral buds : Brussels sprouts;
- the flowers : cauliflower and broccoli **(figure 510)**;
- the stems : Swedes, turnips and kohlrabi **(figure 511)**.

Environment : Brassicas are light-demanding. Ideally, the soil should be moist but not saturated, and fertile. The types which are cultivated for their flowers or lateral buds also thrive on poorer soils, for example, as the last crop in a rotation.

Propagation : Brassicas are usually multiplied by seed. It is better to use selected seeds, sold commercially, rather than home-produced seeds, the reason being that climatic conditions in the low tropics are not particularly suited to the production of Brassica seeds.

Some species of Brassicas can be propagated by cuttings if no seeds are available. In this case, the topped stems are left in the ground. The shoots that develop from the cut

510

511

surface of the stumps are removed and planted **(figure 359)**. As a rule, this mode of propagation produces smaller plants than those grown from seed.

Husbandry : Brassicas are normally sown in nurseries but they can also be sown directly in the field. They must then be thinned to give the plants room to grow. The crop is mulched and watered frequently. Cauliflowers and broccoli are topped to encourage the development of lateral shoots.

Headed cabbages	*Brassica oleracea var. gemmifera*
Brussels sprouts	*Brassica oleracea var. capitata*
Cauliflower	*Brassica oleracea var. botrytis*
Kohlrabi	*Brassica oleracea var. gongylodes*
Indian mustard	*Brassica juncea*
African leaf cabbage	*Brassica integrifolia var. carinata*
Chinese cabbage	*Brassica pekinensis* and *B. chinensis*
Turnip	*Brassica oleracea var. rapa*

SP7 Jutes

Jutes are seasonal plants of the family Tiliaceae. They vary in height from 0.5 to 1.5 metres and often have a bushy habit. There are many species and varieties, each with its own characteristics. The leaves are oval to lanceolate, serrate, with a pointed tip; at their base are two auricles (earlike parts) prolonged by a filament **(figures 512 to 514)**. The flowers attached to the stem are pale yellow, about one centimetre in diameter. The fruits are cylindrical and ridged, and are divided into longitudinal sections. They vary, however, with the species :

- the fruits of **Jew's mallow** or **bush okra** *(Corchorus olitorius)* are beaked capsules, 4 to 7 centimetres long, borne singly in the leaf axils **(figure 514)**;
- the fruits of *Corchorus tridens* are 3 or 4 centimetres long, usually grouped in two's or three's, and have three spreading teeth at the top.

The dark-coloured seeds are about one millimetre in diameter.

The plant is shallow rooting with a few main roots growing from the base of the stem and spreading lateral roots.

Uses : The young shoots and chopped leaves are used in sauces, giving them a sticky consistency.

Jew's mallow is also a fibre-producing plant. Fibres are extracted from the stems and made into jute. In some countries, notably in Asia, jute is widely used for making sacking, fishing nets and carpeting.

512

513

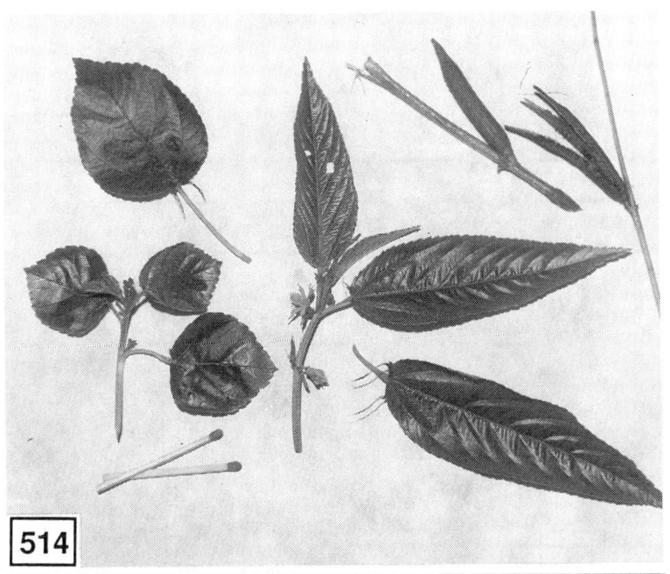

514

Environment : *Corchorus* tolerates poor soil conditions and once the plants are established, withstands drought well. They demand full sunlight but adapt to light shade when interplanted with other species.

Scientific Name	*Corchorus olitorius and C. tridens*
English	**Jute, Jew's mallow, bush okra**
French	corète potagère, mauve des juifs, jute, corète à trois dents
Yoruba	ewudu

Propagation : *Corchorus* is propagated from seeds. These germinate easily if they are moistened by rain. The seeds keep their germination capacity for many years. If the plants are left unpruned, they rapidly produce seeds.

Husbandry : The seeds are broadcast on their own, or in mixtures with vegetables such as bush greens and black nightshade. The seedlings must be thinned soon after sowing. Otherwise, they tend to bolt and produce little foliage. The seedlings can also be transplanted with a ball of soil. Leaf production is promoted by topping the young plants, while the ageing plants are cut back close to the ground.

Storage : The dried leaves and young shoots can be stored, or they may be powdered.

SP8 Costus

Scientific Name	*Costus afer*
English	The scientific name is used.
French	costus

Costus is a member of the family Zingiberaceae and occurs in wet forest regions. It is found bordering valley bottoms or along footpaths or in fallows established on moist soils. It is recognizable by its solitary, erect stem bearing terminal multicoloured, bell-shaped flowers 2 or 3 centimetres long (**figure 516**). The elongated, pointed leaves are between 20 and 30 centimetres long. They are spirally arranged on the stem. Before the inflorescence opens, the terminal bud is typically long and slender, often shaped like the letter S (**figure 515**). The root system is extensively rhizomatous and shallow.

516

515

The juice of the stem is very acid and is used like lemon. Young terminal flowering shoots are used for flavouring sauces and give them a characteristically sharp taste. The plant is propagated by mature stem cuttings or by rhizomes.

SP9 Waterleaf and purslane

Scientific Name	*Talinum triangulare*	*Portulaca oleracea*
English	**Waterleaf**	**Purslane**
French	grassé, épinard de Ceylan	pourpier
Yoruba	gbure	papassan

Waterleaf and **purslane** are two low herbs, 20 to 30 centimetres tall. They are distinguished by their fleshy leaves. They belong to the family Portulacaceae.

The stems of **waterleaf** are round, except when they bear an inflorescence, in which case they are triangular in cross section.

The oval leaves, 6 to 7 centimetres long, are soft green, with notched tips (**figure 517**). The pink flowers are just over one centimetre wide. The fruits are green and fleshy, and contain small brown-black seeds.

517

Purslane (figure 518) has round stems. The leaves are oval, 1 to 2 centimetres wide, 2 to 3 centimetres long, with hardly any petioles. The yellow flower clusters at the tip of short branches produce green fruits in the shape of a hood. The fruits contain black seeds.

518

Uses : The leaves and young shoots are used to thicken sauces.

Environment : These plants flourish when they are cultivated in full light and in fertile soil, but they also adapt to poorer soils. They are drought and heat resistant, and tolerate light shade.

Propagation : By seed. Waterleaf can also be multiplied by stem and root cuttings.

Husbandry : In dry regions, waterleaf and purslane are cultivated plants. They can be interplanted quite easily with other species. In wet regions, waterleaf and purslane grow subspontaneously and are picked as required.

They are sown broadcast or transplanted in the field. Leaf production is induced by topping, cutting back close to the ground and pinching out the inflorescences.

519

SP10 Bastard mustard

Scientific Name	*Gynandropsis gynandra*
English	**Bastard mustard, cat's whiskers**
French	gynandro

Bastard mustard is a bushy seasonal herb between 0.5 and 1 metre high at full maturity **(figure 519)**. It belongs to the family Capparidaceae. **Figure 520** shows its appearance when garden-grown and ready for picking.

The leaves are divided into between 5 and 7 leaflets, more or less palmate, on a stalk 5 to 10 centimetres long. The white flowers, composed of 4 petals, are sometimes asymmetrical and have very long stamens that protrude well beyond the corolla. The fruits are pods 5 to 15 centimetres long, coarse-skinned, more or less round, 3 millimetres wide and with black skins.

520

Environment : Bastard mustard demands exposure to full sun. Leaf production is poor on dry, impoverished soils because, in these conditions, flowering occurs too quickly.

Propagation : By seed only.

Husbandry : Bastard mustard is picked by the wayside or near houses. However, it is sometimes domesticated and thrives both in pure stand and in mixtures.

Seeds are broadcast on well-loosened soil, in pure stands or in mixtures with bush greens, black nightshade or jute plants. Seedlings must be thinned. Topping, cutting back to the ground and removing the inflorescences as soon as they appear are practices that increase leaf production for harvesting **(figure 168)**. The leaves are picked individually or leafy branches are harvested. Whole plants are also uprooted.

SP11 Lettuce

Scientific Name	*Lactuca sativa*
English	**Lettuce**
French	laitue

Lettuce is a seasonal herb of the family Compositae. Some varieties form heads and are called cabbage or head lettuce. The leaves are large, more or less crinkled, sometimes lobate, varying in colour from pale green to purple **(figure 521)**. The rosettes of cabbage lettuce are sometimes very compact. When lettuce plants flower, they produce yellow flowers 0.5 to 1 centimetre wide attached to a branched stem 0.5 to 1 metre high. The seeds are flat, beige to brown in colour, about 2 millimetres long. They are surmounted by a pappus. Lettuce has a taproot system.

521

522

Environment : Lettuce responds well to a moist, rich soil, full exposure to sun and cool weather conditions.

Propagation : By seed. However, the plant does not produce much seed in the tropics, and gardeners are often obliged to buy imported seeds produced by specialized seed-firms.

Husbandry : Lettuce is grown in pure stands or in association with erect plants which only provide light shade. The method of harvesting depends on the type of lettuce plant cultivated, heading or leafy.The heading types (cabbage lettuce) are harvested whole, whereas the tender leaves of leafy varieties are picked as they mature. With these leafy types, you must not cut the leaves too low for fear of damaging the terminal bud and causing the plant to degenerate.

Lettuce is raised in the nursery. The trimmed seedlings are transplanted with a ball of soil or with the roots exposed. They need light shade to start with, and must be watered regularly until they are harvested.

The heads are sometimes tied in order to whiten the hearts and make the lettuce more tender.

Nightshades

Nightshades are vegetables of the family Solanaceae. Three species are widely cultivated. : **Solanum gilo Raddi**, **black nightshade**, and **mock tomato**.

SP12 Solanum gilo Raddi

Scientific Name	*Solanum gilo Raddi*
English	The scientific name is used.
French	grande morelle
Yoruba	igboga igbo

523

Solanum gilo Raddi is a herb that can grow to a height of between 1 and 2 metres. Its leaves are lobed, and fairly smooth. They are dark green and leathery **(figure 523)**. The size and shape of the leaves depends on the variety; the difference in the length of the leaves may be as much as 50 centimetres.

The flowers, white to pale blue, are about 3 centimetres in diameter. The petals are joined to each other, and, because of this structure, form an open bell **(figure 524)**.

524

The erect fruits are round and slightly flattened. They are 5 to 7 centimetres in diameter. Some varieties can bear fruits the size of an orange. The fruits are green, then orange-yellow when ripe, sometimes purple-blue. They are borne in clusters of two or three, sometimes five **(figure 525)**.

Solanum gilo Raddi is a biennial found especially in regions where the dry seasons do not last very long. It normally bears fruits in the second year of cultivation, although the leaves are regularly produced.

The several varieties are distinguished by their lobed leaves which are more or less deeply notched.

Uses : The young leaves are eaten chopped and cooked, often with groundnut paste. They are more fibrous than many other leaf vegetables. Some varieties have to be blanched before cooking in order to get rid of their bitter taste.

Environment : *Solanum gilo Raddi* adapts to soils of low fertility, but it is more productive on soils enriched with organic matter. It fruits early in impoverished soils, with the result that leaf production is low and the leaves, being leathery, are of inferior quality. The plant grows in full sunlight and withstands drought well.

Propagation : By seed only The seeds retain their germination capacity for six to twelve months after drying.

525

Husbandry : *Solanum gilo Raddi* thrives well when cultivated with other species which provide light shade.

The produce is harvested in three ways by picking whole leaves, by harvesting the shoots and the stem, and by cutting back the main stem close to the ground. When this last method of drastic pruning is carried out at the time of harvesting, it rejuvenates the plant. The practice gives very encouraging results where the quality and quantity of leaf production are concerned, but to ensure success, you need well-fertilized, well-watered soils.

Seeds are broadcast either in nursery beds or on the permanent site. Early thinning is required. Seedlings are trimmed and transplanted with a ball of soil or with exposed roots, two or three weeks after emergence. The plants that bear fruits in the rainy season are cut back to within 5 or 10 centimetres of the soil in order to prolong leaf harvesting.

Scientific Name	*Solanum nigrum var. guineense*
English	**Black nightshade**
French	morelle noire
Yoruba	odu, ogunmo

SP13 Black nightshade

Black nightshade is a seasonal herb, 75 to 90 centimetres tall, sometimes more **(figure 526)**. The stems, seen in cross section, are roughly square, and have spines projecting from the angles. As a general rule, the spines are tinged with violet, especially at the base. The leaves are dark green, and vary in length from 5 to 25 centimetres. They may also have violet-coloured ribs or veins. The small flowers, one centimetre in diameter, have five white petals, and a yellow centre. The fruits form clusters of four to seven small, black berries. They are about one centimetre in diameter and contain large numbers of small, flat seeds, dispersed in the pulp. The plant has a taproot.

Some varieties are distinguished mainly by the size of their leaves, a length of up to 20 or 25 centimetres is quite common.

Uses : The leaves and young shoots are consumed as a vegetable mixed in sauces. They are also prepared separately and made into balls. They have a rather bitter taste. The flowers are sometimes used to flavour bitter sauces.

The juice extracted from the leaves is used for treating diarrhoea in children and certain eye infections and jaundice.

Environment : Black nightshade benefits from soils rich in mineral salts. Grown in poor soils, it flowers quickly and produces little foliage. It is a plant that demands full light, and is susceptible to drought.

526

527

Propagation : Black nightshade is propagated by seed or by stem cuttings. The cuttings, 20 to 30 centimetres long, are taken from the main stem and are trimmed before they are inserted. The leaf production from cuttings is said to be inferior to that from plants developed from seeds.

Seeds are collected from seed plants left standing at harvest time. Seed production from these plants is sometimes unreliable, because there is a risk of premature fruit fall. Hence the need to set aside enough plants for seed. The fruits must be picked fully ripe when they are black all over and when the skin begins to wrinkle. The seeds do not keep their germination capacity for long. This is why they must be picked as late as possible in the season, and then sown at the first opportunity.

Husbandry : Black nightshade thrives in association with all light shade plants that have low water requirements. It is a beneficial plant at the start of the cultural cycle because it is a fast-growing cover crop that prevents rain erosion and invasion by weeds **(figure 33)**. **Figure 527** shows black nightshade about to be harvested for the first time. Here, it is interplanted with maize that is still in the early stages of growth. Black nightshade grows well in plots spread with ashes, or burnt trash.

Seeds are broadcast or sown in drills in the field or, if preferred, in nursery beds. It is cultivated in pure stands or in mixtures with plants such as bush greens and jute. It must be thinned at once on emergence.

It is important to control planting distance for good water management. If the seedlings are too closely spaced, less than 15 centimetres, they compete for available water. On the other hand, if they are too far apart, more than 20 or 25 centimetres, they give inadequate soil cover, thus exposing the soil to the drying effects of the sun's rays and also becoming liable to excessive water loss.

Leaf production is induced by practices such as topping, removing the inflorescences, cutting the plant right back to the ground when it has been harvested a few times (figure 183) mulching, weeding and frequent watering.

SP14 Mock tomato

The **mock tomato** is a herbaceous annual that may grow to a height of 1.5 to 1.8 metres **(figure 528)**. The leaves are alternate, lobed, 20 to 30 centimetres long. They are quite widely spaced **(figure 346)**. The inflorescence consists of between 5 and 7 small, white flowers in clusters alternate with the leaves The fruits are round and their colour ranges from green to orange red as they mature. They vary in size from 1 to 2 centimetres in diameter **(figure 529)**. The flat seeds, about 3 millimetres long, are dispersed in the flesh. They are pale-coloured and circular.

Uses : The leaves are prepared and consumed like those of black nightshade. The green, bitter fruits are eaten raw or cooked like tomatoes.

Environment : The mock tomato demands full light and is drought resistant. It is a poorly developed cover plant.

Propagation : The plant is raised from seeds removed from ripe fruits when they are dark orange in colour. The seeds retain their germination capacity for six to twelve months after drying. Seed production is abundant.

Husbandry : The plant is prolific at all times of the year, but it is particularly useful as a dry season crop because it is productive even when water is sparse and infrequent. The mock tomato is harvested by pruning and stooling.

It is raised in the nursery and transplanted with a ball of soil. It can also be sown directly. The fruits and flowers are pruned at the start of the cycle in order to encourage leaf production. However, the plants reserved for seed production are left intact.

The mock tomato is harvested in three ways, by pulling up whole plants, by removing whole shoots, or by picking the individual leaves. This last method decreases leaf production because it stimulates flowering.

528

Scientific Name	*Solanum aethiopicum*
English	**Mock tomato**
French	morelle amère
Yoruba	osun

529

Scientific Name	*Moringa oleifera*
English	**drumstick tree**
French	néverdié, ben ailé
Yoruba	éwé ilé

SP15 Drumstick tree

The drumstick is a small tree of the family Moringaceae. The average plant is 4 to 6 metres tall, rarely more. It produces leafy shoots all the year round, even during the dry season, but yields fluctuate with the seasons **(figure 530)**.

The leaves are divided into many leaflets 3 to 6 centimetres long **(figure 531)**. These are oval and delicately toothed.The flowers are white to pale yellow. The elongated fruits are triangular in cross section, and are 30 to 50 centimetres long **(figure 532)**. The seeds are round, black, and characterized by three wings.

Uses : The young fruits, flowers, leaves, and less frequently the roots, are eaten as a cooked vegetable. The seeds are sometimes used to flavour sauces, and give them a rather bitter, pungent taste. An oil that does not go rancid is extracted from the seeds. The red gum exuded by the bark is occasionally used as a thick, binding agent in sauces.

530

The drumstick is used medicinally as a disinfectant and a restoring tonic, and also as a cure for scurvy.

Environment : The drumstick tree grows in full sunlight. It withstands drought but is susceptible to water-logged soils. It is widespread in the dry savanna regions.

It is propagated by seed or by cuttings These may be matured branches, as much as 4 centimetres in diameter, and one metre or more long.

As a general rule, the drumstick is cultivated, although it may be self-sown in gardens and farms. It is exploited as a tree or a shrub, and is found in hedges and live fences. It can easily be associated with most crops, because of its thin foliage and light shade. Vegetable growers often treat drumstick as an annual and grow it for its leaves only.

531 532

Husbandry : Drumstick reacts well to pruning. Pollarding and pruning to produce poles are frequently carried out. The tree can also be trained to a bushy shape **(figures 157, 159, 164 and 165)**.

Storage : The dried leaves, whole or powdered, keep very well.

533

SP16 Roselle and kenaf

Roselle, also called Jamaican sorrel, is a seasonal plant of the family Malvaceae **(figure 533)**. It has a bushy habit, and is prostrate or erect, depending on the variety. It grows to an average height of one metre, or even two metres in fertile soils. The leaves are simple or lobed, sometimes palmate with between 3 and 9 lobes or leaflets; they are about 10 centimetres long, and variably dentate **(figure 534)**. The yellow or pink flowers are 3 to 4 centimetres in diameter and are borne in the leaf axils. The calyx is distinctive, succulent and very extended up to 7 centimetres long **(figure 535)**. The fruits are globular with black, rounded seeds about 0.5 centimetres in diameter **(figure 536)**. The root system is developed around a tap root which grows about 15 centimetres deep.

Figure 534 shows the leaves of several varieties of roselle occurring in the Sahel.

534

Scientific Name	*Hibiscus var. sabdariffa*
English	**Roselle, Jamaican sorrel**
French	roselle, oseille de Guinée
Yoruba	ichakpa

535

Kenaf or Deccan hemp **(figure 537)** is a species closely related to roselle but with distinctive features. It is, for instance, taller than roselle and can grow to a height of 3.5 metres. Its erect frame is normally characterized by a single stem. The leaf has a long petiole, is simple (occasionally three-lobed), typically drooping. The calyx is covered with bristly spines **(figure 538)**. The plant has a taproot like roselle.

Uses : The leaves of roselle, its tender shoots, succulent calyces and immature fruits are chopped and added to sauces. The succulent calyces are also used for making syrups and infusions. The seeds, sometimes fermented or sprouted, are used in sauces. Oil is sometimes extracted from the seeds. The leaves and fruits are found in many remedies for viral hepatitis, constipation, roundworm infestation and so on.

The leaves and tender shoots of Deccan hemp, and occasionally the seeds, are used in sauces.

Fibres obtained from the stems of Deccan hemp, and occasionally from roselle, are used for making rope.

Environment : Roselle and kenaf grow in full sunlight. They withstand drought quite well and have no particular soil requirements. However, leaf and fibre production are greatly influenced by soil fertility.

538

Scientific Name	*Hibiscus Cannabinus*
English	**Kenaf, Deccan hemp**
French	chanvre de Guinée

536

537

Propagation : By seed only.

Husbandry : It is customary to grow roselle and kenaf in the main cereal fields, in association and also on the edge of the plots. They are also established in home gardens, sometimes as subspontaneous plants. In some regions, in the rainy season, they are systematically cultivated under the leafy canopies of *Acacia albida*

The leaves are harvested either by cutting off the shoots, or by picking the leaves separately with or without the petiole **(figure 205)**.

The seeds are broadcast, or dibbled, three to five per hole. To produce leaves, the seedlings must be thinned so that they are at least 40 centimetres apart. Flower and fruit yields are severely checked by pruning the branches and cutting back to the ground.

For fibre production, the plants are sown very densely on well-manured soil. They are not thinned in order to encourage them to grow upright, with few branches.

Storage : The dried seeds are stored and can be fermented before use if desired. The calyces, and sometimes the leaves and young shoots, are sun-dried and then stored.

SP17 Leek

The **leek** is an erect herb with a single stem. It is a seasonal plant, though it may also be an annual with a cycle varying from six to twelve months **(figure 539)**. It belongs to the family Alliaceae. Mature plants are about 40 centimetres tall, but their overlapping leaves, 'stem', can be up to a metre long. The leaves are elongated and pointed, blue-green, sometimes blue. The inflorescence is produced at the apex of the stem. It is globular with a great many small white-pink flowers. The seeds are black and are irregularly shaped.

539

Uses : The whole plant is edible but the white 'stem' is relished most of all. It is eaten cooked as a side dish.

Environment : The best growing conditions are well-manured, well-watered soils full exposure to sunlight but with moderate temperatures.

Propagation : By seed only

Husbandry : In pure stands or in mixtures with light shade crops. Tender stems are obtained by transplanting the seedlings to holes or drills 10 to 15 centimetres deep. The holes are roughly 5 centimetres in diameter **(figure 540)**. When the holes or the drills close up round the stems, these stay white and tender. If this method is not feasible, you can earth up the plants as they begin to develop. The stems are harvested when they are 2 or 3 centimetres thick, and always before flowering when the stem begins to elongate and becomes hard and barely edible.

540

Scientific Name	*Allium porrum*
English	**Leek**
French	poireau

SP18 New Zealand spinach

Scientific Name	*Tetragonia expansa*
English	**New Zealand spinach**
French	tétragone, épinard de Nouvelle Zélande

New Zealand spinach is a seasonal herb of the family Tetragoniaceae, native to Asia. It is a prostrate, creeping vegetable and looks like a many-branched trailing plant. It has typical pale green leaves, fleshy, oval to lanceolate in shape **(figure 541)**.

All the foliage is edible and is consumed as a leafy vegetable, in sauces or as a side dish.

The plant is grown from seed. It thrives in full sunlight, and is very productive in well-watered soils rich in organic manure.

New Zealand spinach is not widely distributed but it deserves to be better known for the quality of its tender leaves that have none of the bitter flavour associated with some leafy vegetables plants.

541

SP19 Bitter leaf

Bitter leaf plants are shrubs of the family Compositae, and their leaves are used as a vegetable. *Vernonia amygdalina*, *Vernonia colorata*, and *Vernonia calvoana* are the three species usually grown. The characteristics of each of these species are described in **table 545**. However, there are significant variations within individual species so that accurate identification is not always easy.

542

543

Scientific Name	*Vernonia spp.*
English	**Bitter leaf**
French	vernonia
Yoruba	ewuro

The habit of the shrub depends very largely on how the plant is exploited. It develops a shrubby habit if the branches are first lopped for pole production and the stem is then pruned to form a head. A dense, bushy habit is obtained if the stems are pruned severely on a regular basis to stimulate leaf production **(figure 546)**. The plant will develop a tall habit if the stems are allowed to grow unchecked for pole production.

Bitter leaf has a dense root system. Most of the roots arise from the base of the plant and spread in the top 20 to 30 centimetres of soil. Only a few roots are deeply penetrating.

544

Uses : The leaves and young shoots are cooked as vegetables in many regional dishes such as ndolé in Cameroun. They are rich in protein and vitamins.

The bitter flavour of these plants has to be reduced by repeated culinary treatments such as scalding and squeezing with the result that the not-so-bitter varieties and species are very popular. This is why *Vernonia calvoana* has an advantage over other species because its leaves are larger, more tender and sweeter (**figure 542**, on the left).

Vernonia leaves are used medicinally, to treat stomach ache and yellow fever. They are also used as laxatives and diuretics.

Environment : *Vernonia* grows in all types of soil. It is fairly drought resistant, except the species *V. calvoana* which is more sensitive. *Vernonia* plants thrive in full sunlight.

545 Comparative description of three species of Vernonia cultivated in Cameroun gardens (forest zone)

	Vernonia amygdalina	**Vernonia colorata**	**Vernonia calvoana**
Natural habit	low tree, 3 to 5 metres high	shrub	bush or shrub
Main stem (cultivation during one season)	❑ green at the extremity, grey at the base ❑ rough at the base ❑ sometimes with lenticels	❑ dark in colour, sometimes violet to black ❑ with rough patches, sometimes extensive and very noticeable	❑ green in colour, spotted with whitish dots or marks (lenticels)
Wood of the main stem	hard but not brittle, supple when bent	hard, breaks when twisted	soft, relatively pliant, especially the upper part
Leaf	❑ simple, usually with uneven, toothed edges, dark green ❑ main rib pale in colour ❑ rigid, sometimes leathery ❑ petiole 2 to 3 centimetres long ❑ leaf as much as 15 centimetres wide and 30 centimetres long (**figure 542**, to the right)	❑ simple, clearly serrate, rigid ❑ main rib violet-coloured at the base and sometimes throughout ❑ no petiole : at times, the bottom of the leaf curls almost completely round the stem, up to 15 centimetres wide and 30 centimetres long	❑ simple, clearly serrate, supple ❑ main rib pale in colour sometimes pale yellow ❑ petiole often short (one centimetre) ❑ leaf up to 20 centimetres wide and 50 centimetres long (**figure 542**, on the left)
Inflorescence	❑ white, fragrant flowers in dense clusters (capitula) less than one centimetre in diameter **(figure 543)**	❑ white flowers, sometimes blue or mauve in the centre of the capitula, no smell ❑ flowers in large capitula more than 3 centimetres in diameter **(figure 544)**	❑ very fragrant white flowers ❑ arranged in capitula, diameter less than 1 centimetre
Seeds	surmounted by a pappus	surmounted by a pappus	surmounted by a pappus

Propagation : By seed or by cuttings from mature stems, although *Vernonia calvoana* is apparently more difficult to propagate from cuttings. The seeds survive well in dry storage.

Husbandry : The leaves are sometimes gathered from wild or subspontaneous plants **(figure 469)**. But, as a rule, *Vernonia* is cultivated in gardens, farms and orchards. It forms hedges or fills small empty patches or clearings. It can be sown in mixtures with other crops, or in rows on the edge of vegetable beds where it helps to stabilize the soil.

The leaves can be harvested in three ways : by cutting leafy shoots, gathering the leaves with the petioles, or gathering the leaf blades only.

Although housewives find it easy to harvest the leaf blades, this practice is not beneficial for leaf development. The best results are obtained by cutting the leafy shoots in the rainy season because the harvested shoots are quickly replaced. However, in the dry season, picking the whole leaves without cutting the shoots is said to be more productive **(figures 180, 182, 207 and 209)**.

546

Resowing regularly after every harvest period seems advisable because the young plants are more productive. and *Vernonia calvoana* produces larger leaves. If *Vernonia* is to be exploited intensively, a combination of harvesting methods should be considered.

The seeds are broadcast in nursery beds. The plants are pruned when they have four to six leaves and are then transplanted with a ball of soil or with exposed roots **(figure 411)**. Puddling the roots helps the seedlings to establish rapidly.

Cuttings are planted erect or slantwise, but cuttings with more than four eye buds are disbudded **(figures 387 and 388)**.

Vernonia amygdalina and *V. colorata* tend to develop adventitious roots. Consequently, it may be worth earthing up the plants in order to strengthen their root systems.

Topping or stooling the plants every year, and removing suckers stimulates leaf production and ensures the production of larger, more abundant foliage.

Storing the leaves : *Vernonia* leaves are washed and then dried for storage, but the taste is altered. The dried leaves must be steeped in water before they can be used.

Chapter 21

Vegetable and condiment fruits

SP20 | Eggplant

Eggplants belong to the family Solanaceae and are grown as annual or pluriannual plants. They have a densely branching habit, the branches being erect or prostrate. As a rule, the plant is not more than one metre high.

The leaves are entire, often slightly lobed, but rarely serrate. They are of varying sizes ranging from 10 to 30 centimetres in length. Some varieties have thorny stems.

There are at least three widely cultivated species of eggplant that are easily recognized by their characteristic flowers and fruits. They are :

- the **bitter tomato with oblong fruits** *(Solanum esculentum)*, white flowers with the petals at times barely joined, 2 or 3 centimetres in diameter, fruits white to blue-purple, may be tinted with red when ripe, 2 to 7 centimetres long, often in clusters of two's or three's **(figure 548)**;

- the **bitter tomato with globular fruits** *(Solanum incanum)*, blue flowers 2 to 3 centimetres in diameter, petals more or less united **(figure 547)**, green to yellow fruits, deeply segmented, 3 to 10 centimetres in diameter, in clusters of three or more **(figure 550);**
- the **eggplant** *(Solanum melongena)*, violet flowers, petals united, 3 to 5 centimetres in diameter, fruits usually elongated, colour violet, sometimes reddish, 10 to 20 centimetres long, often single **(figure 549)**.

Uses : The leaves and fruits are cooked in water or fried; they are used to season sauces or as a side dish.

Environment : Eggplants grow in full sunlight, but they tolerate some shade. They withstand drought quite well but yields are low when water is scarce.

Propagation : By seed, sometimes by cuttings from mature stems.

Husbandry : Eggplants are grown both in gardens and farms, in pure stands and in associations. They grow vigorously in the shade of other crops. However, fruit production is increased by exposure to full sunlight during flowering and fruiting. This is especially true of *Solanum melongena* .

Fruit harvesting is spread over a long period. It can start two or three months after sowing and last a year or more. During the dry season, fruiting is interrupted if water is not available.

549

Scientific Name	*Solanum melongena*	*Solanum esculentum and S. incanum*
English	**Eggplant**	**Bitter tomato**
French	aubergine douce	aubergine amère

547

548

Eggplants can be made more productive in two ways :

- by picking the fruits before they are fully ripe when they are about to change colour. The green fruits of bitter eggplants *(Solanum esculentum* and *S. incanum)* turn red shortly after picking. Additional fruits will be produced when the ripe or almost ripe fruits are gathered regularly;
- by renewing the plants every season. Eggplants are said to be most productive when three to six months old.

Husbandry : The plant can be sown in the open, in rows or in planting holes. The hardiest plant in each hole is retained, the others are discarded or transplanted.

The plant is also raised in the nursery and the seedlings transplanted about a month after germination. You must leave enough room when transplanting, because the vegetation spreads quite considerably, within a radius of 50 to 70 centimetres of the base.

It is advisable to stake the plants so that the fruits are kept clear of the ground.

Mulching and earthing the stem up to the first branches stimulate growth and increase fruit production.

It would be worth testing practices such as routine pruning (removing the stems that have already fruited) and cutting the plants back close to the ground at the end of the season, or when production slows down.

Storage : Eggplants, whole or sliced, are boiled in water and then dried before being stored. The dried leaves are occasionally stored.

550

SP21 Desert date

Scientific Name	*Balanites aegyptiaca*
English	**Desert date, soapberry tree, thorn tree**
French	balanites, dattier du désert

The **desert date** is a low tree, 4 to 7 metres high, sometimes more, belonging to the family Zygophyllaceae. It is characterized by its dense, often drooping, foliage **(figure 551)**. The green-yellow branches and twigs have strong spines in the leaf axils **(figure 553)**. The leaves are composed of two oval leaflets 3 to 6 centimetres long, on short petioles.The flowers are yellow to green, in small clusters. The yellow oval fruits are 2 to 4 centimetres long and contain a kernel **(figure 552)**.

Uses : The flowers and young leaves are boiled and eaten as a side dish, or used in sauces. The fruit pulp is eaten either fresh or dried. Oil for cooking or for making fatty soaps is extracted from the kernel.

The bark and roots are used in many remedies for treating yellow fever and colic, and as a vermifuge. The whole, macerated fruits are believed to disinfect water efficiently, and, more specifically, to kill the vectors of bilharzia and Guinea worm. The thorny branches are used for fencing.

551

552

553

Environment : The desert date is a tree occurring in dry savannas, and often found on the edge of the desert. It withstands drought remarkably well, and grows on any type of soil, even on badly eroded lands.

Propagation : By seed only. Seeds removed from cattle dung germinate quickly, as do seeds plunged into boiling water for 5 to 10 minutes, and then steeped in lukewarm water for 12 hours.

Husbandry : Spontaneous trees or trees planted on grazing lands, in farms and gardens are harvested. The tree is a good association plant for most crops : it gives moderate shade, the foliage is manageable, the plant reacts well to pruning, and its roots are deeply penetrating. The tree can usefully be grown as a hedge on lands that have to be protected from the wind or from erosive rains.

The desert date grows fairly quickly after germination, but it is better not to exploit it prematurely so that it has time to become well established. Do not harvest the leaves or prune the tree until it is three or four years old. Browsing animals can damage trees.

SP22 Fagara

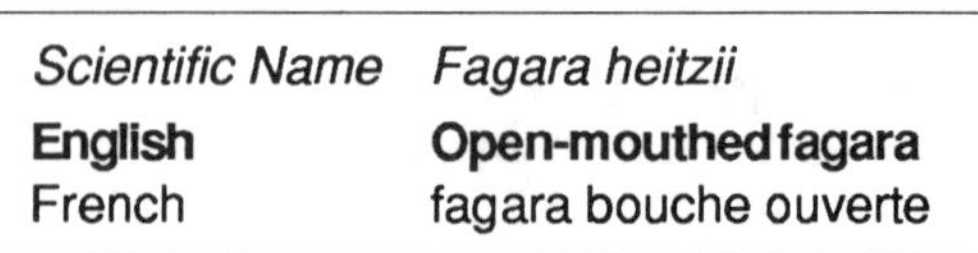

Scientific Name	*Fagara heitzii*
English	**Open-mouthed fagara**
French	fagara bouche ouverte

The **fagara** belongs to the family Rutaceae. It is a tree of average height, 8 to 10 metres tall. Its small dry fruits are used as a condiment. Two species of fagara with a characteristic smell are found in the wet tropics, and are distinguished quite easily by the shape of the fruits **(figure 557)** and the size of the leaves.

Figure 555 shows the leaves and fruits of *Fagara heitzii*, called the 'open-mouthed fagara'. The small, globular fruits split when ripe, and look like an open, smiling mouth. *Fagara macrophylla*, called the 'large-leaved fagara' has fruits like small pears which, as a rule, do not open when ripe.

Fagara trees have a characteristic habit : their branches subdivide into two or three forks, at a certain stage of growth **(figure 554)**, and the trunk is covered with flat, prickly protuberances **(figure 556)**.

The leaves are composed of tough leaflets, the size of these depends on the species. The leaves of the large-leaved fagara *(Fagara macrophylla)* may be one metre or more in length, whereas those of the open-mouthed fagara *(Fagara heitzii)* are 30 to 50 centimetres long **(figure 555)**.

The fagara is a dioecious plant, that is to say, the male and female flowers are not borne on the same plant. When fagaras are cultivated, it is wise to plant many trees at the same time to make sure that fertilization takes place. A single male specimen is enough to pollinate several female trees.

554

555

556

Uses : The fruits of both species are used to prepare a fragrant relish, with a tangy smell. The leaves can also be dried and used as a seasoning.

557

Scientific Name	*Fagara macrophylla*
English	**Large-leaved fagara**
French	fagara à grandes feuilles

Open-mouthed fagara : The young shoots, pounded and macerated and mixed with lemon juice, are used to ease palpitations of the heart. The bark is used for stupifying fish in streams. In South Cameroun, the bark is mixed with crushed grains of paradise *(Aframomum melegueta)* and made into a lotion for treating stiff joints and rheumatism. The wood is light but strong, and is in demand for making dug-outs, beehives and musical instruments.

Large-leaved fagara : The young terminal shoots without leaves are sweet-smelling and are used to flavour sauces. The leaves, finely crushed and steeped in lemon juice, are said to cure snake bites. The bark is used in a remedy for gonorrhoea and as a pain-killer. The timber is suitable for carpentry and building.

Husbandry : Fagara trees are typical regrowth species particularly in secondary forests. They spread easily in fallows, and are usually preserved during clearing operations. They thrive in hedges, in compounds where they are domesticated, or as shade trees in plantations, for example, for coffee crops **(figure 471)**. The fruits are picked from the tree or off the ground, and are then dried. Gardeners could experiment with different ways of pruning the tree in order to develop shorter stems and facilitate harvesting.

Propagation : By seed.

Storage : The fruits and seeds will keep for many years in dry conditions and do not lose their fragrance.

SP23 Fig sycamore

Scientific Name	*Ficus gnafalocarpa*
English	**Fig sycamore**
French	figuier ou ficus sycomore

The **fig sycamore**, a species of the family Moraceae, is a tall savanna tree, 12 to 20 metres high, although much taller specimens up to 45 metres in height also occur. The habit of the tree is characteristic : its trunk supports a very leafy, spreading semi-circular frame **(figure 558)**.

The grey, smooth bark on old trees peels off in large strips. The leaves, which are hairy and almost rectangular in shape, are about 10 centimetres long **(figure 559)**. The fruits, orange when fully ripe, 3 to 5 centimentres long and rounded, are borne on short peduncles in the leaf axils at the end of the fruiting spur **(figure 560)**.

558

559

Uses : The young leaves and ripe fruits are used in sauces. The ripe fruits, which have a delicate sweet flavour, are also eaten raw.

The leaves and unripe fruits which fall to the ground provide excellent fodder.

Many remedies are prepared from the produce of the sycamore. The latex is used for treating dysentery and infections in general, the leaves for jaundice, the bark for coughs and sore throats. The roots are recommended for constipation and worms.

560

Environment : The sycamore needs a well-manured, fairly moist soil. In dry regions, its presence Is a reliable guide to the existence of shallow water tables.

Propagation : By seed. It is said that the tree can be grown from mature stem cuttings in a well-loosened, moisture-retentive soil.

Husbandry : The sycamore is exploited by gathering fallen produce or by harvesting fruits and leaves from spontaneous trees. Its diversified yields are harvested at different times in the year : the leaves and young shoots are ready at the start of the rainy season, the green fruits for livestock at the end of the rains or the beginning of the dry season, the ripe fruits during the dry season.

The sycamore is a common sight in fields, pastures and plantations, but because of its size and spreading foliage, it is more appropriate for hedging and wooded areas.

561

562

SP24 Okra

Okra is a herb of the family Malvaceae. It is widespread in tropical regions and in Africa, in particular. There are many varieties, annual, biennial and short-lived perennials, with differences in the height

563

Scientific Name	*Hibiscus esculentus*
English	**okra**
French	gombo
Yoruba	ila

of the stems, the size of the leaves and fruits, and the habit of the plant which is branched to a greater or lesser degree.

From the farmer's point of view, varieties of okra are divided into two groups : the short-duration varieties with short stems **(figure 563)**, and the long-duration forms with long stems **(figure 564)**. There is also a wide range of plants of in-between heights.

564

Okra leaves are 3-7 lobed, more or less divided, 20 to 40 centimetres long, on a long petiole, and sometimes with crimson streaks **(figure 563)**.

All the varieties have the same shape of flower : five large petals, white, yellow or pink, the claw (centre) of the calyx is crimson **(figure 562)**.

The fruits are green to purple, sometimes black, they are pointed and furrowed. They vary in length and in width depending on the condition of the plant, their position on the stem, the cultural variety and the fertility of the soil. They contain several narrow loculi (small spaces or cavities) full of round seeds, grey or brown when ripe **(figure 561)**.

565

566

On the short-stemmed varieties, the fruits are mostly borne on the top of the stem and generally above the foliage. There are few fruits per plant.

On the long-stemmed varieties, the fruits are borne in the leaf axils or on spurs, and are produced at intervals from the base to the top of the plant **(figure 564)**. Picking is staggered because the fruits reach maturity at different times.

The duration of the **vegetative cycle** depends on the variety of okra cultivated. The short varieties have a short cycle, and the fruits take three months to ripen. The tall varieties have a longer cycle from six to nine months. In some regions, varieties lasting many seasons, two to three years, or even longer, are cultivated. These are cut back drastically at the beginning of every growing season.

Okra has a taproot that anchors the plant deeply in the ground. Many secondary roots branch out from the taproot.

Uses : The leaves and immature fruits are eaten as vegetables. They are mucilaginous and give sauces a typically thick, sticky texture. The very fragrant fruits should be eaten before the seeds become hard, since these are very nutritious when they are under-ripe.

Environment : Okra is an adaptable plant that grows on any type of soil. The plant thrives in full sunlight but also tolerates moderate shade. It is drought resistant.

Propagation : By seed.

Husbandry : Okra is an excellent association plant. Since its foliage gives only light shade and its root system is not extensive, the plant leaves plenty of room and light for intercropped species.

Okra is often planted on the sides of vegetable beds containing lower-growing species such as nightshade, lettuce, bush greens, and jutes. The okra thus acts as a windbreak and protects the other vegetables from sunscald.

The varieties with a long cycle can be exploited for their leaves for the first three or four months of their vegetative cycle. However, picking the leaves delays fruiting and extends the cycle. Some gardeners make the most of this characteristic by gathering the leaves in the rainy season, and picking the fruits in the dry season.

The method of sowing depends on the cultivar. The short varieties are sown more densely than the tall varieties. The seeds are sown at a rate of two or three per hole. Germination is speeded up by steeping the seeds for a day before sowing. Okra can also be sown in the nursery and transplanted when the seedlings have between two and four leaves.

Good results are obtained by pruning and topping the plant, especially okra varieties with a long cycle and the short-lived perennial varieties. Pruning in this case means cutting off the stems that have fruited in the previous seasons; the stems are cut a few centimetres above the buds that will flower in the coming season **(figure 566)**. This cut is carried out at the end of the dry season in order to encourage the growth of a few buds at the onset of the rains.

Topping tall okra plants at 40 or 50 centimetres promotes the growth of many lateral shoots that develop to replace the main stem. If only the most vigorous shoots are retained, the plant can be trained to a bushy habit, something which may be beneficial for fruit and leaf production **(figure 565)**. Topping must be practised when the young plants are in full growth.

Storage : When properly dried, fruits whole, sliced or powdered will keep in dry storage.

SP25 Indian jujube

The **Indian jujube** of the family Rhamnaceae is a thorny shrub of dry and arid savannas, and is 4 to 5 metres tall **(figure 567)**. The oval leaves, a little longer than they are broad (about 6 x 4 centimetres), are marked by three veins which diverge at the base **(figure 568)**. The small yellow flowers with five sepals are velvety in appearance and are borne in clusters on the stem nodes. The round fruits are 1 to 1.5 centimetres in diameter. They are orange to brown and contain a large yellow stone **(figure 569)**.

Uses : The fruits are eaten fresh or dried. They are also ground into flour for binding sauces or for making fritters. The leaves are consumed as a vegetable or as a seasoning. This species is used for preparing many remedies for colic, for venereal diseases and hepatitis. The wood is easily worked and is suitable for carpentry. Its bark contains tannin. The branches are used for fencing.

567

568

569

Scientific Name	*Zizyphus mauritiana*
English	**Indian jujube, Chinese date**
French	jujubier, baouyer

Environment : The Indian jujube is remarkably drought and heat resistant. It grows on very impoverished soils and even in stony soils. It can withstand waterlogged soil for short periods, but is susceptible to atmospheric humidity.

Propagation : By seed, stem cuttings and layers.

Husbandry : The Indian jujube is self-sown in dry savannas where its produce is harvested. It is often planted to form protective hedging near gardens and plantations. The species is valuable in controlling wind erosion because its sturdy, dense root system anchors the plant in the soil.

The tree is sown in nursery beds. It is transplanted with a generous ball of roots and is planted in soil that has been deeply ploughed. Weeding, mulching and watering, if possible, are most beneficial during the first two years when the plant may be slow in getting established.

Fruiting begins in the fourth or fifth year but remains limited until about the tenth year when the tree comes into full bearing.

Storage : The dried fruits keep well.

SP26 Wild or Cameroun cardamom

Scientific Name	*Aframomum melegueta*
English	**Grains of paradise, Melegueta pepper**
French	maniguette piquante, graine de paradis
Yoruba	atare

571

572

573

574

Wild or Cameroun cardamom *(Aframomum spp.)* grows in wet forest regions. This plant, of which there are many species, belongs to the family Zingiberaceae. All the species are quite similar. The undivided stems grow from an enlarged rootstock which is level with the ground. The leaves alternate along the stem, varying in length and width according to the species **(figures 571 and 574)**.

The flowers and fruits are borne at the base of the plants, as seen on the fragrant cardamom in **figure 572**. The flowers are white and yellow, tinted with red or violet.

The fleshy fruits are red to orange when they are mature. **Figure 572** shows the fresh fruits of the sweet cardamom, and **figure 575** shows the same fruits dried and ready for market. The dried fruits are often sold after stringing them onto wooden skewers.

The root system is formed by rhizomes from the nodes of which deep roots originate **(figure 571)**. The rhizomatous habit ensures that new plants are produced from the parent stock.

The seeds of the different species, as illustrated in **figure 576**, vary in shape.

Table 570 sets out the main characteristics of the five cardamom species occurring in Cameroun. One species has a scientific name, *Aframomum melegueta*, or grains of paradise, also called Melegueta pepper. The other four species are called by their local names in Cameroun : the juicy cardamom, the sweet cardamom, the liyambi cardamom, and the fragrant cardamom.

Uses : These depend on the species. The seeds of the **juicy cardamom** are highly fragrant and are used to season various dishes. The seeds are used medicinally to treat a range of disorders. Crushed in oil, they are a disinfectant for scabies. Ground and mixed with palm oil, they are a purgative. Umbilical hernia is treated by massaging the navel with an ointment made from chewed seeds. This cardamom is used on many social occasions, in keeping with traditions that vary from region to region. The fruit is often associated with blessing rituals.

The seeds of the **sweet cardamom** are favourite seasonings, either on their own or mixed with those of the juicy cardamom. They are also crushed on fresh meat to make it tasty. The fruit pulp has a sharp taste and is refreshing to eat.

The seeds of **grains of paradise** are good for the digestion and, for that reason, are an ingredient in certain dishes, cucumber cakes, for instance. Grains of paradise are believed to be an aphrodisiac. They are sometimes mixed in palm wine or in home-brewed spirits. When eaten fresh with a

570 **Comparative description of five species of *Aframomum***

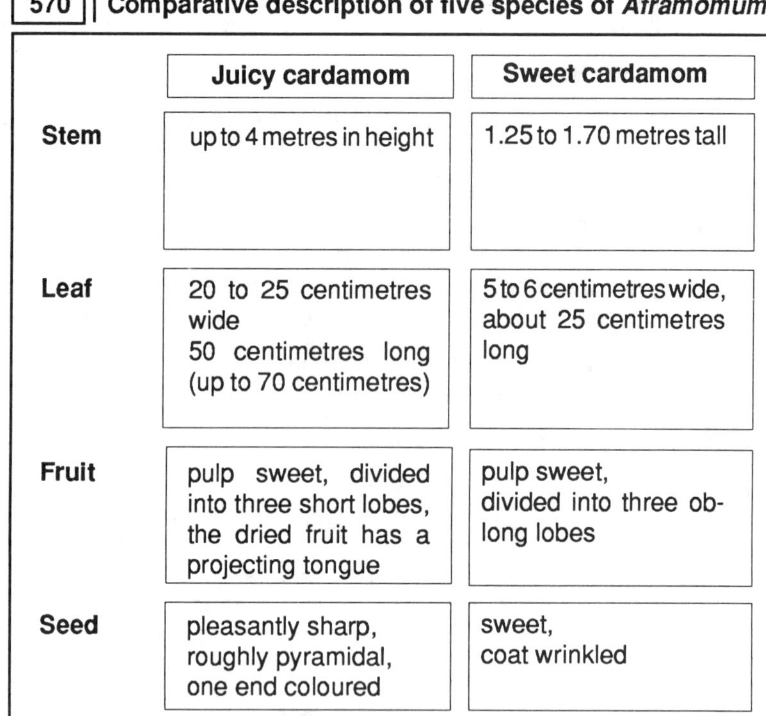

	Juicy cardamom	Sweet cardamom
Stem	up to 4 metres in height	1.25 to 1.70 metres tall
Leaf	20 to 25 centimetres wide 50 centimetres long (up to 70 centimetres)	5 to 6 centimetres wide, about 25 centimetres long
Fruit	pulp sweet, divided into three short lobes, the dried fruit has a projecting tongue	pulp sweet, divided into three oblong lobes
Seed	pleasantly sharp, roughly pyramidal, one end coloured	sweet, coat wrinkled

575

576

occurring in Cameroun (forest zone)

Grains of paradise	Liyambi cardamom	Fragrant cardamom
70 centimetres to 1 metre tall	1.50 to 3 metres tall, colour pale green, pitted as though the skin were wrinkled	2 to 3 metres tall, colour dark green lightly pitted
3 centimetres wide, about 20 centimetres long	10 centimetres wide 30 to 35 centimetres long moderately fragrant, base pale in colour	10 centimerters wide 30 to 40 centimeters long, very fragrant when fresh, base dark in colour
pulp sweet,	pulp sweet	sour pulp
very pungent, roughly pyramidal, but flattened	pleasantly pungent	pleasantly pungent

kola nut, the fruit is said to be an excellent cough-cure. The fruit also plays an important part in all the ceremonies that are in any way associated with magic.

The **liyambi cardamom** is much appreciated for its medicinal uses. The seeds are recommended as a purgative, and for the digestion. The leaves are sometimes used to flavour meat and fish dishes.

Fragrant cardamom leaves have a very pleasant smell and are used in braising meat and fish. Three or four leaves are placed in the bottom of the pan or wrapped round the meat or fish to be cooked. They are sometimes used to prepare an infusion for stomach-ache. The seeds are used in certain remedies for children suffering from measles, and in cures for worms and diarrhoea.

Environment : Cardamom is, by nature, a shade-loving plant growing spontaneously in thickets. It thrives in cool, humid sites in soils rich in organic matter.

The fruits are usually harvested from spontaneous plants growing in fallows, by paths and streams, in valley bottoms and wet lands.

Two species - grains of paradise and fragrant cardamom - are often cultivated in compounds.

The soil should be improved with organic manure, and the plants cultivated in the shade of fruit trees in plantations and orchards. In environments where cardamoms, and particularly grains of paradise, do not grow spontaneously, they are susceptible to competition from undesirable plants, so that weeding around the base is required.

Propagation : By rhizomes or pieces of underground stem with one or more eye buds, occasionally by seed.

Storage : Whole dried fruits keep for long periods.

SP27 Chillies

Chillies are branched shrubs between 1 metre and 1.2 metres tall, sometimes more. They belong to the family Solanaceae.

The many varieties are usually divided into two main species : small chillies called bird chillies *(Capsicum frutescens)* and large chillies called sweet peppers *(Capsicum annuum)*. Bird chillies have very hot fruits **(figure 577)**, while peppers are milder.

The white flowers of bird chillies are 1 to 2 centimetres in diameter. They may be solitary or in clusters of two or three in the leaf axils. They are fertilized by insects, especially ants and bees **(figure 579)**.

The fruits vary greatly in shape, size, pungency and colours depending on the species and variety. The fruits of bird chillies are usually between 1.5 and 3 centimetres long, although some varieties bear elongated fruits 8 to 12 centimetres in length. As a rule, the fruits are bright red when ripe and exceptionally pungent.

The fruits of large chillies (peppers) are milder and fleshier **(figure 580)**. Some, like the sweet pepper, are not sharp in flavour. When ripe, they are red, yellow or green. The ripe fruits are hollow. The many white seeds are attached to the centre of the fruit.

577

578

Scientific Name	*Capsicum frutescens*	*Capsicum annuum*
English	**Bird chillies**	**Chillies, sweet peppers**
French	piment oiseau, pili-pili, piment fort	piment doux, poivron
Yoruba	atawewe, sombo	tatase, atarodo

Large chillies are more popular as a vegetable. Some, like the sweet pepper, are eaten raw in salads. The leaves can also be eaten cooked.

Apart from other medicinal uses, chillies are recommended for constipation and as a painkiller.

Environment : Chillies are plants that thrive in sun and in shade, and grow anywhere, in compounds, gardens and fields.

Propagation : By seed. Ripe stem cuttings can be used for perennial varieties. As chillies cross-fertilize easily, it is advisable to keep seed plants of the different varieties away from each other. The seeds quickly lose their germinating capacity.

Husbandry : Chillies are grown in pure stands or in mixtures, in gardens near compounds or in fields. Market gardeners exploit them as seasonal plants, although African chillies are treated as annuals.

Chillies are sown shallowly in the field or in the nursery. When the seedlings have four to six leaves, they are transplanted with the roots

The branches of chilli peppers, especially the longer duration varieties, are unusual because they bifurcate or divide into two at the internodes **(figure 578)**, and this gives the plant a distinctive appearance. Suckers may develop from the base of the stem.

Bird chillies are biennial, whereas sweet peppers, as their scientific name *Capsicum annuum* implies, are seasonal. (It must be said, however, that some varieties are more or less perennial.)

The chilli has a short taproot and many lateral roots which are mostly spread in the superficial soil layers.

Uses : Bird chillies are used in many sauce recipes. Dried chillies are eaten in powder form or macerated in oil; they are also made into a soft or oily paste.

579

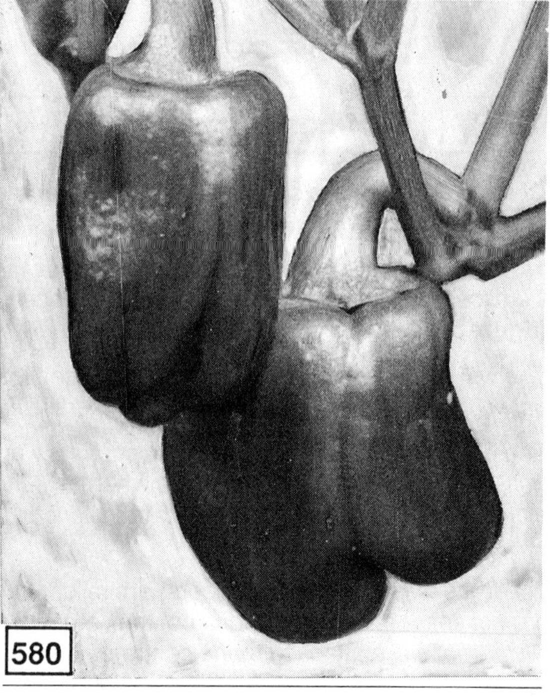
580

exposed, or with a ball of soil. Later on, you can choose between retaining or removing shade. It appears that shaded plants have a longer productive cycle and can be brought to bearing during the dry season provided the season is neither too long, nor too dry. People maintain that when plants are exposed to full sunlight, the fruits mature faster and the production period is more concentrated.

Mulching, earthing up the base of plants; removing suckers and pruning shoots that have fruited; pinching out the buds; pruning back the ageing perennial varieties – these are all ways of stimulating fruit production. (See **figures 194 and 195**.) Training the plants on canes and fences is another possibility.

Storage : Ripe fruits dried in the sun can be stored. The fruits of the fleshy varieties may be scalded before storing.

SP28 Ethiopian pepper

Scientific Name	*Xylopia aethiopica*
English	**Ethiopian, African** or **Guinea pepper**
French	poivre d'Ethiopie, fausse maniguette, piment noir de Guinée
Yoruba	heru

581

The **Ethiopian pepper** *(Xylopia aethiopica)* of the family Annonaceae is a low tree occurring in secondary forests. After forest clearing, the tree is often found with other trees and shrubs associated with secondary forest regeneration.

The trunk is tall, erect and cylindrical, with slender buttresses at the base. The habit of the tree is characteristic, its branches being arranged somewhat like those of a palm. The foliage is sparse.

The leaves are simple, about 15 centimetres in length, tapering to a point 2 centimetres long. The flowers are white, in clusters of two's or three's, sometimes solitary, growing on young branches. The fruits are yellow on the outside and red inside, with seven to eight seeds. When they have dried out, they turn brownish-black and are shaped like small pods 4 to 7 centimetres long, hanging in bunches **(figure 581)**.

Uses : The seeds or pods, whole or crushed, are used in cooking. The seeds are said to be a stimulant. They are also used for treating rheumatism.

The wood is exceptionally hard and is therefore highly rated by builders and carpenters. It is distinctive because it is smooth and shiny under the bark and looks as though it has been polished. In addition, it is believed to withstand termites and other insects destructive to wooden structures.

The bark is used for making partitions inside huts.

Environment : Ethiopian pepper grows in forests, more specifically in wet regions and by river beds. The tree is common in gallery forests. It occasionally grows in the savanna where it acts as a pioneer species in forest regeneration.

Today, Ethiopian pepper is mainly exploited as a wild plant. Cultivators consider that the plant is easily propagated by seed but other modes of propagation would be worth trying.

SP29 Pepper and Guinea pepper

Pepper and **Guinea pepper** (also called **Ashanti** or **Benin pepper**) are perennial climbing vines potentially several metres long. They belong to the family Piperaceae and are widely exploited. Pepper is a native of Asia, Guinea pepper originated in Africa.

The species are closely related : the leaves are alternate, oval and acuminate (pointed) with converging veins **(figure 583)**. The flowers are usually unisexual, borne in pendant spikes arising from the leaf axils. The fruits are globose, without peduncles, 3 to 6 millimetres in diameter, red when ripe, turning black when dried, with a single seed that varies in colour **(figure 584)**.

Guinea pepper is identified by its shorter leaves and fruit spikes. The leaves are 8 to 12 centimetres long – those of pepper measure 8 to 20 centimetres; the fruit spikes are 3 to 5 centimetres long – those of

582

583

pepper vary between 3 and 25 centimetres in length. Guinea pepper also has a more branched habit.

Uses : The fresh and dried fruits, whole or crushed, are hot spices used in cooking.

Environment : Pepper plants are susceptible to drought. They require fertile soil, rich in organic material. They thrive in the shade and are usually associated with the wet forest zones.

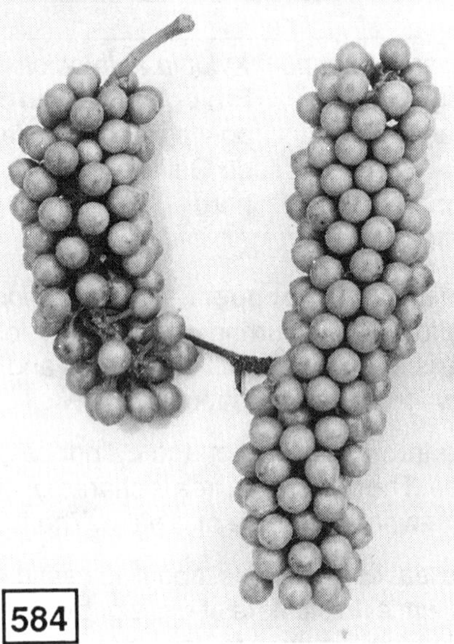
584

Scientific Name	*Piper nigrum*	*Piper guineense*
English	**pepper**	**Guinea pepper, Ashanti** or **Benin pepper**
French	poivre noir	poivre guinéen, poivre du Kissi, poivre des Achantis

Propagation : By cuttings taken from young stems or stem shoots about 50 centimetres long. Occasionally by seed.

Husbandry : The pepper plant is usually cultivated with trees that serve as supports **(figure 582)**. The Guinea pepper is spontaneous in forest regions and is exploited in its natural state.

The cuttings are soaked for a few days before planting. It is advisable to plant on mounds in soils rich in organic matter.

The plants must be trained on a stout post. If a living support in the form of a tree is used, the tree must be able to withstand severe pruning, because shading often needs to be adjusted. Under intensive cultivation, shape pruning is practised in order to develop two or three main climbing stems per plant. Routine pruning is also carried out to check the growth of the main stems which are cut back to about ten nodes. Later, when they have fruited, the stems are pruned to within two or three nodes of the base. By this method, the plant is invigorated and the fruit-bearing nodes are renewed. To stagger production, the three main stems can be pruned at intervals — one now, the second three or four weeks later, the third later still.

Pepper plants benefit greatly from continuous mulching, weeding, mounding of the stumps every season, and lopping the branches of the shade trees used as supports.

SP 30 Bush butter

The **bush butter**, belonging to the family Burseraceae, is a tree native to the wet tropics and is 10 to 15 metres tall. The top of the tree is rounded and the foliage dark green. The frame of the tree consists of crownlike branches arranged in a series along the length of the trunk. The tree remains in leaf in the dry season.

The leaves are divided into a dozen or more leaflets which tend to droop. The young leaves are pink to red in colour; the older leaves are dark green. The foliage is dense **(figure 585)**.

As a rule, the flowers are monoecious (male and female on the same plant), yellow, and arranged in clusters.

Scientific Name	Dacryodes edulis
English	**Bush butter, native pear**
French	safoutier, prunier

585

The fruits are globular and more or less oblong **(figure 586)**. They are 5 to 10 centimetres long, depending on the variety. They are yellow or pink at first, becoming violet or black when ripe.

Uses : The pulp of the ripe fruits is eaten, preferably after cooking, and is rich in starches, proteins and vitamins. The fruits themselves are grilled or boiled in water, and are rather acid.

Environment : The bush butter tree prefers cool, well-manured soils, and grows well in mixed orchards. However, the crown develops laterally in full sunlight and gives dense shade on the ground.

Propagation : Mainly by seed. However, the quality of the trees obtained by this method is uneven. Multiplication by cuttings and especially the grafting of high-yield trees would certainly give good results. Some varieties are propagated by layering.

Husbandry : The bush butter tree is grown in compounds, orchards, hedges and fields. When the tree is interplanted with other species, its shading capacity must be taken into account and the seedlings planted at least 12 to 15 metres apart.

Seeds are sown in the open or in a nursery. Shade and a well-worked soil enriched with organic material are essential. Seeds may even be sown at the foot of a banana as often happens in Cameroun. A seed is laid flat on the ground and covered with one or two centimetres of earth.

Young trees are transplanted when they are about a year old. They are transferred, preferably with a ball of soil, at the beginning of the rainy season. The transplants benefit greatly from shading and mulching.

The bush butter tree comes into bearing when it is about 6 or 7 years old. The first fruits ripen two or three months after the beginning of the rainy season, and production may last for three or four months. There are considerable differences in the production cycles of the various varieties, so that by mixing early and late varieties in orchards, fruits can be available for six or seven months of the year.

586

The growth of the fruit-bearing spurs is stimulated by lopping dead wood and dying branches.

Gardeners should try shaping the framework in order to facilitate fruit picking, encourage the development of the fruit-bearing branches and help the tree to integrate with the other species planted in the orchard.

Storage : The fruits, boiled and dried, keep for three or four months in a dry place. They are reheated in boiling water before consumption.

SP31 Tamarind

The **tamarind** belongs to the family Leguminosae and occurs in dry savannas. It is between 15 to 20 metres tall with more or less permanent foliage, although this is sometimes very thinly spread in the dry season **(figure 587)**.

The leaves are composed of 9 to 12 pairs of leaflets and are about 20 centimetres long **(figure 588)**. The flowers, creamy white to red and 3-petalled, are massed in terminal racemes, and have a pleasant smell. The fruits are elongated pods, sometimes unevenly swollen, about 15 centimetres long **(figure 589)**. The fruit pulp turns brown and sweet as it matures. The pods contain between one and ten brown, shiny seeds, measuring just under a centimetre in length.

Uses : The leaves, flowers and fruits are used to flavour the water in which couscous is cooked. The fruits are used to make cool drinks and syrups. The seeds, shelled, ground and winnowed, are sometimes used in sauces. These are also spiced with the leaves and flowers. A red dye can be extracted from the leaves.

The wood is used in carpentery since it is hard, durable, and resistant to termites.

The many medicinal uses of tamarind include the treatment of asthma, constipation, wounds and skin disorders.

Environment : The tamarind grows on practically any kind of soil, but it does not like water-saturated or very stony ground. It thrives in full sunlight and withstands drought.

Husbandry : The tree is spontaneous in savannas and multiplies without difficulty if it is not subjected to bush fires and browsing animals. It often occurs in fields, orchards and homestead gardens. The tree is said to compete unduly with lower storey plants.

Propagation : The tamarind is grown from seed. In order to break dormancy and facilitate germination, the seeds are soaked in lukewarm water for a day or two, or scalded for about 5 minutes. The tamarind is also reproduced by cuttings taken from branches, and by layering. Propagation by shield budding and by splice and cleft grafting has been carried out successfully. Grafted trees are smaller than those grown by other methods.

The trees multiplied by seed develop on a tall trunk sometimes many metres high, whereas those reproduced by cuttings or layers form a bushier habit from a shorter stem that usually forms a series of branches. These smaller tamarinds are thought to yield more fruits **(figure356)**.

Husbandry : The tree is sown or planted in nurseries, in well-loosened soil. When the seedlings are about 25 or 30 centimetres tall, they are transplanted with a ball of soil as delicately as possible, and will need shading for some weeks. Mulching should be carried out and watering, where possible, is advisable for the first two years.

Scientific Name	*Tamarindus indica*
English	**Tamarind**
French	tamarinier

587

588

589

The first fruits are harvested eight to twelve years after planting.

Storage : The young leaves and shelled pods keep well after drying. They are sometimes steamed and rolled into balls before drying.

The ripe pods are sometimes left to ferment and are then sun-dried, after which they are sold on the market in the form of black-looking, sticky balls.

SP32 | Aidon tree

Scientific Name	*Tetrapleura tetraptera*
English	**Aidon tree**
French	tetrapleura
Yoruba	ahidon

The **aidon tree** *(Tetrapleura)* is a forest tree of the family Leguminosae **(figure 590)**. Its fruits are used as seasonings. The leaves are doubly compound, the leaflets being arranged on secondary petioles **(figure 591)**. The leaves are 25 to 30 centimetres long; the leaflets, flattened at the extremities, are 3 to 4 centimetres long. The foliage gives comparatively light shade. The flowers are tiny, pink to orange in colour, arranged in spikes.

The fruits are 10 to 30 centimetres long and have four ridged sides that can be seen in **figure 591**. They are dark green at fruit set, but turn a dark, glossy brown when fully ripe. The tree sheds its leaves in the dry season.

591

590

Uses : The ripe fruits serve as seasonings and are used medicinally for stomach diseases and obesity.

The fruit has a strong smell that is believed to keep snakes away from dwellings.

Husbandry : The aidon tree is not cultivated. Traditionally, it is preserved during clearing. The fruits are picked off the ground in the dry season.

The tree is self-sown at the present time. Its qualities deserve more attention in relation to agricultural needs. The mature tree gives fairly light shade, especially when it is isolated. Because it sheds its leaves every year in the dry season, it restores a considerable amount of organic matter to the soil.

SP33 | Tomato

The **tomato** is a seasonal, climbing plant of the family Solanaceae **(figure 592)**. The stems, covered with shiny hairs, are usually prostrate, only the tips being erect **(figure 594)**.

The leaves, large and deeply cleft, with many leaflets, are arranged alternately along the stems. Both the leaves and the stems are strong-smelling. Clusters of four to six flowers, sometimes more, form on the stems between the leaves. The flowers are about one centimetre in diameter.

Tomato fruits exist in many shapes, some of which are seen in **figure 593**. The fruits may be large and round, or elongated, depending on the

592

variety. However, varieties of the **cherry tomato** have small fruits not more than 2 centimetres in diameter. These varieties probably became naturalized in Africa a long time ago, whereas the commercial varieties that are popular in urban areas are grown from seeds first imported in the recent past.

The cherry tomato has a bitter flavour that is not found in other varieties. It is productive in difficult conditions such as saline and exhausted soils, where the cultivation of other varieties would be risky. Specifically, the cherry tomato withstands drought and the pests associated with the tomato, so that crop protection treatment is not needed. The cherry tomato is often cultivated in the cropping fields where it spreads along the ground underneath erect plants.

The main root system of the tomato is fibrous. Adventitious roots develop freely along the stems.

Uses : The tomato is eaten raw or cooked, whole or as a purée.

Environment : The tomato prefers moist soils, rich in organic waste. It is susceptible to overheating that can make the leaves turn yellow and cause blossom fall. It can therefore be grown on shady sites for part of the year.

Propagation : The tomato is grown from seed.

If you want to preserve varietal purity, you may have to cultivate the seed plants of each variety on individual plots well away from one another, or separated by barriers such as trees, hedges and houses.

Commercial seeds are selected and, as a rule, can be relied on to bear fruits with the qualities described by the plant breeder, whereas seeds taken from plants under cultivation will not hand down identical characteristics from one generation to the next. If these unselected seeds are used generation after generation, increasingly small, bitter tomatoes similar to the cherry tomato will be produced.

Husbandry : The tomato can be grown in pure stand or in mixtures. It is often subspontaneous in homestead gardens.

In the cropping fields, the tomato is broadcast or sown in holes. In gardens and for commercial production, the tomato is first sown in a germinator, and then transplanted twice – first to nursery beds, and then to the permanent site when the plants are 20 to 30 centimetres high. The plants are transferred with a ball of soil. When the stems are left lying on the ground, adventitious roots grow in abundance.

Ashes, mineral fertilizers and especially organic dressings – manures, compost and mulches - stimulate fruit production.

Scientific Name	*Lycopersicum lycopersicon or L. esculentum*
English	**tomato**
French	tomate

593

594

595

The plants should be earthed up a few weeks after planting out. Regular mulching is needed, and partial shade must be provided in very hot climates with intense sunlight. Staking the plants or training them onto trellises or frames is most beneficial. The frame shown in **figure 595** was made from millet canes.

Pruning, pinching out and removing suckers are also recommended techniques. There is constant competition between fruit production and between the growth of stems and leaves **(figures 151 and 210)**. A balance between these competing elements can be achieved by good pruning.

Pinching out consists of removing the terminal bud of a stem as soon as the first flower cluster appears. By this technique, all the sap rising to the top of the stem is earmarked for the development of the fruits. Later, new stems grow in the leaf axils situated below the inflorescence. One or two stems are retained, the others are eliminated. Then, the new shoots are pinched out when two or three flower clusters have formed there. As the stems are pinched out and the fruits set, the stems are tied with a length of raffia to a support or to a trellis, so that the fruit bearing stems do not collapse or snap under the weight of the fruits.

Pruning tomato plants encourages the growth of larger fruits but reduces the number of fruits per plant. If the stems are not pinched out, suckers can be removed instead. In this case, the main stems are allowed to develop, but the secondary stems are pruned back, thus forcing the sap they would have consumed towards the fruit-bearing branches.

Notice that all the varieties of tomato do not have to be pruned. Some are productive without pruning, while others are more fertile if the pruning described above is carried out.

Chapter 22

Cucurbitaceae

The family **Cucurbitaceae** comprises a wide range of plants of considerable importance in tropical agriculture. These plants have common characteristics : large leaves, creeping or climbing stems usually with tendrils, fleshy fruits with many seeds and a more or less fibrous root system. Their produce – leaves, pulp, seeds and calabashes – have very many uses.

Moreover, these semi-prostrate or climbing plants are often beneficial for interplanted crops when the latter are erect, bushy or shrub-like. Cucurbits play a significant role in controlling soil erosion. They also help growers to maintain gardens and fields and to keep down weeds **(figure 629)**.

This chapter presents thirteen, widely cultivated species of Cucurbitaceae. They are listed in English in **table 596**. However, there is some confusion about names, both in English and in the vernacular. For example, the equivalents of 'vegetable marrow' and 'cucumber' are often used in local languages to label any plant of the Cucurbitaceae family. Actually, it is not easy for the uninitiated to use the right names. The confusion is even greater in English where the words 'squash', 'pumpkin' and 'vegetable marrow' are used indiscriminately, despite the fact that, in certain regions, these names refer to well-defined species.

At the end of the chapter, a section is devoted to the cultivation of Cucurbitaceae and the cultural practices associated with these plants. Some of these practices have already been described in Part I.

596 The main cultivated species of Cucurbitaceae

Scientific Name	English
Sechium edule	Chayote
Citrullus lanatus and *Colocynthis citrullus*	Citrullus and watermelon
Cucumis spp.	Cucumber and gherkin
Cucumeropsis manii and *C. edulis*	Bitter cucumber
Cucurbita pepo and *C. moschata*	Vegetable marrow and courgette
Lagenaria siceraria (L. vulgaris)	Bottle gourd
Telfairia occidentalis	Fluted gourd
Trichosanthes cucumerina var. anguina	Snake gourd
Luffa aegyptiaca (or *cylindrica)*	Smooth loofah
Momordica charantia and *M. balsamina*	Bitter gourd
Cucumis melo	Melon
Cucurbita maxima	Pumpkin

SP34 Chayote

Scientific Name	*Sechium edule*
English	**Chayote, chowchow, christophine**
French	chayotte, christophine

The leaves of the **chayote** are entirc, flat, covered with coarse hairs, 15 to 25 centimetres long and 10 centimetres wide **(figure 597)**.

The male flowers, white, 1 to 2 centimetres wide, are in clusters of five or six, on peduncles measuring about 10 centimetres. The female flowers, also white, are borne in the leaf axils on short, robust peduncles. Male and female flowers appear on the same stem.

The fruits are ovate to pear-shaped, marked by deep, irregular furrows. They are pale green, sometimes with soft prickles. They are 10 to 20 centimetres long, 5 to 10 centimetres wide. The flesh is white.

The chayote has a single seed per fruit. The seed is ovate, 3 to 5 centimetres long.

Uses : The whole plant is edible. The leaves and young shoots are used as a vegetable base in sauces or as a side dish. The cooked tuberous roots are a staple. The ripe and immature fruits are cooked and served as a vegetable.

Environment : The plant thrives at altitudes of 1000 metres and more. It is intolerant of waterlogging.

597

Propagation : As the seed loses its vitality when dried, the whole fruit - pregerminated, if desired - is used for sowing.

SP35 Citrullus and watermelon

Citrullus *(Citrullus lanatus)* and **watermelon** *(Colocynthis citrullus)* are closely related plants as their respective scientific names imply. They are distinguished almost exclusively by their fruits **(figures 599 and 600)**.

The leaves of both species are deeply cleft into fine, irregular lobes, roughly serrate, 10 to 15 centimetres long **(figure 598)**.

598

Scientific Name	*Citrullus lanatus*	*Colocynthis citrullus*
English	**Citrullus, bitter apple**	**Watermelon**
French	Melon à pistache	pastèque
Yoruba	ibara, akussi	

599

The male flowers are yellow, on long peduncles, about 3.5 centimetres wide, with petals united at the base. The female flowers, also yellow, are borne on shorter peduncles, noticeably enlarged at the base containing the ovary. Citrullus and watermelon are monoecious, i.e. male and female flowers grow on the same plant.

The **citrullus**, also known as the bitter apple, has round fruits, green or white or with white markings. The skin is dull, the pulp white. The fruits are between 15 and 20 centimetres in diameter **(figure 599)**. Citrullus seeds are oval, with thick, rough margins, yellow and about 1 centimetre wide and 1.7 centimetres long.

600

Uses : After shelling and grinding, the seeds are made into cakes, or are used for thickening sauces. The bitter pulp is sometimes cooked and fed to pigs.

The fruits of the **watermelon** are much larger. They are oval to round, 30 to 80 centimetres long, more at times. They are green, mottled with white **(figure 600)**. The flesh, red or pink, is sweet and juicy; it is eaten raw. It contains black seeds about one centimetre long.

Environment : Although the citrullus grows well on sandy soils, it prefers soil fertilized with organic manure. It tolerates shade and exposure to sunlight, and is fairly drought resistant.

The watermelon grows in full sunlight. Once it is established, it withstands drought well. The plant is suited to dry season cultivation. The fruits are susceptible to rot at high moisture levels.

SP36 Cucumbers and gherkins

The leaves of **cucumbers and gherkins** are whole, 5-angled, regularly serrate. The surface of the blade is crinkled between the veins. There are regular, symmetrical notches at the base of the leaves. These are about 10 centimetres long **(figure 601**, page 278**)**.

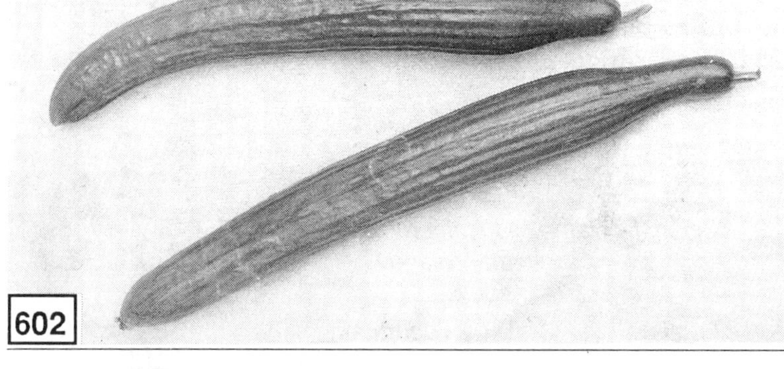
602

The male flowers are yellow, on peduncles, with five partly overlapping petals, 2 centimetres in diameter. The female flowers are also yellow, on short peduncles, the same size as the male flowers. Male and female flowers are on the same plant, and are borne in the leaf axils.

Cucumbers are fruits, dark green, elongated, 10 to 40 centimetres long, rind smooth, sometimes scattered with spines **(figure 602)**.

Gherkins are fruits, pale green to yellow, cylindrical with rind copiously dotted with spinous tubercles. The fruits are about 20 centimetres long when fully ripe, rarely more. However, they are often picked when they measure between 6 and 10 centimetres **(figure 603)**.

A small cucumber is cultivated in wet forest regions. The fruit is regularly cylindrical, pale green, skin smooth but dull, 5 to 7 centimetres long and 3 to 5 centimetres wide **(figure 604)**.

The seeds are flat, white, elongated and half a centimetre long.

Scientific Name	*Cucumis spp.*
English	**Cucumber, gherkin**
French	concombre, cornichon

603

604

Uses : The fruits are eaten raw or cooked. The seeds are shelled and ground for use in sauces.

Environment : Cucumbers and gherkins thrive in full sunlight on fertile soils. They are intolerant of drought.

SP37 Bitter cucumber

The leaves of the **bitter cucumber** are entire, with three regular lobes, evenly serrate. The surface of the blades is crinkled and shiny. The leaves are sometimes simple and cordate on certain portions of the trailing stems. The leaves are 10 to 15 centimetres long **(figure 605)**.

The flowers are yellow, 1.5 to 2 centimetres wide.

The fruits are oval, about 20 centimetres long, yellow-green, with a smooth and shiny rind, and are borne on peduncles about 10 centimetres in length **(figure 606)**. The pulp is white.

The seeds are flat, white, smooth, narrow at one end, about 0.8 centimetres wide and 1.8 centimetres long.

Uses : The seeds are shelled and ground for use in sauces and cakes.

Environment : The bitter cucumber thrives in soils rich in barely decomposed, organic waste. This is why it is often cultivated as a first-crop plant after clearing **(figure 627)**.

Scientific Name	*Cucumeropsis mannii and C. edulis*
English	**Bitter cucumber, Dark egusi**
French	concombre amer

601

605

606

607

SP38 Vegetable marrows and courgettes

Scientific Name	*Cucurbita pepo and C. moschata*
English	**Vegetable marrow, courgette, zucchini**
French	courge, courgette
Yoruba	elegede

Vegetable marrows and **courgettes** are very similar plants. The main difference is in the length of their vines : those of vegetable marrows are several metres long, those of courgettes are between one and two metres long.

The leaves are entire, generally with three well-defined lobes and irregularly serrate. The central lobe is more or less acuminate. The leaves can be 35 centimetres long, but the length varies from leaf to leaf on the same plant **(figures 607 and 608)**.

The male and female flowers, yellow, with petals joined for half their length, roughly star-shaped, are borne on the same plant. The male flowers are 7 or 8 centimetres in diameter, on long, slender peduncles more than 10 centimetres in length **(figure 609a)**.

The female flowers, 12 to 15 centimetres in diameter, are borne on short, stout peduncles, swollen at the base of the flowers **(figure 609b)**.

Vegetable marrows are round to elongated in shape (**figure 610** shows two varieties), dark green, often streaked white, sometimes covered with warts and swellings. The fruits are up to 30 centimetres long. The flesh is yellow or red, depending on the variety.

Courgettes are elongated, sometimes curved. They are green, smooth-skinned, often spotted with white. They are 20 to 50 centimetres long **(figure 611)**.

The seeds are flat, about 1.3 centimetres long, white, tapering noticeably at one end and grooved round the edges **(figure 612)**.

Uses : The young leaves are eaten as a vegetable.

608

609 a b

612

610 611

The pulp of the slightly under-ripe fruits is eaten cooked, and occasionally raw. The immature fruits are cooked. The dried shell of the fruit is sometimes used as a container.

Environment : Vegetable marrows and courgettes need very fertile soil with plenty of organic manure. They do not withstand drought. These are sun-loving plants that tolerate light shade.

SP39 Bottle gourd

Scientific Name	*Lagenaria siceraria and L. vulgaris*
English	**Bottle or calabash gourd**
French	calebasse, courge calebasse

The leaves of the **bottle** or **calabash gourd** are usually entire, cordate, sometimes characterized by three lobes, shallowly marked and irregular, serrate, lightly incurved on both sides of the main vein, very variable in size, up to 30 centimetres long **(figure 613)**.

613

614

615

The male flowers are borne on long peduncles (up to 25 centimetres). They are white and about 5 centimetres in diameter. The petals are joined, but sometimes separate **(figure 614)**. The female flowers are borne on short peduncles 2 to 5 centimetres long. They are white and about 5 centimetres in diameter. They are borne on the same plant as the male flowers.

The fruits, variable in shape, more or less elongated, are often characterized by a long neck, straight or crooked. The rind is hard, smooth and shiny **(figure 613)**. The fruits vary in length from a few centimetres to more than one metre, depending on the variety.

The seeds are flat, about 2 centimetres long.

Uses : The shelled, ground seeds are used in sauces and cakes. The young fruits, leaves and shoots are eaten cooked.

The fruit shells are used to make household utensils such as bowls, funnels and spoons. They are also used for making pipes, musical instruments and decorative objects. For all these uses, the fruits are quite often tied during growth in order to train them to the desired shapes.

Figure 615 shows a crop of bottle gourds growing on an overhead lattice. The gourds are placed in bags and the tops tied to the lattice with raffia. Then, more raffia is wound round the bags in order to shape the fruits.

Environment : Bottle gourds demand well-manured soil. They withstand drought fairly well and dislike shade.

SP40 Fluted gourd

Scientific Name	*Telfairia occidentalis*
English	**Fluted gourd**
French	courge cannelée
Yoruba	iroro

The **fluted gourd** has leaves composed of three leaflets, sometimes five, with veins often converging at the tip of the leaflet **(figure 617)**. The leaves can be 15 centimetres long.

The male flowers are white to pink, small (less than 1 centimetre), arranged on long peduncles up to 30 centimetres in length **(figure 617)**. The female flowers are white on the outside, red-purple in the centre, arranged on small peduncles and solitary in the leaf axils. The petals are delicately frilled and silky round the edges **(figure 616)**. The plants are dioecious, i.e. there are separate male and female plants.

The fruits are long, roughly fusiform, pale green, longitudinally grooved. They have a waxy coating, are up to 20 centimetres in diameter, and more than 35 centimetres long. The flesh is fibrous and bright yellow. The seeds are round, flattened, brown and about 4 centimetres in length.

Uses : The leaves and stems are chopped for use in soups. The ground seeds are also used in sauces. The seeds are also scalded, shelled and dried in the sun and then used like dried fruit. Oil is extracted from the seeds of some varieties.

Environment : The fluted gourd tolerates both sun and shade, and withstands a certain degree of drought. The female plants are said to be the more reproductive.

616

617

SP41 Snake gourd

The leaves of the **snake gourd** are three to seven lobed, deeply cleft, irregular, more or less palmate **(figure 618)**, up to 20 centimetres long.

The flowers are white, on long peduncles up to 30 centimetres. The plant is monoecious. The male flowers are arranged in clusters, the female flowers solitary in the leaf axils.

The fruits are cylindrical, very long, narrow at both ends, green to white, as much as 1.2 metres long and about 5 to 7 centimetres in diameter **(figure 618)**. The flesh is red and fibrous.

The seeds are flat, grey-brown, sculptured, narrow at one end and 1.7 centimetres long.

Uses : The pulp of the ripe fruits is used in sauces and is a good substitute for tomato paste.

Environment : The snake gourd is a climbing vine and is therefore cultivated on a living stake or near a fence or a frame on which it can be trained. It needs organically manured soil. It tolerates both sun and shade, but dislikes drought.

Scientific Name	*Trichosanthes cucumerina var. anguina*
English	**Snake gourd**
French	patole, courge serpent, courge tomate
Kikuyu	tomato eleso

Notes

618

SP42 Smooth loofah

Scientific Name	*Luffa aegyptiaca or L. cylindrica*
English	**Smooth loofah, sponge gourd, dishcloth gourd**
French	éponge végétale, louffa

The leaves of the **smooth loofah** are oval, deeply five to seven lobed, dentate, acuminate, dark green. They are 10 to 30 centimetres long and 5 to 25 centimetres wide **(figure 619)**.

The male flowers, yellow, 5 to 10 centimetres wide, are borne in inflorescences. The female flowers, also yellow, usually solitary, have overlapping petals **(figure 620)**. The flowers open early in the morning and close quickly during the day. Male and female flowers are borne on the same plant.

The fruits are regularly cylindrical, sometimes striped, pale green. When they are retted, a network of fibres is released and forms the loofah sponge that is about 30 to 60 centimetres long and 8 to 10 centimetres wide **(figure 621)**.

The seeds are black, smooth, and about 1 to 1.5 centimetres long.

Uses : The under-ripe fruits are eaten raw or cooked. The ground kernels are used as a basic ingredient in sauces and cakes. The kernels sometimes yield oil.

The fruit fibres are used as sponges and for upholstering mattresses. Loofah fibers have various industrial uses, more especially as engine filters and as shock and sound absorbers.

Environment : Soils should be well-drained and rich in organic waste. Too much rain during flowering and fruit set is harmful.

619

620

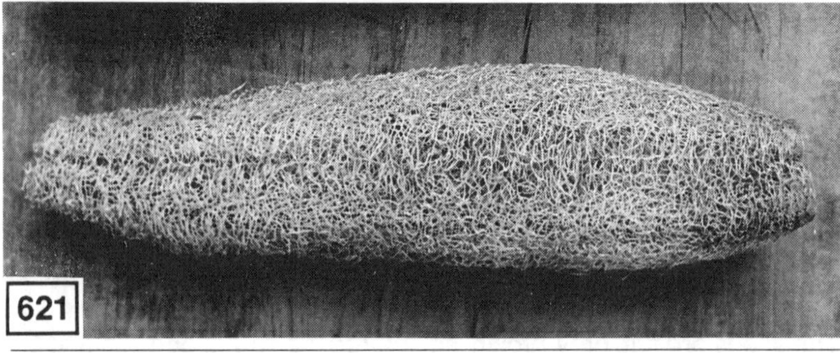
621

SP43 Bitter gourd

Scientific Name	*Momordica charantia and M. balsamina*
English	**bitter gourd, balsam pear**
French	liane merveille, margose

The leaves of the **bitter gourd** are deeply three to five lobed, pale green, about 5 or 6 centimetres long **(figure 622)**.

622

623

The flowers, yellow, are 2 or 3 centimetres wide.

The fruits vary from ovoid to fusiform, with many rows of spines, orange with white patches. The fruits are about 5 centimetres long, sometimes more for certain Asian varieties **(figure 623)**.

The seeds are flat, 1 to 1.5 centimetres long and brown.

Uses : The immature fruits are cooked as a vegetable. The ripe fruits and seeds make a bitter condiment. The young leaves and shoots are treated like spinach.

624

625

626

Environment : The bitter gourd thrives in hot, humid conditions.

SP44 Melon

The leaves of the **melon** are ovate, shallowly five to seven lobed, serrate. They are 5 to 15 centimetres in diameter.

The flowers are monoecious, sometimes hermaphrodite (that is, with male and female reproductive organs on the same flower).

The fruits are globular or ovate **(figure 624)**. The skin can be smooth or rough, and is sometimes furrowed. It is pale green, yellow or orange. The flesh is orange-coloured and sweet.

The seeds are small, white and smooth, between 0.5 and one centimetre long.

Uses : The sweet, juicy flesh is eaten raw. The seeds can be ground and used for thickening sauces.

Environment : The melon thrives in full sunlight. It does not do well in excessively humid conditions.

Scientific Name	*Cucumis melo*
English	**Melon**
French	melon

SP45 Pumpkin

Scientific Name	*Cucurbita maxima*
English	**Pumpkin**
French	potiron, citrouille

The leaves of the pumpkin are entire, with three shallow, irregular lobes, serrate, often slightly acuminate **(figure 625)** and of variable length – up to 50 centimetres.

The flowers are yellow, petals almost completely joined, 7 to 10 centimetres in diameter. The male flowers are on slender peduncles 10 to 20 centimetres long. The female flowers are on thick peduncles 5 to 10 centimetres long. Male and female flowers are on the same (monoecious) plant.

The fruits are round, sometimes flattened, white, grey or green, sometimes yellow or orange **(figure**

626), up to 30 centimetres in diameter. The flesh is yellow to red.

The seeds are flat, ivory to brown, about 2 to 2.5 centimetres long, tapering at one end; the seed margin is noticeably lighter in colour.

Uses : The young leaves are cooked. The pulp of the ripening fruits, more rarely that of the ripe fruits, is cooked or occasionally eaten raw. The seeds are shelled, ground, and used in sauces.

The dried fruit shell is sometimes made into a bowl.

Environment : The plant responds well to soils enriched with ashes, and to sites treated with burnt earth. The melon is light-loving but tolerates a little shade.

Cucurbitaceae : cultivation and husbandry

Cucurbits play an **important role** in cropping fields :

- as **first-crop plants**, or at the start of a cultural cycle. This is particularly true of cucumbers (*Cucumis* and *Cucumeropsis*) that are often sown after clearing. The extensive, spreading vegetation of these species stops the emergence of weeds and of forest regrowth **(figure 627)**. They make the most of the uprooted, decomposing plants and of the ashes from burning;
- as **cover plants** because, thanks to their creeping foliage, cucurbits smother unwanted plants and protect the ground from destructive rains and overheating by the sun's rays. In addition, they fill empty spaces. In **figure 629**, for instance, pumpkins fill the gaps under the maize plants;

627

628

- as **plants in association** with a great many cultivated species, in which case the cucurbits occupy the lowest storey. Sometimes, they have to be cut back if they show a tendency to climb on erect plants. Cucurbits can also be grown in mixtures with each other.

Cucurbits are often grown in compounds and in open spaces such as the sites of former houses. The plants spread on the ground or twine round living or dead poles **(figure 628)**. They are often trained over housetops and supply welcome shade **(figure 630)**.

The **harvests** depend on the varietal characteristics of the plants and the produce to be harvested. When seeds are wanted, the fruits are allowed to ripen as long as possible, before they are picked and split in two for seed removal. When food for consumption is required, the fruits are often picked before full maturity. The leaves are harvested when the plant is in full growth; the young shoots are removed, or the whole leaves are harvested with their petioles.

The snake gourd must be picked just as the skin is changing from green to red, because then the flesh is perfectly ripe, but not over-ripe.

Husbandry : Except for the chayote that is propagated by sowing the whole fruit, cucurbitaceae are **multiplied by seed,** although layers can sometimes be taken from rooted stems. Seeds retain their viability for three to six months, depending on the species. The seeds of the fluted gourd quickly lose their germination power if the fruits are washed or dried. The seeds must therefore be left in the fruits as long as possible.

Cucurbitaceae can be sown in groups on the permanent site, two or three seeds per hole. They are also sown in nurseries. The seeds are planted 2 or 3 centimetres deep. Transplanting takes place when the seedlings have two true leaves.

You must sow cucurbits as early as possible, at the start of the rainy season. The exceptions to this rule are cucumber, citrullus and watermelon. Since the fruits of these plants only ripen properly in dry weather, the plants should not be sown too early. One or two months after the onset of the rains is a good time because the fruits are then sure to ripen in the dry season.

Plants of the Cucurbitaceae benefit from **staking**. Indeed, staking is essential for the snake gourd whose fruits rot before maturity if they are left lying on the ground. There are many ways of supporting plants – on rooftops **(figure 630)**, on upright or criss-crossed posts **(figure 628)**, or on trees. Bottle gourds are sometimes trained in a special way. The vegetation is trained on a raised frame or lattice, and the fruits are suspended in bags **(figure 615)**.

When growing vegetable marrows and pumpkins, you will find that light shade encourages leaf production but hinders fruiting. You must therefore regulate the shade screens in keeping with the production you are looking for, that is to say, leaves or fruits.

It is wise to thin out the young fruits in order to obtain large, ripe fruits. This is done by keeping one or two fruits per fruiting stem and by cutting back the others **(figure 151)**.

Storage : The whole fruits of certain species or varieties, for example, pumpkin, vegetable marrow and chayote, keep in a cool place for some months. The seeds, shelled or unshelled, will keep in dry storage for many years.

629

630

Chapter 23

Miscellaneous fruits

Mangoes, oranges, guavas and pawpaws are examples of fruits that fall into the 'sweet and sour category. Such fruits are usually eaten raw. They are excellent complementary foods because they supply the body with vitamins and mineral salts **(table 46)**.

Apart from the familiar fruit species such as those mentioned above for which detailed descriptions did not seem necessary in the context of this book, there are other fruits, generally overlooked or restricted to particular regions, that deserve to be better known.

The systematic presentations of these neglected fruits are not complete because not enough is known about the best ways of cultivating them in Africa. Further information and corrections from our readers would be welcome, especially data on varieties, cultural practices, pruning, and the possibilities of grafting and propagation by cuttings.

SP46 Annonaceae

The family Annonaceae comprises many fruit trees, five of which are fairly widely distributed in tropical Africa. They are the **soursop (figure 631)**, the **bullock's heart (figure 636)**, the **sweetsop (figures 632 and 633)**, the **cherimoya (figure 634 and 635)**, and the **wild custard apple (figure 637)**. These are all low trees from 4 to 7 metres high.

They have the following characteristics :

- the leaves are alternate, simple and entire;
- the flowers are yellow, with three sepals and three or six petals;
- the fruits are fleshy and soft when ripe, mostly with white, aromatic pulp;
- the seeds are black and more or less elongated.

Uses : The fruit pulp is eaten fresh. The wild custard apple has many medicinal uses - for skin diseases, eye complaints, Guinea worm, as an antidote against snake poisons, etc. The bark of the wild custard apple and the fresh seeds of the sweetsop are said to contain insecticidal properties that are developed by maceration.

Environment : Annonaceae do not tolerate waterlogged soils. They prosper in full sunlight, but adapt to light shade. With the exception of the wild custard apple, these plants are susceptible to drought. The cherimoya is a tree of the highland areas and is badly affected by hot weather.

Propagation : By seed. Splice grafting and budding are known to succeed. It is said that cherimoya, bullock's heart and sweetsop are easily intergrafted.

631

Scientific Name	*Annona muricata*
English	**soursop**
French	Corossol
Yoruba	ebo

Fruits :	green, covered in soft prickles oblong, 10-25 centimetres long
Leaves:	glossy, oval to lanceolate, 10-25 centimetres long, 4-6 centimetres wide

Husbandry : The wild custard apple is spontaneous in dry savannas. The other Annonaceae are cultivated in homestead gardens or in mixed orchards.

The trees come into bearing quickly – in the third or fourth year. If production is intensive, the they would need to be replanted about every ten years.

These species are sown in moderately-shaded nursery beds, in loose, moist soil rich in organic manure. They are transplanted with a ball of soil, and have to be mulched and watered in the first year. Pruning such as shape and routine cutting and thinning is seldom practised, but would probably be beneficial if the best methods were known. More experimentation in this field is needed.

The fruits must be picked when ripe. Otherwise, they deteriorate and losses are severe.

Scientific Name	*A. squamosa*
English	**Sweetsop, sugar apple**
French	pomme-cannelle

Fruits : grey-green, more or less globular, covered in protrudent, rough scales, 5-10 centimetres in diameter

Leaves : lanceolate, blade flat between the veins, 7-10 centimetres long, 3-4 centimetres wide

633

632

635

634

Scientific Name	*A. cherimolia*
English	**Cherimoya**
French	chérimolier

Fruits : green-brown, cordate, light depressions especially on the underside, 8-15 centimetres in diameter

Leaves : oval, sometimes almost rectangular, up to 22 centimetres long and 12 centimetres wide

636

Scientific Name	*A.reticulata*
English	**Bullock's heart apple**
French	coeur de boeuf

Fruits : red, skin nearly smooth, heart-shaped, 7-12 centimetres in diameter,

Leaves : lanceolate, blade convex between the veins, 10-15 centimerters long, 3-5 centimeters wide

Scientific Name	A.senega*lensis*
English	**Wild custard**
French	annone sénégalaise

637

Fruits : yellow, covered with inconspicuous, smooth scales, more or less oval, 3-8 centimetres in diameter

Leaves : lanceolate, dull, prominent venation

SP47 Carambola

The **carambola** is a tree of average height, 5-10 metres, with rather dense foliage. It belongs to the family Oxalidaceae and is a native of tropical Asia.

The pinnate leaves are composed of four to six pairs of leaflets and an odd terminal leaflet **(figure 638)**. The tiny, pink flowers, less than 1 centimetre, are in clusters. The fruits are 5-10 centimetres long, yellow, acutely five-angled or ridged **(figure 639)**. The pulp is acid and full of brown seeds. The ripe fruits are eaten. They are also used like lemons for their juice and to make drinks.

Scientific Name	*Averrhoa Carambola*
English	**carambola**
French	carambolier

638

639

The carambola requires fairly wet growing conditions. It tolerates light shade. The plant is reproduced by seed, and by layering. Propagation by cuttings is suitable for some varieties.

SP48 Cayor cherry

Scientific Name	*Aphania senegalensis*
English	**Cayor cherry**
French	cerisier du Sénégal

The **Cayor cherry (figure 640)** of the family Sapindaceae is a small tree occurring in dry savannas. It has a low, scaly trunk, and a crown with a great many branches.

The leaves are composed of two or four oval leaflets. The flowers, small and green, are arranged in relatively compact inflorescences. The round fruits, 1-2 centimetres in diameter and dark red, are pendant in clusters. They contain a sweet pulp that can be slightly astringent. They are eaten raw.

640

The Cayor cherry grows in full sunlight and withstands drought well. It is self-sown. The fruits are picked in rural settlements wherever the plant grows spontaneously. The tree is noted for its fertility and the quality of its fruits, and would therefore be worth cultivating in gardens and/or orchards.

SP49 Detar

The **detar** is a tree occurring in forests and dry savannas. It belongs to the Leguminosae family. The pinnate leaves are compound and alternate. The leaflets are oval with translucent spots between the veins **(figures 641 and 642)**. The flowers are white, fragrant, and arranged in clusters **(figure 642)**. The rounded fruits are yellow, with fibrous pulp, at least 3-6 centimetres in diameter.

Uses : The fruits are eaten raw or boiled. They are exceptionally rich in vitamins, especially vitamin C **(figure 643)**.

Two species of this tree are often exploited :

- the **detar** *(Detarium senegalensis)* with large fruits, identified by its compound leaves with ten to thirteen leaflets, green on the underside;

641

642

Scientific Name	*Detarium senegalensis*
English	**Detar**
French	détar à gros fruits

Scientific Name	*D. microcarpum*	*D. heudelotianum*
English	**Sweet dattock**	**Bitter dattock**
French	détar à petits fruits	détar amer

- the **sweet dattock** *(Detarium microcarpum)* with small fruits, identified by its compound leaves with seven to ten leaflets, white on the underside.

Another closely related species which is hard to distinguish from the two species mentioned above is the **bitter detar** *(Detarium heudelotianum)* with bitter, poisonous fruits.

Husbandry : Detars usually occur as wild plants, although they can easily be grown from seed. This is done by sowing the stone finger-deep in well-loosened soil. Seed dormancy means that emergence may take a long time.

643

SP50 Monkey guava

Scientific Name	*Diospyros mespeliformis*
English	**Monkey guava, swamp or African ebony**
French	ébénier de l'ouest africain, néflier africain, kaki de brousse

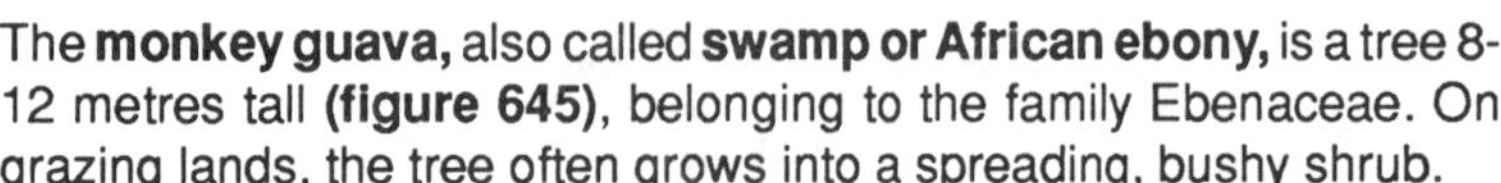

644

645

The **monkey guava,** also called **swamp or African ebony,** is a tree 8-12 metres tall **(figure 645)**, belonging to the family Ebenaceae. On grazing lands, the tree often grows into a spreading, bushy shrub.

The dense foliage is composed of alternate, simple leaves, elongated, about 10 centimetres long, typically brown-pink, at the end of the growing branches. The flowers are white, about 1.5 centimetres long. The male flowers are arranged in clusters, the female flowers are solitary in the leaf axils. The fruits are conical to cylindrical, not more than 3 centimetres long, with a terminal nipple. They are yellow brown when ripe and have four to six blackish seeds **(figure 644)**.

Uses : Its ripe, somewhat acid fruits are the most popular produce, but the leaves are also in demand for animal feed. The wood is of high quality for carpentry and joinery. It turns black like ebony when treated.

Environment : In savanna zones, the monkey guava often grows by temporary pools and streams. It is a good companion tree in flood-retreat fields and gardens and in hedges. However, it also occurs in drier environments, more particularly on rocky hillsides that are cultivated or used for grazing.

Propagation : The monkey guava is propagated by seeds. These are scalded for 5 to 7 minutes in order to hasten germination. The young trees are not easily transplanted, so that sowing on the permanent site is recommended.

646

SP51 Strawberry

Scientific Name	*Fragaria spp.*
English	**Strawberry**
French	fraisier

The **strawberry** is a semi-perennial plant about 20 centimetres high. It is native to Europe and belongs to the family Rosaceae. Strawberry leaves are cordate, regularly serrate, borne on long peduncles. The flowers, about 2 centimetres in diameter, are arranged on erect stems; the petals are white with a yellow centre **(figure 646)**. The fruits are red, fleshy, irregularly conical, 2-5 centimetres long. The skin, glossy and smooth, is incrusted with green-black dots that are actually the seeds **(figure 647)**. The root system is fibrous. Stolons grow on the plant after flowering.

Uses : The fleshy fruits are eaten raw.

Environment : The strawberry is a sun-loving plant, but it needs some shade in very hot weather. It is intolerant of too much rain and also of drought. It requires well-loosened, fertile soil. The strawberry grows mainly in the highland tropics, at over 1000 metres.

Propagation : The strawberry is multiplied by stolons **(figure 352)**, rarely by seed. You should choose stolons stemming straight from the parent plant rather than young shoots produced from stolons.

647

Husbandry : The strawberry is cultivated in pure stands or in association with light-shade crops that do not hamper access to the strawberries at harvest. The planting arrangement can be adapted if necessary. The plants are renewed every year; they are most productive in the first year.

Strawberry plants thrive on soils rich in organic material. Steeping the stolons for a day or two in a little water hastens the growth of the rootlets. The stolons are transplanted, care being taken not to bury the collars. Mulching is maintained at the fruiting stage to stop the fruits from becoming covered with soil and rotting. The stolons that are not going to be used for propagation are cut back.

648

SP52 Cape gooseberry

The **Cape gooseberry** or **Peruvian cherry** from the family Solanaceae is a semi-perennial, bushy plant between 50 centimetres and one metre high. The stem is covered in a soft, white down. The leaves are alternate, cordate, puckered, with bent-back terminal tips and soft pubescence on both sides **(figure 648)**. The flowers are yellow, about one centimetre in diameter, bell-shaped and drooping **(figure 649)**. The fruits are wrapped in thin, hollow membranes, 3-4 centimetres long. They are fleshy, orange, globular, 1-2 centimetres in diameter **(figure 650)**, with many, flat, ivory-coloured seeds about one millimetre long. The plant has a taproot.

Uses : The fruits are eaten raw or stewed.

Environment : The Cape gooseberry thrives in full sunlight and is fairly drought-resistant. It can grow on almost all soils, but is susceptible to waterlogged conditions. It is spontaneous in the highlands.

Propagation : By seed.

Husbandry : The Cape gooseberry is exploited wild, or as a subspontaneous home-garden plant. It is also cultivated in gardens and fields, on its own or with other crops.

Under intensive cultivation, fresh plants are established after two or three growing seasons.

The plants are sown in nursery beds and thinned early. As emergence is often unreliable, the plants that sprout first are selected. After two or three months, they are trimmed and transplanted with a ball of soil. You must keep the crop mulched so that the fruits near the ground are not affected by rain splash. The prostrate varieties are trained on stakes.

Scientific Name	*Physalis peruviana*
English	**Cape gooseberry, Peruvian cherry**
French	groseiller du Cap, coqueret du Pérou, alkékenge coquerelle

649

650

651

652

653

SP53 Mombin

The general heading **mombin** is used here to designate five species. They are : **marvola plum**, **yellow mombin**, **red mombin**, **Golden** or **Otaheite apple**, and ***Trichoscypha ferruginea***. These trees belong to the family Anacardiaceae.

The **marvola plum** is a tree 10-15 metres high, distinguished by its drooping foliage tinged with

Scientific Name	Sclerocarya birrea	Spondias mombin
English	**Marvola plum, cat thorn, kaffir**	**Yellow mombin, hog plum, Ashanti plum**
French	poupartia	prunier mirobolant

Scientific Name	Trichoscypha ferruginea
English	The scientific name is used; **Jamaica** or **Spanish plum**
French	raisin pahouin d'Espagne, casse manguier

Scientific Name	Spondias purpurea	Spondias cytherea
English	**Red mombin, Gambia, Otaheite apple**	**Golden apple,**
French	mombin rouge, prunier	pomme-cythère, casse-manguier

blue **(figure 651)**. The leaves are pinnate with five to ten pairs of small leaflets, 2-3 centimetres long, plus the odd terminal leaflet **(figure 652)**. The silvery hue of the young branches is quite characteristic. The small flowers are borne in clusters at the extremities of the branches. They vary in colour from yellow to red. The male and female flowers are usually borne on separate trees. The fruits, yellow when ripe, are globular and 2-4 centimetres in diameter.

The **yellow mombin** or **hog plum** is a tree of average height, 5-10 metres. It acquires a bushy habit on dry lands. The pinnate leaves are composed of five to ten pairs of leaflets as well as the odd terminal leaflet. They are 5-9 centimetres long, 2-4 centimetres wide, with well-defined veins. The flowers, ranging from white to yellow, grouped at the extremities of the branches, are small, about 1.5 centimetres. The fruits, yellow to brown and oval, form pendant clusters, and are 3-4 centimetres long. The sweet, fleshy pulp contains a stone.

Three species closely related to the marvola plum and the yellow mombin are very common. They are:

- the **red mombin** so called because, in contrast to the yellow mombin, its flowers and fruits are red;
- the **Golden apple**, a tree occurring in wet forest zones. The fruit has a large stone **(figure 653)**;
- ***Trichoscypha ferruginea*** with fruits bright red to pink. These are astringent, sometimes very sour.

Uses : The ripe fruits are eaten raw. The oily kernels of the marvola plum are ground and used in sauces. They yield oil that is sometimes extracted.

Environment : The yellow mombin and, to a lesser extent, the red mombin occur both in forest regions and in dry savannas. The marvola plum is a tree associated with savannas and the semi-arid zones of the Sahel. The Golden apple and *Trichoscypha ferruginea* occur mainly in wet equatorial forests.

Propagation : Mombins are grown from seeds (the stones). The marvola plum can also be reproduced vegetatively, by cuttings from mature stems and by suckers.

654

SP54 Cayor apple

Scientific Name	Parinari macrophylla
English	**Cayor apple, gingerbread plum**
French	pommier du Cayor, parinaire

The **Cayor apple** *(Parinari macrophylla)* belongs to the family Rosaceae. It is a small tree found in dry savannas and characterized by its rounded crown **(figure 654)**.

Its leaves are simple, rounded, leathery, 7-20 centimetres long, with many veins. The flowers, covered in cottonlike felting, grow in terminal racemes and are white. The fruits are grey, rough-skinned, ovoid, not more than 5 centimetres long and 3.5 centimetres wide **(figures 655 and 656)**.

655

There are other species of Parinari with similar characteristics and uses – *Parinari excelsa* with smooth-skinned fruits, and *Parinari curatellifolia* with smaller fruits.

Uses : The ripe fruits are eaten raw. The kernels are eaten raw, grilled, or steamed. Ground kernels are used in sauces (**figure 657**). Oil is extracted from them.

656

657

SP55 Passion Fruit

The genus **Passiflora**, a subdivision of the family Passifloraceae, comprises many species, the fruits of which are edible. Some of these species are wild like the one in **figure 658.** The sepals which first enclose the flower parts and then the fruits later on are noticeably indented and are said to represent the crown of thorns of Jesus Christ. This particular species occurs in savannas and subspontaneous thickets. Its small fruits can be sucked.

The **giant granadilla** *(Passiflora quadrangularis)* and the **passion fruit** *(Passiflora edulis)* are the two commonest garden species.

Passiflora are climbing plants and are therefore good companion plants for hedges and groves, and for big trees.

The leaves of the **giant granadilla** are green, glossy on the upperside, oval and about 20 centimetres long (**figure 660**). The flowers, predominantly purple, are solitary, 5-10 centimetres in diameter. The oblong fruits are green-brown and not more than 5 centimetres in diameter (**figure 661**). The flesh is juicy, yellow in colour, with many brown seeds embedded in translucent pulp.

658

659

The **passion fruit** is different from the giant granadilla in its leaves, palmate with three obovate lobes, and in the colour of its fruits which are purple or yellow, depending on the variety (**figure 659**).

Uses : The fruits are eaten raw.

Environment : Passion fruits do not tolerate waterlogged soils and high precipitation. The plants need to grow on stout supports big enough to let them climb easily. Passion fruit *(P. edulis)* thrives at the higher altitudes.

Propagation : By seed or by mature stem cuttings.

Husbandry : Passion fruits are grown in pure stands on props and trellises, or planted with trees on which they climb. Passion fruits thrive in hedges and on fences near homesteads. They are sometimes trained on housetops and walls.

Although passion fruits can be sown and cuttings planted directly on the permanent site, it is wiser to start with nursery beds. The seedlings need shading for the first few weeks after they emerge. Transplant the young plants when they are 20-30 centimetres long. If the weather is very hot, shade them until they have recovered completely.

Scientific Name	*Passiflora edulis, Passiflora quadrangularis*
English	**Passion fruit, granadilla, giant granadilla, barbadine**
French	maracouja, grenadille, barbadine

Pruning to the desired shape is necessary. Choose one or more main creepers depending on how you intend training the plants, on stakes, on trellises or on the flat. The branches that have fruited are cut back every year. These cuts are designed for intensive production.

Staking or training on trellises is essential. Robust, dead or living supports can be used. Root competition with a living support can be controlled by planting the climbing stems in drums buried at the foot of the tree.

660 661

SP56 Tree tomato

The **tree tomato** belongs to the family Solanaceae and is a native of Latin America. It is a small tree, 3-4 metres high. It generally grows in the highland tropics at 1200 metres or more. It lives for three or four years, and then degenerates **(figure 662)**.

662

663

The bark is green and glossy; the trunk shows prominent leaf scars. The leaves on long peduncles, up to 30 centimetres long, are simple, entire, oval, with a delicate pubescence. The pale pink flowers, 1.5-2 centimetres in diameter, form clusters **(figure 663)**. The fruits, purple to red when ripe, are egg-shaped, 4-6 centimetres long **(figure 664)**. They contain a great many brown seeds scattered in the pulp.

Uses: The ripe fruit is eaten raw, some varieties being more bitter than others.

Environment: The tree tomato is a sun-loving plant. It must have fertile, well-drained soil. It withstands cold and drought fairly well.

Propagation: By seed, though propagation by stem cuttings is also practised.

664

Husbandry: The tree tomato can be interplanted in fields and gardens. The foliage being high and compact, the tree does not give much shade. However, because the tree tomato is short-lived, it is unsuitable for hedges. To maintain high yields, replace the plants after

Scientific Name	*Cyphomandra betacea*
English	**tree tomato**
French	tomate arborescente, prunier du Japon

one or two harvests.

The tree tomato is sown in nursery beds. When the seedlings are about 30 centimetres tall, they are transplanted without delay to well-manured soil. The tree is cut back to ground level every two years, otherwise it degenerates and becomes unproductive. After pruning drastically, select a shoot, two if the tree is vigorous, and remove the others.

Storage : The ripe fruits will easily keep in a cool place for three or four weeks.

SP57 | Lannea

Lannea is a tree belonging to the family Anacardiaceae. It is native to savanna regions and can grow to a height of 15 metres **(figure 665)**.

The alternate leaves are composed of three to seven pairs of lateral leaflets and a terminal leaflet. The leaflets are 8-10 centimetres long **(figure 666)**. The flowers, green to yellow, are arranged in spikes. The fruits are round, about 1 centimetre in diameter, red to purple in colour, and are produced in tight bunches **(figure 667)**.

Two species that are hard to distinguish are commonly exploited :

- *Lannea acida* with inflorescences pendent from the extremities of the branches;

667

665

Scientific Name	*Lannea acida and L. microcarpa*
English	The scientific name is used in both cases
French	raisinier acide et raisinier à petits fruits

666

- ***Lannea microcarpa*** with inflorescences that blend in with the leaves, and with dark, almost black fruits.

Uses : The fresh fruits are eaten raw. The young leaves and the gum exuded by the trunk are occasionally added to sauces. The plant is used medicinally in several ways, especially for treating dysentery, eye complaints, bilharzia and haemorrhoids. Ropes are made from the bark fibres.

Environment : *Lannea* stands up well to drought and bush fires. It is more productive in relatively moist soils.

Propagation and husbandry : These trees can easily be propagated from seed. The seeds are sometimes softened in water to hasten germination. However, *Lannea* species are usually found as wild plants in fields, pastures and compounds where they fit in well. They are often seen in the cropping fields alongside the shea butter and the African locust bean.

SP58 Black plum

The black plum from the family Verberaceae is a tree varying in height from 8 to 20 metres or more. It is characterized by dense foliage, dark in colour, that extends from a clean-cut trunk. The leaves are composed of five to seven leaflets whose petioles all spread from the same base and are palmate in appearance. The leaves are dark green, shiny on the upperside and pale green on the underside where the veins stand out. The leaflets are variable in size, 12-15 centimetres at the most, although the leaflets of young plants may be longer **(figure 668)**. The flowers are white to yellow. The fruits, roughly ovoid, 2-3 centimetres long, change from green to black as they ripen **(figure 669)**. Maturity periods are often staggered and fruit production is slow.

668

669

The black plum is spontaneous in wet savanna regions, in dry and in river forests, by streams and pools; this shows that the tree likes a wet environment. The black plum is commonly planted in gardens, orchards and compounds, but less frequently in the main fields. It is exploited for the leaves eaten as a vegetable. The fruits are eaten raw or made into a fermented drink. The tree also supplies raw materials such as dies, timber, and ash for making soap.

The black plum is easily multiplied from seed. Steeping in water helps emergence.

Scientific Name	*Vitex doniana*
English	**Black plum, West African plum**
French	prune de savane

Chapter 24

Seeds, nuts and kernels

SP59 Cashew

The **cashew** tree belongs to the family Anacardiaceae and is native to Latin America. It is 10-15 metres high; the branches, which are dense and spreading, may almost reach the ground **(figure 670)**.

The leaves, entire, thick and glossy, are oval-shaped, 10-20 centimetres long and 5-10 centimetres wide. The small, yellow flowers hang in terminal clusters on the branches of the current year. The fruits consist of two parts – the cashew apple, which is really the swollen peduncle of the fruit, and the cashew nut containing a kernel rich in oil **(figure 671)**. The cashew tree has a very deep taproot with vigorous lateral roots.

Uses : The kernel of the cashew nut is eaten as a delicacy, or added to sauces. The kernel also yields oil that is sometimes made into a kind of butter. The cashew apple is juicy and astringent; it is eaten fresh or dried. The young leaves and shoots are occasionally used for flavouring stews.

The cashew also has various domestic and industrial uses :

- an oil called CNSL (cashew nut shell liquid) is extracted from the crushed shells;
- an insect repellent is prepared with the crushed shells to which bark gum and an insecticide are added;
- a dye is extracted from the bark and the leaves;

671

Scientific Name	Anacardium occidentale
English	**Cashew**
French	anacardier, pommier cajou

670

- the produce of the tree has various medicinal uses - the gum for warts, CNSL for wounds, and the leaves for burns.

Environment : The cashew requires deep soil which the roots can penetrate freely. It shows good resistance to drought and impoverished soils, but is less productive in these conditions. The cashew grows in full sunlight.

Propagation : The cashew is propagated by seeds and by layering. Mature stem cuttings can also be used. Approach grafting with scions taken from terminal shoots gives good results.

Husbandry : The cashew is grown in orchards either on its own or with other plants. It is sometimes planted in cropping fields and is widely spaced, since the foliage and the root system compete with other plants. In gardens and fields, the cashew is best planted well-spaced out in hedgerows.

Cashews are propagated from seeds that should be soaked for 48 hours or pregerminated in a bed of moist sand. The seeds are sown on the permanent site, with three seeds per planting hole. The most vigorous seedling of the three is selected soon after emergence, the other two are discarded.

The cashew needs to be tended carefully during the early months after germination, so all the practices that preserve soil moisture are recommended – mulching, weeding, hoeing, watering, etc.

Shape and root pruning are required when cashews are planted in orchards or in mixed gardens.

SP60 Kola

The **kola** belonging to the family Sterculiaceae is a tree widely distributed in gardens and forests of the wet tropics. It is between 10-20 metres high. There are many, similar species of kola. *Cola nitida* is the most exploited of these species and is the one described here.

The leaves are entire, simple, alternate, lanceolate, dark green and about 15 centimetres long **(figure 672)**. The flowers are ivory-coloured, often veined or with red markings. The male and hermaphrodite (bisexual) flowers vary in size : the male flowers are about 2 centimetres in diameter **(figure 673)**, the others 3-4 centimetres. The fruits are pods 10-20 centimetres long, dented, and roughly digitate. They contain seeds which are white to red in colour, often pink, to 5 centimetres long. **Figure 674** shows the young fruits; **figure 675 shows** the ripe fruits and nuts.

The various species are distinguished mainly by the shape of the leaves and the fruits.

Uses : The bitter seed is chewed and is appreciated as a stimulant. Small quantities are sometimes used in dishes specially prepared for ceremonial occasions, for example, in the Dioula region in Burkina Faso. There is a large trade in kola nuts.

Environment : The kola grows in wet forest zones, and is susceptible to wind and drought. It thrives on light soils, rich in humus.

Propagation : By seed, though layering is also feasible. Good varieties can be multiplied by splice and approach grafting, but budding is difficult.

Husbandry : The kola is harvested from forests where it grows wild. It is often planted in orchards and in cocoa plantations, less frequently in coffee groves. The tree may form a midway storey or reach the uppermost canopy.

Kola trees are sown in nursery beds and transplanted with a ball of soil when 0.5 metres high. Growth is slow in the early years, especially if mulching and weeding are neglected. The first real harvest is in the

672

673

Scientific Name	*Cola acuminata, C. anomala, C. nitida, C. verticillata*
English	**Abata kola, Bamenda kola, Gbanja kola, Owe kola...**
French	colatier

675

674

seventh or eighth year, but the tree only comes to full production in about the twentieth year. Cuts in the bark are widely practised in Nigeria on ten-year old trees; these incisions are said to induce productivity **(figure 213)**.

SP61 Dika nut

Scientific Name	Irvingia gabonensis
English	**Dika nut, bush mangolo**
French	manguier sauvage, dika

The **dika nut** is a tree occurring in wet forest regions, and is up to 20 metres or more in height **(figure 676)**. It belongs to the family Irvingiaceae. The bark is thin and silvery-grey. The leaves are simple, elongated, 6-10 centimetres long, leathery and shiny on both surfaces. The flowers are brown, arranged in small inflorescences about 4-6 centimetres long.

The fruits, often abundant, are 5-7 centimetres in diameter **(figure 677)**. They are green, tending to yellow, and look like small mangoes. The pulp is yellow and fibrous. The stone, which is fairly hard, contains one flattened kernel that splits very easily in two **(figure 678)**. The tree has a deeply penetrating taproot.

Uses : The fruit pulp is eaten like that of mango. However, the kernels are more highly esteemed because, when they are heated, they yield a thick oil that congeals when cold but melts when warmed. The kernels are also ground to make a thick paste for thickening stews, in the same way as the groundnut and njansan (see page 328). Dika paste gives a characteristic aroma to cooked dishes. The paste can be made into balls and will keep for a year or two after being sun-dried. In Cameroun, the bark is used to make remedies for diarrhoea.

676

677

678

Environment : The dika nut thrives in wet forest regions where it grows towards full light. The tree's productivity seems to depend on this exposure.

Propagation : By seed (the stones). Layering may be possible.

Husbandry : Exploitation is more or less limited to spontaneous trees, although the dika nut seems suitable for interplanting in hedges, wooded areas, mixed orchards and groves.

On well-exposed sites, the dika nut comes into bearing from the seventh year when it is about 10 metres in height.

SP62 Calabash nutmeg

Scientific Name	*Monodora myristica*
English	**Calabash nutmeg**
French	faux muscadier
Yoruba	chacha bakon, sassa bakon (?)

The **calabash nutmeg** is a tree occurring in wet forest zones where it is frequently seen in fields and hedges. It belongs to the family Annonaceae **(figure 679)**.

The leaves are broad and elongated and arranged in terminal clusters of five to six **(figure 680)**. The flowers are solitary, on pedicels up to 25 centimetres in length, with six purple petals, three inside, three outside. The fruits are large, 15-20 centimetres in diameter; they are green, but turn red at the onset of the dry season. A young fruit is seen in **figure 680**. The nuts are brown, oval to oblong. The nuts are shelled to extract the kernel that is very aromatic and is covered with parallel streaks. Nuts ready for the market are shown in **figure 681**.

The calabash nutmeg produces dense shade and is therefore not suitable for planting in fields. However, it is a fine shade tree in villages and hedges, in association with other trees.

Uses : The nuts are extracted from fruits that have fallen to the ground. The nuts are washed to remove their sticky pulp and then dried. They are ground for use in stews.

Propagation : By seed. Germination is slow.

679

680

681

SP63 Akee apple

The **akee apple** of the family Sapindaceae is a tree, 10-25 metres high, occurring in dry forest regions. The foliage, supported by a stout trunk, is massive and dense **(figure 682)**.

The pinnate leaves are composed of three to five pairs of leaflets about 15 centimetres long, oval in shape, and acuminate **(figure 683)**. They are dark-green and shiny on the upper side. The small flowers, less than 1 centimetre, are green-white, arranged in racemes at the leaf axils. The fruits are pink to red, oval, three-angled, 5-6 centimetres long or more at times. They contain one to three black, shiny seeds, surmounted by a fleshy, ivory-coloured aril **(figure 684)**.

Scientific Name	*Blighia sapida*
English	**Akee apple**
French	ris de veau, figuier fisan
Yoruba	lisse

682

Uses : The aril, rich in oil and fragrant, is used in stews. The other parts of the fruit are not edible.

Environment : The akee apple reacts badly to drought and to very heavy rainfall. On the other hand, it adapts to a wide variety of soils.

Propagation : Mainly by seed. Layering appears to give good results.

Husbandry : The akee apple is spontaneous in forest zones. It is commonly planted in orchards and on the edge of fields. As the foliage gives much shade, the trees must be widely spaced when planted in fields.

683

The ripe fruits fall without spoiling the consumable part and the produce is harvested by picking up the fruits as they become available.

The akee apple is sown directly in the field or in nursery beds. It is transplanted with a ball of soil. The tree comes into bearing four or five years after sowing.

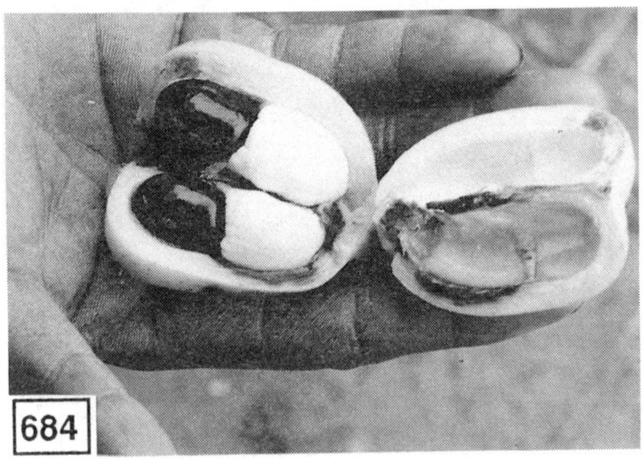

684

SP64 Shea butter

Scientific Name	*Butyrospermum parkii or, Vittelaria paradoxa*
English	**Shea butter**
French	karité

The **shea butter** belonging to the family Sapotaceae is a tree widely distributed in West African savannas. It is usually 10-15 metres high.

The bark is thick, corky and deeply cracked. The leaves, leathery, glossy and 12-15 centimetres long, are borne on long petioles of up to 15 centimetres **(figure 685)**. Like the leaves, the yellow-green flowers grow in bunches. They appear in the dry season, on the tips of the branches,

685

after the leaf fall. The fruits, green-yellow in colour are oval-shaped and up to 8 centimetres long by 4 centimetres wide. They are fleshy and contain a smooth, brown nut, 2-4 centimetres long, with a rough scar at the top **(figure 686)**.

686

The tree exudes a white latex under the bark.

Uses : The sweet pulp of the ripe fruits is eaten. The kernel yields an oil which is solid at air temperature. This shea butter oil is used in all sorts of ways – in cooking, for fuel, and in the preparation of soaps and ointments. The wood, hard and termite-proof, is valued in the carpentry trade. The wood also produces good charcoal.

Environment : The shea butter likes moist soils with plenty of humus. It adapts to poor, even stony, soils but then becomes less productive. It prefers open, airy sites exposed to the sun. The shea butter is therefore not suited to densely-cultivated orchards where it might be shaded by other trees, even partial shade must be avoided. However, the shea butter thrives in cropping fields.

The tree is intolerant of waterlogged soils, but it withstands fire due to its thick, corky bark.

Propagation : By seed, although propagation by suckers and stem cuttings is also practised.

Husbandry : Subspontaneous trees are exploited in fields, pastures and forests where they are generally preserved. The shea butter is also planted widely spaced, in the main fields. But the tree should not be planted in hedges or wooded areas if the aim is to obtain good fruit yields. The ripe, fallen fruits are picked up.

The fresh seeds are sown four to five centimetres deep in nursery beds. The seedlings are transplanted with a ball of soil, when about 40 centimetres tall. A generous amount of compost or well-decomposed manure in the planting hole will contribute greatly to the development of the tree, usually a slow-starter in the early years.

It is essential to mulch and weed the tree and protect it from fires and browsing animals until it has time to become firmly established. This takes four or five years.

The first fruit harvests are late, twelve to fifteen years after planting, and are disappointing. Yields are abundant from the twentieth year, at the earliest, and often only at forty or fifty years.

SP65 Orere

Scientific Name	*Baillonella toxisperma*
English	**Orere, djave, adjab**
French	moabi, oréré

The **orere** *(Baillonella toxisperma)* is a tree of the family Sapotaceae occurring in wet forest zones. It can grow to a height of 50 metres **(figure 687)**. The trunk is tall and straight and is surmounted by a dense crown.

The leaves are simple and 25-30 centimetres long **(figure 688)**. They form rosettes at the extremities of the branches. The tree sheds its leaves every year.

687

688

The small flowers are arranged in small, compact bunches at the tips of the flowering branches. They appear after leaf fall, that is, at the end of the dry season or at the onset of the rains.

The fruits are globular, about the size of an orange, and the pulp is edible. The fruits contain a nut with an edible kernel, rich in oil. The nut

689

is smooth and shiny with a big, rough scar, grey in colour, along one side **(figure 689).**

Uses : An oil much in demand is extracted from orere nuts. The oil cakes are used by fishermen for stupifying fish in rivers and streams. The wood of the orere is of high quality and is appreciated by foresters.

Husbandry : The fallen fruits are gathered from the base of trees growing wild in the forest or protected during clearing operations. The orere is said to be an indicator of fertile soils. It is domesticated in some regions.

Propagation : The tree is grown from nuts sown 4-5 centimetres deep, and emergence may take five or six months if the nuts are not pre-treated; soaking and scarification are suitable methods. Seedlings are transplanted to the permanent site at the start of the rainy season.

The tree, with its elevated habit and lightly-shading foliage, is a good association plant in cropping fields, plantations and hedges.

The orere is slow to fruit, but once it comes into production, yields are abundant and constant.

SP66 African locust bean

The **African locust bean** belonging to the family Leguminosae is a large tree, with a very broad, sometimes pendent crown, supported by a trunk usually short and thickset **(figure 690)**. There are two botanically related species : *Parkia biglobosa* occurring in the Sahel, and *Parkia clappertoniana* occurring typically in wet savanna regions. However, the species are not differentiated in this section.

The leaves are compound, and the leaflets themselves are composed of many, simple, smaller

690

691

693

692

Scientific Name	*Parkia biglobosa and P. clappertoniana*
English	**African locust bean, twoball, nitta tree**
French	arbre à farine, mimosa pourpre
Yoruba	tokoro

leaflets about 1.5 centimetres long by 0.5 centimetres wide. The leaflets are subrectangular with rounded tips **(figure 691)**. The flowers, red in colour, like drooping balls, appear in the dry season after the leaf fall. The fruits are long, narrow pods and flattened, brown or black when ripe. They contain black seeds embedded in yellow pulp **(figure 692)**.

Uses : The yellow pulp of the fruits is rich in carbohydrates and is like flour. It is used in stews. The fermented seeds are used to prepare a condiment rich in protein; this spice is called soumbala or mustard.

The bark and the fruits, with or without seeds, are used to prepare dyes, tannins, narcotics for fishing, etc.

The leaves and the bark are also used in remedies for treating Guinea worm, filiariasis, skin infections and burns.

Environment : The African locust bean is a light-loving tree. It requires deep, well-drained soil, and can withstand drought reasonably well once it is firmly established.

Propagation : The tree is propagated from seed, though suckers are also used. Dormancy is broken by scalding the seeds for 5 minutes.

Husbandry : Generally speaking, the foliage of the African locust bean does not give much shade. The tree is frequently planted in the main cereal fields or in orchards where it forms the uppermost canopy. It fertilizes the ground below and roundabout its crown.

The tree shades pastures. The leaves and pods provide valuable cattle feed.

Growth is fairly slow. The seedlings need a lot of attention. They have to be kept for a year or two in nursery beds, in loose, fertile soil, and must be watered regularly. When the young trees are transplanted to their permanent site, they have to be protected for some years from fire and browsing animals.

The tree first comes into bearing between the eighth and the tenth year, but yields are low until the twentieth year.

Storage : The dry pods keep a long time. The flour (pulp) and the balls of fermented, dried seeds **(figure 693)**.will keep in dry storage for some months.

SP67 Cowpea

The **cowpea** is a seasonal legume. There are many varieties of cowpea – dwarf, climbing, erect, prostrate, bushy and creeping. This explains why the habit of the plant is so variable.

The leaves, alternate and trifoliate, are up to 20 centimetres long. They are dark green, sometimes slightly hairy **(figure 694)**. The flowers are normally yellow, but they can also be white or violet. They are about 2 centimetres long, arranged in pairs on the flowering stems. The fruits are pods 12-25 centimetres long with seeds about 1 centimetre in diameter, variable in colour, white or speckled. The plant has a taproot system.

Uses : The whole plant is edible. The leaves, young shoots and immature pods are cooked and eaten like spinach. The cooked seeds can be served as a staple food or as a side dish.

Environment : The cowpea is a versatile, highly adaptable plant. It is drought resistant and even grows in poor soils. It is intolerant of very wet or badly drained soils.

Propagation : By seed only.

Husbandry : The cowpea is widely cultivated in the main cereal fields, along with millet, sorghum or maize. It occupies the lowest storey, spreading along the ground or climbing up the cereal stems.

Scientific Name	*Vigna unguiculata*
English	**Cowpea**
French	niébé

694

In home and commercial gardens, it is mainly exploited for its leaves. When this is the case, the cowpea is usually sown at the end of the rainy season, sometimes in a mixture with a crop such as eggplant or tomato which has a longer vegetative cycle. The cowpea is then harvested at the start of the dry season when the nursery-raised vegetables are ready for transplanting. This cultural practice makes the most of the last rains. Moreover, the trash left over from the cowpea crop, especially the roots, fertilizes the soil and benefits the transplanted vegetables that occupy the former cowpea beds. The dwarf varieties with a short or a very short cycle, from fifty to seventy days, make full use of the moisture remaining in the soil after irrigation or after flooding. These varieties are able to yield a harvest without supplementary watering.

Cowpea is sown directly on the permanent site, dibbled or in rows. Where possible, it is earthed up two or three weeks after emergence.

Five or six weeks after sowing, the leaves are harvested, either by picking them singly, or by uprooting the whole plant. Cutting back the the plants is said to cause damage, but the effects of this practice need to be tested on the varieties cultivated.

SP68 Njansan

Scientific Name	*Ricinodendron africanum or, R. heudelotii*
English	**Njansan**
French	njansan

The **njansan** belonging to the family Euphorbiaceae is a tall tree occurring in wet forest regions. The trunk is cylindrical, and supports layers of branches, each of which grows and spreads from the same point. The uppermost layer can be seen in **figure 695**.

The bark is scaly and sometimes gnarled **(figure 696)**.

696

695

The leaves are deeply lobed, sometimes compound with three to seven lobes, on long petioles. The leaves are 6-25 centimetres in length **(figure 697)**. The tree sheds its leaves in the dry season.

The tree is dioecious, i.e. the male and female flowers are borne on separate plants. The flowers on the male trees are in large clusters, 30 centimetres long; the clusters on the female trees are smaller. The white petals are joined and are about one centimetre in diameter.

The fruits are yellow-green, about 3 centimetres, with two or three loculi (cavities), and two to three black nuts in a very hard shell. The fruits, a few nuts and their kernels are shown in **figures 698 and 699**.

Uses : The kernels are yellow-ochre in colour and shiny, and have culinary uses. They can be eaten grilled or ground into a paste and used as a thickening agent in the same way as groundnuts. Oil can also be extracted from the kernels. The bark is sometimes used in remedies for wounds. In wet regions, the little white mushrooms that grow on the trunks of felled trees are considered to be a choice food.

Husbandry : The njansan is usually exploited as a wild plant. However, in some regions, it is being taken into domestication.

The tree is propagated from seeds (the nuts) that are removed from the decayed fruits and sown in shaded nurseries. As the nut-shells are very hard, emergence takes place many months after sowing, but, after that, the plant grows rapidly. The seedlings can be transplanted when they

697

698

699

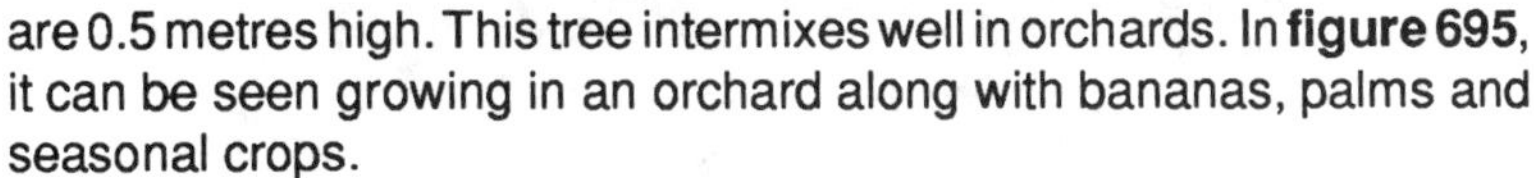

are 0.5 metres high. This tree intermixes well in orchards. In **figure 695**, it can be seen growing in an orchard along with bananas, palms and seasonal crops.

Storage : The nuts are removed from the decayed fruits that are picked up under the trees. They are plunged into boiling water for well over an hour in order to soften the shells. The kernels removed from the split nuts are smoked, and will then keep for years in dry storage.

SP69 Almond nut

The **almond nut** is a forest tree forming a half-way storey and is therefore considered a shade tree. The leaves, 10-30 centimetres long, are leathery, shiny and oval **(figure 701)**. The fruits are globular and green, turning black when ripe **(figure 700)**. They are 3-4 centimetres in diameter with a very hard stone.

Uses : The kernel is used to make very nourishing cakes. Ground almonds are used in stews in the same way as groundnuts for which they are a good substitute.

The wood is extremely hard, and withstands termites and rodents destructive to wooden structures. It is excellent for building purposes and weathers well.

700

701

Scientific Name	*Coula edulis*
English	**Almond nut, African walnut, Gabon nut**
French	noyer du Gabon, noisetier sauvage

Husbandry : The tree occurs spontaneously in wet forests, and is preserved during clearing operations.

Seedlings often grow at the foot of adult trees and can easily be transplanted. During the early years of growth, the tree is intolerant of full sunlight, and therefore develops best when planted under the protective canopy of other trees.

SP70 Pigeon pea

Pigeon pea is a legume (Leguminosae family) of variable habit. The plant is either an annual herb, dense, under one metre tall, or a perennial bush, 1.5-2 metres, sometimes even 4 metres high **(figure 702)**.

The leaves are composed of three leaflets that are lanceolate, sometimes hairy and about 6 centimetres long **(figure 704)**. The flowers are purple or yellow, often yellow and veined with another colour. They are 2 centimetres long, on erect stems in the leaf axils. The fruit is a pod with depressions, beaked, with two to eight seeds about one centimetre in diameter, beige to purple, sometimes grey **(figure 703)**. The plant develops a strong taproot.

Uses : The green seeds and sometimes the immature pods are eaten as a vegetable. The ripe seeds are cooked and eaten as a main dish like beans, or as a side dish with cereals or tubers. The leaves provide excellent fodder.

Environment : The pigeon pea is very drought resistant and adapts to a variety of soils. It does not withstand excess moisture.

Propagation : By seed only for the annual varieties. The perennial varieties can also be propagated from stem shoots and cuttings.

Husbandry : Pigeon pea can be interplanted successfully with most seasonal crops. It is often grown as a hedging plant. Pigeon pea is believed to improve soil fertility, and in wet regions from Nigeria to Ghana, it is cultivated on fallow lands with this aim in mind. The seasonal varieties are an excellent green manure, and the perennial varieties supply valuable fertilizing mulch.

Pigeon pea is sown directly in planting holes. Growth is slow at first, but when the plant is well established, it requires little care. There are a

702

704

703

Scientific Name	*Cajanus cajan var. flavus (seasonal varieties)*
	Cajanus cajan var. bicolor (perennial varieties)
English	**Pigeon pea, red gram, Congo pea, no-eye pea**
French	pois d'Angole, pois Congo
Yoruba	otimi

great many varieties, some of which reach maturity less than six months after sowing, and others that take over a year. The perennial varieties respond well to all kinds of pruning.

SP71 Annato

The **annato** of the family Bixaceae is a very bushy shrub, 2-5 metres high. It is a native of Latin America and now occurs in savanna zones in Africa **(figure 705)**. The leaves, which are cordate and acuminate, are about 15 centimetres long by 12 centimetres wide **(figure 706)**. The flowers have five petals which are white or pink, sometimes notched at the tips, and numerous violet stamens **(figure 707)**. They are about 5 centimetres in diameter, in terminal clusters. The fruits, green to red, covered in thick spines, are up to 5 centimetres long **(figure 708)**. When ripe, the fruit capsules open like a crocodile's mouth. They contain roughly thirty red seeds, pyramidal in shape and about 0.5 centimetres high.

Uses : The seeds, crushed or ground, are used in sauces and are a food colourant. Annato dye, dark red in colour, is obtained by steeping the seeds in water. The dye is used for colouring cloth and wood, and for painting the skin.

705

706

707

708

Scientific Name	*Bixa orellana*
English	**Annato**
French	ro(u)couyer

Environment : The annatto grows on a variety of soils and is fairly drought resistant. It is often cultivated as a compound shrub, on its own or as a bushy hedging plant. It blends well into the intermediate, shrubby layer in mixed orchards.

Propagation : By seed, by stem cuttings, and by layering branches which touch the ground.

Husbandry : The annato is sown in nursery beds and transplanted when about 40 centimetres tall. The plant comes to bearing in the second or third year after planting. Shape pruning and thinning are needed in order to maintain production and to let the plant thrive in the company of seasonal crops.

SP72 Sesame and bungu

Sesame plants belonging to the family Pedaliaceae are seasonal herbs, 1-1.5 metres tall, rarely more, with an erect or a bushy habit. Two species are widely distributed : white sesame *(Sesamum indicum)* and black sesame *(Sesamum radiatum)* **(figure 709)**.

The leaves are variable in shape depending on their position. At the top of the stems, they are simple, lanceolate, 4-7 centimetres long, on short petioles. Elsewhere on the plant, they are more or less lobed, sometimes palmate, irregularly serrate, 10-15 centimetres long, borne on petioles 4-5 centimetres long.

The flowers are of varying colour – yellow, white, pink, sometimes purple, 3-4 centimetres long and shaped like a long tubular bell. The fruits are cylindrical, 1-3 centimetres long, with numerous seeds variable in colour, white, yellow, brown, red or black.

Unlike white sesame, the fruits of black sesame have a terminal beak split in two. As a rule, white sesame seeds are smooth and pale in colour, whereas black sesame seeds usually have dark streaks.

Bungu is a species very similar to sesame **(figure 710)**, although it is a much smaller plant, normally less than 0.5 metres tall. The fruits are flattened, U-shaped, with two divergent terminal nipples **(figure 711)**.

709

Uses : The leaves and young shoots of bungu and sometimes of sesame are used as a vegetable base in stews and give a sticky consistency. The seeds are used to make what are called seed stews. The seeds yield a multi-purpose oil; it is used, for example, in cooking, as a lubricant and for lightning, and as a skin preparation.

Environment : Sesame adapts to a wide variety of soils provided they are well drained. The plants withstand drought well but are intolerant of shade.

Propagation : By seed only.

Husbandry : Sesame is usually cultivated in pure stands in the cropping fields in the first or second year of the cultural cycle, sometimes in little clearings in cereal fields. They have poor ability to compete with other plants in the early stages of growth. Their sowing calendar is very flexible. The fruits must be picked as soon as they are ripe in order to avoid seed shedding.

710

711

Bungu is a plant grown in gardens, in a mixture with other vegetables, often as an edging plant. It is also cultivated in tuber fields between the mounds. Its cultural cycle varies from four to six months depending on the varieties and the time of sowing. It is subspontaneous in the whole of West Africa.

Scientific Name	*Ceratotheca sesamoides*
English	**Bungu**
French	boungou, tambacounda

Scientific Name	*Sesamum indicum and S. radiatum*
English	**Sesame, beniseed, gingelly simsim**
French	sésame

Sesame and bungu are sown broadcast, although sowing in drills, on mounds or on ridges is preferable on soils that are clayey or badly drained. Weeding and thinning soon after emergence are required. These plants are harvested at maturity.

Chapter 25

Palms

712

713

Six palms are included in this chapter: date, dum and oil palm, coconut, raffia and African fan palm. With a few exceptions, they share the following characteristics :

- a cylindrical trunk, unbranched, sometimes hollow, its height dependent on the activity of the terminal bud;
- huge leaves, palmate or composed of numerous leaflets;
- small flowers, normally unisexual, crowded in pendant inflorescences borne in the leaf axils;
- fruits usually composed of a nut, a shell, and pulp, variably fleshy and fibrous, and a kernel;
- multiple uses.

SP73 Date palm

The **date palm** is a tree growing to 20 metres in height, occurring in arid regions with very sandy soils. It is characterized by its many leaves pointing slightly upwards, with leaflets 20-40 centimetres long **(figure 712)**. The fruits are red brown in colour and 3-8 centimetres long **(figure 713)**. The date palm is dioecious.

Uses : Its uses are multiple :

- the very sweet fruits are eaten fresh or dried. The fruit stone contains a kernel that is sometimes used in stews;
- the wood, durable, termite- and rot-proof, is widely used for building purposes – for framework, bridges, water conduits, etc.;
- the fibres obtained from the leaves are used for all sorts of domestic products, for example, basketwork, brooms, and padding.

Environment: The date palm is exceptionally resistant to high temperatures and dry atmospheric conditions; it adapts to a variety of soils provided there is moisture in the deeper layers. It also withstands saline soil and water. The date palm is a shade tree ideally suited for growing in gardens and orchards in desert and Sahel regions. It is propagated by sowing the nuts or from suckers.

Full production is obtained about five to six years after planting. One male tree for about thirty female trees is enough to ensure natural fertilization.

Fruit production is increased by artificial pollination, i.e. cutting some male flowers and shaking them over the female flowers so that the pollen comes in contact with the pistils.

Scientific Name	*Phoenix dactylifera*
English	**Date palm**
French	dattier

SP74 Dum palm

Scientific Name *Hyphaene thebaica*
English **dum palm, doum palm, gingerbread palm**
French palmier doum

714

The **dum palm**, often called doum palm, is common in dry regions and is distinctive because it has a branched stem that divides into an even number of secondary stems **(figure 714)**. Its leaves are palmate like those of the African fan palm, but smaller. The fruits are more or less globular **(figure 715)**, pale brown, shiny, about 5 centimetres along the side and on short, thick peduncles, about 8 millimetres long

Uses : Like other palms, the dum is used in numerous ways. The ripe fruits are eaten raw; the buds are eaten raw or cooked like palm cabbage; the dried, powdered fruits are used as spices.

715

The wood is durable, and known for its solidity. Fibres are obtained from the leaves and the roots. The wood as a fuel is a source of great heat.

SP75 Oil palm

The **oil palm** occurs in savannas and in wet forests almost everywhere on the African continent, provided there is sufficient soil moisture and exposure to sunlight **(figures 716 and 717)**. The oil palm can stand temporary waterlogging.

Uses : The various ways in which the oil palm is used have already been described in Chapter 1 (page 26). Its uses are numerous as for most palms.

Propagation : This is by seed only. The seeds must necessarily be subjected to heat to ensure germination, for example, in ashes or over a flame (In a germinator maintained at 39° C, the process might take anything up to three months).

The oil palm is established in orchards and plantations. In both cases, it is usually interplanted with seasonal crops. The tall varieties fit in well with other plants in fields and mixed orchards. The same cannot be said of the dwarf varieties although these are much more easily harvested and yield more oil.

716

717

Husbandry : Many **cultural practices** encourage the growth and productivity of the oil palm. These

Scientific Name *Elaeis guineensis*
English **Oil palm**
French palmier à huile

include weeding and hoeing, superficial tillage of the soil under the foliage, and applications of organic manure. To obtain good oil yields, remove the older leaves which have no fruits in their axils.

718

Scientific Name	*Cocos nucifera*
English	**Coconut**
French	cocotier

SP76 Coconut

The **coconut** is a large tree 20-30 metres in height characterized by its single, unbranched stem, often curving downwards **(figure 718)**. The trunk swells at the base, usually revealing countless adventitious roots stripped bare by the passage of time. Male and female flowers are on the same tree but in separate inflorescences. The fruit is a hard nut, 10-20 centimetres in diameter, in a fibrous envelope.

There are dwarf and tall varieties.

Uses : The nuts are eaten fresh or grilled. Oil is obtained from the dried endosperm of the nut. The residues obtained after expressing this oil provide cakes called copra; this is a valuable food for cattle. The leaves and stems are used like those of the oil palm.

Environment : The coconut prefers sandy soils; it tolerates saline soils in coastal regions but it must have adequate moisture. The coconut requires relatively high temperatures and a high atmospheric humidity and exposure to sunlight.

This palm is propagated by sowing the nut. The top of the nut can be split to quicken emergence.

The coconut is cultivated in orchards, or in plantations in pure stands. It is intolerant of shade in orchards. Like other palms, it can easily be interplanted with seasonal crops.

719

Scientific Name	*Raphia spp.*
English	**Raffia palm**
French	palmier raphia

SP77 Raffia palms

There are many kinds of **raffia palms** which are so alike as to be confusing. Some species are only found in wet forest swamps, whereas others thrive in highland regions. Raffia palms have a typically short trunk (these palms are sometimes stemless), and exceptionally long leaves, up to 15 metres in length, arranged in bunches **(figure 720)**.

Uses : Raffia palms are used in various ways. The sweet sap is tapped to make the highly regarded raffia wine; the fruits of some species yield oil **(figure 719)**. The scaly envelope of the fruit is used as a bitter

720

condiment in stews, sometimes instead of the cola nut. The white parasitic worms which live on the fruits are considered to be a delicacy.

The leaves and dried fruits are used by craftsmen in many ways – for weaving, basketry and ornaments, as well as for building.

Environment : Raffia palms prefer moist soils, and even tolerate waterlogged land and swamps. They usually respond well to shade, even to the fairly dense shade of the taller plants by which they are dominated.

Propagation : Raffia palms are usually propagated by seed but some species can be propagated by suckers.

SP78 African fan palm

The **African fan palm**, up to 25 metres in height, is common in savanna regions **(figure 721)**. It is recognized by its palmate leaves with petioles, 2 to 3.5 metres long. The male and female flowers are green, borne on separate (dioecious) plants. The globular fruits, 10-20 centimetres in diameter and green-orange in colour, hang in long bunches under the leafy crown **(figure 722)**.

Uses : The oily pulp of the fruit is eaten fresh. The seeds and sometimes the pith which is rich in carbohydrates are added to stews. The terminal shoots are a delicious vegetable called palm cabbage, but their removal kills the tree. The young, freshly germinated shoots are also cultivated and eaten as a vegetable.

721

722

Scientific Name	Borassus aethiopicum
English	**African fan palm**
French	palmier rônier

The base of the terminal bud is pierced in order to tap a very sweet drink that is left to ferment and gives palm wine.

The wood, hard, termite- and rot-proof, is highly regarded in the building trade – for frames, scaffolding, roofing and piping. The leaves are the main raw material for many handicrafts such as basketwork, thatching, and roping for nets.

Medicinal uses include remedies for sore throats, bronchitis and skin ulcers.

Environment : The African fan palm is intolerant of the slightest shade. It needs plenty of superficial soil moisture.

Propagation : By seed only.

Husbandry : The African fan palm grows spontaneously in moderately dry savanna zones. It is subspontaneous and preserved or cultivated in the main cereal fields and homestead orchards where it forms the uppermost canopy.

As a rule, the sap for palm wine is tapped from female trees at least fifteen years old. This practice is harmful and sometimes fatal for the tree in regions where the rainfall is less than 700 or 800 millimetres per annum.

The pregerminated fruit is planted in soil that has been deeply ploughed or hoed and well broken up. It is a good idea to earth up the plant in the early years. Since growth is slow to begin with, it is better not to remove the leaves of plants until the fifth year after planting, nor to extract the sap till the tenth year.

Chapter 26

Bulb and root vegetables

Scientific Names	
Garlic	*Allium sativum*
Onion	*Allium cepa*
Shallot	*Allium ascalonicum*
Chives	*Allium Schoenoprasum*

SP79 Garlic, onion and shallot

Garlic, onion, shallot and chives are plants belonging to the family Alliaceae. They are about 40 centimetres high when fully grown. The leaves of onions, shallots and chives are cylindrical and hollow, all arising from the swollen stem that takes the form of a bulb, as illustrated for chives in **figure 723**. Garlic leaves are flat and very slender. The inflorescence is composed of numerous flowers, white to pink, with peduncles of variable length. The flower is spherical on a stem which is hollow like the leaves, but rigid. The seeds are dark in colour, of variable shape , and about 2 millimetres long and wide. The root system is fibrous.

724

723

Uses : All the plant parts are edible, but the bulbs and the lower stem sections are the most popular as seasonings or as vegetables in stews **(figure 724)**, except for chives of which the leaves are more in demand.

Environment : Most members of the Alliaceae are light-loving plants that will withstand heat and drought reasonably well. The plants dislike wet soils that are rich in badly decomposed organic waste, especially manure, and may rot in these conditions.

Propagation : This is by seed for onion, and by bulbils for garlic, shallot and chives. In hot climates with short days, the Alliaceae cannot be relied on to flower.

Husbandry : Onions, shallots, garlic and chives originated in temperate regions, where the bulbs have the ability to remain dormant during the cold winters and begin growing again when the weather becomes warmer. In tropical Africa, however, they are cultivated as seasonal plants rather than as perennials, because the bulbs are consumed.

Onions are sown in well-watered nursery beds. The seedlings are transplanted when 10-15 centimetres high, and spaced at about 15 centimetres. The transplants benefit from trimming.

Garlic and shallot bulbils are sown in the open, buried in the ground to about two-thirds of their height. Harrow the soil lightly, and water frequently but moderately to avoid saturation.

The bulbs are harvested when the leaves have dried up completely, otherwise they may rot.

725

Scientific Name	*Daucus carota*
English	**Carrot**
French	carotte

Storage : Whole bulbs can be **stored** after drying the leaves well. The bulbs can be thinly sliced, dried in the sun and, if desired, ground into powder.

SP80 Carrot

Carrot of the family Umbelliferae is a seasonal vegetable of European origin **(figure 725)**. All the leaves, which are dark green, arise from the base of the plant. They are markedly dentate and between 15 and 25 centimetres in height. When the plant flowers – this is unusual in the tropics - the flowers are borne in clusters on the tips of the branched, leafless stems. The fruits are flat, the colour of straw. The plant has a tap root which is swollen and orange in colour.

Uses : The taproot is eaten raw or cooked as a vegetable.

Environment : The plant requires deep, well-loosened soil, without stones, fertile and moist but not waterlogged. Carrot thrives in full sunlight but light shade is acceptable in very hot weather.

Propagation : By seed only.

Husbandry : In gardens, with other vegetables that give little shade.

Carrot is sown in rows or broadcast, and is thinned soon after emergence, leaving the seedling spaced 5 centimetres apart. Well-loosened soil is worked on the flat. Other soils will have to be ridged or formed into raised beds. Carrots need to be watered regularly. They are harvested about three months after emergence.

726

SP81 Coleus

Coleus from the family Labiatae is a bushy, seasonal herb about 30 centimetres tall. Its stem sections are square. The leaves, opposite on the stems, oval, serrate, irregularly puckered and 5-7 centimetres long, are covered with short hairs **(figure 726)**. The flowers, white to pink, are arranged in spikes on the stems ((**figure 728)**. The seeds are black. The shallow, fibrous root system produces tubers which are roughly cylindrical and 5 centimetres long **(figure 727)**.

The species described above is the commonest *(Coleus dysentericus)*. However, there are other, very similar species cultivated on a more regional basis. They are distinguished by the size and shape of the tubers. For example, *Coleus rotundifolius* , called ussuni-gué in the Bambara region, has tapering tubers, 10-20 centimetres long.

Scientific Name	*Coleus dysentericus (Coleus rotundifolius)*
English	**Hausa potato, frafra potato**
French	coleus, pomme de terre du Soudan

727

728

Coleus dazo has spread out tubers, 5-10 centimetres long. This species is called bi n'gombo in Zaire, ingombo in Rwanda and rizga in Hausa country.

Uses : The tubers are eaten as a vegetable or as a staple.

Environment : Coleus thrives in full sunlight, on well-loosened soils, moist but not saturated. It tolerates drought.

Propagation : By sets from tubers, whole or in sections.

Husbandry : In clearings, in pure stands, or interplanted with low-growing crops.

Coleus is planted on mounds or ridges, at a depth of 10 centimetres. The plant must be earthed up again before flowering; this is essential in sandy soils.

Whole plants can be harvested with their tubers attached, but tubers can also be lifted as they reach maturity by gently excavating them from the hills **(figure 74)**.

Storage : Seed tubers can be stored in buried silos. They are also kept in houses, in baskets stuffed with straw.

SP82 Ginger and turmeric

Scientific Name	*Zingiber officinale and Curcuma domestica*
English	**Ginger and turmeric**
French	gingembre et curcumin

Ginger is a herb of variable height (30-90 centimetres) and is seldom taller. It belongs to the family Zingiberaceae **(figure 729)**.

The green leaves are narrow (1-3 centimetres wide), from 5-25 centimetres in length and arranged at right angles to the stems. The stems are erect and not more than 3-6 millimetres in diameter.

The flowers, yellow in colour, are rarely produced; they arise on a basal stem.

The root system is in the form of an enlarged rhizome, 2-3 centimetres in diameter, 3-10 centimetres long, more at times, white to yellow and sometimes a delicate pink in colour **(figure 730)**. The adventitious roots branch out from the rhizome in the superficial soil layers.

Turmeric looks very like ginger, so much so that the plants are often confused with each other. Turmeric is another plant species, *Curcuma domestica* . It is distinguished from ginger by the shape of its leaves. These are broader than those of ginger, about 7-8 centimetres, and longer, as much as 50 centimetres. They are borne on sturdy petioles arising from the base of the plant. The leaves tend to curl outwards **(figure 731)**.

Uses : Ginger rhizomes fresh or dried, crushed, grated or powdered, are used to season sauces and stews, and give food a characteristic, rather spicy, flavour. The rhizomes are also used to prepare a refreshing drink.

Medicinally, ginger is said to be a stimulant and to have aphrodisiac properties. It is used on its own or with other products in remedies for stomach ache. It is believed to help the digestion of the foods with which it is consumed.

Turmeric is used in cooking in the same way as ginger. It is also used as a food colourant. Some varieties make foods yellow-ochre in colour.

729

730

731

Environment : Ginger and turmeric grow best in soils rich in organic material, sufficiently moist but not waterlogged. They thrive in full sunlight.

Propagation : From portions of rhizomes, 3-5 centimetres long, with at least one bud. The rhizomes set aside for propagation will keep for some months buried in dry, fresh sand. Damping the sand shortly before planting induces the emergence of young shoots.

Husbandry : Ginger and turmeric are exploited in compound gardens and in the fields. They are grown in a mixture with many other plants. However, planting in a pure stand will increase production.

The plants can be harvested nine to ten months after planting. If the harvest is at seven-and-a-half to eight months, the rhizomes will be much smaller but more tender and easier to grind into powder. The crop can also be harvested by cutting some of the rhizomes and leaving the rest of the plant in position for the coming season. The rhizomes produced in this way are supposed to be larger.

The soil must be of good tilth, rich in organic matter. The rhizomes are planted at a depth of 5-7 centimetres at the onset of the rains. Mulch spread when planting activates the emergence of the rhizomes, encourages growth and protects the new shoots. After emergence, you should earth up the shoots as they appear : they must not be allowed to remain on the soil surface because they are then of inferior quality, too fibrous and less aromatic.

Storage : Ginger and turmeric rhizomes can be stored whole or in pieces after thorough drying. The dried rhizomes also keep in powder form.

SP83 Tiger nut

The **tiger nut** is a herb of the family Cyperaceae, 30-50 centimetres in height **(figures 732 and 733)**. The pointed leaves, 30 centimetres long, are pale green tinted yellow at maturity. The inflorescence is on a stem triangular in section and grows above the leaves. It consists of small spikes, on slender peduncles all arising from the same point on the stem **(figure 735)**. The fibrous taproot produces small tubers 1-3 centimetres long, roughly cylindrical, with circular markings which look like superimposed sections **(figure 734)**.

Uses : The tubers are eaten cooked or raw as side dishes, occasionally as a staple meal. Sometimes the tubers are dried and made into flour for doughnuts which are a delicacy.

Environment : The tiger nut is intolerant of waterlogged soils. Yields are disappointing on impoverished soils or when the plant is shaded.

Propagation : By tuber sets, seldom by seed.

Husbandry : It is planted in fields, often with Bambara groundnuts or cereals, sometimes in a pure stand, in large or small clearings. The tiger

732

733

Scientific Name	*Cyperus esculentus*
English	**Tiger nut, earth almond**
French	souchet

nut competes significantly with interplanted crops, hence the need for land preparation and for appropriate plant arrangement as shown, for example, in

735

734

figure 732 where tiger nuts and Bambara groundnuts are planted on ridges.

In order to induce germination, the tuber sets are soaked for a few days before planting. They are positioned at a depth of 5 centimetres in well-loosened soil, preferably on mounds or ridges. The tubers are picked as soon as they come to maturity because they are quickly infested if they are left in the ground. Depending on the variety, they are pulled three or four months after planting.

Storage : After drying in the sun or with another source of heat, tiger nuts can be ground into flour and stored.

Chapter 27

Edible bark and flower producing trees

SP84 Garlic tree

Many trees emit through the bark, fruits or leaves, a potent smell similar to that of garlic. This is true of the garlic tree *(Scorodophleus zenkeri)* of the family Leguminosae.

The **garlic tree**, 25 metres or more in height, occurs in forests. The leaves are compound with ten to twenty small leaflets, oblong and acute **(figure 736)**. They are shiny on the upper surface, dull and paler beneath. The main vein is prominent on the underside of the leaflets. Leaf fall normally occurs in the dry season. The fruits are flat pods, about 10 centimetres long, black when dry. They contain a single seed, dark in colour, flattened, about 2 centimetres in diameter **(figure 737)**. The pods burst and release the seed in the dry season.

Scientific Name	*Scorodophleus zenkeri*
English	**Garlic tree**
French	arbre à ail

736

The garlic tree has a characteristic, deep taproot giving rise to short lateral roots.

Uses : The bark **(figure 738)** and seeds are peeled and used as seasonings in stews. They taste of garlic. Sometimes, they are singed or placed on hot coals before grating. When prepared in this way, they make stews black.

Environment : The garlic tree grows in forests. It thrives in light soils; it is intolerant of even temporary waterlogging.

Propagation : The tree is easily propagated from seed.

Husbandry : Generally speaking, only spontaneous trees growing in forests or trees preserved in fallows are exploited at the present time. However, the tree would be worth planting in fields and plantations, because its light foliage filters the light without overshading, and the root system penetrates to a considerable depth.

The bark is removed in the wet season (Chapter 6, **figures 211 and 212)**. If removal is staggered, say every two or three years, thicker, better quality bark is obtained.

Seeds of the garlic tree are sown in nursery beds, at a depth of 2 or 3 centimetres. Make sure that the soil is loose and deep at the time of sowing because the radicle arising from the seed reaches a considerable length before the shoot appears. Seedlings with straight, unbranched stems are transplanted, when they are between two and three years of age and are 1.5-2 metres tall.

It is easier to harvest the bark from stout trunks and branches which are straight and well-shaped. All the cuts that produce these branches should be practised. For example, shape pruning and lopping one or two years after transplanting will remove the laterals which tend to divide the trunk.

It is advisable to stake the transplants with supports two metres high.

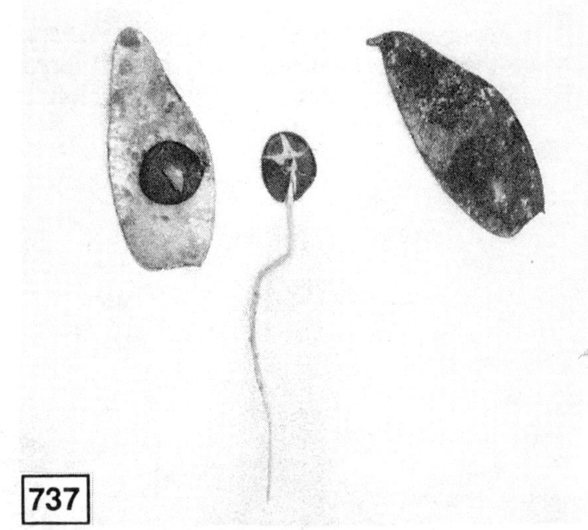

737

738

SP85 Red flower silk and silk cotton trees

739

The **red flower silk** of the family Bombaceae is 10-20 metres high, more at times, with typical conical spines on the branches, and sometimes on the stems of young plants. The tree occurs, often singly, in forests and dry lands.

740

Scientific Name	Bombax costatum	Ceiba pentandra
English	**red flower silk, cotton tree**	**silk cotton tree, kapok**
French	kapokier rouge, faux kapokier	fromager, kapokier

The leaves are composed of five to seven digitate leaflets on petioles 15 centimetres or more long **(figure 740)**. The flowers, red in colour, elongated and about 5-6 centimetres in diameter, appear in the dry season after leaf fall. The ripe fruits burst into five segments or valves, discharging a cottonlike floss called kapok. The tree has a deep, vigorous root system.

The **silk cotton tree** or **kapok** is closely related to the red flower silk **(figure 739)**, but is distinguished by its small, white flowers and sturdy buttresses at the base of the trunk. The fruits are fusiform, straw-coloured and 10-20 centimetres long **(figure 741)**.

Uses : The entire flower of the red flower silk, or only the calyx, is used for preparing sauces because of its mucilaginous properties. The immature fruits and the leaves of both trees are added to soups and stews. An edible oil is obtained from the seeds. Kapok is used for stuffing and padding.

741

Environment : The red kapok is a sun-loving tree that grows on a variety of soils and withstands fire and drought remarkably well. The silk cotton tree needs more moisture.

Propagation : By seed.

Husbandry : Mostly by gathering or picking up the flowers of subspontaneous trees. These trees are well suited to fields, pastures and gardens. They should be widely spaced to avoid competition with crops. Every year, they produce abundant, organic litter.

The red flower silk is preferably sown in the open because the seedlings have very deep roots and are difficult to transplant successfully.

Storage : The dried calyxes of the red flower silk will keep for many years in dry storage.

SP86 Triumphetta

Triumphetta belongs to the family Tiliaceae. Two species (*T. cordifolia* and *T. pentandra*) are commonly cultivated; a third species *(T. tomentosa)* occurs less frequently.

These plants are perennial herbs with abundant foliage **(figure 742)**. When they are harvested in their natural state, they are 0.8 to 1.5 metres tall, but trained on other plants, they can easily reach a height of 2-3 metres.

The leaves are pale green, notched, lightly serrate on the margins and acute. They have three to five characteristic veins arising from the same

742

743

Scientific Name	Triumphetta spp.
English	**The scientific name is used**
French	The scientific name is used

point on the leaf base. The leaf edges often curl lightly inwards and are sometimes covered in thick down *(T. tomentosa)* .

The stem is smooth; the upper section is the same colour as the leaves, the base is rough and dull grey. The plant tends to scramble along the ground when it is not supported. Many adventitious roots appear at the base of the stems. The flowers are yellow, on slender peduncles 15-20 centimentres long.

The fruits are grey-brown when ripe, shaped like tiny sea urchins **(figure 743)**.

Uses : The bark of the leafy stems contain substances that give stews a typically sticky consistency. These substances are extracted by softening the bark in hot water, and then kneading it in a little clean water. During the kneading process, the sticky agents are released into the water.

Environment : *Triumphetta* usually grows in wet conditions. It also occurs near water courses in river forests. When the soil is abundantly watered, *Triumphetta* will thrive in full sunlight.

Propagation : By cuttings from leafy stems.

Husbandry : As *Triumphetta* is not productive in the dry season, plants growing wild in wet valley bottoms are sometimes harvested. When cultivated, *Triumphetta* thrives when associated with tall plants.

At harvest, the branches are cut leaving one or two buds at the base, with the result that a single plant can be cropped for many years.

Leafy cuttings are planted in well-watered soil. Earthing up, mulching and shade – under a banana, for instance – are most beneficial. Staking is important when cultivated. This is because the best stems are straight and wide, with tender barks. But *Triumphetta* stems are pliable and when left to grow untrained, they tend to trail on the ground, quickly developing adventitious roots that make the plants unusable. Only the most vigorous stems are retained. This practice lets the remaining stems thicken and produce more bark from which a good-quality, sticky agent is then extracted.

Storage : The bark peeled from the stems keeps for many months.

Appendices

Glossary of the botanical terms used in Part II

Acuminate leaf	tapering to a point **(figure 515)**
Acute leaf	ending in a point **(figure 512)**
Alternate leaf	arranged at different levels of the stem **(figure 571)**
Annual	plant living or lasting for one year only
Aril	appendage that forms on certain seeds after fertilization, sometimes as a pulpy covering
Biennial	plant that lasts two years, usually producing flowers and seeds the second year
Blade	that part of the leaf contained between the veins or ribs
Cake	fibrous residue when oil has been obtained from seeds or fruits
Calyx	outer whorl of protective leaves of a flower, usually green
Capitulum	inflorescence with flower clusters arranged side by side on a hollow or enlarged receptacle
Climbing stem	flexible stem that develops by growing on other plants or on a support
Compound leaf	composed of several separate leaflets **(figure 736)**
Convex	curving outward like the surface of a sphere
Cordate leaf	rounded at the base on both sides of the petiole **(figure 706)**
Cordiform leaf	heart–shaped **(figure 500)**
Creeping	refers to a long root or rhizome growing near the soil surface
Dentate leaf	prominently toothed leaf margins **(figure 598)**
Denticulate leaf	finely dentate **(figure 005)**
Digitate leaf	having finger–like divisions **(figure 498)**
Dioecious	species producing male and female flowers on separate plants
Foliage	all the leaves of a plant, leaves collectively
Fruit set	the moment when the ovule of a flower becomes a fruit
Fruiting spur	small twig or branch on which fruits are borne
Fusiform leaf	spindle–shaped
Globular/globose	shaped more or less like a sphere
Habit	the tendency of a plant to grow in a certain way – an erect habit, a bushy habit
Hermaphrodite	bisexual flower with male organs (stamens) and female organs (ovaries)
Imparipinnate or odd leaf	pinnate – with pairs of leaflets and an odd terminal **leaflet (figure 665)**
Inflorescence	cluster of several flowers **(figure 504)**
Lanceolate leaf	lance–shaped **(figure 672)**
Leaflet	small leaf that is part of a compound leaf **(figure 555)**
Lenticellate	stem with bark irregularly mottled
Lobed leaf	with major divisions (lobes) that extend almost to **the base or centre (figure 622)**
Locule	compartment or chamber of a fruit
Monoecious	male and female flowers borne on the same plant
Mucilaginous	thick and sticky, producing or secreting mucilage
Notched	said of a leaf blade with base hollowed out **(figure 660)**
Obovoid	not quite oval
Opposite leaf	arranged on opposite sides of the stems on the **same node (figure 502)**
Ovoid/ovate	egg–shaped **(figure 664)**
Palmate leaf	palm–shaped
Pappus	tuft of hairs surmounting the fruits or seeds of certain plants, and assisting in their dispersal by wind
Paripinnate leaf	with an even number of leaflets
Pedicel	small stem bearing a flower
Peduncle	small stem bearing flowers and fruits
Pentagonal	five-sided **(figure 639)**
Perennial	lasting many years
Petiole	small extension of the base of the leaf attaching the leaf to the main stem

Pluriseasonal refers to plants planted in one season and harvested in another, sometimes one year later (see Chapter 1).

Prostrate habit of a bushy plant with branches and shoots that tend to spread on the ground

Pubescence soft down covering the surface of many plants

Pubescent covered with a soft down

Pyriform leaf pear–shaped **(figure 597)**

Raceme an inflorescence with flowers in clusters at equal distances along the main stem **(figure 667)**

Rachis a main axis, such as that of a compound leaf

Rugose rough to the touch

Scabrous/scabrid rough to the touch

Semi-perennial lasting some years

Senescent growing old, ageing

Sepal any of the usually green, leaflike parts of the calyx

Serrate leaf lightly toothed like a saw **(figure 542)**

Simple leaf with the blade in one piece, that is, not divided into lobes or leaflets **(figure 534)**

Spike raceme with the flowers essential sessile, that is, attached directly to the main stem

Spontaneous self–sown, reproducing itself without man's intervention

spp. the abbreviated plural form of species, used when the characteristics of the species are not known or not described

Stem section what is seen when a stem is cut crosswise

Subspontaneous a plant that is not fully spontaneous because reproduction is encouraged by man's presence

Taproot a main root growing almost vertically downward, from which small branch roots spread out

Terminal bud, flower or fruit positioned on the top of a stem

Valve any of the segments into which a pod (capsule) separates when it bursts open

Venation arrangement of the veins (ribs) of a leaf.

English and Latin names of plants

English	Latin
African Elemi	*Canarium schweinfurthii*
African Fan Palm	*Borassus aethiopicum*
African Leaf Cabbage	*Brassica integrifolia var. carinata*
African Locust Bean	*Parkia biglobosa and P. Clappertoniana*
African Marigold	*Tagetes spp.*
Aidon Tree	*Tetrapleura tetraptera*
Akee Apple	*Blighia sapida*
Almond Nut	*Coula edulis*
Amaranthus dubius	*Amaranthus dubius*
Annato	*Bixa orellana*
Avocado	*Persea americana*
Banana	*Musa sapientum*
Baobab	*Adansonia digitata*
Basil	*Ocimum spp. and Basilicum spp.*
Bastard Mustard	*Gynandropsis gynandra*
Bauhinia	*Piliostigma reticulata and P. thonningii*
Beniseed, Sesame (white)	*Sesamum indicum*
Bird Chillies	*Capsicum frutescens*
Bitter Cucumber, Dark Egusi	*Cucumeropsis mannii and C. edulis*
Bitter Gourd	*Momordica charantia and M. balsamina*
Bitter Leaf	*Vernonia amygdalina, V. colorata, V. calvoana*
Bitter or Sour Orange	*Citrus aurantium*
Bitter Tomato	*Solanum esculentum and S. incanum*
Black Nightshade	*Solanum nigrum var. guineense*
Black Plum	*Vitex doniana*
Borreira	*Borreira princea*
Bottle Gourd	*Lagenaria siceraria and L. vulgaris*
Breadfruit	*Artocarpus communis*
Brussels Sprouts	*Brassica oleracea var. gemmifera*
Bullock's Heart	*Annona reticulata*
Bungu	*Ceratotheca sesamoïdes*
Bush Butter or Native Pear	*Dacryodes edulis*
Bush Greens	*Amaranthus hybridus*
Cabbage	*Brassica oleracea var. capitata*
Calabash Nutmeg	*Monodora myristica*
Cape Goosebery	*Phusalis peruviana*
Carambola	*Averrhoa carambola*
Cardamom	*Aframomum spp.*
Carrot	*Daucus carota*
Cashew	*Anacardium occidentale*
Cassava	*Manihot esculentum*
Castor	*Ricinus communis*
Cattail or Reed Mace	*Typha australensis*
Cauliflower	*Brassica oleracea var. botrytis*
Cayor Apple	*Parinari macrophylla*
Cayor Cherry	*Aphania senegalensis*
Celery	*Apium graveolens*
Celosia	*Celosia argentea and C. trigyna*
Chayote	*Sechium edule*
Cherimoya	*Annona cherimolia*
Chillies	*Capsicum annuum*
Chinese Cabbage	*Brassica pekinensis and B. chinensis*
Chives	*Allium schoenoprasum*
Citronella	*Cymbopogon nardus and C. citratus*
Citrullus	*Citrullus lanatus*
Citrus fruits	*Citrus spp.*
Coconut	*Cocos nucifera*
Cocoyam	*Xanthosoma sagittifolium*
Coffee, Arabica	*Coffea arabica*
Coffee, Robust	*Coffea canephora*
Coleus	*Coleus rotundifolius, C. dysentericus and C. dazo*
Common bean	*Phaseolus vulgaris*
Cork or Hissing Tree	*Parinari curatellifolia*
Costus	*Costus afer*
Courgette	*Cucurbita pepo*
Cowpea	*Vigna unguiculata*
Crotalaria	*Crotalaria retusa*
Cucumber	*Cucumis sativus*
Dark Egusi	*Cucumeropsis edulis and C. mannii*
Date Palm	*Phoenix dactylifera*
Deccan Hemp	*Hibiscus cannabinus*
Desert Date	*Balanites aegyptiaca*
Detar	*Detarium microcarpum and D. senegalensis*
Dika nut	*Irvingia gabonensis*
Diodia	*Diodia scandens*
Dracaena	*Dracaena spp.*
Drumstick	*Moringa oleifera*
Dum palm	*Hyphaene thebaica*
Earthpea	*Voandzeia subterranea*
Eggplant	*Solanum melongena*
Elephant Grass	*Pennisetum purpureum*
Eleusine	*Eleusine coracana*
Endive	*Cichorium endivia*
Ethiopian or African Pepper	*Xylopia aethiopica*
Eucalyptus	*Eucalyptus spp.*
Euphorbia balsamifera	*Euphorbia balsamifera*
Fagara	*Fagara heitzii and F. macrophylla*
Fig Sycamore	*Ficus gnaphalocarpa*
Flemingia	*Flemingia congesta*
Fluted Gourd	*Telfairia occidentalis*

Foetid Cassia	*Cassia tora*
Fonio	*Digitaria exilis*
Gardenia	*Gardenia triacantha*
Garlic	*Allium sativum*
Garlic Tree	*Scorodophleus zenkeri*
Gherkin	*Cucumis anguria*
Giant Granadilla	*Passiflora quadrangularis*
Ginger	*Zingiber officinale*
Gnetum	*Gnetum spp.*
Grains of Paradise	*Aframomum melegueta*
Grapefruit	*Citrus maxima*
Groundnut	*Arachis hypogaea*
Guava	*Psidium guyuva*
Guiera	*Guiera senegalensis*
Guinea or Benin Pepper	*Piper guineense*
Hilleria	*Hilleria latifolia*
Hog Plum	*Spondias mombin*
Hyptis	*Hyptis spicigera*
Indian Jujube	*Zizyphus mauritiana*
Indian Mustard	*Brassica juncea*
Indian Spinach	*Basella alba and B. rubra*
Indigo	*Indigofera tinctoria*
Jute, Jew's Mallow	*Corchorus olitorius and C. tridens*
Kanda	*Beilschmiedia obscurea*
Kohlrabi	*Brassica oleracea var. gongylodes*
Kola	*Cola spp.*
Lannea	*Lannea acida and L. microcarpa*
Leek	*Allium porrum*
Lemon	*Citrus limon*
Lettuce	*Lactuca sativa*
Lime	*Citrus aurantifolia*
Lotus	*Nymphea lotus*
Maize	*Zea mays*
Mandarind	*Citrus nobilis*
Mango	*Mangifera indica*
Marvola Plum	*Sclerocarya birrea*
Melon	*Cucumis melo*
Millet	*Pennisetum americanum*
Mock Tomato	*Solanum aethiopicum*
Monkey Guava	*Diospyros mespeliformis*
Neem	*Azadirachta indica*
Negro Coffee	*Cassia occidentalis*
Nettle Tree	*Celtis integrifolia*
New Zealand Spinach	*Tetragonia expansa*
Njansan	*Ricinodendron heudelotii or R. Africanum*
Oil Palm	*Elaeis guineensis*
Okra	*Hibiscus esculentus*
Onion	*Allium cepa*
Orange	*Citrus sinensis*
Orere	*Baillonella toxisperma*
Otaheite or Golden Apple	*Spondias cytherea*
Palmyra Palm	*Borassus flabellifer*
Parsley	*Petroselinum sativum*
Passion Fruit	*Passiflora edulis*
Pawpaw	*Carica papaya*
Pea	*Pisum sativum*
Pepper	*Piper nigrum*
Pigeon Pea	*Cajanus cajan var. flavus and C. cajan var. bicolor*
Pineapple	*Ananas comosus*
Plantain	*Musa paradisiaca*
Potato	*Solanum tuberosum*
Prickly Amaranth	*Amaranthus spinosus*
Pumpkin	*Cucurbita maxima*
Purslane	*Portulaca oleracea*
Radish	*Raphanus sativus*
Raffia Palm	*Raphia spp.*
Red Amaranth	*Amaranthus cruentus*
Red Flower Silk	*Bombax costatum*
Red Mombin	*Spondias purpurea*
Rice	*Oryza sativa*
Roselle, Jamaica Sorrel	*Hibiscus sabdariffa var. sabdariffa*
Rough-skinned or Guinea Plum	*Parinari excelsa*
Sage	*Salvia spp.*
Sapodilla	*Achras sapota*
Sesame (black)	*Sesamum radiatum*
Sesame (white)	*Sesamum indicum*
Shallot	*Allium ascalonicum*
Shea Butter	*Butyrospermum parkii or Vittelaria paradoxa*
Siam Weed	*Eupatorium odoratum*
Sierra Leone Bologi	*Crassocephalum biafrae and C. cecropioides*
Silk Cotton or Kapok Tree	*Ceiba pentandra*
Smooth Loofah	*Luffa cylindrica or L. aegyptiaca*
Snake Gourd	*Trichosanthes cucumerina var. anguina*
Solanum gilo Raddi	*Solanum gilo Raddi*
Sorghum	*Sorghum bicolor*
Soursop	*Annona muricata*
Soya	*Glycine maximum*
Strawberry	*Fragaria spp.*
Sugar cane	*Saccharum officinarum*
Swede	*Brassica napus*
Sweet Pepper	*Capsicum annuum*
Sweet Potato	*Ipomoea batatas*
Sweetsop	*Annona squamosa*
Tamarind	*Tamarindus indica*
Tannia, Cocoyam	*Xanthosoma sagittifolium*
Taro	*Colocasia antiquorum*
Teak	*Tectona grandis*
Tef	*Eragrostis abyssinica*
Tevesia	*Thevetia neriifolia*

Tiger nut	*Cyperus esculentus*	**Waterleaf**	*Talinum triangulare*
Titonia	*Tithonia spp.*	**Watermelon**	*Colocynthis citrullus*
Tobacco	*Nicotiana tabacum*	**Wheat**	*Triticum aestivum*
Tomato	*Lycopersicum lycopersicon or L. esculentum*	**Wild Custard Apple**	*Annona senegalensis*
		Wild or Green Amaranth	*Amaranthus viridis*
Tree Tomato	*Cyphomandra betacea*		
Trichoscypha	*Trichoscypha ferruginea*	**Yam**	*Dioscorea spp.*
Triumphetta	*Triumphetta cordifolia, T. pentandra and T. tomentosa*	**Yard-long Cowpea**	*Vigna unguiculata var. sesquipedalis*
		Yellow Mombin	*Spondias mombin*
Turmeric	*Cucurma domestica*		
Turnip	*Brassica oleracea var. rapa*	**Zamena**	*Acacia macrostachya*
Vegetable Marrow	*Cucurbita pepo and C. moschata*		

Bibliography

Some books on tropical agriculture and horticulture

DUPRIEZ, H. and DE LEENER, P. (1988), *Tropical Agriculture in Rural Communities,* Macmillan, London, U.K.

CHLEQ J.-L. and DUPRIEZ, H. (1988), *Vanishing Land and Water,* Macmillan, London, U.K.

GRUBBEN, G.J.H. (1976). *The cultivation of amaranth as a tropical leaf vegetable,* comm n° 67, Dept. Agricultural Research, Royal Tropical Institute, Amsterdam.

IRVINE, F. (1979). *West African Crops,* Oxford University Press, Oxford, United Kingdom.

MESSIAN, C.M. (1974 and 1975), *Le potager tropical,* 3 volumes, ACCT, 19 avenue de Messine, 75008 Paris, France.

MARTIN, F.W., and UBERTE, R. (1975), *Edible Leaves of the Tropics,* Antillan College Press, Mayaguez, Porto Rico.

PURSEGLOVE, J.W. (1979 and 1981), *Tropical Crops,* 2 volumes, Longman Group Limited, Harlow, United Kingdom.

TERRA, G. (1966). *Tropical Leaves,* Department of Agricultural Research, Royal Tropical Institute, 63 Mauritskade, 1092 AD Amsterdam, Netherlands.

TINDALL, H. (1983), *Vegetables in the Tropics,* Macmillan Press, Houndmills, United Kingdom.

TINDALL, H. (1968), *Commercial Vegetable Growing,* Tropical Handbooks, Oxford University Press, 300 p.

TOUTAIN, G. (1979), *Eléments d'agronomie saharienne,* GRET and L'Harmattan, 16 rue des Ecoles, 75005 Paris, France.

THOMAS, A. (1965), *Gardening in Hot Countries,* Faber and Faber, London, United Kingdom.

VAN DEN PUT, R. (1981), *Les principales cultures en Afrique Centrale,* A.G.C.D., 5 Place du Champ de Mars, 1050 Brussels, Belgium.

VAN DER ZON, A. and GRUBBEN, G. (1976), *The wild and cultivated leaf vegetables of South Benin,* Department of Agricultural Research, Royal Tropical Institute, 63 Mauritskade, 2 Ad Amsterdam, Netherlands.

VAN EPENHUIZEN, C.W. (1974), *Growing native vegetables in Nigeria,* F.A.O., via delle terme di Caracalla, 00100 Rome, Italy.

Reference books on the identification of plants and their uses

AUBREVILLE, A. (1950), *Flore forestière soudano-guineenne,* Société d'editions géographiques, maritimes et coloniales, Paris, France.

BERHAUT, J. (1971 to 1976), *Flore illustrée du Sénégal,* Vols 1-0, Ministère du Développement Rural, Direction des Eaux et Forêts, Dakar, Sénégal.

DALE, R.V. and GREENWAY P.J. (1961), *Kenya trees and shrubs,* Buchanan Kenya Estates Ltd., Nairobi, London, 654 p.

BERHAUT, J. (1967), *Flore du Sénégal,* Editions Clairafrique, Dakar, Senegal.

DALZIEL, J. (1937), *The Useful Plants of West Africa,* Crown Agents for the Colonies, London, United Kingdom.

IRVINE F. (1961), *Woody plants of Ghana with special reference to their uses,* Oxford University Press, London, 868 p.

KERHARO, J. and ADAM, J. (1974), *La pharmacopée sénégalaise traditionnelle. Plantes médicinales et toxiques,* Vigot Frères, Paris.

PALMER E. and PITMAN N. (1972), Trees of Southern Africa, A.A.Bolkema, Cape Town, Vol 1-3, 2235 p.

REEKMANS, M. and NYONGERE, L. (1983), *Lexique des plantes vasculaires du Burundi,* Faculté des Sciences, Université du Burundi, Bujumbura, Burundi.

VON MAYDELL, H. (1983), *Sahelian Trees and Shrubs,* G.T.Z., Dag Hammaskjold weg 1, 6236 Eschborn, Federal Republic of Germany.

In most African countries, there is a government department in charge of studying the country's flora. As a rule, information is freely available.

Illustrated books on pest identification and crop protection

AUTRIQUE, A. (1981), *Principaux ennemis des cultures de la région des Grands Lacs,* I.S.A.B.U., B.P. 795, Bujumbura, Burundi, and A.G.C.D., 5 Place du Champ de Mars, 1050 Brussels, Belgium.

BOLHEN, E. (1978), *Crop Pests in Tanzania and their Control,* Editions Paul Parey, Lindenstrasse 44/47, 1000 Berlin 61, Federal Republic of Germany.

C.D.H. (Centre pour le Développement de l'Horticulture), *Fiches techniques illustrées sur les principaux ennemis des cultures maraîchères,* B.P. 154, Dakar, Senegal.

COLLINGWOOD, E.F., BOURDOUXHE, L. and DEFRANCQ, M. (1981), *Les principaux ennemis des cultures maraîchères au Sénégal,* C.D.H., B.P. 154, Dakar, Senegal.

KRANZ, J., SCHMUTTERER, H. and KOCH W. (1981), *Diseases, Pests and Weeds in Tropical Crops,* Editions Paul Parey, Lindenstrasse 44/47, 1000 Berlin 61, Federal Republic of Germany.

LOZANO, J.C. *et al.* (1981), *Field problems in cassava,* CIAT, Colombia.

STOLL, G. (1986), Natural Crop Protection, AGRECOL, c/o Oekozentrum, CH-4438, Langenbruck, Switzerland

THURSTON, H.D. (1984), *Tropical Plant Diseases,* The American Phytopathological Society, 3340 Pilot Knob Road, St Paul, 55121 Minnesota, USA.

Information on nutrition and the composition of foodstuffs

JARDIN, C. (1967), *List of Foods used in Africa,* F.A.O., Via delle terme di Caracalla, 00100 Rome, Italy.

LATHAM, M.C. (1979), *Human Nutrition in Africa,* F.A.O., Rome, Italy.

OOMEN, H. and GRUBBEN, G. (1978), *Tropical Leaf Vegetables in Human Nutrition,* Koningklijk Instituut voor de Tropen, 63 Mauritskade, 1092 AD Amsterdam, Netherlands.

PELE, J. and LE BERRE, S. (1966), *Les aliments d'origine végétale au Cameroun,* Centre ORSTOM de Yaoundé, available from ORSTOM, 70-74 route d'Aulnay, 93140 Bondy, France.

TOURY, J. and others, *Aliments de l'Ouest Africain,* O.C.C.G.E., ORANA, B.P. 2089, Dakar, Senegal.

Answers to specific problems may be obtained by writing to the bodies and agencies listed below

AGRECOL, Oekozentrum, 4438 Langenbruck, Switzerland. Tel : (41) 62-601420.

APICA, B.P. 5946, Douala Akwa, Cameroun. Tel : (237) 421228.

ATOL, 9 Blijde Inkomststraat, 3000 Leuven, Belgium. Tel : (32) 16-224517.

BERPS, Bureau d'Etudes et de Recherches pour la Promotion de la Santé, B.P. 1977, Kangu-Mayombe, Zaire, for documentation on nutrition.

COTA, 18 rue de la Sablonnière, 1000 Brussels, Belgium. Tel : (32) 2-2181896.

TCA, Post Box 380, 6700 AJ Wageningen, Netherlands. Tel : (31) 8380-20484; telex 30169 TCANL.

ENDA, B.P. 3370, Dakar, Senegal. Tel : (221) 224229.

GRET, 213 rue La Fayette, 75010 Paris, France. Tel : (33) 1-42391314.

ILEIA, Information Center for Low External Input Agriculture, P.O.Box 64, 3830 AB Leusden, Netherlands. Tel : (31) 33-943086.

IRED, 3 rue de Varembé, case 116, 1211 Geneva 20, Switzerland. Tel : (41) 22-341716.

RISED, Regular Information System on Environment and Development, 29 rue Vautier, 1040 Brussels, Belgium. Tel : (32) 2-6470199.

TOOL, 68a/69a Entrepôtdok, 1018 AD Amsterdam, Netherlands. Tel : (31) 20-264409.

General Index

Acaricide 154
Active agent 155
Acute toxicity 159
Adhesive 155
Adjab 303
Adventitious bud 75
Akee apple 301
Aidon tree 273
Allies, the farmer's 152
Almond nut 307
Amaranths 239
Anatomy 212
Animal manure 56, 144
Annato 99, 309
Annonacea 286ff
Anthracnose 109, 136
Ants 102, 118, 152
Aphid 118, 121
Apical bud 75ff
Apple 287, 293, 301
Approach grafting 220
Ashes 59, 140
Axillary bud 75

Bacteria 101, 120ff
Bacterial diseases 120
Bacterial wilt 125ff, 135
Bactericide 154
Bait 148ff
Baobab 240
Barbadine 294
Bark beetle 117
Barrier effect 126ff
Basal shoot 166, 170
Base dressing 61
Basil 143, 242
Bastard mustard 247
Bauhinia 22
Bed 40, 233
Beetle 117, 150
Beniseed 306
Biological control 122, 152ff, 165
Biomass 49
Bitter cucumber 278
Bitter dattock 289
Bitter leaf 225, 255
Bitter orange 213
Bitter tomato 258
Blight 107
Black nightshade 250
Bordeaux mixture 158
Borer 89, 102, 107

Breadfruit 30
Broad-spectrum insecticide 157
Brussels sprouts 244, 245
Bud cutting 217ff
Bud excision 179
Bud grafting 217ff
Bug 117
Bulb 23, 166, 187, 315ff
Bulbil 166, 187
Bullock's heart apple 288
Bungu 310
Burning-over 60
Bush butter 270
Bush greens 239
Bush mangolo 300
Bush okra 245
Butterfly 117

Cabbages 244
Calabash nutmeg 300
Callus 213
Cambium 212
Canker 112, 132f
Cape Gooseberry 291
Carambola 288
Carbohydrate 28ff, 68
Cardamom 265
Carrot 316
Cashew 143, 298
Caterpillar 117
Cat's whiskers 80, 247
Cauliflower 245
Causal agent 114
Cayor apple 293
Cayor cherry 289
Cellulose 59
Celosia 240
Centipede 115
Cereal 30
Chayote 276
Cherimoya 287
Chillies 267
Chives 315
Chlorophyll 68
Chronic toxicity 159
Citrullus 276
Cleft grafting 215
Climbing plant 70
Clove 166, 167
Coconut 313
Cold compost method 53
Coleus 316

Commercial farming 10
Complementary foods 29ff
Compost 53
Condiment 7, 30, 31
Contact insecticide 155
Costus 246
Cotton tree 320
Cotyledon 174ff, 186
Courgette 279
Cricket 115
Crop in pure stand 16
Cross-fertilization 188
Crown (pineapple) 170
Crown slip (pineapple) 170
Cryptogamic disease 120
Cucumber 277, 278
Cucurbitacae 275ff
Cultural calendar 204ff
Cultural cycle 204
Cultural variety 24
Curative control 122
Cutting 166ff, 176ff, 187
Cutting back 79

Damping off 108
Dark egusi 278
Date palm 311
Deccan hemp 252
Decoction 144
Deficiency 101, 105, 123
Deficiency disease 101, 123
Defoliating caterpillar 104, 119
Dehiscent 172
Desert date 259
Detar 289
Dibbling hole 183
Dieback 108
Dika 300
Dioda 177
Dioecious 108
Disbudding 79
Disinfection 132, 137
Djave 309
Domestication 223ff
Dormancy 12, 179
Dormant bud 75, 179, 218
Drain 41, 233, 235
Drainage pit 205
Dracaena 144
Drip irrigation 234
Droppings 57, 144
Drumstick 251

Dum palm 312
Dusting 140, 141,

Early blight 109
Early produce 205
Early variety 205
Earthing up 43, 133
Ecological cost 159
Eggplant 257
Elytron (wing-sheath) 117
Emulsion 142
Epigeal germination 186
Epiphytic plant 103
Ethiopian pepper 269
Euphorbia tirucalli 127, 153
Excision (buds) 177, 179

Fagara 199, 260
Fallowland 10
Family 24
Fan palm 314
Fertilizer 60ff, 106, 123
Fig sycamore 261
Fire 132
Flemingia 55, 56
Flood irrigation 228
Floral cushion 93
Fly 103, 118
Foetid cassia 224, 243
Fonio 30
Food chain 149ff, 159, 163
Food refining 35
Framework 80ff, 222
Fruit drop 92, 108
Fungicidal disease 90, 120
Fungicide 154, 157ff
Fungus 101, 106, 119, 120

Gall 107, 113, 119
Gardenia 22
Garlic 315
Garlic tree 97, 319
Gene 137
Genetic selection 139
Germination energy 172
Germination power 172
Germinator 191
Gherkins 277
Ginger 317
Girdling 179
Gnetum 223
Golden apple 292
Gourds 280ff
Grafting 167, 211ff
Grains of Paradise 265ff
Granadilla 294
Gravity irrigation 232ff
Green manure plants 54ff
Gross productivity 21
Guiera 143
Guinea pepper 269
Gummosis 112

Habit 182
Half-standard (tree) 214
Haussa potato 316
Heel cutting 176
Hilleria 69, 224, 225
Herbicide 154
Hoe 46
Hoeing 47
Homopter 117, 118
Honeydew 118
Horticulture 7
Hot compost method 53ff
Humus 49
Hypogeal germination 186
Hyptis 142

Imbibition 174
Immunity 138
Improved seed 139
Incidence 137
Indian mustard 245
Indian spinach 241
Infusion 144
Insecticide 154
Insecticide by ingestion 156
Insecticide by inhalation 156
Insectifuge (repellent) 137, 156
Interrow 64

Jew's mallow 245
Jujube 264
Jutes 245

Kaolin 32, 141
Kapok 321
Kenaf 252
Kola 299
Kohlrabi 245
Kraal 11, 57
Kraaling 57

Lannea 296
Larvae 113, 116, 121, 130
Larvicide 156
Laterite 141
Layer 167, 179
Leaching 48
Leaf miners 102
Leaf spot 110
Leafhopper 118
Leek 254
Legume 30
Lettuce 248
Life cycle 130, 190, 227
Light-loving plant 69
Lime 61, 141
Lipids 28, 68
Locust bean 304
Lodging (crops) 71
Loofah 282
Lopping branches 78
Lotus 22

Maceration 143
Maize borer 129
Mallet cutting 176
Malnutrition 32
Marigold 127
Market gardening 7
Marling 60
Marrow 279
Marvola plum 292
Mass selection 139
Mediterranean fruit fly 130ff
Melon 283
Microbial disease 101
Microorganism 53, 101, 119ff
Millipede 115
Mineral salt 29ff, 48
Mineralization 49
Mistletoe 102
Mixed farming 10
Mock tomato 251
Mombin 292
Monetary productivity 20
Monkey guava 290
Monoculture 10
Morphology 74
Mosaic virus 111
Mounding 43
Mulch 51
Mulching 51, 184
Mutagenic substance 159

Natron 31
Necrosis 109ff, 113
Neem 143
Negro coffee 243
Nematicide 154
Nematode 107, 121
Net income 21
Net productivity 21
Nettle tree 85
New Zealand spinach 255

Nicotine 141
Nitrogen-fixing bacteria 175
Njansan 306
Nursery 190ff
Nursery grafting 214

Off-season crop 173
Oil cake 30
Oil palm 312
Oilseed 30
Okra 262
Orere 303
Onion 315
Organic manure 58
Organic matter 49
Otaheite apple 293
Ovary 165
Ovicide 156
Ovule 165

Palm 311ff
Parasitic chain 103
Parasitic plant 102
Passion fruit 294
Patch 40
Pea 190
Pedunculate 94
Pepper 269
Perennial 7
Peruvian cherry 291
Persistence 156
Pest control 130
Pesticide 154ff
Pineapple 169, 170
Photosynthesis 68
Phytotoxic 159
Pigeon pea 308
Pinching out 79, 91
Plant parasite 102, 121
Plant spacing 16ff, 64, 128
Plant species 24
Plantation 17
Planting hole 44, 198
Plough 46
Plum 293, 297
Pluriannual 7
Pollard 77
Pollen 165
Positioning the graft 214
Predator 150
Pregermination 181
Preventive control 122, 139
Primary stem 75
Proteins 29ff
Protid 28
Pruning knife 214
Pruning saw 98
Psylla 117, 118
Puddling 175
Pulse-beetle 117
Pumpkin 283
Purslane 246
Pyrethrum 143

Quarantine 136
Quelea quelea 115, 119, 147

Raffia palm 313
Rainfed crop 228
Rainfed market gardening 228
Rainsplash 132
Raised bed 40
Rake 46
Ratoon (pineapple) 170
Refined salt 31
Removing mineral salts 49
Repellent 156
Resistance 137ff, 162, 164
Return from a crop 20
Rhizobium 57, 121, 175
Rhizome 167, 169, 180
Ridging 44
Ringing 179
Ripe wood 169, 177, 212
Rock salt 31
Rodenticide 154, 158
Root collar 90, 106, 197ff, 214
Root pruning 88
Root rot 106, 119
Root-sucker 166, 187
Root vegetables 315ff
Rootstock 211
Roselle 252
Rotation 17, 132
Rotenone 143, 160
Rounding-off food 29ff, 32
Row planting 65
Runoff 17, 228

Sanitary pruning 87, 89
Sap-drawer 222
Sapwood 97, 212
Scalding 34, 174
Scale insect 107, 117
Scarecrow 147
Scarification 174
Scion 211
Sea salt 31
Seasonal plant 7
Secateurs 98, 214
Secondary stem 75
Seed 135ff, 165, 182ff
Seed density 64
Seed inoculation 175
Seed plant 168
Seed rich in oil and protein 30
Seed rich in protein 30
Seed tuber 135, 180
Seeding broadcast 63
Selected seed 136, 139
Self-pollination 165
Semi-perennial plant 7
Sesame 306
Sessile 94
Shade plant 69
Shallot 315
Shea Butter 302
Siam weed 126
Sierra Leone bologi 223
Silk trees 320
Slug 115
Slurry 51, 57, 144
Snail 32, 115
Snare 148ff
Soaking cuttings 137
Soil crust 47, 183
Solanum gilo Raddi 249
Sole 15
Soursop 286
Sowing in the field 182ff
Spade 46
Spectrum 155, 157, 160
Spider 118
Spontaneous plant 223
Spore 120
Sprinkler irrigation 234
Stabling animals 57
Staking 69, 92, 131
Stamen 165
Standard tree 214
Staple food 7, 29ff
Stem shoot 166, 169, 181
Stem sucker (pineapple) 170
Stock 211
Stolon 166
Stomata 68
Stratification 194
Strawberry 291
Streak virus 111ff
Subspontaneous plant 223
Sucker 79, 86, 166, 170
Sugar cane 171
Supplemental foods 7
Supplementary irrigation 229ff
Susceptibility 138
Sweet dattock 289
Sweet peppers 268
Sweetsop 315ff

Symptom 103, 105
Systemic insecticide 155

Tagetes 126
Tamarind 271
Tef 30
Termite 108, 116
Tevesia 142, 148
Thinning 72, 183
Thinning branches 72
Thrips 118
Tiger nut 318
Tined hoe 46
Tithonia 56
Tobacco 142
Tolerance 139
Tomato 273
Topworking 220
Total control 140, 151
Toxin 151
Trace element 106
Tracheomycosis 107
Transplanting hole 198
Transplanting in the root ball 197
Tree tomato 295
Trimming (transplant) 178
Trichoscypha ferruginea 292
Triumphetta 320
Tuber 30, 180
Tumeric 317
Turnip 245
Tying plants 76

Uncertified seed 136
Underground stem cutting 181
Urine 51, 57, 144

Variety 24, 137, 187ff
Vegetable cropping 7
Vegetable farming 7
Vegetable garden 7
Vegetal salt 31
Vegetative cycle 7, 104, 182, 226ff
Vegetative seed 134, 165
Viral disease 101, 110
Virus 101, 111, 121, 139
Vitamin 29ff

Waterleaf 246
Water table 227
Weakness pests 123
Weeding 134, 154
Weevil 117, 134, 148
Wetter 155
Whip grafting 217
Whitefly 118
Wild custard apple 143
Wilt 105ff
Wilting 105ff
Witches' broom 86, 112
Worms 117

Zamena 224

TERRES ET VIE

rue Laurent Delvaux 13, 1400 Nivelles, Belgique

English-Language Editions in association with Macmillan Publishers and CTA

* **Vanishing Land and Water. Soil conservation in dry lands,** by H. Dupriez and J.-L. Chleq, 1988, 117 pages (ISBN 0-333-44597- X, ISBN 2-87105-007-04).
  An illustrated book on water management techniques and crafts at village level : fight against erosion, small dams, wells, bore holes, pumps, surface water storage.

* **Agriculture in African Rural Communities,** by H. Dupriez and Ph. De Leener 1988, 294 pp. (ISBN 0-333-44595-3, ISBN 2-87105-006-6)
  An illustrated book on agriculture in African rural communities, designed for use by small farmers,

French-Language Editions
in association with CTA, L'HARMATTAN, APICA, ENDA

* **Paysans d'Afrique Noire,** de H. Dupriez, 1982, 256 pp, 2ème édition, ISBN 2-87105-002-3.
  Les vues d'un agronome-économiste sur les pratiques du "développement rural" en Afrique Noire.
  The views of an agro-economist on "rural development" in Black Africa.

* **Agriculture tropicale en milieu paysan africain,** de H. Dupriez et Ph. De Leener, 1986, 282 pp, 2ème édition, ISBN 2-87105-000-7.
  Un livre abondamment illustré consacré à l'agriculture paysanne, destiné aux agriculteurs, aux élèves, aux cadres ruraux et à tous ceux qui s'intéressent au milieu agraire.

* **Eau et terres en fuite,** de J.-L. Chleq et H. Dupriez, 1984, 136 pp, ISBN 2-87105-001-05.
  Divers métiers de l'eau pratiqués dans le cadre villageois : lutte contre l'érosion, micro-barrages, puits, forages, pompes, retenues de surface (texte illustré).

* **Jardins et vergers d'Afrique,** de H. Dupriez et Ph. De Leener, 1987, 370 pp, ISBN 2-87105-005-8.
  Un manuel pratique consacrés aux cultures maraîchères, fruitières et condimentaire propres à l'Afrique tropicale.

* **Langue française et Agriculture tropicale,** de F. Tsoungui, 1985, 193 pp (ISBN 2-85319-145-1/ISBN 2-87105-003-1), coédité avec le CILF (Conseil International de la Langue Française)
  Un outil d'apprentissage de la langue française se basant sur les textes du livre "Agriculture tropicale en milieu paysan africain".
  A manual for learning French, based on the texts of Agriculture tropicale en milieu africain.

* **Ecocultures d'Afrique** (Shifting Cultivation in Africa), de P. de Schlippé (†), 1986, 201 pp, ISBN 2-87105-004-X. Traduction et adaptation.
  Un peuple, un milieu, une agriculture. L'auteur fait une analyse fouillée de la relation qui lie les Azande à leur terroir (aux confins du Zaïre, du Soudan et de la République Centrafricaine).
  The author describes in detail how the Zande tribe living on the borders of Zaïre, Sudan and the Central African Republic practise shifting cultivation. Illustrated text translated and adapted from the original english version titled Shifting Cultivation in Africa, The Zande System of Agriculture (1956), Routledge & Kegan Paul, London.

Titles in the Tropical Agriculturalist series

Title	ISBN
Sheep	ISBN:0–333–52310–5
Pigs	0–333–52308–3
Goats	0–333–52309–1
Dairying	0–333–52313–X
Poultry	0–333–52306–7
Rabbits	0–333–52311–3
Draught Animals	0–333–52307–5
Ruminant Nutrition	0–333–57073–1
Animal Breeding	0–333–57298–X
Animal Health Vol. 1	0–333–61202–7
Animal Health Vol. 2	0–333–57360–9
Warm-water Crustaceans	0–333–57462–1
Livestock Production Systems	0–333–60012–6

Title	ISBN
Upland Rice	0–333–44889–8
Tea	0–333–54450–1
Cotton	0–333–47280–2
Weed Control	0–333–54449–8
Spice Plants	0–333–57460–5
Cocoa	0–333–57076–6
The Storage of Food Grains and Seeds	0–333–44827–8
Sugar Cane	0–333–57075–8
Maize	0–333–44404–3
Plantain Bananas	0–333–44813–8
Coffee Growing	0–333–54451–X
Food Legumes	0–333–53850–1
Cassava	0–333–47395–7
Sorghum	0–333–54452–8

Other titles published by Macmillan with CTA (co-published in French by Maisonneuve et Larose)

Title	ISBN
Animal Production in the Tropics and Subtropics	0–333–53818–8
Coffee: The Plant and the Product	0–333–57296–3
The Tropical Vegetable Garden	0–333–57077–4
Controlling Crop Pests and Diseases	0–333–57216–5
Dryland Farming in Africa	0–333–47654–9
The Yam	0–333–57456–7

Land and Life series (co-published with Terres et Vie)

Title	ISBN
African Gardens and Orchards	0–333–49076–2
Vanishing Land and Water	0–333–44597–X
Ways of Water	0–333–57078–2
Agriculture in African Rural Communities	0–333–44595–3